# EPIPHANY

---

## A PRIDE & PREJUDICE VARIATION

## JESSIE LEWIS

Quills & Quartos
PUBLISHING

Edited by Debbie Styne and Beth Flintoft

Cover by Penny Dreadful Book Cover Design

ISBN 978-1-956613-10-0 (ebook) and 978-1-956613-11-7 (paperback)

*For everyone who ever yearned for a little more time with Darcy and Elizabeth.*

# PROLOGUE

*Darcy House*
*1 Arlington Street, London*
*December 1811*

*Dearest Anne,*
*I am heartily sorry to hear your mother has been called away. I know she has been intimate friends with Mrs Fortescue for an age. How sad that lady should be so unwell! Let us hope she recovers swiftly, and you are not required to remain alone overlong.*

*I thank you for your kind invitation. Regrettably, we cannot join you at Rosings at the present time. Brother has only recently returned from Hertfordshire, and we are both much occupied with Mr Bingley and his sisters. Besides, no matter how dearly Miss Bingley wishes her brother and I would form an attachment, he clearly wishes to be at Netherfield still. And since my brother evidently took such pleasure in the society there, I cannot think it will be long before they both return. I hope to join them if they do. I know, however, you must have many other friends on whom you may call for company, thus I shall not feel too wretched for depriving you of mine.*

*On the subject of Hertfordshire society, I am afraid you have quite mistaken what I wrote in my last letter in regard to Miss Elizabeth Bennet. I do not believe my brother found her at all vexing. When I relayed to you that they had argued, I phrased it ill. Rather, they debated, and as you know, my brother enjoys that activity far too well. Indeed, I do not believe I have ever heard him speak so favourably of any lady.*

*You will understand my surprise to hear your rector has expressed such severe censure of her—and she his own cousin! Do you know the nature of his grievance? I understand Miss Bennet is exceptionally quick-witted. Perhaps Mr Collins construed it as impertinence. I assure you, however, it does not seem likely. My brother described her as compassionate, intelligent, and perceptive. I really do not think she can be as objectionable as Mr Collins has implied. Pray, do not continue to think ill of Miss Bennet, for I should be miserable if my careless words gave you a poor impression of an acquaintance my brother holds in such high esteem, and whom I dearly hope you and I shall both one day meet.*

*I pray Lady Catherine returns home very soon. Do write again to tell me how you get on with your new ponies when they arrive.*

*Yours &c.*
*Miss Georgiana Darcy*

Anne de Bourgh folded the letter with such energy that she tore the page. She gestured at a footman. "Have my phaeton brought around." Then, she gestured at her companion. "Come, Mrs Jenkinson. We are to pay a call on Mr Collins at the parsonage."

Then, she gestured to the heavens. This was not to be borne! Yet, if her cousin would not put an end to it, it fell to her to act.

# CHAPTER 1

It was a dull, unforgiving day—the sort that eroded one's spirits. The leaden sky clutched selfishly to all but the most miserly scattering of sunlight, leaving barely enough to differentiate day from night. The remnants of the previous day's snowfall had been shoved into heaps of blackened slush at each side of Arlington Street. A wintry chill stifled the aromas of the freshly served breakfast, leaving the room smelling no better than the damp newspaper that had been brought up with the post.

Darcy's head throbbed with the legacy of an evening that ought to have cheered him but had only deepened the objectionable melancholy he could not dispel, and the heavens were doing their damnedest to parody. He sipped his coffee and glowered down upon the street, daring the world to give him a reason to be cheerful. He felt singularly inclined for a battle.

Behind him, his sister opened a letter with an obvious and vain effort to make as little noise as possible. He rued his surly responses to her several attempts at conversation, but he was in no humour for tittle-tattle. Knowing it was neither the triviality of Georgiana's discourse nor the aching of his head, the temperature of the room nor the colour of the blasted sky that was responsible for his persistent dejection, only inflamed his rancour.

There came a soft exclamation from behind him, one he thought likely he had not been meant to hear. He twisted his head slightly, listening for further signs of distress, but Georgiana was silent. Unaccountably wary, Darcy turned away from the window to regard her. She was all agitation, the fingertips of one hand pressed to her lips and her head shaking as she read.

"What is it?" he enquired brusquely, his last vestiges of civility stolen by the horrible certainty that her answer would somehow pertain to Wickham.

Georgiana winced, glancing at him but briefly before returning her eyes to her letter. "It is Anne."

"Anne?" he replied, thrown by the unexpected answer. "Anne *de Bourgh*?" When his sister nodded, he pressed, "What of her? Is she unwell?"

Georgiana hesitated, inhaled, and at last raised her eyes to properly meet his gaze. "She has gone to Hertfordshire."

For a moment, Darcy thought Georgiana had said *Hertfordshire*, and he reviled not only the preposterous lurch his heart gave at the mention of the word, but the very fact that his mind had contrived to hear it in yet another conversation. He was grown inordinately weary of his every passing thought being trespassed upon by his preoccupation with that place. Anne never left Kent. He had evidently misheard.

"I am sorry, Brother."

He felt another unpleasant lurch, and now his headache was reasserting its presence with a more determined pounding. "For what?"

"For having caused you yet more trouble. It was unconsciously done. I had no intention of misleading Anne with what

I wrote. Indeed, I had not the smallest idea of my words being ever felt in such a way. I simply did not wish to go to Rosings."

"I have no idea what you are talking about. Pray explain to me what has happened."

The dregs of last night's overindulgence roiled in Darcy's stomach when he beheld the turn his sister's countenance then took. It was precisely the expression she had worn that past summer as she admitted her design to elope with George Wickham—the pitiful mix of a child's fear of reproof and a young woman's self-reproach. When she swallowed and held out the letter for him to take, he did so reluctantly, privately railing at the world for taking him so literally in his challenge of a fight.

*Georgiana,*

*What a shame you are too busy to visit me, though I am pleased you and Darcy are enjoying your time with the Bingleys. I daresay you are mistaken about either gentleman's wish to return to Netherfield, however. If they would not be pleased with Kent, then Hertfordshire cannot boast anything they would regret. Certainly not sharp-tongued country misses.*

*Regrettably, my mother has not yet returned. Mrs Fortescue's condition has worsened. Terribly sad, if a little inconvenient, yet there are two very good reasons that you need not fear I shall be downhearted. The first is that you were correct in your conjecture that I do not want for other sources of entertainment. Indeed, I have been well attended by Mr Collins this past fortnight. His manner is somewhat affected, but I can forgive it, for such a mode of oration must be a necessary habit for a man who delivers sermons for a living. He is certainly eager to please me, an inclination that disposes me to be far better pleased with <u>him</u> than I might otherwise have been. I must say he has painted a very different picture of his cousin than you sketched in your letter. He has very little good to say of her at all, in fact, other than she is* *handsome—and looks are of far less importance to sensible men than good breeding and fortune. Therefore, despite your panegyric of Miss Elizabeth Bennet's charms or Darcy's unfathomable forbearance of her impertinence, I am disinclined to think any better of her.*

*The second reason you may set aside all concern for my entertainment is that I have decided to accompany Mr Collins when he returns to Hertfordshire on Monday. Since it was on my mother's advice that he affianced himself in the first place, and since he is so eager that she and I approve of his choice, it seems fitting that I employ my newly unencumbered time travelling to meet this Miss Lucas to give my consent in person. It is a stimulating prospect, for I have not left Kent for above two years, and I vastly anticipate the change of scene.*

*If I should happen to meet Miss Elizabeth Bennet while I am there, and she should happen to see for herself the vast distinction in our relative situations in life, then all the better. Perchance she will drop whatever false hope Darcy might have given her when he singled her out for a dance at his friend's ball. This I learnt from Mr Collins. Whatever was your brother thinking?*

*Wish me well. It will be quite the adventure, I am certain.*

*Yours &c.*
*Anne de Bourgh*

Darcy stared at the letter, incredulity steadily curdling into fury. He had left—Devil take it—he had *left* Hertfordshire, left *Elizabeth* and her blasted impertinence behind! He had come away—and *stayed* away—despite the insuperable urge that plagued him to return at every moment, waking or otherwise. He waited, day after day, for the cloying feeling of having made a mistake to pass. He told himself repeatedly that his only mistake had been in allowing so many preposterous imaginings of what might have been had he stayed. For had he not indulged in *those*, it might not presently be taking such a damnably long time for the infernal fascination to loosen its grip.

Nevertheless, he had not gone back. Nor had he admitted his partiality to anyone, for it could lead to nothing, give nobody any pleasure, and end no other way than in disaster. Yet, somehow, he was discovered, and *Anne* of all people had gone to Hertfordshire with what appeared to be a resolve to intimidate Elizabeth out of any misplaced aspirations towards the family—towards *him*.

*Hell's teeth!*

Darcy held his countenance motionless, unwilling to reveal any hint of vexation. Yet, oh, how he wished to rage at his sister! To demand of her what she thought she knew of his acquaintance with Elizabeth, to enquire what madness had induced her to discuss it with Anne, to upbraid her for being so indiscreet after all *his* endeavours to protect *her* reputation the previous summer—but what did it matter? Though she was likely to be as subtle as an ox, Anne's visit would ultimately serve him well. It would do no harm for Elizabeth to be told categorically that he would never return for her, and it would save him having to waste any further thought on the matter.

He handed the letter back to Georgiana. "I suggest you are more careful what nonsense you write to our cousin in the future. Lady Catherine appears to have allowed her to become unduly fanciful of late." He walked towards the door.

"You are not angry?" Georgiana enquired timidly.

He paused without looking at her. *Angry* was a term applied when one had spilt coffee on one's ledgers, or been spoken to uncivilly, or dropped a precious trinket in a puddle.

Whereas in his case, his hapless sister had somehow begun a rumour that he was romantically attached to the penniless young woman from an unheard-of and vulgar family, with whom duty and good sense forbade him from *ever* considering an alliance, but whose extraordinary wit and captivating eyes he had been entirely unable to banish from his thoughts at any point in the eight weeks, two days, and twelve hours since he first met her, who had bewitched him to the point that he knew not where his memories of her ceased and his dreams of her began.

Now, thanks to his sister's imprudence and his cousin's unaccountable precipitance, any hope of somehow finding a way to overcome every impediment and give in to his incessant longing to be with Elizabeth was lost forever. It was possibly why what he felt was far more visceral, far more alarming, far uglier than mere anger.

"No," was all he said. Then he left the room.

❧

The fields surrounding Longbourn were crisp with frost, but since Elizabeth's stockings had been soaked through within five minutes of leaving home, she was not discouraged. She put her foot to the next stile she reached, determined to venture farther than the lane on her morning's walk.

"Lizzy!"

She stopped mid-clamber and stood tall on the stile to see her two youngest sisters dashing towards her along the lane, waving frantically. She withdrew her leg from over the rail and jumped back down to greet them.

"Lizzy," Lydia panted, first to reach her. "Mr Collins has arrived, but he is not to stay with us after all."

"Really? Well, I cannot say I am sorry, though such short notice is inconsiderate. Mama will be most put out. Do you know where he does mean to stay?"

"At Lucas Lodge, and you—"

"You will never guess whom he has brought with him!" Kitty interrupted, catching up with them. She promptly found herself in receipt of a vicious swipe of Lydia's reticule. "Ow!"

8

"Let *me* tell her!"

"I do not see why I should. I saw her first."

"Saw who?" Elizabeth enquired as she confiscated Lydia's reticule with an admonishing look.

"Miss Anne de Bourgh," both girls said at once.

Elizabeth stared, all astonishment.

"It is why Mr Collins declined to stay at Longbourn," Kitty said quickly, as though to share all the news before Lydia could. "Apparently, Miss de Bourgh insisted they stay with his new family. Sir William is well-nigh bursting with pride to have such a distinguished guest."

"And Lady Lucas is furious, for Miss de Bourgh sent no word of her visit," Lydia added.

*How much like her cousin Mr Darcy she is, to expect the world to be at her disposal!* Elizabeth reflected. "And Charlotte?"

"We did not see her. We left as soon as Mr Collins arrived, for the whole house was in uproar."

"Heavens, what a turn of events!" Elizabeth set off in the direction of Longbourn. "Was anything said of why she has come? I understood from Mr Collins that ill health prevented her from travelling much."

"And I daresay he is right, for she looked very ill indeed," replied Lydia, her nose wrinkled in distaste. Elizabeth was about to ask that she expound on her description but was anticipated by Kitty.

"What does it matter why she is come? At least we shall not have to put up with our cousin at home."

Elizabeth could not argue with that. After she refused his offer of marriage the month before, Mr Collins had been excessively cold in his manner towards her. Moreover, since he had two-and-seventy hours after that rejection become engaged to her dearest friend, Charlotte, she had been unable to view him with anything other than contempt, for a man who betrayed such flagrantly insincere affections could never command her respect. A reprieve from all his absurd affectations was most welcome. Yet, there were other circumstances to consider aside from her own.

"It might matter to Jane," she pointed out.

"How so?"

"Miss de Bourgh is Mr Darcy's cousin, and according to Mr Wickham, they are engaged. If *she* is come, it might signal *his* return. And if *he* were to come back, so might Mr Bingley."

"But Miss Bingley's note said the party had not any intention of returning."

Elizabeth huffed a sceptical sigh. "Miss Bingley's note said that *Miss Bingley* had not any intention of returning. I have never believed she spoke for her brother."

Lydia's countenance lit with interest. "It would please Jane very well if he did. She has been excessively dull since he left. Do you think he will?"

"I do not know. We can but hope—for *his* return, if not his friend's." Elizabeth felt a pang of apprehension at the prospect of seeing Mr Darcy again. She had received her fill of supercilious quarrels and disdainful looks the last time he was in Hertfordshire. From the first moment of their acquaintance, he had proven himself the proudest, most ungentlemanlike of men, which only heightened her curiosity in his betrothed. She opened her mouth to enquire again about the lady but was forestalled a second time by Kitty.

"I daresay Mama will be pleased not to have to host Mr Collins, too. It makes much more sense for him to stay at Lucas Lodge now that he is engaged to Charlotte. It was unaccountably strange that he still meant to stay with us."

"Yes, well, he is an unaccountably strange man," Elizabeth replied. "Though I should not be surprised if his purpose was to remind us that he is still heir to Longbourn, regardless of whom he marries."

Kitty looked rather offended by this. Lydia looked outraged.

"And that is also why I fear you are wrong about Mama," Elizabeth added resignedly. "She has not yet recovered from the indignity of forfeiting Longbourn's future to the Lucases. She will not be at all pleased that the honour of such a prestigious guest has gone to Lady Lucas as well. And since that is all ostensibly my fault, I expect I shall be the object of a good deal of her displeasure for as long as Miss de Bourgh is in Hertfordshire."

Both her sisters winced in commiseration, and neither of them attempted to tell her she was wrong before leaving her to walk behind them when the path became too narrow to admit three. Elizabeth fell back, content with her own thoughts as the two younger girls hopped about ahead of her, giggling as they helped each other over and around the muddiest bits of ground.

When the path widened sufficiently to allow it, Elizabeth came abreast of her sisters once more and enquired, "What was she like?"

"Miss de Bourgh? She did not seem particularly friendly."

"Aye," Kitty chimed in. "She had a superior air that made her look very severe."

"She is not handsome, then?"

Kitty screwed up her face in thought, and Elizabeth reflected that anybody whose looks required that much deliberation could not possibly be considered beautiful.

"She is not ill-favoured, per se," her sister answered at length. "I daresay she looks well enough beneath the sneer. Not as pretty as Jane, though."

"Or me," Lydia added.

"Well then," Elizabeth replied, nodding towards the end of the path wither lay Longbourn. "Let us see what Mama has to say about it all."

They arrived mere moments after a letter was delivered, announcing Mr Collins's altered plans. Mrs Bennet, note in hand, appeared to be suffering some manner of apoplexy and was resolutely ignoring Jane's attempts to persuade her to sit down. Upon espying Elizabeth, her mother grew unnervingly quiet, drew herself up tall, clasped her hands across her stomach, and tucked her resentment away beneath her bosom with several indignant nudges.

"This is all your fault, Lizzy," she said in a clipped tone. Then she swirled around and strode out of the hall with a flourish that was lent uncharacteristic elegance by her pique.

Lydia and Kitty both snorted with laughter, but seeing Jane let out a quiet sigh, Elizabeth sent them on their way. "I am sorry I was not here to help with that," she said as she closed the front door.

"It was probably better you were not," Jane replied with a small shake of her head. "Mama was excessively vexed, but do not concern yourself on my account. Papa took the brunt of it and Mary the rest. I ought to see whether she is well. She was on the verge of tears when she ran upstairs."

"Oh Lord! Let me go. I need you to save your strength to work on Mama." Elizabeth had gone only two steps up the stairs before Jane called her back.

"Why do you think Miss de Bourgh is come, Lizzy? Do you think her visit has anything to do with Mr Darcy?"

Elizabeth sighed discreetly, understanding that it was not Mr Darcy about whom her sister truly cared. She had never seen Jane as happy as in those few weeks that Mr Bingley showered her with his attentions, nor so dispirited as in the weeks since he left without explanation or farewell. She hoped beyond anything that he might return to mend her sister's heart, but she would not say anything that might give false hope.

"Truly, I do not know. What did Mr Collins say in his note?"

"Only that he was sorry for the short notice, but that he was obliged to honour the wishes of his patroness's daughter, and that *she* has expressed a wish to become acquainted with Charlotte. There was no mention of her cousin."

"Or her cousin's friend?" Elizabeth pressed gently.

Jane shook her head.

"Then we shall have to wait and see. If she is, as Mr Collins once assured us, the British court's brightest ornament, who knows how many gentlemen might follow her here. Hertford-shire could soon be inundated with eligible young men, and Mr Bingley will have to fight his way back in."

That drew a gentle laugh from her sister. "I shall not set my heart on his coming back. It seems more and more unlikely."

Elizabeth gave a lopsided smile of sympathy.

Jane returned it with a small but sad smile of her own. "I do think it is strange that she is come. Mr Collins said she hardly ever left Kent."

"Indeed it is. I cannot help but wonder what sort of woman she must be."

"To have made such a journey?"

"To be engaged to Mr Darcy."

"Is she?"

"Yes, do you not recall? Mr Wickham mentioned it the same evening he gave me the account of his history with the Darcy family. The two cousins are pledged to unite their estates."

"Well, the dismay of hearing you tell me the former must be my excuse for entirely forgetting the latter. Still, it is not uncommon for two cousins to marry." Jane raised an eyebrow and smiled more sincerely than before. "Unless one of them refuses."

Elizabeth shushed her sister loudly, grinning and peering pointedly in the direction her mother had gone. "Not so loud, if you please. Mama does not need reminding." As an afterthought, she added, "She must be clever, do you not think? And handsome. I refused *my* cousin because he is ridiculous and certainly not to my taste in appearance. If Mr Darcy has no such objections, then Miss de Bourgh must be a more appealing prospect."

"Perhaps, though recent experience has taught me that neither looks nor understanding will guarantee a man's affections."

A shrill summons came from the parlour. "Jane! Jane, come here at once!"

The sisters shared a knowing look, and Jane departed to wait upon Mrs Bennet.

"Was that your mother shrieking orders?" enquired Mr Bennet, stepping out of his library, book in hand.

Elizabeth replied that it was. "She is not pleased with Mr Collins's desertion."

"Nor am I, Lizzy. For what sport shall we have now? I had set my heart on more of his sermons on flattery. And to think, with the legendary Miss de Bourgh accompanying him, we might have seen him at work. Indeed, I am at least as put out as your mother that he will not be staying here."

"Do not be too disheartened. You may depend upon an invitation to dine at Lucas Lodge arriving imminently, for Sir William will not wish to keep his illustrious guest a secret. You will have ample opportunity to discover whether she is as pleased by our cousin's delicate compliments as he claims her to be."

Her father observably brightened. "A good point, my girl. Let us hope she proves to be every bit as absurd as her travelling companion."

Elizabeth smiled for her father's benefit, but she was not convinced. "I would find it odd if she were *entirely* ridiculous. Indeed, I wonder quite what virtues she must possess to satisfy a man as difficult to please as Mr Darcy."

"Well, we all know *you* do not please him, so we must presume she has a few that you do not, eh?" Mr Bennet replied, grinning gleefully. "But we all know Mr Darcy to be a proud, disagreeable man, so you ought not to let it trouble you."

"I assure you, it does not," she replied, rather more heatedly than she intended. Ignoring the way her father's eyebrows rose, she excused herself to leave in search of Mary.

# CHAPTER 2

It was not Sir William who imposed his esteemed houseguest upon the Bennets but the lady herself. Miss de Bourgh arrived long before the hour for morning calls, one of two ladies sitting up front in a gig being driven apace towards the house and identifiable as belonging to Sir William only by dint of his future son clinging frantically to the luggage shelf at the back.

"What does Mr Collins mean, bringing her here at this time of day?" Mrs Bennet cried, attempting to shoo her children about the room until they, or at least the furniture, appeared to best advantage.

"I am not sure we can lay the blame for this at his door," Elizabeth replied. "It looks rather more as though *she* has brought *him*."

Mr Bennet, peering from the window with her, smiled at this. "And only just at that, for she does not look as though she would have stopped to scoop him up if he had fallen off."

"Who is that driving them?" Mary enquired from her spot at the next window along.

Lydia left her seat at the table to look, drawing an exasperated cry from her mother, who had only moments before finished arranging her into it. "That is Miss de Bourgh."

"Are you sure?"

"Yes, I am sure," Lydia retorted petulantly.

"Do you not recall?" Kitty said, standing up from the sofa and drawing more strident objections from Mrs Bennet. "Mr Collins told us that Miss de Bourgh drives a little phaeton and ponies all the time around Rosings Park. A gig with one horse cannot present much bother."

"She is evidently quite the horsewoman," Jane remarked from the spot where her mother had positioned her and where she dutifully remained.

"There you are, Lizzy," said her father, nudging Elizabeth with his elbow. "We have already found a way in which her talents surpass yours, and she has not yet set foot in the house."

"Thank you, Papa," she replied sardonically. She did not argue, however, for she could claim no extraordinary skill with horses.

Mrs Bennet abandoned her object of titivating her children to come to the window and see for herself, whereupon she tutted indignantly. "It is all well and good for those who can afford the extravagance of a phaeton and ponies. Some of us must make do with walking."

Elizabeth glanced sidelong at her mother, surprised to hear something that sounded so much as though it was in her defence. She was more used to being scolded for her frequent sorties out of doors, Mrs Bennet's favourite lament being that the maids could spend their time in better ways than scrubbing her petticoat and boots clean.

"I imagine she is too frail to walk such a distance. Wait until you can see her closely. She looks as though she would snap in a sharp breeze," Lydia opined.

"Would, then, that she had stayed at home out of the wind," said Mrs Bennet, turning away from the window to sit defiantly in her chair.

All speculation was brought to a halt when the visitors reached the house. Mr Collins led his companions into the parlour and presented them with a preposterous degree of cere-mony. The lady who had been passenger in the gig was intro-duced as Mrs Jenkinson, Miss de Bourgh's companion.

Miss de Bourgh herself was hale enough to walk into the parlour unaided but was wrapped in so many shawls as made it difficult to determine much more about her constitution. It was not immediately clear whether she was tall or short, broad or slight, graceful or ungainly. All that could be said of her was that she was frightfully pale, and she had a pinched, troubled look about her, as though she had lost something and was looking for it. She bore absolutely no resemblance to Mr Darcy that Elizabeth could perceive. She supposed it fortunate, since it would be exceedingly strange for anybody to be married to the mirror image of themselves.

"These are my daughters," Mrs Bennet said once she and her husband had been introduced. She did not trouble herself to point out who was who as she rattled off their names.

Miss de Bourgh nodded but said nothing. There was an awkward silence as she sat down and waited impassively for Mrs Jenkinson to arrange each of her many layers, presumably to plug all gaps where a draft might find ingress. Tea was poured and handed around, and Mrs Jenkinson tested the temperature of hers before nodding to her charge that it was acceptable. Even after that, Miss de Bourgh did not speak. She only gazed slowly around the faces in the room, fixing finally and silently on Jane.

Elizabeth exchanged an amused glance with her father, who shrugged, indicating his equal bemusement. "It is a shame

Charlotte could not join you, Mr Collins," she said. "I hope she is not indisposed."

He answered somewhat haltingly that she was not. "Indeed, she would most certainly have joined us had she known we would call here."

"You did not tell her you were coming?"

"Sneaking out already, sir?" enquired Mr Bennet. "That does not bode well for your connubial felicity."

Mr Collins laughed in a way that did not mask how ill he liked the remark. "We did not—I would not—that is to say, it was not our intention to call at Longbourn."

Mrs Bennet made a noise of affront and stiffened her spine.

"Of course," Mr Collins continued hastily, "we meant to call on your good selves eventually, but today, the object was merely to show Miss de Bourgh a little of the neighbourhood. Only, when we happened to drive along the lane that leads to Longbourn, she expressed a wish to see it, no doubt aware that it is entailed upon me."

"No doubt," muttered Mr Bennet.

"Once the house was within sight, she quite reasonably pointed out that it would make sense to call and make the acquaintance of my relations while we were here, rather than come back again later. Miss de Bourgh is just like her esteemed mother in that respect," he added with a sycophantic smile in her direction. "Always making sensible suggestions that will save others bother."

Miss de Bourgh inclined her head at the compliment, apparently unaware that the only person she had saved from bother was herself.

"And is the neighbourhood to your liking?" Elizabeth enquired.

Miss de Bourgh glanced in her direction, her top lip puckered in a way that suggested it was not, and said, "It is very quaint." She then swivelled her head back to continue peering at Jane.

"We understand from Mr Collins that Rosings Park is very grand," Jane said. "It must be very different here from what you are used to at home."

"It is."

"Yes, well," said Mrs Bennet peevishly, "a man of Sir William's preponderance will always make a house feel smaller than it is. If only, Mr Collins, you had held to your previous arrangement and stayed at Longbourn, Miss de Bourgh would certainly have felt more at home."

"Madam, please! One cannot *begin* to compare Longbourn to Rosings Park!" Mr Collins blustered, looking with alarm at Miss de Bourgh as though the momentary lapse of veneration might cause her physical harm.

"It will do well enough for you when Mr Bennet dies, I should wager," Mrs Bennet murmured.

"Mr Collins, have you and Charlotte set a date for the wedding yet?" Elizabeth enquired.

"No, not as yet, although we hope it will be early in the New Ye—"

"Have you been presented at court?"

Everybody paused to look at Miss de Bourgh, who had thrown out this interjection with no preamble and was still staring with uncommon penetration at Jane.

"No, madam, I have not," Jane answered.

"None of my girls has been presented at court, and none of them is worse off for it," said Mrs Bennet.

"I wish you had told me this was your real opinion sooner, my dear," said her husband. "I should have wasted far less of my time concocting excuses not to go to London."

"And do you play?" Miss de Bourgh enquired, ignoring them both and continuing to look only at Jane.

"I used to play the pianoforte, but it is many years since I conceded that my ambition did not match my ability. I prefer to listen to my sisters play."

"Oh yes," said Mrs Bennet. "Mary is particularly talented.

Mary, open the instrument and play us that pretty little air you were practising this morning."

Mary did as she was asked, though she might as well have walked the mile to Meryton and played the tune on her Aunt Philips's pianoforte for all the notice Miss de Bourgh paid her, persevering instead with her questions to Jane.

"Do you draw?"

"Not with any degree of proficiency," Jane answered with a sweet, unassuming laugh.

"But you dance, I am told."

"Indeed—and take great pleasure in it."

Elizabeth wondered at the sincerity of Jane's smile. She herself was bristling at such an insolent inquisition by a lady whose ill health had, according to Mr Collins, prevented her from making progress in *any* accomplishments of note.

"Do you have much opportunity to dance at Rosings?" Elizabeth asked in an attempt to draw the conversation away from her sister.

Miss de Bourgh looked rather alarmed to have been thus addressed, but Mrs Jenkinson soon leapt to her defence.

"Miss de Bourgh's health does not permit her to engage in rigorous activity. We generally pursue gentler diversions."

"Such as playing and drawing?" Elizabeth asked.

Miss de Bourgh looked at her with a mixture of alarm and annoyance for a second or two and then she coughed—a breathy, extravagant exhalation that sent her companion into a frenzy of cushion plumping, shawl tightening, and brow soothing.

Mr Collins looked on in dismay. "Have a care, Cousin Elizabeth. Miss de Bourgh is of a delicate constitution."

Miss de Bourgh's head whipped around, her eyes narrowed, and her cough clean forgot. "*You* are Miss Elizabeth?"

"I am."

"Then who is that?" she demanded, pointing at Jane but never taking her eyes off Elizabeth.

"That is Jane, my eldest," Mrs Bennet answered.

"I see," Miss de Bourgh replied. "I had assumed—but never mind that." She looked Elizabeth up and down, then broke into a small but self-satisfied smile. "I see I was mistaken."

Elizabeth had time to do no more than frown in bewilderment before the door was opened, and Charlotte Lucas was announced.

"Mr Collins!" cried she upon entering the room. "What are you doing here?"

Mr Collins paled and tripped over a largely incoherent explanation. "Uh, oh, ah, good day, dear. You look lovely."

Mr Bennet snorted with mirth. Elizabeth took pity on her friend. "Miss de Bourgh expressed a wish to meet us."

"I see," Charlotte replied. After a momentary hesitation, she threw a belated and somewhat panicky curtsey at the lady in question.

"And why are *you* here?" asked Mrs Bennet rudely, clarifying for anybody who was unsure that she had not yet forgiven Charlotte for inveigling her way into position as Longbourn's mistress-in-waiting.

"I came to—" Charlotte glanced awkwardly at Miss de Bourgh. "To offer my—"

Seeing her friend visibly flounder, Elizabeth asked her, "Have you come to look at the brooch I told you about?" To Mr Collins she added, "For the wedding. Something borrowed."

Charlotte gave her a look of intense gratitude. "Yes, if it is not too inconvenient. Thank you."

Miss de Bourgh seemed excessively put out by this. It did not escape Elizabeth's notice that she gave her a piercing look before turning to her companion to complain that she was cold and wished to leave. Mrs Jenkinson began explaining that her charge suffered terribly in cold weather, and as Elizabeth led Charlotte into the hall, Mr Collins started eulogising over the very great number of fireplaces that were always kept ablaze at Rosings.

"I am sorry," Charlotte whispered as they hastened away from the parlour.

"It is hardly your fault."

"No, but what must your mother think? I do not blame her for being angry. I came with the specific purpose of apologising for the slight in Mr Collins's change of plans. I cannot fathom why Miss de Bourgh should demand that he give them up, only to insist that he bring her here at the very first opportunity."

Elizabeth was increasingly certain *she* knew the reason. Miss de Bourgh had evidently discovered Charlotte was not Mr Collins's first choice of wife and had come to inspect the woman who had refused him. Her mistaken assumption that it must have been Jane, the undisputed beauty of the family, confirmed it in her mind.

Unable to guess what Charlotte's feelings on the matter might be, she chose not to mention it, saying instead, "She is a strange woman—frail yet still overbearing. The latter must be a family trait, but her fragility makes for a curious addition."

"Indeed it does. One moment she, or at least her companion, is complaining that she feels, or looks, or might *become* unwell. The next, she is demanding conversation or entertainment or—"

"Or the use of your father's gig."

"Precisely! My mother is exhausting herself attempting to satisfy her every whim—of which she has an astonishing number. Maria is terrified of her. John has taken to teasing Mr Collins for being hobbled to too many women, which is making *him* ill-tempered."

"Oh dear! How long does she plan to stay? Surely, she cannot intend to impose on you for very long. 'Tis Christmas next week."

"Until Saturday."

"Well, that is not too bad."

"It is four days, Eliza." They reached Elizabeth's bedchamber, and Charlotte turned to her with an exasperated expression. "What am I to do with her for *four* days?"

"She might improve on closer acquaintance," Elizabeth replied, laughing as she began searching through the drawers of her dressing table. "You never know, you might become friends."

Charlotte scoffed. "People of Miss de Bourgh's sphere do not make friends with women like me. Her uncle is an earl!"

Elizabeth was put in mind of Mr Darcy and his disdain for Meryton society and agreed that her friend was probably correct. "In which case," she added, "you had better use this time to learn to tolerate her, for friendly or not, she will soon be your closest neighbour. Here." She held out her favourite brooch. "What do you think?"

Charlotte angled it towards the window and smiled when the sunlight amplified its opalescence. "I think it is beautiful. You know you do not actually have to lend it to me, do you not?"

"I should dearly love you to wear it," Elizabeth insisted and meant it. For though she could not respect Charlotte's decision to marry Mr Collins, they had nevertheless been friends for a very long time.

Charlotte thanked her sincerely. "Will you come to Lucas Lodge tomorrow to help me keep Miss de Bourgh occupied?"

"I shall certainly come, if you would like me to, though it is you she desires to know, not me."

Charlotte insisted that she *would* like it, and thus it was agreed. The ladies returned downstairs, where they found Mr Collins in a state of some distress.

"I humbly beg your pardon, madam," he was saying in an anxious tone, "but I do not know that Lady Lucas has issued an invitation." Upon noticing Charlotte had returned, he pounced to her side and grabbed her arm. "My dear, do you know whether your mother means to invite the Bennets for dinner tomorrow?"

"She will when you inform her that I wish it," Miss de Bourgh replied before Charlotte was able to speak. "Come, Miss Lucas. We are leaving. You may ride with me."

Mr Collins made a noise and held up a finger as though he wished to object but did not dare say the words aloud. He was promptly informed that he should walk back.

With one last, prolonged glare at Elizabeth, Miss de Bourgh left the room, her slow, shuffling gait completely at odds with her vastly superior air.

"I can see why you are so charmed by the de Bourghs, sir," said Mr Bennet to Mr Collins. "What splendid neighbours they must be. An endless source of sport, I imagine."

Mr Collins looked at him blankly for a moment, then shook his head and excused himself to scuttle home after his future wife.

"Well," exclaimed Mrs Bennet expressively, "all I can say is, thank goodness she is not staying under my roof! Have you ever met such a peevish, complaining woman?"

Nobody replied, though everybody looked at her, which Mrs Bennet took as invitation to elaborate.

"If she grumbled less, I might be disposed to show more sympathy, but if you ask me, anybody whose every other utterance is a complaint deserves no such attention, for if they are well enough to complain, then they are well enough, and that is all there is to it. I should know. I daresay I have endured more aches and chills in the last week than she has in a lifetime with all those fires burning at Rosings Park. She does not know what it is to suffer. Not as I do."

With an angry growl, she twisted to face Elizabeth. "If you had only done your duty and agreed to marry Mr Collins, you could have insisted he not bring her here. Charlotte Lucas has none of your impertinence. She will never tell him no, and so we must continue to suffer both him *and* his tiresome connexions. Oh!" She pressed her palm to her forehead. "All this distraction has unsettled my poor nerves. I must lie down." She paused in her sweep from the room to say to her husband, "If an invitation comes from Lucas Lodge, be sure to send word that we shall *all* be in attendance. I shall not sit back and allow Lady Lucas to take the credit for introducing Miss de Bourgh to the neighbourhood. She is, after all, *our* cousin's connexion." She gave another groan and stumbled heroically to the door.

Mr Bennet stood up to leave also, though he stopped in front of Elizabeth and shook his head. "I am sorry, my girl. Anybody who is able to induce your mother to admit that complaining is a dreadful habit is a more accomplished person than I have ever met. I am afraid Miss de Bourgh has quite the lead on you at the moment."

❧

Darcy forced himself to smile, though he could not hold it for long. He turned to look into the fire to avoid giving offence to Miss Bingley, whom he was finding singularly irritating that evening. Had they been at Bingley's house, he might have made up an excuse to leave. Alas, Bingley and his sisters were dining with him at Number One, and he could scarcely absent himself from his own soirée.

"What about you, Darcy?" Bingley enquired. "Will you go to Chamberlain's ball?"

Darcy had no intention of going, for dancing was never high on his list of favoured amusements at the best of times—and this was assuredly *not* the best of times. Nevertheless, a peevish whim compelled him to say whatever was in contradiction to Miss Bingley, who had spent the last few minutes maligning the man's new wife.

"I am considering it, if only to congratulate him on his marriage and welcome Mrs Chamberlain to England."

"There you have it, Caroline. Darcy is not afraid of her," Bingley replied.

"I never said I was afraid of Mrs Chamberlain," she retorted.

"And I never said I would not go. Indeed, perhaps I *shall* go and make it known she has one friend, at least, here in London."

Darcy could see in the periphery of his vision she was watching him, but if she hoped he would offer to accompany her, she would be sorely disappointed.

"I should like to go to another ball," Mrs Hurst said with a sigh. "I have not been to one since we were at Neth—" She stopped abruptly when her sister delivered a quick elbow to her ribs.

Indelicate though it was, Darcy was not sorry. In this, if in nothing else, Miss Bingley and he were in accord. They had barely managed to dissuade Bingley from returning to Meryton—and Jane Bennet—and it was not such a complete triumph that Darcy had any confidence of his friend's mind staying resolved. Reminders of his time there were best avoided.

"You are right, Louisa. It was a splendid ball," Bingley said longingly. "Though that was as much to do with the company as the dancing."

*Too late.*

"Charles," said Miss Bingley, glancing expressively at Darcy's sister, "you will give Miss Darcy the wrong impression." Turning to speak directly to Georgiana, she said, "We had a pleasant enough time there, but we much prefer being back in town. The society here is far superior."

*Usually,* Darcy thought, reflecting grimly on Miss Bingley's less than superior company. He was used to her attention, but even by her standards, she was being absurdly obsequious this evening.

"You would have liked it there, I think, Miss Darcy," Bingley said, apparently indifferent to his sister's attempt to redirect the conversation. "There were several young ladies of your age."

"Yes, all wild and ill-bred," Miss Bingley added.

"No, indeed, not all!" her brother objected.

"Most of them were, you must admit," Hurst put in. "Never

have I witnessed such a raucous gaggle as overran the card room after supper that night."

"They were lively, to be sure," Bingley argued, "but who wants a ball without a bit of liveliness? Apart from Darcy, maybe."

Darcy did not rise to that challenge. He was watching his sister, who was growing observably more uneasy with every passing moment. He did not wonder at it. She was under strict instructions not to mention Meryton—or, more particularly, Anne's jaunt there—and was no doubt fretting over how she might evade the subject now that it had been broached. He felt somewhat guilty for having overemphasised it so, but Bingley would almost certainly take Anne's presence there as reason to go back. And since returning and reuniting with Miss Bennet would be seriously detrimental to his friend's prospects, Darcy meant to do all he could to keep Bingley away.

"On the contrary," he said. "The only thing worse than an excessively lively ball is an excessively dull one."

"Oh certainly," Miss Bingley said. "One ought to be able to have fun at a dance. I should find no pleasure in sitting about, philosophising all evening."

Darcy stared at her fully sensible, even if she was not, that she had said precisely the opposite at Netherfield when they were planning the wretched ball. Would that she grow a mind of her own!

"Have you heard Lord Liverpool's latest idea?" he said to Hurst, deliberately taking the conversation where he hoped Miss Bingley would not follow.

"No politics, Darcy, I beg you!" cried Bingley before Hurst had a chance to swallow his mouthful of wine.

"Come, Charles, can we not discuss anything more serious than dancing? I think it admirable that Mr Darcy keeps abreast of such matters," Miss Bingley simpered.

Darcy took a gulp of his own wine to prevent snarling with vexation. Was there nothing he could say that she would not advocate? "There is a new turnpike road being built at Evesham. They plan to set the toll for a chaise-and-four at a shilling."

Bingley raised an eyebrow. "You are a veritable spark in a powder keg this evening, Darcy. First, politics, now roads. What will it be next—taxes?"

"Politics and roads are both matters of great importance to landowners," Miss Bingley told him. "You really ought not to ridicule that which you do not understand."

Darcy reviled the ingratiating look she tossed his way. "It could be considered a worse evil to ridicule a want of understanding," he said stonily.

Miss Bingley gave a nervous laugh. "I beg your pardon?"

"You accused Bingley of ridiculing me to disguise his ignorance, but a disinclination to discuss something does not equate to mockery."

"Well no, but I think we all know he was implying that you were being dull."

"I *was* being dull."

"No sir!" she cried, leaping to his defence, where she was clearly most comfortable. "You were only making conversation, and that shows good manners." She turned to address her sister, but Darcy, unsatisfied, pressed on.

"But if I chose to discuss something of which, as you say, my companions were ignorant, does that not make me *ill-mannered*?"

She exchanged an uneasy look with Mrs Hurst before answering hesitantly. "I suppose, if it was your purpose to expose Charles's ignorance, then yes, but you will not convince me there was any such intention in what you did."

"But if that *had* been my design?"

Her brow furrowed, and she gave a tight smile. "You will not make me accuse you of meanness, Mr Darcy."

"*Did* you do it on purpose?" Bingley enquired.

"That is irrelevant. I am merely trying to establish whether it is discourteous to initiate a conversation without giving due consideration to the preferences and abilities of one's company."

"Much as you are now?"

"What?"

Bingley shook his head. "What has got into you this evening, man? 'Tis midweek—you have no excuse for your usual Sunday evening doldrums. Why are you trying so hard to start an argument?"

"I am not."

He was. He had wanted Miss Bingley to respond with wit, intelligence, a glint of challenge in her eye. To hell with it, he wanted her to argue with him like Elizabeth would have! The realisation amplified his ill-humour tenfold.

"What would *you* have us talk about, Bingley?"

The infuriating devil smirked at him. "I wished to talk about balls."

"You wished to talk about Netherfield, and I have told you there is no point. We have discussed this. There is no advantage in going back. You had much better stay away."

Bingley sighed and sank further into his chair. "Yes, yes, I know. There is no need to repeat the entire sermon. I remember it all perfectly. Nevertheless, I cannot help but think it is the height of poor manners to have left without word. I promised Mrs Bennet I would dine with them on my return." He looked at Georgiana. "Do you not agree, Miss Darcy? Would you not be offended if I said I would dine with you and then I disappeared without a word?"

Georgiana's eyes widened, and she swallowed so hard Darcy saw it from across the room.

"Bingley," he said through gritted teeth, "we are not returning to Hertfordshire."

"Do not concern yourself, Charles," Miss Bingley said, with a reassuring glance at Darcy that he absolutely did not deserve. "I shall write to Jane again to confirm that we mean to winter in town. That will certainly suffice, for we have no particular connexion to them that would lead them to expect more. Indeed, I should think Mrs Bennet will be relieved at not having to entertain another family so close to Christmas."

Bingley nodded disconsolately, and the room fell into a gloomy silence, all topics of conversation having been established as either too tedious or too incendiary for an ordinary Tuesday evening in December.

# CHAPTER 3

Charlotte's younger sister snuck out of a side passage to greet Elizabeth when she arrived at Lucas Lodge the next day. "Thank goodness you are here," she whispered as she attached herself to Elizabeth's arm and clung to it tightly. "We have run out of ideas."

"Good morning, Maria. Ideas for what?"

"Ways in which to please Miss de Bourgh. She has been dissatisfied with everything we have done thus far."

Elizabeth frowned. "She chose to impose herself upon you. I should say the onus was on her to be a pleasant houseguest, rather than to expect you to keep her entertained."

Maria nodded her head. "That is as my mother says, yet nothing has satisfied her. Even my father has begun to show signs of vexation."

Miss de Bourgh must be trying indeed if even Sir William had grown weary of her. "How do you know she is dissatisfied? Is she uncivil?"

"If silence can be taken as incivility, aye. She has not yet said a word to me. Even after I played the pianoforte for her last night. It was as though I was not there."

Elizabeth declined to comment. Sweet girl though Maria was, she was so timid that it often seemed as though she were not there. "Does she speak to anyone else?"

"Sometimes she asks a question but usually only of Charlotte or Mr Collins. Mostly, she just sits and looks disapproving."

"She is bearing a greater resemblance to her cousin by the moment. Let us see whether we can draw her out a little this morning, shall we?"

Maria nodded and squashed herself hard against Elizabeth's side as they entered the morning room.

Miss de Bourgh reddened upon seeing them enter and turned to whisper urgently to her companion. None of the men of the house were present—only Charlotte and her mother.

"How delightful to see you, Eliza! But I am sure you young ladies have plenty of things to discuss that you would not wish me to overhear. I shall leave you alone to talk amongst yourselves." Lady Lucas promptly hastened away.

Elizabeth found herself pulled to the sofa, where she sat heavily, thanks to Maria's insistent tugging.

"How nice of you to call, Eliza," Charlotte said, her tone thick with apology.

"Is it usual for people to pay calls so early in the day here?" Miss de Bourgh enquired tersely.

Maria whispered to Elizabeth, "Do you see?"

"Eliza and I are good friends. We often visit each other outside of the customary hours for calling," Charlotte explained.

"Which are the same here as everywhere else," Elizabeth added, wondering whether Miss de Bourgh were even conscious of what time she had called at Longbourn the previous day. The information was apparently not of interest to her, however. She had turned to talk to her companion again, though with so little effort to lower her voice as convinced Elizabeth she was meant to hear every word.

"I know of many young ladies who claim to be visiting friends when their real purpose is to put themselves in the path of their friend's handsome brothers."

Elizabeth laughed before she could help herself.

"You are amused, Miss Bennet? I would have thought that finding a husband *amongst your acquaintance* was a matter you might take more seriously."

"Forgive me. Mr Lucas and I have known each other all our lives. I am sure he would be flattered to know you consider him handsome, but I could never think of him in that way. We are more like cousins." No sooner had she closed her mouth on the words than she realised her mistake. She had intended no insult, but Miss de Bourgh evidently perceived one, for her eyes narrowed and the colour returned to her cheeks.

"Oh yes, I recall now. You are not in favour of cousins marrying." She stretched her neck long, which gave the impression of leaning forward without shifting her weight. "You will have to take my word that, in my sphere, it is not only considered acceptable but eminently sensible."

"I am not against cousins marrying in principle." She glanced at Charlotte and hastily added, "When they are well suited to each other in disposition. Only, sometimes it transpires that one of the two finds a better match elsewhere."

Her attempt to placate her friend only seemed to fluster Miss de Bourgh more, and in an attempt to appease her, Elizabeth was on the verge of explicitly congratulating her on her engagement to Mr Darcy when Charlotte intervened.

"Eliza, you must be thirsty after your walk here. Maria, will you call for some tea?"

Maria nodded enthusiastically and hastened to ring the bell.

"You *walked* here?" Miss de Bourgh repeated. She looked just as disgusted by the revelation as her cousin had the morning Elizabeth walked to Netherfield two months ago.

"I did. My mother would have had me ride, but—"

"Can you not drive?"

"It would not matter if I could, madam, for we do not possess the means."

This remark seemed finally to mollify Miss de Bourgh. She relaxed back into her seat with a slight smile. "No, that is true. I had forgotten your circumstances were so reduced compared to my own."

Maria sidled back to the sofa, taking a wide berth around Miss de Bourgh. There seemed little need, however, for her earlier observations had been proved correct. The lady had deigned to give her no attention whatsoever. Elizabeth might have suggested that Maria sneak out of the room if she thought the girl had the courage to go.

"Mr Collins has said he will teach me to ride his gig," Charlotte said to Miss de Bourgh. "He has always spoken very highly of your skill with a phaeton. My father never thought it necessary for his daughters to learn, but I believe it is because of your example that Mr Collins deems it a vital skill for his wife."

Miss de Bourgh nodded, her eyes on Elizabeth as she agreed. "I presume you do not have the correct clothes for riding, either. Do you stay abreast of the latest fashions?"

"When I can, though I do not have much opportunity," Charlotte replied.

Miss de Bourgh flicked a vexed look at her and then repeated her question to Elizabeth.

"Charlotte has greatly the advantage over me, being the oldest daughter in her family. I must make do with whatever my eldest sister, Jane, no longer wishes to wear." This was not entirely true. She and Jane shared their clothes by choice. Aware how dearly her friend wished to appear in a favourable light, she added for good measure, "Charlotte always dresses beautifully."

"That is well. My mother will expect you to dine often at Rosings, Miss Lucas. It will be imperative that you dress and behave appropriately. Have you spent much time in company with people of higher rank?"

"A little. As you know, my father has been knighted. We occasionally accompany him to court."

"You have an advantage over your friend, then. Miss Bennet's father apparently dislikes town."

Elizabeth grinned. "It is an advantage to which Charlotte is more than welcome."

"You do not care for polished society, Miss Bennet?"

"With one or two exceptions, I do not consider the society I keep *un*polished. And what I have seen of the manners of those who frequent more fashionable places has not left me with any peculiar sense of deprivation. Besides, a woman ought not to be judged by the company she keeps or the places she visits but on her own merits. Would you not agree?"

Miss de Bourgh did not answer immediately and regarded Elizabeth with puzzlement. When another minute went by without her speaking, Mrs Jenkinson began to fuss.

"Are you quite well, Miss de Bourgh? Should you like a measure of your tincture? Allow me to fetch it."

"I am sorry she is being so difficult," Charlotte said quietly, leaning over the arm of her chair towards Elizabeth.

"*I* am sorry I am not doing much to help make her more bearable."

"You are doing wonderfully," Maria whispered. "This is the most she has said since she arrived."

Charlotte nodded her agreement, and Elizabeth huffed a small laugh. "Perhaps because she is not getting the answers she desires. I shall try and behave myself better."

"No, pray carry on as you are. The more opinions you give, the more complying you make *me* look. At this rate, I shall be her absolute favourite by dinner," Charlotte replied with a sly smile.

Elizabeth duly continued to give detailed responses to an increasingly arbitrary succession of enquiries until, without warning, Miss de Bourgh announced, "I shall drive you home now, Miss Bennet."

"Home?"

"Yes, whilst the weather holds."

Elizabeth had intended to stay longer but did not wish to gainsay the woman outright by insisting upon it. Nevertheless, she could see no justification for taking the gig. "I thank you, but Longbourn is not far from here. There is no need to have the horse brought out."

"It is no trouble," Miss de Bourgh replied, once again demonstrating that her understanding of the word did not extend beyond any imposition to her own person.

At least, Elizabeth supposed, a ride in the gig would fulfil her promise of helping to keep the woman entertained. Thus, after less than an hour at Lucas Lodge, Elizabeth found herself being driven back to Longbourn at an interminable pace and in painful silence. What little of Miss de Bourgh's face could be seen beneath her bonnet and a dozen scarves looked pale and drawn, and were it not for the steady control with which she drove the gig, Elizabeth might have worried she was sickening in the cold.

"It was good of you to take the time to come and meet Charlotte before she moves to Kent," she said at length.

Miss de Bourgh stared ahead at the road and sniffed. "My mother was called away. I had no other demands on my time."

"I see." This was not information Elizabeth would be sharing with either Charlotte or Mr Collins. Better they continue in the belief that it was a kindly meant condescension. "My cousin speaks very highly of your mother. She sounds like an estimable lady."

"People always admire my mother. She has an overactive sense of charity and a predilection for frankness. She frightens everybody into reverence, eventually. I understand you are acquainted with my cousin Mr Darcy."

Elizabeth was so busy being amused by the first remark that

the second took her aback. She had not expected to hear his name, which was silly really, given that he was one of only two acquaintances she and Miss de Bourgh had in common.

"Yes, I know him a little."

"You know him well enough to have danced with him."

"Dancing with Mr Darcy and knowing him are not mutually connected endeavours. He did not say very much."

"All praise to him, in that case. Would that more gentlemen could learn to be less fascinated by the sound of their own voices."

"Perhaps, though *some* conversation whilst one is dancing can be pleasant."

"That depends on what is being said. Given the choice between enjoying the moment and having it ruined by an inane discussion that is of no real interest to either party, I should always prefer companionable silence."

*Companionable silence!* Elizabeth reflected with amusement. She rather thought *misanthropic taciturnity* a better description, but she kept the notion to herself.

"What about when you were not dancing? Did you have occasion to speak to Darcy much at other times?"

"Not overmuch, no."

"You did not spend much time with him, then?"

"Other than the few days I stayed at Netherfield with him, no." Upon receiving a rather horrified look and hearing Mrs Jenkinson's muffled gasp from where she perched behind them on the parcel shelf, Elizabeth explained. "My sister had a fever and was instructed by the apothecary to stay there until she was well enough to return home. I stayed to nurse her."

Miss de Bourgh flicked the reins and the horse skittered forwards, drawing another, louder gasp from her companion. "How convenient!"

"Excepting Mr Bingley, and perhaps my mother, I do not think anybody involved considered it so, least of all my sister."

"So, you had no conversation with Darcy the entire time you were there?"

"Well, obviously we had *some.*"

"What did you discuss?"

"Goodness, I can scarcely recall," Elizabeth lied. In fact, she could remember almost every one of their exchanges, for most had left her either laughing or fuming for hours afterwards. She recalled, with perfect clarity, questioning his vanity and pride, his opinion of Mr Bingley's character, his treatment of Mr Wickham, and his opinion of what constitutes an accomplished woman. On reflection, almost every interaction had centred upon a challenge to his integrity. Elizabeth rebuffed a twinge of guilt, certain that Mr Darcy's conceit was more than robust enough to withstand the scrutiny. "It was just general chatter."

"I doubt that. My cousin does not *chatter.*"

"No, I suppose he does not. Very well, I believe we had debates and the like. The usual sort of discussions one has over breakfast and dinner and coffee."

"So, actually, you had plenty of conversations with him."

Elizabeth sighed. If all Mr Darcy's relations were this supercilious, she did not wonder at his having turned out proud and disagreeable. It was not behaviour conducive to cordiality.

"Hardly. On the last day I was there, he all but ignored me."

Miss de Bourgh looked distinctly unimpressed. "Was that before or after he asked you to dance?"

"Both, strictly speaking," she replied testily, for she was growing increasingly tired of being interrogated. "He asked me to dance three times, though one was only a tease, and I only agreed once."

She was rewarded with a venomous look but was denied any further response when a pheasant dashed into their path, and Miss de Bourgh was forced to pull the horse violently to one side to avoid it. Mrs Jenkinson let out a terrified squawk. Elizabeth clutched at the seat and held her breath until the gig righted itself, which it only did thanks to some impressively quick-witted and calm manoeuvring on Miss de Bourgh's part.

"That was very well done," Elizabeth said breathily.

"I do try to avoid the pheasants in particular. I like their iridescent plumage."

Rather unfairly, the admission of such a simple, honest enjoyment of wildlife surprised Elizabeth. It disposed her to be a little less guarded.

"May I ask why it matters what I talked about with your cousin?" she enquired in what she hoped was a conciliatory tone.

If the question startled her, Miss de Bourgh disguised it well. "By your own edict, we must discuss *something*. Would you rather we discussed *your* cousin?"

"Not really."

"I thought not. Mine is infinitely more interesting and worldly. I am not surprised you felt you had little to discuss with him. His knowledge no doubt far exceeds yours."

"Yes, I expect it far exceeds *everybody's* who hardly ever leaves the place in which they grew up."

Miss de Bourgh pinched her lips together, and her nostrils flared. "My health might have prevented extensive travel, but *I*, at least, had a governess. I am able to engage with my cousin on many subjects."

"I do not doubt it, madam," Elizabeth replied coolly, "though I believe I just about managed to make myself understood."

"What a relief! But then, Darcy is very generous and will only have engaged you in discussions on which he could be sure you would be able to comprehend him."

"If you mean that Mr Darcy only disagreed with everything I said because he thought I had the wit to match him, then I suppose I ought to be flattered that he did nothing *but* argue with me."

"Except when he did *not* argue with you and was silent, but that did not please you either, did it? I think it is a very good thing he has left Hertfordshire. You are obviously horribly unsuited as acquaintances and best kept out of each other's way."

"I could not agree more," Elizabeth replied, though she heard less vehemence in her voice than had been in her thoughts.

Miss de Bourgh let out a long breath, her shoulders dropped, and she turned to Elizabeth with a small but satisfied smile. And there, hidden behind the pallor and the perennially dissatisfied hauteur, was her loveliness. And there, too, was the familial resemblance.

Elizabeth looked away swiftly, unsettled that only in Miss de Bourgh's handsomeness could she see Mr Darcy. She was inordinately pleased when they bounced over a deep rut, and Mrs Jenkinson let out another yelp, for it gave her the excuse to insist upon being allowed to walk the rest of the way to let the poor woman ride in comfort.

Miss de Bourgh consented with a haste that made her insistence upon driving Elizabeth home in the first place seem utterly absurd. She turned the gig with enviable skill, waited barely long enough for her companion to scramble into the seat next to her, and departed without a word of farewell.

Elizabeth shook her head in bewilderment and set out for home, pitying Charlotte a lifetime in servitude to such a woman.

The next morning brought an invitation from Lady Lucas, an icy drizzle, and a dismal pall over Longbourn. Mrs Bennet passed the chief of the day flouncing from room to room in search of an audience for her complaints.

As promised, she was resolved to dine with her usurper, if for no other purpose than to exhibit her husband, whom she had fiercely instructed to say, wear, drink, and generally *do* whatever was necessary to convince the world he was in the finest possible fettle, in absolutely no danger of dying for the next forty years at least.

Elizabeth's youngest sisters, put out at being prevented by the weather from walking to Meryton to see the officers, lounged about the house lamenting their ennui. And the delivery of a letter for Jane just after two o'clock ruined any hope of the day being redeemed.

"Where is everybody?" Elizabeth said to Mary upon finding her alone in the parlour.

"Papa is in his library, Lydia and Kitty went upstairs, Mama is speaking to Cook, and Jane went to read her letter in private."

"A letter? Do you know who it was from?"

Mary shook her head. "She did not say."

Elizabeth thanked her and went directly to find Jane, confident that any privacy her sister sought would not exclude her. She found her already finished with the letter and turning the folded missive over and over in her hands.

"They are not coming back," Jane said with a sad smile. "Miss Bingley writes that it is now certain they are all settled in London for the winter."

Elizabeth's heart sank. "May I read it?"

Jane handed the letter to her but shook her head as she did so. "You will not find any other meaning in it. They are spending all their time at Mr Darcy's house, and although she has attempted to spare my feelings by not saying it directly, it is clear Miss Bingley wishes me to understand that Miss Darcy is now the focus of her brother's attentions."

Elizabeth sat down next to Jane and read the letter with mounting indignation. "There is nothing in here that convinces me these are anything other than Miss Bingley's own wishes."

"Have you read to the end? Mr Bingley sends his regrets for not having had time to pay his respects to his friends in Hertfordshire before he left the country. Those are not the wishes of his sister. He is his own master."

"But Miss de Bourgh is—"

"Here to see Charlotte. Please do not look for signs that are not there. I do not think I could withstand any more disappointment. Miss de Bourgh's visit is unrelated to Mr Darcy or any of his friends, and I shall not torment myself by continuing to hope otherwise. I beg you would not, either."

Elizabeth did not argue, for it looked increasingly certain that Jane was right, and Mr Bingley was not coming back. Refraining from argument was not the same as withholding her opinion of Miss Bingley, however, and she expressed her dislike with great energy. If her litany of complaints drowned the small and vastly disconcerting voice in her head that whispered, '*Mr Darcy is not returning, either,*' then she did not have the least objection to allowing her censure to flow long.

# CHAPTER 4

"What a delightful observation," Mr Collins simpered. "The plums are, as you say, glazed to perfection. But then, you are looking particularly radiant yourself this evening, madam. Your charms would outshine even the glossiest of fruits."

This compliment, absurd—and inaccurate—though it was, might have been better received had it been paid to his betrothed. Instead, it was lavished upon Miss de Bourgh, in keeping with what appeared to be a well-established method. First, Mr Collins complimented her. Next, he complimented himself for having paid her such a pretty compliment. Then, he waited eagerly for some sign that his blandishments had pleased her.

He had so far been waiting three and a quarter hours, which was precisely how long it had been since the soiree began. Miss de Bourgh seemed neither diverted nor vexed and certainly not flattered by his ongoing panegyric. Her attention seemed to be elsewhere entirely, begging the question why she was there at all.

"You have spent your time wisely today, I see, Mr Collins," said Mr Bennet. "Not only arranging an entire bank of subtle little compliments to please the ladies but taking the trouble to discover what delights were being planned for dinner so that all your praise would be perfectly apt. A day well spent, sir."

Mr Collins thanked him. "I consider it an imperative part of my duties to be fully prepared to offer whatever encouragements I can that might afford comfort or pleasure."

Mr Bennet gave a nod of appreciation. "I commend your commitment to your craft, sir."

Charlotte's youngest brother scoffed loudly. "Anybody can compare a person to food and call it a compliment. Watch this. Charlotte, you look like a cabbage."

"Thank you, Timothy," Charlotte replied drily, "though I do not think you have quite mastered Mr Collins's finesse just yet."

"Almost," Mr Bennet mouthed to Elizabeth with a mischievous expression that nearly ruined her composure.

"Indeed. You look nothing like a cabbage, my dear," Mr Collins objected, "except that your gown has a greenish shade to it. That is no bad thing, I should add. Miss de Bourgh often wears green and wears it well, too, for it enhances the colour of her eyes." After casting her an unctuous and toothy smile, he glanced back to inform the rest of the dinner guests, "I take care to mention often that Miss de Bourgh's indifferent health has, in no way, diminished the magnificence of her eyes and flatter myself that such reassurances are always gratefully received." He stopped speaking and regarded Miss de Bourgh with all the patient adoration of a puppy.

Miss de Bourgh did not look up from her plate as she replied, coolly, "My eyes are blue, Mr Collins."

Elizabeth barely stifled a laugh.

"Oh—ah—pardon me," he stammered. "Perhaps I was thinking of your mother and assumed a family resemb—"

"Her eyes are also blue."

"Or perhaps your cousin, Mr Darcy?"

"Mr Darcy's eyes are brown," Elizabeth corrected him.

"How very observant, Miss Elizabeth," said Miss de Bourgh, looking up at her. "Do you recall the eye colour of every man with whom you barely converse and dance with but once?"

Elizabeth, wholly unaware that she possessed this nugget of information until she said it, felt her cheeks redden. "Apparently."

"Well, whatever colour his eyes are, Mr Darcy is a *most* estimable gentleman," said Mr Collins, "and one of the most illustrious personages in the country."

Elizabeth caught Jane's gaze and rolled her eyes. Evidently, having failed to impress Miss de Bourgh with his attentions to her, Mr Collins meant to move on to eulogising about her relations instead. She doubted he would find the present company particularly receptive to such a scheme—a suspicion that was substantiated in the next moment by her mother.

"Mr Darcy does not even *like* the country. He considers it nothing at all, in fact."

"Come, come, Mrs Bennet," cajoled Sir William. "That cannot be true. Mr Darcy has a house in the country the same as the rest of us."

"It certainly *is* true," she replied heatedly. "He told me himself that he considers the society *constrained and unvarying,* by which you can be sure he meant to disparage anyone who does not live at least half the year or more in town."

Mrs Bennet was quite mistaken about the conversation in question, but Elizabeth felt no inclination to defend Mr Darcy until she noticed Charlotte's discomfort. Following her friend's gaze to Miss de Bourgh, she could easily discern that lady's displeasure. It was hardly surprising, she supposed, that one might take offence at the censure of one's relation and future husband, and so for Charlotte's sake, she resolved to correct her mother's misapprehension.

"You have quoted Mr Darcy out of context, Mama. That is not what he meant."

"But it *is* what he said, and therefore, I shall take whatever meaning from it I choose."

"Let us leave the gentlemen to their port," Lady Lucas announced, coming to her feet abruptly and indicating to a footman to clear the table.

The ladies all duly filed out and busied themselves finding cups of coffee, talking partners, and places to sit in the drawing room. Elizabeth had assumed with some relief that was the end of any discussion about Mr Darcy. She soon discovered otherwise.

Charlotte cornered her at the refreshment table and, whilst maintaining a perfectly composed smile, began whispering in a decidedly uncomposed manner. "I mean no disrespect to your mother, Eliza, and I am very sorry if Mr Darcy was uncivil to her, but her words have angered Miss de Bourgh, and I know not what to do to put things right."

Elizabeth dared not look at Miss de Bourgh, for it would too clearly mark her as the object of their discussion. She smiled innocuously into her coffee cup and enquired, "Has she said she is displeased?"

"No, but she has a face like thunder, and Mr Collins is beside himself that she has been offended."

"Then I am very sorry, but if you are hoping my mother will apologise, I think I had better warn you it might be better to let the matter drop. She will only make it worse if you bring it up again."

Charlotte shook her head. "I was hoping *you* would speak to Miss de Bourgh."

"Me?"

"Yes. You said your mother quoted Mr Darcy out of context. I thought you could explain that she had misunderstood him."

Elizabeth restrained herself to a quiet sigh before conceding. "Very well. But only because it is you."

She reluctantly made her way to sit next to Miss de Bourgh. Elizabeth received no more than a cursory nod in greeting and sipped her coffee in silence as she attempted to fix on how to broach the subject.

"The dinner was very pleasant," came a squeaky voice. Miss de Bourgh had not moved her lips, and Elizabeth looked around in bewilderment until Mrs Jenkinson made her presence known by leaning forward in her seat on the other side of Miss de Bourgh. "The lamb was cooked to perfection."

Elizabeth smiled and nodded back. That appeared to be the extent of the lady's contribution. She leant back in her seat, disappearing from view once more. Miss de Bourgh glowered ahead as though neither of them were there.

"I must apologise for my mother," Elizabeth said quietly. "I assure you she quite mistook Mr Darcy's meaning."

"I doubt it." At last, Miss de Bourgh turned to face Elizabeth, and Charlotte's description of her countenance proved to be remarkably accurate. "It sounds just the sort of thing he would say. I scarcely blame your mother for being offended. Those of us who have little choice but to avoid London can do without the disdain of those with the luxury of going there whenever they choose."

Surprise kept Elizabeth quiet too long, and Miss de Bourgh snapped, "I cannot imagine why you should be astonished at my saying so. It was *you* who told me a woman ought not to be judged by the company she keeps or the places she visits."

"That is true, I did. Though, if you will pardon me, it was *you* who remarked on the disadvantage of my having spent so little time in London myself."

"Do not fool yourself into believing it is *not* a disadvantage, Miss Elizabeth. It will certainly be viewed as such by any gentleman wishing to attach himself to you."

Elizabeth began to suspect what was truly at play. Miss de

Bourgh feared her cousin would think less of her for having been similarly deprived of what he considered refined society.

*She seeks to comfort herself by undervaluing me.* It might have rankled had Elizabeth cared for Mr Darcy's good opinion. As it was, she pitied Miss de Bourgh for being made to feel as though her intended thought ill of her. She had no great fondness for him, but it was unfair that Mr Darcy should be in disfavour with his future wife for something he had not said.

"That is as may be, but whether or not that is Mr Darcy's true opinion, in this instance, it really is not what he said. I had remarked that I like to study people's characters. He merely observed that there was a greater variety of people to study in London than in the country."

"I see."

Elizabeth could not tell from Miss de Bourgh's countenance whether she was convinced. "Truly," she insisted, "he was not in any way disdainful." *On that occasion,* she did not add aloud.

Rather than appearing any more persuaded, Miss de Bourgh merely began to look vexed.

Elizabeth had begun, however, and thought she might as well finish the job. "I assure you my mother's indignation was not Mr Darcy's fault. Once she takes a dislike to somebody, she does not easily shake it off. Mama was determined to take offence, and when she thought she saw an opportunity, she took him to task directly."

"For what reason was your mother determined to be offended by Darcy? Had he insulted her in some other way before this..."

Miss de Bourgh's voice faded, replaced by Mr Darcy's, as Elizabeth recalled him telling her that his good opinion once lost was lost forever. She had ridiculed him for admitting as much, but in retrospect, it was no different from the implacable resentment she had just attributed to her mother without censure. She twisted her mouth in chagrin to have caught herself exercising such contrasting principles. She might even have felt guilty had she not presently been engaged in saving him from the ire of his betrothed. That was surely enough to compensate for one captious remark.

"Miss Elizabeth?"

"I beg your pardon. What was that?"

"I asked what else my cousin did to earn your mother's disapprobation?"

Elizabeth smiled wryly. She may not have been her mother's favourite, but Mrs Bennet did not suffer criticism of any of her daughters from any*one* other than herself. That Mr Darcy had spurned Elizabeth's looks and refused to dance with her upon first making her acquaintance had set him firmly in her mother's bad books from the start. She did not explain that, however. Despite having laughed about it often enough, Elizabeth found herself strangely averse to divulging his slight to Miss de Bourgh.

"They merely got off on the wrong foot," she said instead. "I am not aware that Mr Darcy was ever directly uncivil to her. Indeed, I believe he was the recipient of rather more of my mother's spleen than she was of his."

Miss de Bourgh looked taken aback. "How did my cousin act? He is not known for suffering fools."

Overlooking the insult to her mother, largely because it could not easily be contended, Elizabeth replied, "Nothing, except to treat her to some of his *companionable silence* until she gave up arguing with herself and went home."

Miss de Bourgh laughed, then observably stopped herself and scowled instead. "A woman ought to try not to be handsome *and* witty, Miss Elizabeth. She will get a reputation for being greedy."

Elizabeth closed her mouth on her first response and, after a moment, replied, "Thank you for the advice. I shall bear it in mind."

"Oh! Is Wickham coming?" Lydia shrieked from across the room, saving either of them from saying any more.

"They are all coming, my dear," replied Lady Lucas. "Even Colonel Forster."

"What is this?" Elizabeth asked of Kitty, sitting nearest to her.

"Lady Lucas says Sir William has invited the officers to join us for supper."

"Will there be cards?" Lydia enquired of no one in particular, veritably bouncing in her seat. "And dancing? Please let us have some dancing. I have not danced with Wickham since we were at Mrs Long's last week."

"Wickham?" Miss de Bourgh said. "I know that name. Who is he?"

"He is the late Mr Darcy's godson. His father was Pemberley's steward." Elizabeth wondered whether they were acquainted. Did Miss de Bourgh know that Mr Darcy had refused to honour his father's will, refused to give Mr Wickham the living he was promised? Would she be as disdainful of Mr Wickham's straitened circumstances as her cousin had been? Elizabeth could scarcely keep her countenance as she watched Miss de Bourgh for any sign of recognition.

"Oh yes," she said presently, her brow creasing faintly. "I vaguely recall that Mr Darcy used to fish with him."

"You know him, then?"

"I know *of* him. I did not fish with them, if that is what you are implying."

Elizabeth longed to ask more but dared not. "I do not believe *they* fish together anymore," was as much as she would venture.

The next hour passed interminably slowly as Elizabeth awaited the officers' arrival. She was pleased for the opportunity to see Mr Wickham, for he was exceptionally good company, but she hoped he would not be distressed by Miss de Bourgh's presence.

She began to worry he would not come, for surely Sir William had mentioned his guest when issuing the invitation, and if Mr Wickham had eschewed the Netherfield ball to avoid Mr Darcy, then it was not inconceivable that he would find a reason to avoid Miss de Bourgh as well.

At last, Colonel Forster arrived, with seven of his officers in tow, and Mr Wickham one of the party. He caught her eye almost immediately and sent her a small, private bow. The contented smile he directed at her lingered only a moment, however, vanishing when Sir William, with great ceremony, announced Miss de Bourgh's presence. Elizabeth watched closely and did not miss that Mr Wickham blanched, just as he had the day he encountered Mr Darcy in Meryton.

In contrast, Miss de Bourgh seemed wholly unaffected, seemingly uninterested in any of the soldiers, let alone Mr Wickham in particular. Nevertheless, the manner in which he shrank back into the midst of his company made it seem likely that *he* believed there was good reason to avoid her notice.

Elizabeth rose to her feet angrily. Mr Wickham was the wronged party, and it was unpardonable that he should be made to feel unwelcome. She attempted to make her way to him, but Lydia anticipated her, pulling Mr Wickham into a dance almost immediately. After completing a reel with her, he then danced with Kitty, Miss Long, Miss King, and finally Maria Lucas before allowing himself to be drawn into a game of loo. Only when John Lucas gave up his seat at the card table half an hour later was Elizabeth able to get close enough to speak to Wickham.

He greeted her with a plaintive look and an entirely unnecessary apology. "I thought it best to avoid the guest of honour. I regret it has kept me away from you all evening also."

"There is no need to apologise, sir. I completely understand, although I do not think you need to worry. Miss de Bourgh scarcely remembers you."

He observably brightened at the news. "You are sure?"

"I am. She recalled your name and that you used to fish with Mr Darcy as a boy but no more."

"That is a relief."

"How so?" Elizabeth objected. "That she is ignorant of how her cousin has mistreated you is hardly something to be celebrated. It only means that Mr Darcy has concealed his abhorrent actions from all his relations."

"Perhaps, but it means I shall not have to dishonour my godfather's name by discussing his son's misdeeds."

It was not a perspective Elizabeth had considered. She grinned ruefully. "And there I was about to insist that you tell her everything and demand justice."

He shook his head. "I have long since given up hoping for justice, Miss Elizabeth. I have learnt to survive well enough on what I have. It would only cause trouble were I to speak up now, and I hate to cause trouble. In fact, now that I can be sure there will not be any, why do we not go and speak to her?"

Elizabeth could hardly refuse, and she accompanied Mr Wickham to the sofa where Miss de Bourgh yet held court and presented one to the other in an odd exchange that was more of a reminder than an introduction.

"You look remarkably well, madam. Lovelier even than I recall," Mr Wickham said, bowing low.

Elizabeth wondered at that. She had seen glimpses of Miss de Bourgh's handsomeness, but the woman's prevailing features were sallowness and hauteur, and this evening in particular she looked very ill indeed. It rendered Mr Wickham's praise hollow and made her wonder what his real opinion had been when he said the same to her.

"Wickham!" Lydia shouted, dashing over to join them. "Tell me you are still coming to the Meryton assembly tomorrow. Lieutenant Denny said he was not sure whether you meant to."

"Lydia, you are interrupting," Elizabeth admonished.

"I shall be there, Miss Lydia," Mr Wickham assured her.

"You knew my uncle well, I understand," Miss de Bourgh said, entirely ignoring Lydia, who sighed loudly and stomped away to pester another unwitting officer.

"Exceedingly well," Mr Wickham replied. "He was an excellent man."

"He was—as is his son, who has grown very much in his father's image."

Elizabeth looked at Mr Wickham with pity, anxious that he might be pained by this, but he betrayed no hint of discomfort.

His smile was undiminished as he replied, "Well, if he is only half as honourable as his father was, then yours will still be an excellent marriage."

Miss de Bourgh cast Elizabeth a triumphant look. Yet, with growing evidence of how difficult to please both she and her cousin were, Elizabeth was increasingly disinclined to think it a good match. Some of her doubt must have shown on her face, for Miss de Bourgh's pride changed instantly to indignation.

"It will be," she said haughtily, "and those who think otherwise are quite mistaken. Mr Collins?"

The rector hastened to her side. "Yes, madam?"

"I hear there is an assembly tomorrow evening in Meryton. I wish to attend."

Mrs Jenkinson let out one of her expressive gasps. Mr Collins's eyes widened in panic, and he swallowed hard.

"Miss de Bourgh, you know I would do anything to serve you well, but this wish, I fear, is not one I am able to grant. I must return to Hunsford tomorrow. The curate cannot stay beyond noon, and there is nobody else to—"

"That is not my concern. I should like to attend the assembly. Therefore, we cannot return to Kent tomorrow."

"But madam, you cannot—*I* cannot—the parish—your mother!"

"Miss de Bourgh, I beg you to reconsider," Mrs Jenkinson pleaded urgently. "You cannot possibly attend a dance. It would be too much. You would surely be overcome. Just the thought of all those foul humours in one room! You must not attend, I beg you. I dread to *think* what might become of you."

Such nonsense provoked Elizabeth to hiccup a tiny laugh

before she could prevent herself. She bit it back instantly but too late.

Miss de Bourgh glared at her malevolently, then all but snarled at Mr Collins. "I suggest you begin to make the necessary arrangements directly, if your curate is to be prevented from leaving at noon tomorrow." Turning to her companion, she said, "And I suggest you do whatever you must to ensure that I am not *overcome,* as you put it, because if I am, my mother will be seriously displeased."

"Bravo, madam," Mr Wickham said with an amused smirk. "May I be so bold as to secure your hand for the first two dances?"

Miss de Bourgh's consent drew another gasp of horror from Mrs Jenkinson, who began to lament the very grave dangers of overexerting oneself, a whimper from Mr Collins as he watched his preferment teeter on the edge of an abyss before him, and a small frown from Elizabeth as she attempted not to be offended that Mr Wickham had overlooked her for the honour of dancing the first set.

# CHAPTER 5

Darcy was interrupted by a knock at the door. He set his papers aside when Mrs Annesley answered his summons to enter. His sister's companion had not come to his study since he first interviewed her for the post. Her presence and her expression made him disagreeably wary.

"Pray forgive the intrusion, Mr Darcy, but Miss Darcy has received a letter that has caused her a good deal of distress. I would not usually trouble you with it, except I understand the matter relates in some way to Mr Wickham, though I have not been able to discover the details, for she is too upset to speak of it."

Darcy held himself very still—no easy feat, considering the flips his stomach was performing. "Thank you, madam. Where is she?"

Mrs Annesley directed him to Georgiana's private saloon, whither he went with quick steps and burgeoning rage. He ought not to be surprised that Wickham had the audacity to write to his sister despite innumerable warnings to leave her alone. Nevertheless, Darcy was incensed. He would have to involve his cousin Fitzwilliam in this. Clearly, Wickham required a more tangible deterrent.

He heard his sister before he arrived. She was sobbing again. *Do all young ladies cry this much?* he wondered, sure that his sister had spent at least two thirds of every other day weeping since the age of about eleven. She paused briefly when he opened the door, only to redouble her efforts when she saw him, slumping over the letter in her hand and howling wretchedly. Darcy supressed the urge to tell her to collect herself and was inordinately grateful when Mrs Annesley did it for him.

"Come now, Miss Darcy, this will not do. Your brother wishes to speak to you. Sit up and compose yourself this instant."

Georgiana nodded and sniffed ineffectively into the handkerchief Mrs Annesley gave her. She glanced at Darcy, a doleful look that made her appear a decade younger than her fifteen years. He did not want for compassion, and angry though he was, he did not like to see her thus anguished. Yet, he had little experience of consoling young women and had no idea what manner of comfort she desired. He wondered what Elizabeth would do—no doubt make her laugh and tease her out of her misery—then he cursed himself for allowing the thought ingress.

"What has he said?" Darcy asked, more curtly than he intended but angry at his own weakness.

Georgiana swallowed a sob and looked at him in confusion. "What has *who* said?"

"Wickham. What has he said in that letter that has upset you this much?"

She shook her head. "This is not from Mr Wickham."

Relief forced the breath out of Darcy. It was fortunate, for it meant he had none left with which to swear an oath when Georgiana added, "It is from Anne. She says Mr Wickham is in Meryton, and she has dined with him! She is going to a *ball* with him this evening and has agreed to dance the first set with him." Her breathing had grown ragged and her voice higher in pitch. "What if he tells her what happened in Ramsgate? What if he tells her and she tells my aunt? She would be furious! Oh my life! I cannot—" More gasping breaths. "I cannot *bear* the thought of Lady Catherine knowing of my disgrace."

"Calm yourself, Miss Darcy. Calm yourself this instant!" cried Mrs Annesley, taking Georgiana's hand and rubbing it firmly as one does for sufferers of shock.

Darcy was grateful for it. He had not the capacity to administer to his sister while he battled his own agitation and dismay. He was confounded as to how this eventuality had never occurred to him.

No, that was untrue. He knew precisely why this very obvious, very feasible encounter had not struck him as likely. It was because he had been too busy convincing himself he did not care what was happening in Hertfordshire. Too busy forbidding himself from thinking about what Anne might be saying about him to Elizabeth. Too busy feigning indifference to the fact that, judging by her remarks at Bingley's ball, Elizabeth was sympathetic to Wickham's tales of woe. *Far* too busy refusing to contemplate the possibility that the cur might succeed in seducing *Elizabeth* to recognise the danger of him encountering Anne.

Yet, troubling though all that was, it was not Darcy's greatest source of consternation. Nor was his sister's prediction that her indiscretion would be discovered. He doubted that would happen, for there was no profit to Wickham in revealing it. What *was* likely—inevitable, really—was Wickham setting his sights on Anne's fortune, which was substantially larger than Georgiana's.

Yet, even that was not Darcy's chief concern. Nay, the reason he could scarcely contain his vexation was that after all his endeavours to give no consideration whatsoever to anything that was occurring in Meryton, he was now obliged by honour and duty to return there. He must rescue his cousin as he had done his sister, and to do it he must put himself back in the path of the one woman he most wished, most *needed* to avoid.

"Damn!"

He only realised he had said it aloud when Mrs Annesley took a sharp intake of breath and Georgiana began crying again. "Forgive me," he murmured. Pulling a chair from the side of the room, he sat before his sister and rested his elbows on his knees. "You must not distress yourself. Wickham will not say a word about Ramsgate, of that I am convinced."

Georgiana slowly unfurled herself and took a shuddering breath. "How can you be sure?"

"Because it will do him no favours to admit to someone with Anne's potential that he attempted to seduce her young cousin."

"But what if he tells someone else and Anne hears of it?"

"He has not said anything so far. He is not likely to change tack now."

Georgiana's eyes widened. "What do you mean? How long has he been there?"

*Blast it!* He had not meant to reveal that! After a sigh, he admitted, "He arrived with the militia whilst I was there last month."

"You did not mention it!"

"I did not wish to distress you. Besides, there was little to tell. I encountered him but once. We did not speak then or afterwards. He knew better than to provoke me."

"But what was he doing there? What brought him to the same town as you?"

"Nothing more sinister than happenstance. The point is, whatever he may have said about *me*, it is very clear he said nothing about *you*, for I should certainly have heard of it if he had." Darcy waited for Georgiana to nod, then added, "Pray, do not be anxious. I shall collect Anne myself before Wickham can cause any more harm."

"It is four days before Christmas. I cannot ask it of you." It was obvious from her expression how much she wished him to do just that.

"It is as much for Anne as for you," he assured her. God knew what his aunt was about, allowing her frail and sickly daughter to gad about the country in the midst of winter in such a fashion. "Besides, Meryton is less than thirty miles distance. If I were travelling alone, I could be there and back in a day." He knew this, because he had contemplated making the journey more times in the last few weeks than he cared to admit. "With your cousin, I may take longer, but still, if I leave first thing on Monday, I shall be back on Christmas Eve."

Georgiana smiled an apologetic but grateful smile. "Thank you, Brother. You are very good."

He reached to give her hand a quick pat, offered her a reassuring smile, then left the room to begin barking orders at his man to pack his trunks in an effort to release some of his own violent perturbation.

⁊

Charlotte attached herself to Elizabeth's arm as soon as she entered the Meryton assembly rooms. "Where have you been? Why are you so late?"

"Good evening, Charlotte," Elizabeth replied, laughing. "And, to the best of my knowledge, we are not late."

"Forgive me. 'Tis only that Miss de Bourgh made such a fuss about coming, we were the first to arrive, and she has been asking after you ever since."

Elizabeth directed them to their usual seats near the large front window, favoured for being the only source of fresh air in what was always an unbearably hot place. She opened one of the casements and set the stay on its catch.

"Why on earth has she been asking after me?" She turned back in time to see Charlotte shrug.

"I presume she wished to know who was coming. I think she has bundled all of your family into one entity in her mind, and you represent every Bennet there is."

"There are enough of us," Elizabeth admitted. "Well, we are here now. But where is she?"

"In the cloakroom. Mrs Jenkinson has taken her there three times already to ensure she does not overexert herself."

"How can she be overexerted? The dancing has not yet begun."

"I am sure I do not know. Mr Collins speaks often of her indifferent health, but I am not aware of any specific illness. There is truth to it though, for she occasionally betrays uncommon frailty, and she is very easily fatigued."

"Mrs Bayley used to suffer similarly. Do you recall? She would be in perfect health one day and bed-ridden the next, unable to lift a cup to her lips."

"I do recall, now that you mention it. Whatever happened to her?"

"Her husband moved her to the coast in the hope that the sea air would help. I pity Miss de Bourgh if she is afflicted in the same way. It seemed a debilitating condition." The acknowledgement made Elizabeth rather more sympathetic to Miss de Bourgh's want of accomplishments, which she had hitherto, rather uncharitably, attributed to indolence. "But you do not look as though you agree."

"If she is that unwell, she ought not to have come. If something happens to her, Lady Catherine is sure to blame Mr Collins for having allowed it."

Elizabeth laughed at that. "Miss de Bourgh does not strike me as the sort of woman who requires permission to do anything she wishes. Wilfulness seems to be a strong family trait."

"That will not stop Lady Catherine from laying the blame at Mr Collins's door."

Elizabeth thought Mrs Jenkinson must surely take her share

of the blame, the sole purpose of her employment being to safe-guard Miss de Bourgh. Nevertheless, she could perceive that Charlotte was genuinely anxious and thought it better to ease her mind than argue the point.

"Then we had better ensure no harm comes to her."

Thus, Elizabeth found herself sitting with Miss de Bourgh, Mrs Jenkinson, Charlotte, and thankfully, Jane as they waited for the room to fill and the dancing to begin. There were glances aplenty directed at them as whispers of Miss de Bourgh's wealth and rank rippled around the gathered company. Elizabeth fancied there may have been more than one appraisal of her person as well, for Miss de Bourgh was very elegantly turned out in an exquisitely embroidered gown and with her hair dressed in a most becoming style. If not for the pallor of her cheeks and the heavy shawl across her knees, she might have looked every bit the young beauty. As it was, she appeared older even than the seven-and-twenty years that Mr Collins reported to be her true age.

"What do you make of our assembly rooms, Miss de Bourgh?" Jane enquired. It was her third attempt at beginning a conversation. Elizabeth had given up after her first.

"They are hot and crowded," Miss de Bourgh replied.

Elizabeth felt Jane give her a surreptitious nudge with her elbow, forcing a giggle into her throat which she disguised by saying, "Full of people enjoying themselves." She received no response.

"Are you engaged for the first dance, Eliza?" Charlotte enquired.

"Yes, I am dancing with Mr Douglas."

"I suppose you must have a lot of admirers in the neigh-bourhood, Miss Elizabeth," said Miss de Bourgh.

"I am flattered that you should think so, madam, but Mr Douglas is merely a friend. I do not have any admirers of whom I am aware."

Mr Wickham, with whom she had enjoyed so many gratifying walks and conversations, flitted across her mind, but even before humility prevented her mentioning his name, some other, unaccountable reluctance decided her against it.

"Why not?" Miss de Bourgh replied, sounding almost angry. "Are they put off by your unclassical looks?"

Elizabeth regarded her incredulously, but she seemed perfectly sincere, without any meanness in her expression, as though stating a fact. "Perhaps they are," she replied coolly.

"It must be difficult, having a sister who is handsomer than you," Miss de Bourgh continued. "Though not as difficult as it must have been for Miss Lucas, suffering the *pair* of you as such close neighbours." Nobody responded, but she was not deterred. "You must wish to find a husband in the vicinity, though, Miss Elizabeth. You cannot wish to be settled too far from your family."

"I cannot say that I have ever been particularly troubled by the prospect," Elizabeth replied, beginning to be diverted by the flagrancy of her offensiveness.

"Someone as uninterested in venturing out into high society as you purport to be, *must* be satisfied with a husband from the area in which she grew up."

"Perhaps. Though, if I were going to love any of the gentlemen with whom I grew up, I should think I might know by now."

Miss de Bourgh looked at her aghast. "I was speaking of marriage, not love."

Jane and Charlotte's gazes weighed heavily upon Elizabeth, the one's entirely unromantic engagement and the other's thoroughly romantic heartbreak persuading her against any grand declarations in favour of marrying for affection.

"Of course. We must not confuse the two."

"Good evening, ladies," said Mr Wickham, appearing out of the crowd and bowing low. "You all look in excellent health this evening."

They each thanked him perfunctorily, for no compliment

shared between four women could ever truly please any of them.

"I hope you will not be angry when I tell you that I overheard some of your conversation just now, and I feel obliged to speak up in favour of romance. Though I risk appearing foolish, I confess I have been used to thinking of real affection as essential to a successful union. I do not mean to say that contentment must elude those who marry for convenience, but there is no harm in aspiring to true felicity—the sort of deep and lasting admiration that is not always possible when one marries where one is expected."

He addressed this to Elizabeth, and anybody who knew she had refused her cousin would think it perfectly natural that he did so. Except, to the best of her knowledge, Mr Wickham did *not* know, and his sly glance at Miss de Bourgh at the end of his speech made her suspect it had not been meant for her.

"You hope to marry for love, do you, sir?" Elizabeth enquired.

His mouth lifted in a smile so casual it might have been an incidental consequence of the shrug he gave. "But of course, should my situation allow. Though, as you know, I am limited by circumstance."

"Indeed," said Charlotte. "A modest situation often requires a less romantic resolution."

"Ah, but it is not only those of modest means who are thus constrained. Is it, Miss de Bourgh? We all have our crosses to bear, our duties to uphold." He waited a moment while that lady frowned at him in puzzlement, then said, "But enough of such serious matters. I hear the musicians warming up. Come, madam. You have promised me the first two dances, and I am all anticipation. I beg you would not keep me waiting any longer."

Miss de Bourgh, her cheeks flushed either by flattery or trepidation, pulled the shawl from her lap and passed it to her companion. She, in turn, began pleading with her charge to take care, not to dance too quickly, to stop should she feel faint, to—

She was silenced when Mr Wickham took Miss de Bourgh's hand and pulled her to her feet. "She will be perfectly well, madam. I shall take good care of her." He promptly whisked her away to join the set.

"I hope you are not too put out that Mr Wickham has over-looked you for the first dance, Lizzy," Jane said.

"I am happy to report I am not," she replied, pleased that it was true. She had expected to be at least a little vexed, watching him pay his attentions to another—particularly given that the *other* in question was Miss de Bourgh, who had been nothing but quarrelsome towards her since she arrived in Meryton. But there was something in Mr Wickham's air this evening which, though she could not explain it, made her grateful to avoid the obligation of dancing with him.

As she observed them cross the room, Elizabeth noticed other people watching also. Lydia, for one, viewed them with an expression she more commonly reserved for one of her sisters who had bought a bonnet or slippers she wished were hers, and Miss King, who looked positively crestfallen when Mr Wickham walked past her, chatting convivially with Miss de Bourgh.

Denny arrived to claim Jane for the first dance, and once she was gone, Charlotte said quietly, "I, too, am glad you are not upset about Mr Wickham. I have heard that he has taken an interest in Miss King. I believe she has recently inherited ten-thousand pounds."

"Yes, I heard the same figure mentioned. I imagine there are few people who would not be interested at the mention of such a sum. A person must have something on which to live, and I certainly have nothing of the kind to offer a husband."

After a pause and a shrewd look, Charlotte replied, "I am glad you are coming to see things in the same way I do."

Elizabeth winced at the half-admonishing remark. Perhaps she had been less clear-sighted in Mr Wickham's case than in her friend's. Nevertheless, Miss King's new wealth did not seem to be enthralling him overmuch at present.

"Her fortune seems to have lost its allure."

"I am not surprised. Miss King's ten-thousand pounds is nothing to Miss de Bourgh's fifty-thousand. Not to mention that she is the heiress to Rosings Park."

Elizabeth knew not how to respond. She did not wish to think of him as mercenary, but if even her most sensible, least romantic friend was alarmed by the vagaries of Mr Wickham's attentions, she must concede there were grounds for misgivings.

The uncertainty made Elizabeth grateful for Mr Douglas's friendly face and easy manners when he arrived to greet her. She accepted his hand with pleasure and threw herself into the dance with zeal. It was a lively set, and she enjoyed herself prodigiously—until it was interrupted by a commotion farther down the line. The dancers all stumbled to a halt atop each other, the musicians screeched to the end of their refrains, and Mrs Jenkinson came rushing forth, wailing in dismay.

"Miss de Bourgh! Oh heavens, Miss de Bourgh!"

Elizabeth could see nothing through the throngs of onlookers until the crowd parted, and Mr Wickham strode through, bearing Miss de Bourgh in his arms. Mr Collins came scurrying after them, loudly lamenting the disastrous turn of events. Sir William and Lady Lucas hastened along behind them with expressions of grave concern. Charlotte seized Elizabeth's arm and dragged her along in their wake.

"What has happened?" Elizabeth enquired urgently.

"Miss de Bourgh fainted."

"Oh good Lord!"

Mr Wickham carried Miss de Bourgh out of the main ballroom and laid her on a chaise longue in an antechamber, which Sir William cleared with a few choice phrases and some startlingly energetic arm waving. Mrs Jenkinson shoved a bottle of smelling salts under Miss de Bourgh's nose and cried out in relief when she coughed and spluttered to life.

"Get that vile stuff away from me," cried the patient, flapping at the bottle.

"I begged you not to do it!" Mrs Jenkinson wailed. "Would that you had listened! What will your mother say?"

"My mother will not say a word because my mother will never hear of this. Is that understood?"

Mrs Jenkinson nodded. Miss de Bourgh looked sternly at Mr Collins and Charlotte until they gave similar assurances.

"But are you quite well?" Mr Collins asked. "You did not hurt yourself when you fell? Your mother will wish to know the cause if you have been injured."

"I did not fall, for Mr Wickham caught me," she replied, smiling in that gentleman's direction. "And until that point, I was having an exceedingly pleasant time. I am only sorry we could not finish the set."

Mr Wickham gave an affected shake of his head. "You must not concern yourself, madam. There are *some* people too high in the instep to enjoy a bit of excitement at a ball, but *I* thought you swooned as delightfully as you danced."

"Oh, I quite agree. Rarely have I seen such exquisite dancing," said Mr Collins.

Elizabeth wondered if they had all been watching the same person, for while she would grant that Miss de Bourgh's skill was commendable for one who rarely had the opportunity to practice, delightful and exquisite it was not.

"You must not allow me to keep you from the dance, sir," Miss de Bourgh said to Mr Wickham. Her smiled seemed fixed in place, and there was a slight tremor to her voice. Charlotte heard it too, it seemed, for she swiftly ushered her father and Mr Wickham from the room. Mr Collins could not be persuaded to leave, and Miss de Bourgh either did not care or had not the energy to object.

"What a miserable display!" she exclaimed, collapsing back onto the sofa with her eyes closed.

"I assure you Mr Wickham will not think any less of you for it," said Lady Lucas. "He is a most amiable gentleman."

"I do not care what the son of my late uncle's steward thinks. What I care about is being able to host balls for my husband, which I can hardly do if I have not the strength in my legs to walk from here to the door. What sort of wife cannot even dance one dance?"

"I do not think Mr Darcy will mind," Elizabeth said. "He abhors dancing."

It was evident that Miss de Bourgh had not known Elizabeth was still in the room, for she twisted around and stared at her in dismay.

"Why would you say he does not like dancing? He danced with *you*."

Elizabeth walked to stand where Miss de Bourgh could see her more easily, and from there she could perceive, beneath the discourtesy and hauteur, a vulnerability that moved her to reveal what she had previously preferred to keep private.

"Yes, he did, but that was at his friend's ball, where it would have looked very odd indeed had he not danced with *somebody* outside of his circle. But the first time it was suggested that he stand up with me, he refused and declared that I was not handsome enough to tempt him."

She tried her best not to be offended by how obviously this cheered Miss de Bourgh, who pulled herself farther upright in her seat and accepted a glass of wine from Charlotte.

"I always thought he *did* enjoy dancing. I know he dances often enough with his sister, for she is forever mentioning in her letters that he has helped her practise again." She shook her head slightly. "No matter. Mr Collins, I am ready to return to Lucas Lodge now. You may summon the carriage."

He blinked at her a few times, his entire demeanour that of exasperation. "You have danced but one dance, madam."

"Not even that, Mr Collins, yet I am ready to return. Now, make haste and summon the carriage."

Elizabeth smiled sympathetically at her friend and excused herself, for there was nothing more she could do. She returned to the main room where she answered the barrage of questions about Miss de Bourgh's well-being with as much consideration for the lady's dignity as she could summon.

Mr Wickham could not be avoided all evening, and Elizabeth was eventually obliged to join him for a set. His interest in Miss de Bourgh was diametrically opposed to the rest of Meryton's—he did not ask after her once. She paid it and him little attention, however. Her thoughts were largely taken up imagining how pleasant it would have been to have an older brother with whom to practise dancing as she grew up. And how surprising it was, in a strangely endearing sort of way, to discover that the austere and fastidious Mr Darcy would do such a thing for his sister.

# CHAPTER
# 6

"Darcy, what brings you here at this time on a Sunday? I do hope nothing is amiss." Bingley ushered Darcy into his study and offered him a drink.

"No, thank you. I have an early start in the morning."

"Oh? Going anywhere pleasant?"

Darcy clenched his teeth, partly at the now familiar flare of vexation at Anne, Wickham, and the world in general, and partly against the surge of anticipation that had been intermittently assaulting him ever since it became apparent that he would need to travel to Meryton. There was no reason to anticipate the trip, for he would not see Elizabeth while he was there. He had briefly considered taking advantage of the opportunity to ensure she was safe from Wickham but had ultimately decided that if she had chosen to believe that blackguard's account of things, it was her prerogative. He would not intervene. He would retrieve his cousin and leave.

"A pressing matter has arisen, and I find I must go away for a day or two to resolve it."

"You are leaving London? Two days before Christmas?"

Darcy nodded.

"Will you tell me the reason?"

"No." The word sounded officious, even to his ear, but he would not demean his friend by making up a fictitious excursion to evade suspicion. Neither would he reveal his true destination. Bingley was evidently still in danger of succumbing to Jane Bennet's charms, and since those charms consisted of naught more than a handsome countenance, a vapid smile, and her mother's tenacious aspirations, Darcy had no intention of permitting his friend to be taken in. Better that the word 'Meryton' remain unspoken, lest it dislodge Bingley's resolve to stay away. "It is a family matter. The timing is regrettable, but it cannot be avoided."

Bingley, as ever, took him at his word. "Then I wish you a safe journey. I hope the weather holds for you. Does this mean we shall not see you for dinner tomorrow evening after all?"

"That is why I have called. I wondered whether you would still be good enough to welcome Georgiana in my absence. I am loath to leave her alone again so soon after returning."

"But of course! I assumed she would be travelling with you."

"Not on this occasion. I hope to be back in London on Tuesday. It will not be a leisurely trip." Anne would have to remain in town for now. Darcy had no intention of returning her to Kent before Christmas.

"Consider it done. And, should you be delayed, you may of course count on us to keep her spirits up over Christmas as well."

"That is good of you, Bingley. Thank you."

Darcy wished he had accepted the offer of a drink. He was uncomfortable with how close he was sailing towards disguise, and speaking of his sister only served to remind him about their unpleasant conversation earlier that day.

What had begun with a simple request that Georgiana not reveal his destination to Bingley had transformed into a highly unpleasant exchange in which she expressed several objections to his inducements for separating Bingley from Miss Bennet. He had been forced to remind her that not all suitors were motivated by genuine affection. This she took as reproof for her own recent misadventure, and matters had deteriorated from there. Nevertheless, in the course of their quarrel, Georgiana had confirmed his own suspicions that Bingley was still very much in love with Miss Bennet, hardening his mind to his present course.

"You never know," Bingley said, interrupting Darcy's reflections. "A quick spell out of town might do you good."

"In what way?"

"Well, it might cure you of this ill-humour of yours." His affront must have shown, for Bingley hastily added, "I mean no disrespect, my friend, but you have not been at all yourself of late."

Darcy knew not what to say to that. All he knew was that Elizabeth's name reverberated in his thoughts, burying every rational denial. Evidently, he had not triumphed over his fascination as well as he imagined.

"I know I have been somewhat distracted myself since we returned from Netherfield, but I still know how to enjoy myself. You seem perpetually dissatisfied," Bingley went on. "Now, do not glower at me in that way. It is true. Nothing pleases you anymore. You are uninterested in everything, and you seem to have entirely forgotten how to smile."

Bingley's accusations provoked a sensation of panic in Darcy, as though his friend were diagnosing him with some incurable disease. It made him wish to deny them, immediately and emphatically. He restrained himself, stating calmly, "Are you certain you are not imposing your own recent disappointment onto me?"

"Oh, I suppose I might be," Bingley said morosely. His shoulders slumped, and Darcy felt a wretched sense of duplicity. "Pay me no mind. You have enough of your own problems to resolve. Be off with you to do whatever you must and then come back and see how cheerful I can be at the Christmas dinner table. And if I cannot be merry, then as long as you are there, at least Caroline will be happy."

Even in his dejection, Bingley managed a mischievous smile, reminding Darcy why he treasured his friendship so dearly. He was a breath of fresh air to Darcy's typically staid existence.

And one breath of fresh air was quite enough. He had no need of another. And he definitely did not need to see her while he was in Meryton.

On the following Monday, Mrs Bennet's brother and his wife came to spend Christmas at Longbourn as usual. Mr Gardiner was bustled away into Mr Bennet's library to discuss whatever either could think of that would keep them there until dinner. Mrs Gardiner was drawn into the parlour, where her four children were permitted to remain and play while Mrs Bennet—and her daughters, whenever they were able to squeeze in a word—regaled her with news of all that had befallen them since last they were together.

"Two of my girls almost married," Mrs Bennet lamented. "Yet, both of them are still single. I am quite as broken-hearted as Jane, though Lizzy has not a care for it."

Mrs Gardiner sent Elizabeth a private look of commiseration. Between the two of them and Jane there was an intimate understanding that ensured most of Mrs Bennet's censure was met with sympathy, rather than scorn.

"Now we must suffer Charlotte Lucas parading about the place as though she already owns it," she continued. "Though I do not know why she should be in such a hurry to be Mrs Collins. If I were her, I should seriously reconsider my decision to shackle myself to such a horrid woman."

"*Woman?*" Mrs Gardiner asked in some confusion. "If Mr

Collins is not a man, does that not resolve the entire problem of the entail?"

"I believe my mother is referring to Miss Anne de Bourgh," Elizabeth replied, laughing. "She is his patroness's daughter." She and her sisters then explained Miss de Bourgh's strange and eventful stay in Meryton, after which Mrs Gardiner puffed out her cheeks in wonder.

"I see. And Miss Lucas will have to answer to this lady and her mother when she becomes Mrs Collins? Poor woman."

"Poor woman nothing!" Mrs Bennet objected. "Charlotte will have this house as soon as Mr Bennet dies. I have not one iota of sympathy for her. Besides, she is clearly going about pleasing the woman in the wrong way, for Miss de Bourgh is nowhere near as awful to Lizzy." She turned to her daughter and said, "Further proof that it ought to have been *you* who married Mr Collins."

"What is this?" Mrs Gardiner enquired.

"Miss de Bourgh has singled Lizzy out as her favourite," Mrs Bennet replied, preening as though this were not a highly dubious honour. "She asks after her constantly and speaks to her more than she does to anybody else."

"I think Miss de Bourgh only feels more drawn to me because she discovered that I am slightly better acquainted with her cousin than most, having stayed with him at Netherfield," Elizabeth demurred.

"Who is her cousin?" her aunt enquired.

"The friend of Mr Bingley's we told you about, Mr Darcy."

"Mr Darcy of Pemberley in Derbyshire?" she replied, all astonishment. "Her pride begins to make more sense. With such connexions, she has a good deal of which to be proud."

"That is precisely what Charlotte said about *him*, though having met both, I am inclined to think the advantage is far more in Miss de Bourgh's favour than Mr Darcy's. He may be disagreeable, but she is awful."

"Really, Lizzy?" said Jane doubtfully. "I should not have expected you to say so."

Elizabeth had not expected it either and had quite surprised herself with the sentiment.

"Mr Darcy is disagreeable?" continued Mrs Gardiner, relieving Elizabeth of the necessity of answering Jane. "I confess that surprises me, for his father was highly regarded when I lived in the area."

"Aye, Mr Wickham speaks fondly of him, too."

"Mr Wickham?"

"He is an officer with the militia encamped in Meryton," Mrs Bennet explained.

"And the late Mr Darcy's godson," Elizabeth added.

"And he is the handsomest of the officers by a mile," Kitty said wistfully.

Lydia scoffed. "He is all looks and no manners."

"What makes you say that?" Elizabeth enquired.

"He promised her the first set at the last assembly and then danced it with Miss de Bourgh," Kitty explained.

"I did not know he had done that," Jane said. "How unkind."

"Oh, I do not care," Lydia replied. "Denny said he owes him ten shillings from their last game of loo, and I could never love anybody who cannot win at cards."

"Or pay his debts," added Mary.

"How odd that so many people connected to one family should have arrived in the same place all at once," Mrs Gardiner observed.

"Mr Darcy seems to have that sort of influence," Elizabeth replied. "Everybody follows him about the country. I am convinced Mr Bingley would still be here if his friend had not left."

"That does neither gentleman much credit," Jane said softly. "Nor me."

"Forgive me. I do not mean to pain you, but Mr Bingley was so obviously in love with you, I cannot believe he left of his own accord. And I can easily believe that if Mr Darcy had made up his mind to go, nothing would persuade him to remain, no matter how it might affect his friend, who was too complying to refuse."

"It is strange that the son should have turned out so disagreeable if his father was as excellent as you say, Aunt," said Mary.

Mrs Gardiner turned from Jane, whom she had been regarding with a worried expression, to frown instead at Mary, this time pensively. "I spent some years in that part of the country, and I cannot recall ever hearing it said that Mr Fitzwilliam Darcy had turned out markedly unlike his father. I think I heard it said that he was reserved. Perhaps that was the beginning of a more conceited sort of pride." She shrugged. "I left Derbyshire some years ago. Anything could have happened since then to affect his character."

There was much in what her aunt said that was of interest, yet Elizabeth could attend to only one part of it. "Fitzwilliam? Is that his Christian name?"

"Yes. It was his mother's maiden name, I believe."

She knew not why this information gave her such a sense of satisfaction. Perhaps it was that knowing his name made him seem less forbidding. Perhaps it was how well the name suited him—pompous, imposing.

*Distinctive. Striking.* Elizabeth blushed deeply at the direction of her thoughts and, undesirous of being asked to account for it, rose to help herself to another cup of tea.

"Well, if both of them are disagreeable, at least they will be well suited in marriage," Mrs Gardiner said, holding out her cup for Elizabeth to fill.

"The same can be said for the Collinses. I wish them all the happiness they deserve. Which is none," said Mrs Bennet.

A commotion erupted elsewhere in the house that grew louder and louder until the parlour door was thrust open, and Mrs Philips burst into the room. "Sister! Oh—and Sister!" she added upon noticing that Mrs Gardiner was present. "How wonderful to see you, dear. But attend, I have such news! You will never guess who I have just seen arriving in Meryton."

"Tell us quickly, then," Mrs Bennet said eagerly.

Mrs Philips grasped her sister's outstretched hand. "Why, none other than Mr Darcy!"

Mrs Bennet cried out in delight and began to rhapsodise about what this meant for Jane's romantic aspirations, for surely, they had just settled it that Mr Bingley followed Mr Darcy everywhere!

Elizabeth hoped her mother's transports would mean nobody noticed how the tea she was pouring shot over the side of the cup and pooled in the saucer, but Mrs Gardiner's querying gaze was awaiting hers when she glanced up to return the cup. She prayed she would not be called upon to account for herself, for she had not the slightest idea why that gentleman's name should startle her.

It was likely because she had talked about him so frequently of late, courtesy of his cousin. Or perhaps because she had just that moment surprised herself with the recollection that he was uncommonly good looking. Mayhap she was simply pleased for Jane. Indeed, upon reflection, Elizabeth thought it most likely that it was her *aunt* who had moved her hand, and that *she* had not flinched at all. She turned her attention to Jane, who looked considerably less collected than she herself was bound to feel once her heart slowed to a more natural pace.

"I beg your pardon, Mr Darcy, but your fair cousin is not here. Mr Collins has taken Miss de Bourgh to Longbourn for one last visit before she returns home. But pray, come in. You are more than welcome to await her return here with us."

Darcy stared at Sir William, trying his hardest to neither snarl nor swear. He had not thought his day could deteriorate any further. The journey had been long and difficult thanks to inclement weather, a broken wheel, and the tide of memories that harried him along the way. Despite his man's most persuasive efforts, the only lodgings they had been able to secure this close to Christmas were at the George and Crown—the least salubrious establishment in Meryton, with a name disagreeably reminiscent of the reprobate who had necessitated his trip hither.

To make matters worse, he had stepped down from his carriage onto the High Street at precisely the same moment as Mrs Philips had come out of the milliner's shop. She had curtseyed, blasting his hopes that she had not recognised him and making a mockery of his wish to remain incognito. He could envisage her, even now, announcing his arrival to all her acquaintances. To all her relations. To Elizabeth. As though all of that were not objectionable enough, he discovered now that he need not have come at all, for Anne was about to leave anyway!

"No, I thank you, Sir William," he replied. "I have some business in Meryton. I shall make use of the time and see to that whilst I wait." That his business consisted of skulking in his lodgings to avoid any more unwanted encounters was neither here nor there. He took his leave and with the promise to come back in two hours, mounted his horse and returned in the direction of the inn.

He reached as far as the end of the lane before his resolve began to waver. What was to be gained by avoiding Longbourn? Anne was already there. He did not doubt that Mrs Philips was already or had recently been there, telling them all he was in town.

*Elizabeth will be there.*

He abhorred the way his guts twisted at the thought. Good God, was he so little master of himself that he could not set eyes on her without incident? He clenched his fist around the reins. There was no danger for him at Longbourn, and he would not be frightened into inaction by the pathetic fluttering of his recalcitrant heart. Better to get it over with—fetch Anne and leave Hertfordshire this very afternoon.

Ever angrier at the irrepressible feelings that had plagued him for the last three months, making every decision ten times harder than it ought to be, Darcy turned his mount and set out defiantly towards Longbourn.

# CHAPTER 7

Mrs Philips stayed only a quarter of an hour. Any longer and she would have forfeited the chance of being first to announce Mr Darcy's return to the rest of her acquaintances. She might have chosen to stay had she known who would call next at Longbourn. As it was, the pleasure of revealing Mr Darcy's arrival to his cousin fell to Mrs Bennet.

"Darcy has come for me?" Miss de Bourgh replied with an air of ingenuous satisfaction. It was a fleeting look. Her countenance rapidly hardened into a more superior expression. "Of course, he is devoted to me."

"You were not aware he was coming?" Elizabeth enquired.

"No, I understood he was occupied with his friends in town, but I expect he wishes for me to accompany him there."

Elizabeth did not doubt it. Mr Darcy seemed intent on whisking everybody he knew away from Hertfordshire.

"Ought I to understand that you will be travelling with him now?" Mr Collins enquired, looking thoroughly miserable.

"Of course! What an absurd question! I do not know why

you look so unhappy about it. You have been desirous of returning to Kent for days. Now, you may go." Miss de Bourgh turned to Mrs Bennet abruptly. "Are you planning to introduce this lady to me?"

Mrs Bennet floundered but was rescued by Jane, who calmly introduced Mrs Gardiner.

"And you are Mr Bennet's sister, are you?"

"No, madam. My husband is Mrs Bennet's brother. We are come up from London for Christmas."

"Whereabouts in London?"

"Gracechurch Street. Near Cheapside."

"Oh," Miss de Bourgh replied, managing to imbue the word with the whole of society's disgust for the middle class. It marked an end to her interest, and after an appraising look and a sniff, she turned away from Mrs Gardiner to address Mr Collins. "You certainly have some unfortunate connexions, sir."

Mrs Gardiner's polite smile never faltered, yet Elizabeth could perceive she was offended. It rankled deeply that some-body as intelligent and genteel as her aunt could be considered an unfortunate connexion. Indeed, given Miss de Bourgh's conduct, she rather thought the fastidious Mr Darcy might consider her just as objectionable a connexion.

"As have we all," she retorted.

Miss de Bourgh's eyes snapped to hers. "Oh yes, you are not much better pleased with mine, are you? No matter. You do not have to like Darcy. *You* are not marrying him. Are you?"

"No, madam. The distinction of that connexion is all yours."

"Quite so. When one's own connexions are exceptional, it would be nonsensical to even *consider* marrying elsewhere."

Lydia snorted indecorously and murmured to Kitty, "That was not enough to convince Lizzy to marry Mr Collins."

"Lydia!" hissed her mother, aunt, and eldest sisters in unison.

Elizabeth pitied Mr Collins his obvious embarrassment, yet she had been certain Miss de Bourgh already knew this.

Though, if she did, that did not account for the present turn of her countenance, which was narrow-eyed suspicion.

"Pray excuse my sister's indiscretion, though I must confess, I thought Mr Collins had already informed you of this. Your remark about my not approving of cousins marrying made it seem—"

"I was obviously referring to myself and Mr Darcy, not you and Mr Collins."

"I see. But why would I disapprove of you marrying your cousin?"

"Why did you refuse *yours*? You told me you had no suitors."

"And I spoke true. I do not."

"You must have had one in mind, otherwise why would you ever have refused an offer from the heir to your family home?"

Elizabeth could feel her mother's eyes on her and prayed she would not speak out to worsen matters. "The answer is very simple. As I said to Mr Collins at the time, I did not believe we could make each other happy."

"And who was it, exactly, you believed *could* make you happy?"

"I assure you, I had nobody particular in mind."

Everybody began to speak at once—Mrs Bennet to lament the sorry truth of Elizabeth's claim, Jane to try and change the subject, Mary to sermonise about the perils of insincere regard, and Mrs Gardiner to restore them all to calm. Mr Collins made a noise that might have been choking on his own mortification as he attempted to shrink into the crack between the cushions on the sofa.

"I do not believe you," Miss de Bourgh said angrily over them all. "I have shown you all the condescension you could have wished for, Miss Elizabeth. Now you will do me the honour of being honest. Did you or did you not refuse your cousin because you hoped to receive an offer from—"

"Mr Darcy, ma'am."

All eyes turned to the housekeeper, who had entered the

parlour at some point during the argument and evidently did not think the announcement could wait any longer.

Behind her, Mr Darcy stood tall, imposing, and motionless. His eyes were fixed unblinkingly upon Elizabeth, and an infuriating smile played about his lips as though he were vastly satisfied to have found her and all her family behaving exactly as he had expected.

Elizabeth could have screamed. Of *course* he would arrive at that precise moment, when her relations were giving their worst performances, and she was arguing heatedly with his enfeebled future wife. She turned fully to face him and curtseyed, refusing to be unsettled by the intensity with which his presence filled the room.

"Thank you, Hill," said Mrs Bennet, recovering her voice. "Mr Darcy, you are very welcome. Pray, come in. Your cousin is here."

"He knows that, Mama. That is why he is come," Elizabeth said crossly.

Miss de Bourgh held out her hand. "Darcy, what a delightful surprise!"

It did not seem as though he meant to acknowledge any of them. Mrs Bennet waited, her hands fussing fretfully with her handkerchief. Miss de Bourgh's raised arm drooped back into her lap, her complacency shrivelling with it. Jane looked anxiously at Elizabeth, and even Mrs Gardiner seemed uneasy. Indifferent to it all, Mr Darcy maintained his silence.

Elizabeth suppressed the urge to roll her eyes. "I shall be terribly disappointed if what you say next does not have all the éclat of a proverb, sir."

Mr Darcy's slight smile abruptly broadened in a manner that made Elizabeth feel absurdly flushed and therefore, even more provoked. "Ought I to fetch a pen and paper so it can be written down?"

"I defer to your judgment on the matter, Miss Elizabeth," he replied in a wholly unperturbed and discomposingly resonant tone. To her mother, he said, "I beg you would excuse my unannounced visit, madam, but it could not wait. My cousin and I shall need to make haste if we are to return to London by nightfall."

"Come now, there is no need to rush off," Mrs Bennet replied. "You must stay for dinner."

Elizabeth stared at her mother, knowing she disliked Mr Darcy as much as she did his cousin. Inviting either to dine with them seemed an entirely avoidable punishment. Mrs Bennet's reasoning soon became clear, however.

"When Mr Bingley went to town last winter, he promised to take a family dinner with us as soon as he returned, and you would naturally have been included in his party. Therefore, you are as much in our debt as he. I have not forgot, you see, and I assure you I was very much disappointed that he did not come back and keep his engagement." She paused, but just as Mr Darcy opened his mouth to reply, she added, "Does Mr Bingley have any plans to come back, do you know?"

"None of which I am aware, madam," replied Mr Darcy, after which he closed his mouth and ventured no more.

A brief glance at Jane revealed her misery. With pain and mortification hewn into every line of her rigid pose and her smile so brittle it looked liable to shatter at any moment, she refused to meet Elizabeth's gaze and stared instead at a point in the middle of the floor.

"What are your plans for Christmas, Mr Darcy?" Elizabeth asked in a wild attempt to direct the conversation away from Mr Bingley. It failed.

"My sister and I planned to spend it with Bingley and his sisters."

"I hope they will not mind an addition to the party," Elizabeth replied, indicating his cousin.

He smiled again and shook his head. "I am sure there will be no objection."

Miss de Bourgh, Elizabeth noticed, was *not* smiling but

glaring at Mr Darcy with undisguised displeasure. Which could most likely be attributed to the fact that he had not said a word to her since he arrived. Elizabeth could not but think that odd. It showed a peculiar want of affection on his part. Perhaps in cases such as these, it was not expected that there should be any affection, though if that were true, she thought it prodigiously sad.

"Bingley rarely objects to anything," Mr Darcy went on. "He is entirely too good-natured."

*Would that he cease mentioning his friend! Does he not comprehend how it will distress Jane?*

"May I introduce my aunt, sir?" Elizabeth asked almost desperately. Consent was given and the introduction made. "Before she was married, Mrs Gardiner spent some considerable time in Lambton, which I understand is near Pemberley," she explained. Better to mention *his* home than subject her aunt to any more scorn for hers.

She was foiled again when Miss de Bourgh leant to speak to her companion in a whisper that would likely have been audible in the garden. "She has not mentioned that Mrs Gardiner and her husband live in Cheapside."

"No wonder," Mrs Jenkinson replied, equally loudly.

There was a short pause, then Mr Darcy said, "It is rumoured that Defoe stayed at The White Hart in Lambton when he toured Derbyshire."

"That is right," Mrs Gardiner agreed happily. "There is a particular window seat—"

"—that overlooks the Derwent, yes."

"They say he preferred it to every wonder of the peaks lauded by Hobbes and Cotton. Though I suspect all the owners of The White Hart have embellished that part of the tale over the years."

"Oh no. Defoe was famously unimpressed with Derbyshire."

Elizabeth thought he looked offended as he said this, as though he took it as a personal slight that somebody should think ill of his home county. She thought it rather endearing, if a little silly. It compelled her to take his part.

"Oh well! *I* was unimpressed with *Robinson Crusoe*. Perhaps Mr Defoe would do better to stick to desert islands."

Mr Darcy laughed—actually laughed—which ought not to have surprised her, except that she could not recall seeing him do it before.

"Darcy, Mr Collins needs to get all the way back to Hunsford today," Miss de Bourgh announced abruptly, coming unsteadily to her feet. "It would be unpardonably rude to detain him. Let us be on our way."

As unpardonable rudeness went, Miss de Bourgh was an expert and, therefore, most qualified to know what would constitute an offence. Nevertheless, her cousin seemed disinclined to comply. Elizabeth was diverted by how obviously Mr Darcy disliked being told what to do, though her amusement waned as his brief show of graciousness was eclipsed by a sudden change of temperament.

His wistful smile disappeared, his forbidding glower returned, and he ceased talking altogether as his party readied themselves to leave. Miss de Bourgh, apparently at the limit of her powers, was bundled into the passenger seat of the gig. Mrs Jenkinson was relegated once more to the parcel shelf. Two servants hoisted Mr Collins, squealing, onto Mr Darcy's enormous horse and propelled him in the direction of Lucas Lodge.

Mr Darcy himself bowed a wordless goodbye to Mrs Bennet and climbed into the driver's seat of the gig without so much as a sideways squint at the rest of the family. It would have perfectly substantiated Elizabeth's impression of him, had he not looked back at her from the end of the drive. It was brief, but their eyes met, and Elizabeth felt it all the way to the very pit of her stomach.

"Thank heavens they have gone! A stranger family I have never come across in my life," cried Mrs Bennet. "Imagine if you had married Mr Collins, Lizzy? You would have had to put up with both of them as your neighbours whenever they were at Rosings. What a lucky escape!"

The incredulity this remark induced went a long way to dispelling the unsettling sensation still jostling Elizabeth's insides, and she was able to give a credible smile. "From my cousin's nonsense and Miss de Bourgh's incivility, certainly." She wondered whether she might have better tolerated Mr Darcy's authoritative efficiency—but only fleetingly, for he was gone, and her musings were immaterial.

They travelled in silence for a time. Whosoever's gig they were in was old and ill-balanced, and the horse was uncooperative. Darcy was glad of the distraction of trying to control it, for it helped take his mind off the tendrils of sullenness creeping back into his thoughts, souring his mood.

It was not that ill temper fazed him. He was not naturally disposed to sanguinity and was well acquainted with vexation and impatience. What troubled him was the inescapable fact that for a few sublime minutes at Longbourn, he had been neither ill tempered, nor vexed, nor impatient. For the first time in months, he had felt utterly and completely at peace. So happy that at one point, he had laughed aloud for sheer joy. He had walked into Long-bourn resolved to be unaffected, yet there she had been, exactly as he recalled—fierce, defiant, magnificent. He cared not that she had teased him. On the contrary, he had revelled in it, aware only then how acutely he had missed her wit. In those few sweet moments, every layer of bitterness and frustration had sloughed away from him, leaving nothing but pure delight to be once again in Eliza-beth's company. And it had downright terrified him.

Only when it had come time to go had he realised what was happening, and then he had wished to run and run and never look back. What foolhardy conceit had led him to think he would be in no danger once he saw her again? The sooner Anne's trunks could be loaded onto his carriage and they could set out for London the better. He knew from experience that distance would not banish his feelings, but it might diminish them to a less alarming intensity.

"Are you intending to say anything to me at all, or are we to travel the entire way in silence?"

Darcy looked down at his cousin in surprise. The words were so similar to those Elizabeth had said to him at Bingley's ball, the very conversation to which she had alluded moments ago, that he half expected to see her sitting next to him instead of Anne.

"Forgive me," he forced himself to say. "I was distracted, thinking about the journey ahead."

"To what journey do you refer?"

After a pause, during which Darcy failed to divine her meaning, he replied, "Back to London."

"You are leaving again so soon?"

"I am in no humour for games, madam. You must know I have come to take you back to town with me."

"I do not wish to go to town."

"I cannot take you back to Rosings this side of Christmas. You may travel with Mr Collins if you prefer, but unless he means to travel overnight, he will have to lodge in London this evening anyway. Better to come with me and stay at Number One, surely?"

"You mistake my meaning. I do not wish to go to Rosings, either."

Darcy reined in the horse and when the gig came to a halt, he turned to glare at his cousin. "What?"

"How kind of you to ask," Anne replied sardonically. "It is terribly noble of you to come all this way to escort me, but had you troubled yourself to ask what I wished first, you might have saved yourself a trip, for I do not wish to go."

"Sir William is under the impression that you were planning to leave this afternoon."

"I have changed my mind. I do not feel well."

Darcy regarded her for a moment. She looked no more indisposed than usual, though he could not imagine why she should invent such a claim. "I am sorry to hear it, but if that is the case, you would certainly be better coming with me and being seen by my physician."

"For heaven's sake, they do have physicians outside of London, you know, Darcy. But that is immaterial. I wish to stay here."

"You cannot mean to be away from Rosings for Christmas. What has my aunt to say about all this? Has she objected to your being here?"

"It would be difficult, given that she does not know."

Darcy made a concerted effort to prevent his expression from reflecting his thoughts. "Pray explain how she can possibly be unaware that you are not at home?"

"Because she is not there, either. She has been called away to visit a dying friend."

"She believes you are still at Rosings? Anne, please tell me you have not obliged the servants to conceal this from her?"

"Do not be ridiculous. She knows I am not there."

"And?" he pressed, his displeasure escalating. "Where does she think you are?"

"At Number One. With you."

He turned away sharply so she would not see the oath he mouthed. If there had not been reason enough to get her out of Hertfordshire before, there was no possibility of her remaining now. He had no intention of exposing himself to Lady Catherine's wrath should any harm befall her daughter whilst ostensibly in his care. This was precisely why he abhorred disguise.

"I have never observed this streak of cunning in you before," he remarked icily.

"No, well, I am discovering some less than agreeable parts of *you* that I never noticed before, either."

Darcy was taken aback as much by the turn of her countenance as the charge she flung at him, yet he would not knowingly cause her distress and thus moderated his tone as he attempted to explain his concern. "There is a man in the vicinity, a Mr Wickham, who—"

"Yes, I am acquainted with him."

"So I understand. But he is not the sort of man whose company it would be prudent for you to keep."

Anne narrowed her eyes. "You have an excessively low opinion of my intelligence."

"It is not my opinion of you that matters. It is my opinion of him."

"In that case, you need not concern yourself. It will be no punishment at all for me to stay away from him. Meryton is a large enough town that avoiding him ought to be easy."

"It would be considerably easier in a *different* town. Why are you so insistent upon staying here?"

She shifted uncomfortably in her seat. When she replied, it was not with an answer to his question. "You behaved very strangely just now at Longbourn. Miss Elizabeth was exceedingly rude to you, yet you said nothing. You only smiled at her. It is most unlike you to tolerate such an affront."

Darcy glanced pointedly at Mrs Jenkinson, whose studied indifference to their conversation was convincing nobody.

Anne ignored him. "I thought I understood you did not care for her," she continued, "but if you truly do not find her handsome enough to tempt you, then why do you allow her to be so insolent towards you?"

A shard of uneasiness shot through Darcy's gut. How the devil did Anne know he had said that? "Miss Elizabeth was not insolent. She was merely teasing."

"Teasing? What are you thinking, allowing her to believe it

is acceptable for her to *tease* you? You cannot continue to raise her expectations in this merciless manner, Darcy. It is cruel."

"I have given nobody *any* just cause to believe they may expect attention from me," he said gravely. He may as well have claimed he did not possess a head.

Anne banged her hand on the side of the gig. "Do not be absurd! Simply by coming back to Longbourn you have led her on. I know not what possessed you!"

Darcy tugged sharply on the reins, and the gig clattered into motion once more, almost erratically enough to eclipse the burst of unease that had spurred him into action. "It is a very good thing that we are returning to London, then."

Anne did not reply. She only pulled her shawl more tightly around her and turned her face away. Darcy made no attempt to draw her out, content to justify her original complaint by travelling the rest of the way in silence. He had never known his cousin to behave in such a way. It vexed him to such a degree that he left Mrs Jenkinson and a footman to assist her down when they arrived at Lucas Lodge.

He crossed the stables to speak to the driver of his own carriage but had time only to ask whether his cousin's trunks had yet been loaded before they were interrupted by a pitiful wail and several shouts of alarm. Hastening back to the other side of the gig, the cause was soon discovered to be Anne, who had apparently swooned as she disembarked.

"Good Lord!" cried Sir William, approaching from the house. "Bring her indoors directly. Hodges, quickly, ride out and fetch Mr Jones."

Darcy ignored him and knelt next to his cousin where she lay with her head in her companion's lap. The conviction instantly settled upon him of Anne being no more unwell than the servant who had been ordered to scoop her up and carry her indoors. Manners, pride—nay straightforward decorum—made it impossible that she might have feigned a swoon, however, and he was forced to swallow his spleen.

"Forgive me, Anne. I did not comprehend how unwell you were."

She gave him a wan smile. "I am sure it is nothing a good rest will not cure."

"I fear she has over-exerted herself," Mrs Jenkinson said in a nervous whisper. "It is precisely what the physician warned would happen."

"Stop fussing, Penny," Anne said, breathless either from asperity or infirmity, Darcy could not tell which.

"I am sure she will be well, madam," he assured Mrs Jenkinson. Then he stood up and indicated with a curt gesture for the servant to convey Anne indoors as per Sir William's instructions. With a sinking feeling, he allowed himself to be shown inside and given a cup of tea he did not want as they awaited the apothecary's appearance. It was another hour before Mr Jones arrived, by which time Darcy had resigned himself to the inevitable verdict: Anne was not to be moved.

He felt all the awkwardness that Elizabeth must have suffered the previous autumn when she arrived at Netherfield to nurse Jane, for Lady Lucas and her daughters made little attempt to conceal their dissatisfaction. Sir William was everything that was gracious, but even he could not muster an entirely persuasive air of approval. Mr Collins appeared on the brink of a nervous collapse, and Darcy was obliged to give his word that he would smooth any difficulties with Lady Catherine that arose as a result of Anne's misadventure. The man was sent on his way to resume his duties in Hunsford, and Darcy took his leave to return to the inn.

Several hours later, he sat alone before a dwindling fire, staring into a flagon of insipid mead. He ought to be livid. He had every right to be furious with Anne for having drawn him into her preposterous scheme, or the apothecary whose remedy for every ailment was apparently to confine the patient indefinitely to their bed. He would be perfectly justified in blaming Georgiana for inflicting her demonstrably terrible romantic instincts upon him. Any self-respecting gentleman would be disgusted by the unsavouriness of such lodgings. And he had no idea what to do to rectify any of it—a circumstance that would ordinarily have put him in the very worst of humours.

There could be only one explanation for the small grin that repeatedly accosted him, preventing any of his troubles from taking root. And he could not help but wonder, if five minutes in Elizabeth's company could bring him such contentment, what a lifetime might be like.

# CHAPTER 8

D arcy had never met a person who would not, eventually, construe his complete silence as a cue to cease talking—until that day. He had been seated on Sir William's intolerably hard sofa for the best part of an hour while the man himself spoke without pause, undeterred by the want of any response. He had listened as attentively as he was able, but with horsehair and springs jabbing him in the thighs and a succession of hysterical demands emanating from his cousin's part of the house, he had been too distracted to summon much enthusiasm for discourse.

What Anne was about he could not suppose. One moment she was screeching for somebody to rub her calves, the next, she was protesting at being manhandled. She called for salts, then she complained they made her bilious. She begged for a drink, then declared it tasted foul.

*Bring back Jane Bennet,* was all he could think, as each of Anne's laments put the former's convalescence at Netherfield in a better light and further compounded his mortification.

"Pray, excuse me," said a footman, silencing Sir William at last. "Miss Elizabeth Bennet is here, sir. I was unsure whether you meant to receive any *more* guests today."

Darcy lurched to his feet, then cursed himself for it. Was he a green boy to be leaping about idiotically at the mention of a woman's name? He clasped his hands behind his back and clenched his jaw shut, refusing to betray any discomposure. Even when Sir William exclaimed effusively that, of course, all callers were welcome, for it was Christmas and the more the merrier.

Elizabeth was shown in and received by Sir William with preposterous ebullience. She took it in her stride, returning his greeting with equal cheer if not equal fervour. She had evidently come on foot, for the walk had made her eyes gleam in a way Darcy recognised well. He could not decide how he liked them best, brightened by exercise or flashing with challenge. Her complexion was flushed, and one or two strands of her hair had been plastered to her cheeks by the damp winter air. The tip of one was caught in the crease at the corner of her mouth until she unconsciously looped a finger under it and tugged it free.

"Mr Darcy, you are still here!" Her exclamation startled him, though his heart was already thundering at such a pace that it scarcely signified.

He gave her a quick bow. "My cousin is unwell. The apothecary deemed her too ill to travel yesterday. We were due to leave this morning, but—"

Anne helpfully chose that moment to groan loudly, and Darcy let it stand in lieu of finishing his explanation.

"I am very sorry to hear that," Elizabeth replied, though she said it to Sir William, which Darcy suspected was deliberate. He wished he were not diverted, but he did so enjoy it when she was sly.

"Will she be well enough to travel today?" she asked.

"It is not certain." The strained reply came from the lady of the house, who had appeared in another doorway. She did not come into the room but remained where she was, looking extremely weary. "Good day, Eliza. Husband, might I have a word?"

Sir William's cheerfulness faltered as he excused himself to leave with his wife. When they were gone, Darcy let out a quiet sigh and rubbed the bridge of his nose with a knuckle. Blast Anne and her cosseted ways! He needed to return to Georgiana!

"You must be very worried about her."

He dropped his hand. Elizabeth was regarding him with a searching look that made her remark seem to contain more question than concern. Part of him wished to confess his suspicion that there was nothing the matter with Anne other than contrariness, for there were few people who would enjoy such nonsense more than Elizabeth. He constrained himself to grimacing very slightly and inclining his head, leaving her to construe it as she chose.

"I am particularly worried about my sister, to whom I gave my word that I would return to London no later than today."

"Oh dear! Can you not go to her and allow Mr Collins to take Miss de Bourgh back to Rosings when she is recovered?"

"Your cousin was obliged to return to Kent yesterday. He could stay away no longer this close to Christmas."

"Oh yes, of course."

She had a faint line between her brows that deepened when she frowned. Darcy had first noticed it when she nursed her sister in the autumn and ofttimes since. It appeared whenever she was concerned, a signifier of her compassion that augmented her beauty in a way handsome features alone never could. He was not able to enjoy it for long. It was snatched away from him when her attention went to the footman, who was ushering in another visitor. The servant faltered when he discovered his employer gone from the room, but at Elizabeth's encouragement, he continued with the announcement.

"Mr Wickham, for Miss de Bourgh."

Darcy could not contain the incredulous huff of air that

escaped him. He would never cease to be amazed by the sheer audacity of the man he had once called a brother. It took him a moment to recognise his vague sense of nausea for what it was: a vast aversion to witnessing Elizabeth's partiality for the reprobate. He clenched his teeth against the feeling.

Wickham waltzed in, every bit the cocksure dandy, and searched the room for his quarry. He seemed only vaguely surprised to see Elizabeth. He was significantly more perturbed to espy Darcy. The leer he had laid out for the former vanished, replaced by a nervous gulp and a countenance gone ashen.

"Darcy, what are you doing here?"

"Continuing to outmanoeuvre you."

After a bit of awkward bluster and a brief glance at Elizabeth, Wickham affected a swagger he evidently did not feel. "Come now, that is no way to greet your father's favourite."

A muscle twitched in Darcy's temple, but he held himself still. Evoking his father's memory was reprehensible, yet he was acutely aware of the intensity with which Elizabeth was watching their exchange. Watching *him*. Never had he been confined with two people who provoked in him so intense a desire for physical action, though of wholly opposing kinds.

Wickham smirked at his silence. "Let us set our differences aside for today. 'Tis Christmas, after all, and Miss Bennet does not wish to see any unpleasantness."

"There will be no unpleasantness, Wickham. You ought to know I shall make sure of that."

"Upon my life, I forgot how peevish you can be. I came only to express my best wishes to Miss de Bourgh before she leaves Hertfordshire."

To Wickham's left, where he could not have seen her, but where Darcy clearly could, Elizabeth raised one eyebrow in a supremely disbelieving look. He hoped to God that meant she had Wickham's measure.

"My cousin is not receiving callers," he said flatly. "You have had a wasted trip."

After a moment's hesitation, Wickham conceded, in as much as he licked his lips and took a step backwards. Still, he parried on the retreat.

"I think not, Darcy." Turning to Elizabeth, he said, "It seems the Lucases are all otherwise engaged, and Lord knows there is nothing else to entertain you here. May I have the honour of escorting you home?"

Darcy willed her to refuse, but before she could answer, they were joined by Miss Lucas and, to Darcy's relief, Anne. His cousin was leaning heavily on her companion's arm, her complexion the same pallid hue as usual, giving no indication as to the true state of her health.

"Miss de Bourgh, what a pleasure to see you looking so well," said Wickham, moving towards her.

Whether he still believed he had a chance at Anne's fortune or his design was purely to vex *him*, Darcy had no patience for it. He stepped in front of him, quelling his schemes with a quick, dark look before turning to address his cousin.

"Has whatever was the matter ceased troubling you?"

"Hardly," she replied.

"Good day, Mr Darcy, Mr Wickham, Eliza," said Miss Lucas. "Mama said you were come, Eliza. I am very pleased you have. Miss de Bourgh has expressed a wish to speak to you."

Apprehension splintered Darcy's gut.

"Me?" Elizabeth enquired.

"Yes, I should like a word in private. Let us take a turn about the garden," Anne said in a tone that could only have been learnt from her mother.

Everybody objected in unison, though Darcy's protests were loudest of all. "Anne, I shall not have you do anything to prevent us leaving. That includes making yourself ill again with unnecessary midwinter rambles out of doors."

"I should go," Elizabeth said quietly.

"No, you should stay," Anne replied, "for I have said I would speak to you. If you will not walk in the garden, perhaps you would do me the honour of coming upstairs with me."

It seemed Miss Lucas shared Darcy's reservations. She winced and stumbled over her words as she searched for a way to rescue her friend.

"You found it difficult to come down the stairs just now, Miss de Bourgh. Perhaps it would be best if you spoke to Eliza here."

"Perhaps it would be best if you struck up a correspondence and wrote everything you wish to say in a nice long letter *once we reach London*," Darcy interjected, his patience exhausted.

It discomposed him completely when Elizabeth tried unsuccessfully to stifle a laugh. He knew not whether she was laughing at him or with him, but the sound of it gave him a thrill that turned very rapidly to panic and then to anger.

"Anne, you are up and dressed. Let us go now before we lose the light."

"I am not going anywhere until I have spoken to Miss Bennet."

Though he suspected, Darcy could not be sure what she wished to say, but he would not risk her divulging his inclination, not when he was this close to evading the peril Elizabeth presented.

"Cousin, it is Christmas Eve," he said tersely. "I insist we leave now. I *must* get home."

Anne gave him an impatient, dismissive look. "If you are worried about your sister, she will be perfectly well where she is."

Darcy's every sinew tensed. He dared not look at Wickham, but his mind raced as he attempted to think of a way to evade further mention of Georgiana in his presence.

"Anne, this is not—"

"She has Mr Bingley at her disposal, does she not?" she continued, heedless of the gravity in his glare. "Miss Bingley is there to direct their attachment. You would only be in the way of that. If you are as keen as she is for them to come to an understanding, you had much better stay away."

A small gasp from Elizabeth drew Darcy's notice. She had changed colour, and her lips were pressed tightly together.

"My, my, Darcy. Have you been separating more young lovers? This is becoming quite the habit."

He rounded on Wickham, who he could only presume had been emboldened by the presence of so many people whose ignorance must be maintained. The blackguard leant nonchalantly against the fireplace, his mouth an ugly, lilting curve that made Darcy's blood boil.

"Do not dare, Wickham."

But he *had* dared, and it was already too late.

"What is your meaning, sir?" Elizabeth asked, but Wickham only affected an air of helplessness, and with an expressive glance in Darcy's direction, he shrugged.

"What did he mean?" she demanded of Darcy instead. "Did you persuade Mr Bingley to leave so you could encourage a match with your sister instead?"

Darcy hesitated. He had not expected her to ask about Bingley.

"Who could blame him if he had?" Anne interjected. "You really must overcome this foolish conviction that anyone in your family could marry so far above themselves."

Elizabeth's astonishment was clear as was her displeasure. "Excuse me, madam, but Jane is a gentleman's daughter. Pray tell me, in what respect is she not good enough for Mr Bingley?"

Wickham chimed in. "And how is it that a tradesman's son is suddenly good enough for your sister, Darcy? 'Tis a notable change of heart."

"It may be difficult for you to comprehend," Darcy snarled, "but a good match rests as much on excellent character as sufficient fortune."

Elizabeth emitted a wordless cry of indignation. "You thought Jane's character wanting?"

Darcy spun back to her. "What—no! What did—" He paused, distracted by Wickham's broadening smirk and the disagreeable feeling of the conversation slipping away from him in a direction he could not grasp.

"You mistake Mr Darcy's meaning, I am sure," said Miss Lucas, laying a hand on Elizabeth's arm. "I have said before that Jane was very guarded in her affections. Perhaps it was not clear she was in love."

"Well, it has certainly been clear since Mr Bingley *left*," Elizabeth retorted. "She has been utterly miserable."

Darcy barely had time to frown over this before his attention was pulled to the other side of the room where Anne had dropped noisily into a chair.

"Do dispose of your airs, Miss Bennet. If my cousin has separated his friend from your sister, then he has done him a very great service. Only *consider* the situation of your mother's family."

"Anne!" Darcy admonished. No matter that it was true, there could be no justification for saying it to Elizabeth.

"Nay, I am serious, Darcy. The want of connexion could not be so great an evil to Mr Bingley as to you, but it is hardly to be overlooked."

He stared at her, appalled. He might have *thought* it all—indeed, these were the very reasons he had not put an end to his torment and offered for Elizabeth months ago—but aloud, it sounded as vain as it did insolent.

"Madam, you are unjustly severe. We both made the acquaintance of Miss Bennet's relations yesterday, and they were evidently people of fashion and *good manners*." Darcy emphasised the last part, wishing rather than believing his cousin would take his meaning. He could scarcely credit it when Anne, so far from perceiving his warning, persisted instead with more censure.

"A fashionable wardrobe does not a fine connexion make. What of Mrs Bennet? Will you tell me her behaviour would not be a cause of repugnance to any potential suitor? She betrays a total want of propriety as do most of Miss Bennet's sisters."

"Younger sisters, eh? Troublesome lot," said Wickham, drawing upon himself the full force of the displeasure that Darcy was prevented by good breeding from directing at his cousin.

"You have said quite enough." Controlled fury made his voice harsher than usual, and he noticed with grim satisfaction its effect on Wickham. "Leave this place before I am minded to act upon the particulars laid out in my last letter to you."

Wickham blanched, and when Darcy said nothing more and only glowered at him with seething hatred, he hastily left. Only once he had gone did Darcy realise that so had Elizabeth. He ought to have been pleased, but what he felt was an iron band tighten about his chest that prevented him from catching his breath.

"As for *that* one—Miss *Elizabeth Bennet*," Anne went on, pointing at the spot where Elizabeth had been. "*She* seems to think that the inferiority of her connexions, her condition in life —so decidedly beneath our own—can be made up for by impertinence and flirtation. She—"

"Anne, that is *enough!* I do not wish to hear you speak another word against any of the Bennet family. You are in no position to disparage anybody. Your shocking behaviour these past few days has surpassed *anything* I have witnessed from Elizabeth's relations. Would that you displayed half *her* sense and disposition rather than exaggerating your ill health and taking to your bed like a spoilt child. What on earth were you hoping to achieve?"

Anne paled further still, if such a thing were possible. "You... You *love—*"

"Is anything amiss?" asked Lady Lucas. She crept into her

own room as though entering a bear pit, wringing her hands together and almost cringing as she awaited an answer.

Darcy closed his eyes briefly in mortification. He prided himself on his impeccable manners and reviled such weaknesses as a quick temper and uncivil tongue. Never would he have believed himself liable to raise his voice in another person's house, scaring away their guests and reducing them to cowering pleas of conciliation.

"I beg your pardon for the disturbance, madam," he said solemnly.

"I thank you, Lady Lucas," Anne interrupted. "I am glad *you* are able to see how I suffer, even if not everybody is so perceptive. I do not feel at all well. I wonder if you could help me back to my chamber. I need to rest else I fear I may swoon again."

❦

Darcy could scarcely remember the order of events that followed. All he knew was that for the second day in a row, dusk found him seated before a dying fire, nursing his manifold indignities over a tankard of disgusting mead at the George and Crown. The warmth that had enveloped him the previous evening as he reflected on Elizabeth's teasing had, this evening, been replaced with dismay as he recalled the abhorrence with which she had regarded him at Lucas Lodge. Where she had gone afterwards, he knew not. He was doing his damnedest not to think about it, without much success.

Wickham, at least, was on his way to another regiment. Darcy cared neither where nor how much it had cost him to bring it about. All that concerned him was that the man was away from him and anyone connected to him. Darcy wished he had seen to it the last time he was in Meryton, though he had no reason to suspect then that he would be back so soon.

Anne remained abed at Lucas Lodge. He was certain she was not any more unwell than she had been these past seven-and-twenty years. Whatever had ailed her that long had not killed her yet, and he sincerely doubted thirty miles of good road would have finished her off. He could not, for the life of him, fathom her purpose in feigning illness.

Neither could he reconcile himself to her selfishness. Quite apart from her indifference to the fact she had made him look an absolute fool, rendering all Elizabeth's relations decorous and refined by comparison, her performance had put paid to all his hopes of returning home in time for Christmas.

He had been sorely tempted to leave without her, yet he had been required to deal with Wickham first, and daylight had waned long before Anne's histrionics. Thus, after Georgiana's terrible year and despite all his promises to her, his sister must now pass the holiday without him. He sipped his drink, grimacing as he swallowed it.

He had offered his manservant the chance to return home, though Carruthers had refused, excellent man that he was. He regretted he had not persuaded Anne to offer Mrs Jenkinson the same opportunity. All that remained for him to do was send expresses to Georgiana and Bingley, informing them of his delay. This he was attempting to do in the George and Crown's public saloon, for there was no table in his room and only one candle by which to admire the want of it.

He picked up his pen to add a line or two to what he had written already. Rereading his own words recalled him to Miss Lucas's earlier that afternoon. *'Perhaps it was not clear she was in love.'* He twirled his pen back and forth between his finger and thumb.

In the tumult of the moment, when his mind had been wholly engaged in attempting to keep Georgiana's name out of the conversation and away from Wickham's notice, this allusion to Jane Bennet's affections had confused him greatly. But, of course, nobody here knew about Georgiana and Wickham. They had all understood him to be speaking of Miss Bennet and Bingley.

"Ah, there you are, Mr Darcy. May I interrupt you for a moment?"

Darcy looked up and was astonished to see Mr Bennet standing before him. "You may, sir." He folded away his letter and gestured for him to sit. "What can I do for you?"

Mr Bennet sidled into the opposing bench and fixed him with a smile that he disliked partly because he knew not what diverted the man and partly because it reminded him of Elizabeth.

"It is more what I can do for you," Mr Bennet answered. His gaze wondered about the dingy parlour. "It has come to our attention that for reasons outside of your command, you are facing the prospect of spending Christmas Day on your own in this *delightful* establishment."

Darcy was unsure how to answer. He certainly would not be going home, but as to where else he might pass the day, he had not considered. Lady Lucas had not issued an invitation for him to join her.

"So it would seem," he replied at length.

"Well, in Mrs Bennet's esteemed opinion, that will never do."

"I beg you would tell Mrs Bennet that it is not in my power to do anything about it."

"Fortunately for you—or unfortunately, depending on your perspective—my wife has a strong aversion to any matter in which she cannot be involved. She, therefore, very often thrusts herself, with a zeal I am quite unable to contain, into matters the rest of us might be forgiven for thinking have absolutely nothing to do with her. Which is why I am come, at her insistence, to invite you to dine with us tomorrow at Longbourn."

Darcy stared at him. The memory of Elizabeth's final look, rife with pain and anger, had haunted him all afternoon. Now, it seemed that would not be their last encounter, for apparently, he was to spend Christmas Day with her. His life was growing more ridiculous by the moment.

"That is an exceedingly generous offer."

"I thought so, too. But then, as well as suffering from a vast number of nervous complaints and being staggeringly silly, Mrs Bennet is an exceedingly generous-hearted woman."

"Even so, I hope you will not be offended if I observe that she has not always seemed to care overmuch for my company."

"No, but slight one of her girls and you will rarely be treated to her gentlest side."

"I beg your pardon," Darcy said tightly, affronted by the insinuation, "but never have I and never would I slight one of your daughters."

Mr Bennet displayed that disquieting smile again. "Perhaps I misunderstood, then. But to business! Can I engage you for attendance? Mrs Bennet will be offended beyond repair if I return with the report that Mr Darcy of Pemberley would rather dine at the George and Crown than at her table."

Darcy knew not why he was prevaricating. Because it would be an imposition? Because most of Elizabeth's relations were ghastly? Because being in Elizabeth's presence made him ache for her in a way he did not think he could bear? He sighed discreetly. It was for all those reasons, but he had not the resolve to stay away from her.

"I should be delighted to join you, though I have one small problem in the form of my cousin. I am unsure whether she will be expected to dine at Lucas Lodge tomorrow."

"I doubt it, from what Lady Lucas was saying about her in my parlour not two hours ago."

*For the love of God!* If he ever escaped Hertfordshire, Darcy swore to himself he would never return for as long as he lived. "Then I am afraid, if you have me, you will be obliged to have her and her companion as well."

"Excellent! If I am to spend Christmas Day with a house full of my own silly women, the least you can do is bring a few of your own."

Darcy could not accustom himself to the man's irreverence,

and the comparison of Anne to any one of Elizabeth's younger sisters was sobering, thus he did not smile as they stood to shake hands. "Before you go, might I ask you something about your eldest daughter?"

Mr Bennet pulled a face that made clear his curiosity. "You may."

"Was she *particularly* disappointed when my friend Bingley left the country?"

Mr Bennet's countenance relaxed into one of comprehension. "More so than her mother, do you mean? Aye, Jane does appear to have been in low spirits since, but do not all girls like to be crossed in love at some point, Mr Darcy? But Jane is usually less apt than her sisters to make a fuss of things, and Lizzy seems to think her melancholy is genuine. And Lizzy, you understand, is the most sensible of all my girls. If anyone is likely to have the right of it, 'tis her."

Darcy thanked him, and they parted ways. When he was gone, Darcy threw his letter to Bingley on the fire and wrote it out anew. He sent a boy out with it and a bag of coin heavy enough to ensure it would find its way to London despite it being almost Christmas. Then he retired for the night to fight a losing battle against the pangs of agitation that assailed him every time he thought of seeing Elizabeth on the morrow.

# CHAPTER
# 9

Hostages were exchanged at church on Christmas Day. Mr
Darcy retrieved his cousin and her companion from Sir
William's carriage and sat with them at the rear of the nave, as
far away from both the Lucases and the Bennets as the modest
building permitted. To Elizabeth, this was proof of his disdain
for both families. Charlotte, who had wasted no time retrieving
Elizabeth from *her* family party, was more inclined to think his
intentions good.

"I am sure he means only to spare us all as much inconvenience as possible, Eliza. Mr Darcy was most sincere in his
apology to my mother for the trouble they have given us. In
truth, I think he was rather embarrassed."

"Who would not be? Miss de Bourgh has made a nuisance of
herself from the very first." Seeing Charlotte sigh resignedly,
Elizabeth checked her tone and added, "I am sure she will not
always be so unreasonable. In any case, I expect they will live at
Pemberley once they are married, and you will not have to deal
with her at all."

"Perhaps," replied her friend with a humourless smile. "Though I suspect she may not be so tiresome when she is away from here."

They were obliged to cease conspiring to join in a hymn. Elizabeth did so with uncommon eagerness, for when she was not singing herself, she could hear Mr Darcy doing so. She could not have said why she preferred not to listen to him, except that it made her lose her place so often.

"It was very good of your mother to invite them both to dine with you today," Charlotte whispered when they were seated again.

"She only invited Mr Darcy. And only because *your* mother was not disposed to have him—for which none of us blame her, you understand. Miss de Bourgh is quite enough bother on her own, but he would not come without her."

"He ought to be applauded for that. It shows an affection for his future wife that is very pleasing."

"It certainly shows more affection than he has exhibited for her thus far." Elizabeth stole a sly glance at them, then wrinkled her nose in ambivalence. "If either of them is pleased by it, they are disguising it well."

Charlotte laughed lightly. "I am sure *she* is delighted. But their happiness notwithstanding, my mother is exceedingly grateful for the reprieve. Mrs Bennet has demonstrated true Christmas spirit with this generosity."

"She might have been a good deal less generous had she heard what Miss de Bourgh said about her yesterday."

"I am sure. It was excessively unkind of her to say all those things."

There was something in Charlotte's intonation that made her meaning ambiguous, and her sudden interest in the rector's oration was telling. Elizabeth decided against questioning it, for it was Christmas, and she had no wish to quarrel with her friend. Yet, Charlotte said no more, either, and her willingness to abandon the subject grew more vexing the longer her silence persisted. By the time the last hymn of the service was sung, Elizabeth could resist commenting no longer.

"You think she was right."

Her answer came in the colour that tinged her friend's cheeks. She turned irritably to glare at the pulpit.

"Not for the most part," Charlotte said gently. "And no matter what her motivation, saying any of it *to* you was unpardonably ill-mannered. But you and I have ever valued each other's honesty, and just as I did not blame you for questioning my decision to marry Mr Collins, I hope you will not blame me for saying that there was *some* truth in what Miss de Bourgh said."

Elizabeth's ears rang with indignation. "The part where she said Jane was unworthy of being Mr Bingley's wife or the part where she accused my mother of being a cause of repugnance?"

"Oh Eliza!" Charlotte reached for her hand and, because it *was* Christmas, Elizabeth did not pull it away. "When you reflect on this later, I hope you will be sensible enough to acquit me of thinking anything of the sort. I *know* you are sensible enough to recognise which of her accusations had merit and which are to be ignored entirely."

Confined as she was to a pew, Elizabeth was unable to act on her most immediate wish to walk anywhere fast until her anger was burnt off. She took a deep breath and forced herself to give Charlotte's hand a quick answering squeeze before letting it go.

It was a relief when the service was done, and she was able to stand along with the rest of the congregation to file out of the church. It was less of a relief to see Mr Darcy and Miss de Bourgh just outside the door, speaking to her mother and Jane. *Dear* Jane, who was yet unaware that the wretch at whom she was smiling so sweetly had been the means of separating her from the man she loved.

Elizabeth checked herself. She had gone over this a thousand times in her mind since the previous day, and in no iteration of events had she been able to come to any conclusion other than

Mr Darcy truly had not known Jane was in love. The indifference with which he had spoken of Mr Bingley without embarrassment or concern upon his first return to Longbourn, his confusion when she questioned his motives for dividing them, and that he had asked her father about Jane's regard, all spoke of his miscalculation there. None of it justified his officious interference or his disdain for the match. But it was enough to exonerate him of the cruelty of detaching Mr Bingley from her sister without *any* regard to the sentiments of either. It was not enough to make Elizabeth anticipate an entire day in his company.

At that moment, Jane and her mother walked away, and Mr Darcy turned in her direction, but he frowned immediately upon setting eyes on her. What displeased him was of no interest to her. Elizabeth suppressed a sigh, gave him a perfunctory curtsey, and hastened away to wish Mrs Goulding a happy Christmas.

"Do you always indulge so early?" said Miss de Bourgh with the utmost disdain as she accepted the glass Kitty thrust at her.

"Only at Christmas," answered Mrs Bennet, accepting hers from Lydia and settling into her usual chair in Longbourn's parlour.

"It helps get through the rest of the day," Mr Bennet added. One of the Gardiners' children squealed and slammed a door at the back of the room, and Mary played the opening chords of a regrettably cheerless tune at a volume that threatened to make further conversation impossible. Mr Bennet raised his voice to add, "I heartily recommend you drink it, madam."

"I certainly shall not," Miss de Bourgh replied. "It is most unseemly at this hour, no matter the occasion."

Mrs Bennet bristled, but her husband only shrugged. "Do not say I did not warn you."

Miss de Bourgh set her glass aside, then took Mrs Jenkinson's glass from her, setting that aside also. Elizabeth was diverted to see that Mr Darcy took such a swig as almost drained his dry. He was very quiet, which was hardly out of character, but she did not doubt he was uncomfortable.

Even in the grand halls of Netherfield he had been reserved, fastidiously proper. It would be almost impossible for him to retain the same air of dignity in such a chaotic family setting as Longbourn on Christmas Day. Then, though she had looked upon his coming as an intolerable invasion, Elizabeth began to pity him—*a little*—for being so far removed from his usual surroundings.

"It is one of our little traditions," she said to him. He looked startled to have been addressed, and Elizabeth qualified her statement by pointing to his glass. "For as long as I can remember, we have had a glass of punch after church on Christmas Day. We have been doing it for so long I cannot recall how it began."

"It began the year you were in London, Lizzy," said her father. "Mr Gordon's wife had a baby in the early hours of Christmas Day, and he had a tipple before the service to celebrate."

"A tipple?" said Mrs Bennet. "He could barely stand up in the pulpit."

"And I said that if it was acceptable for the clergy to enjoy Christmas that well, then so would I. And, of course, we were all missing you, Lizzy, so we had Hill prepare us something to soothe our spirits."

Mr Darcy looked as though he might speak, but Mary made a mistake at the pianoforte and attempted to disguise it by banging out the correction with even greater energy.

Miss de Bourgh made a great show of being alarmed, pressing a hand to her chest dramatically and grumbling, "Is that really necessary?"

Mr Darcy looked at her sullenly but said nothing. *Probably because he agrees*, Elizabeth thought bitterly. Then she smiled, for she scarcely *dis*agreed herself.

"As Christmas traditions go, I like this one better than most," said Mr Gardiner, raising his glass to the room and taking a sip.

"I like it better than Mary's playing," said Lydia, quite as meanly and not so discreetly as Miss de Bourgh.

"You and I have a tradition, Lydia, do we not?" Elizabeth said. She was under no illusion that distracting her sister would constrain her poor manners, but she hoped that distracting Mr Darcy might save him from being mortified by them.

"Yes," Lydia replied. "I put a pebble in your punch one year in the hope that you would choke on it."

Mr Darcy almost choked on *his* punch, somewhat dispelling Elizabeth's hopes.

"It does not appear to have been a successful gambit," remarked Miss de Bourgh.

"No, I found it before I choked and thought it was meant as a gift," Elizabeth replied. "But Lydia had quite forgiven me for whatever I had done by then, so she made it into a necklace for me instead. Now she gives me a new pebble every year."

"Then there is hope one of them will work eventually."

Despite not much liking Miss de Bourgh, Elizabeth was nevertheless inclined to laugh at this. The cause of the woman's animosity was a mystery, but with four sisters, three of whom had on numerous occasions wished her ill, it was an easy enough sentiment to disregard.

Indeed, Lydia *did* laugh. Mr Darcy did not appear quite so ready to overlook it, but Elizabeth supposed he was ill used to the occasional pettiness of so many women in one place and pitied him even more for being thrust into the thick of it without any practice.

"Do you have any Christmas traditions, Mr Darcy?" Jane asked.

"No, I have not that pleasure," he replied succinctly.

Elizabeth thought he looked a little saddened by the admission. She felt a little sad *for* him.

"We keep to the more conventional, refined traditions of the season in our circle, Miss Bennet," said his cousin.

Mr Darcy closed his eyes very briefly. It could almost have been mistaken for a blink, but Elizabeth fancied he was close to losing his temper with his cousin.

"I assure you there is quite as much of that going on in our circle as any other," cried Mrs Bennet.

"Sister," cautioned Mrs Gardiner in a low voice but to no avail. Mrs Bennet persisted.

"We go to church, rejoice, feast well, drink merrily, and sing jolly carols the same as every other person, regardless of in which sphere they were brought up. In fact—Mary, stop playing that song! Lizzy, play that one you were practising this morning. Girls! Come and sing with your sister. Come along! Let us demonstrate that we know perfectly well how to observe traditional Christmas...*traditions*."

"There, you see, Mr Darcy," called Mr Bennet. "You have made a good effort, but my ladies are by far and away sillier than yours."

Elizabeth pushed herself to her feet and made her way to the pianoforte. As she passed in front of Mr Darcy, she gave him a satirical smile that she hoped was expressive of their mutual mortification. He did not return it, but she was not offended. He looked so miserable now that she was tempted to think of an excuse to have him sent out of the house. Still, since he had accepted the invitation to come of his own volition, he would just have to bear the ignominy.

Elizabeth played and sang several carols before ceding the instrument to Mrs Gardiner. Miss de Bourgh was invited to play, but she refused. She looked rather dismayed to have been asked, her gaze flicking anxiously between her cousin and the pianoforte. Elizabeth recalled too late Mr Collins's report that she had never learnt and hastily offered her eldest niece a turn.

Even Mr Gardiner was prevailed upon to exhibit his skill, proving to vast amusement that his claim to modest talent had not been exaggerated.

"Think you it is time to allow the children their moment, Sister?" he enquired, closing the instrument in defeat. "I believe my performance has marked a low point in proceedings that only something special will salvage."

"By all means," Mrs Bennet replied, "if they are ready to indulge us."

Upon receiving their enthusiastic assurances, Mr Gardiner leapt to his feet and swept his youngest daughter into his arms. With Jane and Mrs Gardiner's help, he shepherded the other three children from the room.

Mr Bennet stood with a groan. "I hope this year's performance is less eventful than last year's. My banyan still has a burn hole in it."

Seeing their guests look thoroughly confused, Elizabeth said, "My cousins have prepared a little performance to entertain us."

"Another tradition?" said Miss de Bourgh in a condescending tone.

"It is only the second year they have done it, and they only wished to repeat it *this* year because last year's attempt went so very awry. But I sincerely hope it becomes a tradition."

"You never know, Anne, you might enjoy it," said Mr Darcy.

Elizabeth looked at him, as did his cousin, but his countenance was a mask of disinterest. "I hope you both will," she said. "If you would come this way?"

She led them into the morning room, where the furniture had been arranged to give the impression of a stage with seats fanned out in front for an audience. Mrs Bennet had instructed that the best sofa, nearest the door, be left for their distinguished guests, something Elizabeth pointed out to them upon entering. Miss de Bourgh sat on it directly, instructing her ever-faithful companion to do the same.

"I should prefer a better view, if there is space nearer the front," said Mr Darcy.

"By all means, sir, take my seat!" Mr Bennet replied. Bending down to one of his nephews, he said in a grandfatherly tone that he did not often employ and which Elizabeth suspected bespoke the amount of punch he had consumed, "I shall happily sit farther away where there is less chance of being roasted like Cook's goose."

"We are not using real candles this year, Uncle Bennet," Matthew replied, wide-eyed.

"Best not, lad, though I should like to see Mr Collins's face if we did manage to burn the place down."

Elizabeth took her seat, and Mr Darcy took her father's, next to it. She was not sorry to be seated by him, for she found herself intrigued by his enthusiasm. Nay, enthusiasm was the wrong word, but he was certainly interested, as though he was discovering something that he had not expected to enjoy. She watched him, as slyly as she was able, whilst he watched her cousins begin their very sweet, very stilted version of the Nativity story.

In her opinion, it was impossible that anybody should *not* enjoy the sight of Joseph—played by dear little Matthew—struggling to haul the old rocking horse to the centre of the room with his brother, Edward, applying the only true forward momentum to the creature's hindquarters with his shoulder. Mary—her youngest cousin, Lucy, wearing a cushion tied haphazardly about her midriff with a cord—clung desperately to the horse's neck the entire way, only to slide off upon arriving centre stage.

They all laughed at little Emily who, sporting one of Mrs Bennet's hair pieces as a beard, repeatedly misspoke the solitary line, "There is no room at the inn," which gave her innkeeper all the appearance of being foxed on his own ale. Edward's attempt to simultaneously portray a shepherd and a wise man resulted in a calamitous costume mishap that reduced Emily to insensible giggles. Whatever message her Angel Gabriel had been meant to impart was abridged to several minutes of uncontrollable laughter. By the time Mr Gardiner burst into their midst dressed all in black with a bronze cooking pot for a crown, bellowing for the heads of every baby in the kingdom, Elizabeth was holding her side from laughing overmuch.

The end of the performance was met with hearty applause, at which point it dawned on her that she had entirely forgotten her object of studying Mr Darcy. Elizabeth glanced at him, then looked away again hastily. *She* may have been too engrossed in the play to attend to anything else, but it seemed he had not been similarly affected. She wondered that she had not noticed him looking, for his gaze was singularly intent. Part of her wished to know what his slight smile signified. A greater part of her was certain she would not like the answer. It was that part which propelled her from her chair to congratulate her cousins.

"Very good, children," Mr Bennet agreed. "I am heartily diverted—and relieved, for there were no injuries but to Edward's pride. And you, Miss de Bourgh? Were you amused by the children's efforts?"

Elizabeth felt a flash of shame, for it was obvious to her if to no one else that her father's purpose was to ridicule his guest. Miss de Bourgh wore a pinched, unhappy expression and did not appear at all diverted. Indeed, she looked almost bewildered, as though she wished to partake in the fun but knew not why everybody was laughing. This sort of silliness evidently did not appeal to her sensibilities. There was no reason it should, for she had no children of her own and passed her time surrounded by people who had made it the study of their lives to take themselves far too seriously. It was very wrong of Mr Bennet to make sport of her discomfort.

"They did well, did they not?" Elizabeth said, enabling Miss de Bourgh to escape the matter with but a nod of her head and a vague smile.

"Did you em-joy the per-lay, sir?"

Such a darling enquiry could only have come from little Emily. Elizabeth looked around and smiled to see her cousin standing at Mr Darcy's feet, her neck craned so far back as she peered up at him that it seemed she might topple over. There was no reason to expect him to be unkind in his response, but neither could Elizabeth have anticipated what he did, which was to crouch down and very formally kiss the back of Emily's hand.

"I thought it a better production than any I have seen in London, Miss Gardiner. It was an honour to be in the audience."

Emily beamed, curtseyed, then abruptly reverted to being terrified and looked to Elizabeth in silent entreaty.

"Run along, precious," she told her. "Auntie Bennet will be wanting her beard back."

Mr Darcy stood up, his curious little smile still in situ.

"That was very kind of you," Elizabeth remarked.

"Extending kindness to cousins seemed to be the order of the day. Besides, it was true. I enjoyed it very much. Both Miss Gardiners remind me of my sister at that age."

"Of course! I forget that your sister is so much younger than you."

His expression altered to a more wistful one. "She has just turned sixteen. This is the first Christmas we have ever spent apart."

Elizabeth saw him waver towards melancholy and resolved not to allow it on Christmas Day. She smiled broadly instead.

"There is your tradition, sir. And a very fine one it is, too."

# CHAPTER
# 10

Darcy was in agonies—some sublime, some infernal, all of them insufferable. Elizabeth's relations embodied almost every trait he had been taught to despise, yet the longer he was amongst them, the more he envied their contentment, the more he resented Anne's paltry meanness, the unhappier he was not to be with his sister, the more he missed his father and, for the first time in many years, his mother.

And the more drawn he felt to Elizabeth.

It was a confounding and unpleasant state in which to find himself, and it diminished his appetite to the point that eating became a struggle. That was a shame, for the dinner Mrs Bennet served was astonishingly good. Her table and the dining room itself were handsomely decorated with red ribbons and boughs of fir and holly, giving a remarkably festive air to the occasion, but he was too uncomfortable to truly enjoy it.

Further detracting from his pleasure were the seating arrangements that placed him at the opposite end of the table to

Elizabeth but next to her mother, from whom he received an excruciating barrage of poorly veiled allusions to Bingley's departure. By the time he forced down the large glass of mediocre port with which Mr Bennet furnished him after dinner, he was exhausted—and, annoyingly, hungry. Only the thought of his revolting bed at the inn prevented him from announcing his early departure. That, and his unwillingness to part ways with Elizabeth for what would likely be the last time.

It was with no little alarm that he discovered her absent when the gentlemen joined the ladies in the drawing room. The possibility that she had retired, denying him his last goodbye, struck a deep, hollow note in his stomach that would not fade no matter how much coffee he drank to drown it. When the door opened and she returned, when she came into the room looking for someone and stopped searching once her eyes met his, when all the air flowed out of his lungs in one, uneven breath, and the hairs on his arms stood on end, he understood how far beyond *danger* he had strayed. He knew he ought not to engage with her anymore, but he knew he could no more prevent himself than he could prevent the moon from orbiting the earth.

She collected a cup of coffee and came to sit down next to him. "I have something for you."

She handed him a strange little item—a doll, he realised—small enough to fit in his palm and fashioned from what looked like clothes-pegs. He took it, for he would never refuse anything she gave him, but he looked askance at her as he did.

"Her name is Hegarty. My uncle Gardiner made her for me that Christmas my father mentioned earlier. I had the measles, so I was sent to stay in London away from my sisters. It was the first Christmas I ever spent apart from Jane, and I was wretched. I thought she might cheer you up while you are away from Miss Darcy."

Darcy looked at it, then he looked at her. He was eight-and-twenty years old, master of one of the largest estates in the north of England, and revered by half the *ton*. And Elizabeth had given him a wooden peg-doll called Hegarty as a gift. She was also biting her lips against a smirk, her eyes sparkling as she watched him, and he knew she was anticipating his confusion, possibly even his contempt. What he would not give to be able to kiss away her misconception! His mouth fought for a broader smile than the slight one he allowed himself.

"You thought correctly. Thank you."

She looked surprised though not displeased with this answer and, with a nod, settled back into her seat to take stock of the rest of the room as though catching up with what she had missed.

"Your uncle and mother are playing piquet," he said quietly. "Miss Mary has been reading a book to your father, and the rest of your family is attempting to explain the plot of *Othello* to Miss Catherine, though I confess how that conversation came about quite escaped my understanding."

These observations evidently surprised her as well, though she did not remark on them directly. She only smiled as she said, "Yes, discussions in this house can be rather convoluted. It can get a little lively at times."

"On the contrary. It has been an agreeably peaceful evening."

"Indeed," Anne interposed to Darcy's consternation, for it signified her having listened to all that had been said before. "We have been expecting the celebrations to devolve into raucous parlour games at any moment."

Darcy shot her a furious look, but before he could think how he might civilly frame a reproof, Elizabeth had turned to address her over the arm of her chair.

"Alas, my father loathes parlour games, my mother is terrible at them, and my younger sisters do nothing but argue over who won and who cheated. We gave up playing them years ago, but I should be happy to request a bowl of raisins and a bottle of sherry from the kitchen if you would like a game of Snapdragon."

Anne pursed her lips, and Darcy uncharitably thought to himself it was probably because she had not the wit to extract herself from the situation in which her own incivility had landed her.

"Perhaps another time," Elizabeth said, more forbearingly than Anne deserved.

His cousin's enmity towards Elizabeth gave Darcy an uneasy feeling. He wished to apologise for her ingratitude but could not while she eavesdropped his every word, though that problem, at least, was soon resolved. Miss Bennet moved to sit next to her and spoke with such patient kindness that eventually, Anne condescended to converse.

"Jane is very good," Elizabeth said quietly. "If anybody can make your cousin feel more at ease, it is my sister."

"I do not know why my cousin should feel ill at ease. You have all been extremely welcoming."

"Oh, come now, sir," she replied with a bewitching expression. "Miss de Bourgh has all the same reasons to feel uneasy as you have."

He ought to have known he could not conceal his disquiet from Elizabeth, studier of character that she was. Still, she was not completely correct in this. "Not all."

She looked perplexed, and Darcy felt a stab of alarm at having come far closer than he meant to an admission of his feelings.

"I have no doubt that your sister will be unperturbed by any surliness," he said hastily. "She is one of the most serene ladies I have ever encountered."

Elizabeth sighed unhappily. "Aye, though that composure of temper has served her very ill of late. Jane's uniform cheerfulness hides a great strength of feeling, but once you know it is there, her unhappiness is plain to see. It is in the tilt of her head, and the brevity of all her smiles."

This speech made Darcy inordinately glad to have written to Bingley, though he was not in a position to say anything on the matter. Instead, he asked, "What of you? How does one know when you are happy or sad?"

She seemed to accept the change of subject well enough. "When I am happy, I laugh."

"And when you are unhappy?"

"That is the tricky bit, for I usually laugh then, too."

"Not always. You were not laughing when you came out of the church earlier."

Her smile faltered. "No, not always. But despite what you might think, my first object in life is not a joke."

It took Darcy a moment to place the reference, but at length he recalled it from one of their debates at Netherfield. "I assure you I never thought that." With a pointed look at his cousin, he added, "Yet, it would be to the advantage of *some* to joke more often. Regrettably, my cousin's upbringing has not taught her much appreciation for life's simpler diversions." He wondered whether the same could be said of him. He hoped not.

"I had noticed, sir. But humour is a fickle creature, and we shall never all be diverted by the same things. It is good that you comprehend Miss de Bourgh's nature. That will give you the best chance for happiness in the future."

He was still frowning over this peculiar remark when a servant entered with two expresses, just arrived—one for Mr Bennet, and one for him. Both contained the news that Bingley was, at that very moment, unpacking his trunks at Netherfield. Mr Bennet and all his family were invited to dine there tomorrow. Better still, Darcy and Anne were invited to decamp from their various lodgings and move there that evening.

Mrs Bennet's rejoicing was immediate and noisy. Elizabeth's was quieter but sincere. It was Miss Jane Bennet whom Darcy watched most carefully. She made no noise at all but, as per Elizabeth's directions, he was able now to perceive that she did indeed seem to be holding her head a little higher, and her smiles, though not any broader, no longer vanished whenever she thought nobody was looking. He despised Bingley in that moment, a sentiment that shocked him out of his seat.

"Might I have use of a writing desk, Mr Bennet? I must send word to Lucas Lodge and the inn at Meryton to have our effects moved."

As he followed his host to a dark room at the front of the house, Darcy sent a silent apology to his friend. He did not despise Bingley—far from it. But he found he did resent his friend's certain happiness with Jane Bennet. Resented it with an intensity for which he could not account, for resentment implied regret, and he would never regret avoiding a similar alliance with the Bennets, no matter how well he admired Elizabeth. No matter how well he had enjoyed his day, against all expectation. No matter how every reason that opposed inclination was crumbling away to nothing.

He owed his family too much. Duty forbade him from even contemplating it. In fact, he was glad Bingley's notes had arrived when they did. It was high time he left. Before he fell so far under Elizabeth's spell that leaving became impossible.

Elizabeth took her shawl with her as she stole away from the excitement in the drawing room to the quiet but cold entrance hall. She shared her mother's hopes for Jane, but she also shared Jane's quietly expressed anxiety, for there had been no mention in Mr Bingley's note of his purpose in returning. There was every possibility that he had come merely to open his house for his friend's convenience.

One thing was certain, however. Jane had suffered enough doubt. It was Christmas Day, and Elizabeth would have her dearest sister enjoy this happy turn of events, instead of being tortured by it. It was why she had resolved to eschew all propriety and ask Mr Darcy directly why his friend had come.

"Miss Elizabeth, a word?"

She turned in surprise. Miss de Bourgh had followed her into the hall, which she supposed meant the word was unlikely to be a pleasant one, else she would have said it in company.

"If you like."

Perhaps she had not expected Elizabeth to agree, for she floundered a little before continuing stiltedly. "You can be at no loss to understand the reason I have been desirous of speaking with you."

"Indeed, you are mistaken, madam, but if you would come to the point, then we might return to the warmth of the drawing room."

Miss de Bourgh huffed in displeasure. When she spoke, Elizabeth thought she could detect a note of agitation in her voice, though she was evidently striving to sound superior.

"Very well, I shall speak plainly. The fact that your sister is on the verge of being most advantageously married should not be taken as encouragement for any of your preposterous aspirations towards my cousin."

Elizabeth looked at her with unaffected astonishment. "I beg your pardon?"

"May I remind you that he is engaged to *me?*"

"You may, though it is entirely unnecessary, for I had not forgot."

"That only puts your behaviour in a worse light. But you have not a hope of ensnaring him. From our infancy we have been intended for each other." Her words had become hurried, muddling her delivery of what sounded very much like a rehearsed speech. "It was the favourite wish of his mother as well as mine. We are descended from the same noble line. Our fortune on both sides is splendid. We are destined for each other by the voice of every member of our respective houses, and the upstart pretensions of a young woman without family, connexions, or fortune will not divide us. Honour, decorum, prudence, nay—interest forbid it. If you are not lost to every feeling of propriety and delicacy, you will stay away from Netherfield tomorrow, and you will promise me *never* to enter into an engagement with Darcy."

Elizabeth's incredulity had increased with Miss de Bourgh's every word, but now that she was silent, it began to ferment into indignation. "I wonder at your believing my word necessary, if you think so highly of his honour."

"I have seen how you try to work on him! You are relentless in your flirtation, but you will not draw him in. Do not be fooled by what you think are his attentions. He is only being civil."

"And barely that!" Elizabeth tugged her shawl tighter, not chilled but greatly discomfited. "Miss de Bourgh, you *really* need not have mortified us both in this manner. Before today, I should have said your cousin did not even *like* me."

Miss de Bourgh gave a bitter laugh. "Gratifying though it is to hear you believe that, I would still have your promise."

"I hope you will not be too disappointed when I tell you that you will never succeed in extracting any promise of the kind from Lizzy," said Mrs Bennet, appearing out of the shadows like a menacing pantomime dame. "She will no more marry your cousin than she would marry her own, for she dislikes the one even more than she did the other, but you can be sure that she will neither accept nor refuse any man because someone *else* demands it of her. She will do as she pleases. She always does."

Miss de Bourgh blushed deeply enough for it to be visible even in the nocturnal gloom of the hall. "This is a private conversation, madam."

"I am afraid I must correct you there, also, for I heard every word. I must say, I really think you ought to concern yourself less with Lizzy's aspirations and attend more to your own. Mr Darcy would be a terrible match for you. His fortune may be as splendid as yours, but you are ill-suited in other, more pertinent ways. You are too sickly, too inactive. Besides, he is in desperate need of a wife who will teach him some liveliness, and you are hardly qualified in that regard. No, you ought to aspire to a man of the cloth, or better yet, a physician. He could practise on you and make himself rich."

"You presume to address me in such a way? Do you know who I am?" Miss de Bourgh spluttered. Then, looking as though she were anxious this was not threatening enough, she added, "Who my *mother* is?"

"I know who your cousin is. I have just fed him Christmas dinner."

Elizabeth had never enjoyed her mother's impropriety so well, though she was too shocked to laugh properly. It came out more as a nervous exhalation that halted altogether and turned into a held breath when the door to her father's library opened, and Mr Darcy himself stepped into the hall.

That he was surprised by the scene before him was obvious. He looked alarmed and inordinately wary as he took it in. In fact, he looked a lot of things, and Elizabeth suddenly could not comprehend how she had ever thought him inscrutable.

Mostly, however, he looked *at her* piercingly, as though he were trying to know her thoughts. Elizabeth's heart began to hammer against her ribs as the implication of Miss de Bourgh's speech, indeed the entire purpose of her visit to Hertfordshire, dawned on her. Mr Darcy *did* like her—possibly *more* than liked her. At least, so his cousin suspected and strongly enough to think she needed to intervene.

Elizabeth did the only thing she knew how to do: she laughed. It threw a picture of confusion over his features, which of course it would, since she had told him only moments ago that she laughed regardless of her sentiments.

"Forgive me," she said, attempting to collect herself.

"Darcy, I wish to go," said Miss de Bourgh. "I am feeling unwell again."

He inhaled deeply but conceded.

Elizabeth was glad. Her thoughts were awhirl, and she could not recall ever feeling so awkward. She excused herself to return to the others in the drawing room, where she picked up the first book she could find, sat in the farthest seat from the door, and pretended to read in the hope that she would not be required to speak to anyone. Mr Darcy and his cousin soon followed to wait in the warm while their carriage was readied. Elizabeth did her best to ignore his persistent gaze but was eventually required to join the whole party in going outside to wave them goodbye.

She did then look at him—and instantly felt awful for not having done so sooner. Mr Darcy's expression was profoundly pained. He looked at her as though he wished to say a thousand words. His eyes, shining black in the wintry darkness, seemed to hold myriad questions, all of them urgent. And there was something in the intensity of his pose, the way he leant slightly towards her, the way he watched her with his brow almost imperceptibly furrowed, that convinced her a good deal of his anxiety was for her, rather than himself.

All she could do with so many people about was smile, but when she did, he all but staggered with relief. It was not something she had ever thought to see the proud and forbidding Mr Darcy do—certainly not at a look from her. She wondered whether she had imagined it and cast her eyes around to see whether anybody else had noticed, but nobody remarked upon it, so she supposed they had not.

"We shall look forward to seeing you both again tomorrow," said Mrs Bennet. "Pray, tell Mr Bingley we are all anticipation."

"I shall, madam," Mr Darcy promised. He handed Mrs Jenkinson and the utterly silent Miss de Bourgh into the carriage, then turned back, ostensibly to continue talking to Mrs Bennet, though he looked at Elizabeth when he said, "I am particularly anticipating introducing my sister to you."

"Your sister?"

"She is at Netherfield," Mr Darcy explained as he climbed up behind his cousin. "Bingley has brought her with him."

Jane's small gasp was drowned by the sound of the carriage door slamming closed and the horses pulling away, but Elizabeth heard it, and her heart broke to see the dismay overspreading her sister's countenance.

# CHAPTER 11

"Caroline is furious. I am not sure whether at me or you," Bingley called over the sound of pounding hooves. "You, I think."

"Would she have had me conceal it from you?" Darcy shouted back.

"Probably. She still does not believe Miss Bennet's affections are genuine."

Darcy was inclined to think Miss Bennet's affections, genuine or otherwise, were of no importance to Miss Bingley whatsoever, and she only claimed to be unconvinced to justify her continued opposition to the match. If she had expected him to do the same, she had severely misjudged his character. He might yet oppose it, but he would not manipulate his friend out of it with falsehoods and concealments.

"Either way, Caroline refused point-blank to come, so we shall have to do without her," Bingley grumbled. "Are you sure your sister will not mind playing hostess? She agreed, of course, because she is a dear, but I must say, she did not seem overly enamoured of the idea."

"Mrs Annesley will assist her. As will my confounded cousin. She owes me a favour."

"That she does," Bingley replied with a laugh that was curtailed into a warning shout. "Dash it! The blasted gate looks shut. Think you can jump it?"

"I shall not even attempt it in this weather," Darcy called back. "In any case, is it not *that* way?"

He smirked to see Bingley look all around him in perplexity. It had snowed slightly overnight, and the light dusting had rendered the landscape unfamiliar. Not enough to put Bingley off coming out, however. At three o'clock that afternoon, he had appeared in the doorway of the library, thrown Darcy's own hat at him, declared that he had not come all this way to watch him stalk about the place like a cantankerous old bear, and insisted that he join him to ride off his snit.

Darcy was sorry to have dampened his friend's festive spirits, though he fancied Bingley might be rather more grateful if he comprehended his efforts to limit himself to mere sullen silence when what he wished to do was rage and storm.

He had not managed to make Anne divulge what passed between her and Elizabeth the previous evening. She had demurred, prevaricated, and—he was convinced—outright lied. It mattered not. He could guess without being told. Had she not undertaken in her letter to Georgiana to ensure Elizabeth 'dropped whatever false hope' he might have given her?

"Ride faster!" Bingley shouted. "And do not give me any more of your objections about the blasted weather. Cantering is clearly not sufficient. You still look as though you might bludgeon the first person to come within ten yards of you, and I shall have no violence under my roof at Christmas." He kicked his horse into a gallop and sped off in the new direction.

It was a fine idea. Darcy spurred his horse onwards and soon overtook his friend, who hooted his enjoyment of the chase. Earth and snow were flung into the air in Darcy's wake, and icy wind whistled past his ears as he raced ever faster across the field.

His miseries kept pace with him the entire way, inescapable, unconquerable. How he reviled that despicable creature, Providence, for taunting him thus! The one woman—who in temperament and understanding, deeds and thought, liveliness and loveliness, who was perfect for him and would bring him happiness in every conceivable form—had been thrown not *into* his path, but near enough to torture him with the knowledge that she would never be his. He reined in his horse. There was no point laming the beast attempting to escape troubles that could not be outrun.

Bingley thundered up behind him and came to a skidding halt, his horse steaming with exertion. "I hope that did the trick, for any more of that nonsense and one or both of us will end up with a broken neck."

"Forgive me, Bingley. I have much on my mind."

"As always, my friend. You are the master of weighty problems, the original troubled soul." He dropped the sardonic tone with which he had said this to add more seriously, "I think you take too much upon yourself, Darcy."

"Perhaps." He urged his mount back in the direction of the house. "I certainly ought not to have taken on the superintendence of your romantic affairs. I apologise for thinking it was my place."

"I must say, your note was a surprise. As was its postmark."

Darcy grimaced. "I must apologise for that as well. I only concealed my destination from you because I knew you would wish to accompany me, and at the time, I believed Miss Bennet to be still indifferent to you. I thought it would only pain you. Besides," he added irritably, "I only intended to be in Meryton one night and had no intention of seeing the Bennets."

"Yes," his friend said, laughing. "From what you have told me, it seems your cousin has given you quite the merry chase. Is she usually this audacious?"

"No, she is not. But then, she has never before been free of my aunt's watchful eye." *And she has never before had cause to suspect that her cousin was about to ruin the whole family with a staggeringly imprudent marriage,* he thought privately.

They rode for a while in silence, then Bingley cleared his throat. "Your letter was somewhat short on details, old fruit."

"What further details do you require?"

"A man needs more to go on than an observation that the woman he admires 'might not be indifferent' to him. Have you nothing else for me?"

"Not a great deal. But her sister Elizabeth insists she admires you. Her father confirmed she was miserable when you left. And she looked very well pleased when your letter arrived announcing your return."

Nevertheless, Miss Bennet's modest smile had been *nothing* to the look Elizabeth had given *him* when she met his gaze on the drive outside Longbourn. It was a look which, many years hence when he would likely not have laid eyes on her for an age and may even be married to another woman, he would probably still treasure better than any other Christmas gift he had ever received. It had plagued him all day, for one such look could never be enough to last a lifetime. He desperately wanted more.

"You are right," Bingley replied. "That is not a great deal, but it is a start. I shall just have to hope for better luck at dinner."

Darcy only nodded. Dinner! Another major source of his present misery. Good sense told him he ought to have returned to London at first light, rather than torture himself with another evening of Elizabeth's company, but though he abhorred his own weakness, he simply could not tear himself away. He would give himself one last evening of bliss before he must return to life without her.

ॐ

Two hours into the evening, Darcy reflected that 'bliss' was not a word *anyone* could use to describe proceedings thus far. The Bennets had arrived promptly at seven o'clock, with only their three youngest daughters in tow. The Gardiners had arrived almost half an hour later with their two eldest nieces, claiming one of their young children had delayed them.

There had been no heart-stopping looks directed at either him or Bingley from either lady. Elizabeth had stepped down from the carriage and attached herself firmly to her sister's arm, where she remained, watching her possessively throughout her re-introduction to Bingley and sparing nary a glance for anybody else.

The introduction to Georgiana, for which Darcy had been so very anxious, had been even less inspiring. Elizabeth was perfectly civil, but she seemed largely unaffected by the honour of the presentation, far more interested in her own sister than his, almost as though she expected Miss Bennet to disapprove of the acquaintance. Georgiana had been typically meek, stammering and wincing her way through her hostess's duties with humiliatingly frequent prompts from her companion and vexingly few from her cousin. The whole thing had left him vastly dissatisfied, a far cry from the joyous meeting of kindred spirits he had foolishly envisaged.

As for Miss Bennet, gone was the lady who had blushed happily at the mention of Bingley's return. She scarcely seemed able to look at him, replied to his questions with monosyllabic responses or looked to Elizabeth to answer for her, and generally acted as though she would rather be anywhere but in Netherfield's dining room. Darcy began to wonder whether he had slipped from his horse and hit his head upon arriving in Meryton and hallucinated everything that had occurred since, for nothing he had witnessed this evening corresponded to his previous observations.

"I must say, Mr Bingley," said Mrs Bennet, who then instead of saying it, took a large gulp of claret. "That was a delightful meal. Your cook did a wonderful job, considering she had less than a day's notice to prepare it all."

"Or have we just eaten the meal *you* were supposed to have the day you took your leave without warning?" said her husband, chuckling to himself. "It was worth the wait. Nothing like well-aged beef."

Bingley coloured slightly but forged valiantly onwards. "No, indeed, I had it all brought down from London with this dinner in mind." Looking at Miss Bennet, he added, "I had a fancy that it should be as enjoyable as possible."

Miss Bennet did not look pleased. She only smiled weakly and continued eating.

"Beef is your favourite, Georgiana, is it not?" Darcy said to cover the intervening silence.

His sister stammered an inarticulate reply. It was all his senseless remark warranted, to be fair. Damn, he hated inane pleasantries!

"Goodness, Mr Bingley. What a lot of trouble you have gone to for your friends," Elizabeth said coldly, confirming Darcy's impression that she was exceedingly angry about something. He wished he knew what.

He had, at first, assumed it to be whatever Anne had said to her, but he was less certain now, for her resentment did not appear to be reserved for him or Anne but included the whole Netherfield party. He wished also that her expression, so like the one she had worn when they danced at Bingley's ball, was not so devastatingly alluring. Unsmiling severity sharpened the contours of her face, plumped her lips, and made her beautiful eyes flash dangerously. He could not look away, and his thoughts were in chaotic, brutish uproar.

"Indeed," Bingley replied. Still looking at Miss Bennet, he said, "I aspire to please." It did him no good. She was not looking at *him,* and his earnestness was wasted.

"You may take heart then, Mr Bingley. Many people have aspirations. Yours, at least, are attainable," Anne remarked.

Elizabeth looked at her darkly. Her sister paled and attended more diligently to her meal.

"Oh, you did listen to me yesterday then, Miss de Bourgh?" said Mrs Bennet. "I was worried you would not take my advice to heart."

"Is that what it was, madam? Advice? You will have to forgive me. I mistook it for impertinence."

Mrs Bennet gave an affected laugh. "Oh no. *Impertinence* would have been to ask one of my daughters to decline Mr Bingley's kind invitation and not come today."

Anne flushed scarlet and said no more. Darcy fixed her with a furious glare, which she refused to meet. *Surely, she did not?*

"Have there been many more dances in Meryton of late?" Bingley quickly enquired.

"Aye, there was one last Saturday," Miss Lydia replied. "Miss de Bourgh swooned halfway through her dance with Mr Wickham."

Several hissed reproaches went up around the table, all of which were drowned by the sound of Georgiana dropping her knife and fork. They clattered noisily onto her plate, and one fell into her lap, drawing a whimper from her lips as she fumbled to reclaim it. Darcy swore to himself and tried desperately to catch her eye, but not even Mrs Annesley's cleared throat could persuade her to raise her head.

"I understand he has gone out of the country now," he said in as steadying a voice as he could.

Georgiana still did not look at him, and her countenance had turned ashen, but she nodded slightly, retrieved her cutlery, and resumed eating.

Elizabeth, of course, observed the entire exchange. She looked away when she noticed Darcy's gaze, thus he could not tell what she made of it. He only knew that he must want her beyond reason when he briefly considered throwing more cutlery into his sister's lap to draw her attention back his way.

"Your stumble that evening was most unfortunate," said Mrs Bennet to Anne, "but that was precisely the point I was making yesterday. Now, *Jane* danced with Mr Mountbatten—did you not, Jane? He would have been a far better match for you, Miss de Bourgh. A stout fellow, not too fast on his feet. And short sighted, which I should think would be of benefit to some, though Jane would be quite wasted on him."

"Mr Bingley, I hear your ball in the autumn was a fine affair," Mrs Annesley interposed with such gracefulness as made Darcy vow to increase her stipend.

"It was, madam, even if I do say so myself. I am excessively fond of dancing."

"It shows," said Mr Bennet indiscreetly to Mr Gardiner. "I have never known any man dance around a question for as many months as he."

"Do you often get the chance?" Mrs Gardiner enquired.

"I had the chance yesterday, as it happens," Bingley replied. "My sisters and Miss Darcy were attempting to teach me a new cotillion. I daresay *you* would like it, Miss Bennet. You dance so very prettily. Perhaps, Miss Darcy, you could teach Miss Bennet the steps?"

Georgiana had not yet recovered, and it was too soon for her to speak with any confidence. Miss Bennet looked mortified by the mere suggestion. Both ladies appeared on the verge of tears.

Bingley glanced helplessly at Darcy, and well he might, for the warm welcome he had been promised was nowhere to be seen. Instead, awkward silence pervaded the company as the central turret of one of the cook's castellated ices slid off sideways and landed on the tablecloth with a dull splat.

Darcy knew matters had reached a decided low when he found himself wishing Miss Bingley were there to rescue them all with some of her insipid but well-honed social graces.

*I was right,* he thought to himself. *I ought to have left this place at first light.*

&.

Elizabeth would gladly have complied with Miss de Bourgh's wishes and remained at home. It was Jane who had insisted upon coming, too well-mannered to renege on an invitation already accepted. If Mr Bingley had not chosen her, she insisted, then she would neither resent him for it nor be so petty as to refuse his olive branch. That was all well and good, except that for the last several hours, Elizabeth had watched Jane struggle to maintain her composure as the man she loved flaunted his new paramour in front of them.

Mr Darcy was little better, obstinately promoting the match at every opportunity. Miss de Bourgh was, as always, being insolent and superior—an air made worse by dint of Elizabeth's mother, father, and younger sisters determinedly betraying every bit of the disdain for propriety of which the woman had accused them. By the time the ladies separated from the gentlemen after dinner, Elizabeth was so angry she was tempted to ask for her pelisse and steal away home.

The only person at whom Elizabeth could not be vexed was Miss Darcy, though she wished to be. Indeed, she had begun the evening determined to find her as objectionable and proud as Mr Wickham had described her. That, perhaps, was the reason her resolve had crumbled so rapidly, for Mr Wickham's testimony held little water with her of late. It had been the work of less than a few minutes to determine that Mr Darcy's sister was only painfully shy. Neither had it escaped Elizabeth's notice the effect Mr Wickham's name had upon her, nor her brother and companion's concern for her after its mention. It was a turn from which Miss Darcy had yet to recover, though Miss de Bourgh appeared oblivious to her cousin's distress.

"What possessed you at dinner, Georgiana?" Elizabeth heard her say in a harsh whisper. "You are aware, I suppose, that the saying 'When in Rome' is proverbial and not to be taken as instruction."

"I am sorry, Cousin Anne. I was nervous."

"When will you learn it is for people like this to be nervous in *your* presence, not the reverse? Now you have splashed gravy on yourself."

Miss Darcy gasped in mortification and inspected her gown for the offending stain.

Little though Elizabeth was inclined to take her part while Jane looked on, it tugged at her conscience to see the young lady's embarrassment over the regrettably obvious mark. It persuaded her to swivel in her seat to fully face them and lean forward so she could whisper. "'Tis hardly noticeable, Miss Darcy. You must not concern yourself."

Miss de Bourgh fixed her with a rancorous glare. "Do not attempt to ingratiate yourself this way, Miss Elizabeth. It will not work." To her cousin, she added, "What will Mr Bingley think?"

"I—I do not think Mr Bingley will mind," Miss Darcy replied in a stilted voice. "He is too kind, and I believe he is altogether too engrossed in Miss Bennet to care about my gown."

Elizabeth was instantly alert but uncertain how to proceed without knowing whether the remark had been made in bitterness or innocence. She had not long to wait before Miss de Bourgh demanded the answers she herself was so desirous of hearing.

"What is your meaning? Is he chasing after another under your nose? Need I speak to your brother?" More to herself than to her cousin, she added, "Though he is little better. I doubt he will be of much use."

Miss Darcy's expression was one of the oddest Elizabeth had ever seen. It was as though somebody had taken all Jane's diffidence and all Lydia's meddlesomeness, and mixed them together in one countenance that was too noble to give either a good home.

"Mr Bingley was never chasing after me," she said quietly and almost excitedly.

"You said in your letter he was."

"Pardon me, Cousin Anne, you misunderstood me. I—I said that was his sister's dearest wish. It always has been. It is a silly notion of which none of us has ever disabused her, for we are all such good friends. And I expect my brother would agree if Mr Bingley and I were ever to decide upon each other—but we never shall. Mr Bingley does not wish to marry me any more than I wish to marry him. We are too much like brother and sister." She wrinkled her nose. "And he is rather old, do you not think?"

"He is three-and-twenty, Georgiana."

"Exactly."

Elizabeth bit the insides of her cheeks to keep them straight. Beneath her reserve, there was definitely more of Lydia than of Jane in Miss Darcy. The notion tickled her no end, and she wondered whether Mr Darcy were aware of this rebellious streak in his sister. Mrs Annesley looked as though she might have an inkling, for she watched her charge with obvious unease. It seemed Miss de Bourgh's authority superseded her own, however, for she did not intervene.

"If you recall," Miss Darcy said breathlessly, managing to make herself seem simultaneously eager and reluctant to speak, "in the same letter, I said that I should not be surprised if my brother and Mr Bingley soon returned to Hertfordshire because they both liked it so well the last time they were here. Mr Bingley is quite in love with your sister, Miss Elizabeth."

"Oh, for heaven's sake, Georgiana!" scolded Miss de Bourgh. "I do not care how young you are, spouting this sort of nonsense is a ridiculous way to carry on."

Rebellious she may be, but brave she was not. Miss Darcy sank back into her seat with a meek apology. Elizabeth assured her none was necessary, then excused herself to speak to Jane.

The gentlemen joined them moments after she finished relaying the whole conversation, giving her sister not the time to collect herself before she must face Mr Bingley again.

She clutched Elizabeth's hand and whispered, "I am not formed for this much upheaval. First, he is gone. Next, he is back. Then, he is to marry Miss Darcy. Now, he loves me again. My heart will not stand the tumult."

"Your heart will do perfectly well if you would only cease allowing other people to decide what it ought to feel. But you had better talk to Mr Bingley soon, or he will think you do not love *him*. We have not exactly been friendly towards him this evening."

When Jane's eyes widened in alarm, Elizabeth assured her there was plenty of evening remaining to remedy that. She nodded in encouragement when Mr Bingley came directly to sit with them, but seeing Jane blush and stumble for something to say, she determined to set them off on a better path.

"My sister was just saying how well she enjoyed dinner, Mr Bingley. You might not be aware, but beef is her favourite, too."

"Oh, but I *was* aware," he replied with an expansive smile that made Elizabeth think she could very easily fall a little in love with him, too. It was quite the sweetest compliment she had ever heard. Jane was suitably gratified by it, and to Elizabeth's relief, they soon proved they had no further need of her to advance their conversation. She shuffled back into the corner of the sofa and let out a deep sigh.

Her sigh turned to a smile as she mused over the absurdity of the misapprehension that had almost ruined Jane's happiness a second time. That smile froze in place when Elizabeth looked up to find Mr Darcy watching her, the turn of his countenance plunging her back into Longbourn's hall the evening before, recalling her to all that was said then, and paralysing her with embarrassment.

She had all but forgotten. Jane's distress the previous night, her tears and turmoil all that day, and Elizabeth's own indignation had overtaken everything. Well, she remembered now! It would seem from the way he was regarding her, so did he. The intensity of his gaze made her shiver.

Then, it made her want to laugh. She had spent the better part of four months in contempt of this man who had once disdained her looks. One whiff of possibility that he admired her, and suddenly, a brief, unsmiling glance was enough to knot her stomach. And she had accused *him* of vanity! It diverted her enough that she was much better able to dismiss the flicker of tension she felt when he excused himself from his conversation with Mr Gardiner and came towards her.

"Sit here, Darcy. Mrs Jenkinson will make room for you," called Miss de Bourgh, shooing her companion out of her seat to make room for her cousin.

Elizabeth thought Darcy hesitated, but her aunt chose that moment to move to the seat he would have taken, and the moment was lost.

"Lizzy," began Mrs Gardiner, "your mother has just reminded me that I never told you what happened to my new lady's maid."

"Oh, you keep servants, do you?" said Miss de Bourgh.

Mrs Gardiner replied with perfect equanimity that she did, then continued. "She came into my room one evening by mistake—"

"That is hardly surprising," Miss de Bourgh said to Mr Darcy in a loud aside. "There is so little difference in rank between them, one cannot blame the poor woman for being confused."

"—instead of Lucy's room," Mrs Gardiner finished pointedly. "And she missed the step down inside the door and turned her ankle. She will recover, but for all the trouble it took to appoint her, I am without her again for now."

"You must be used to not having servants Mrs Gardiner," Miss de Bourgh persisted. "You cannot always have had them, for Mr Gardiner's money is so very *new*. It must be agreeable to you to have been able to elevate your condition in life by employing a maid. How easy it is to give the impression of bettering oneself by hiring someone beneath you."

"Your army of servants at Rosings would rather discredit that theory, Cousin," said Mr Darcy icily. "Georgiana, can you be persuaded to play for us?"

Elizabeth knew not whether to be amazed or amused. In the end, both sentiments ceded to pity, for it was a shame Mr Darcy must marry a woman he so evidently did not respect.

"I should rather not, if it is all the same," Miss Darcy replied.

Mrs Annesley's gentle but firm encouragement was interrupted by Miss de Bourgh's firm and not at all gentle rebuke.

"Why would you refuse? Believe me, you have nothing to fear. I heard everyone here play yesterday, and you are by far the most talented among them."

Curious, the way anger honed Mr Darcy's features. Elizabeth found herself rather caught up in the way his clenched teeth accentuated the line of his jaw, and his furious glare made his dark eyes gleam. It afforded him an air of restrained potency that gave an exhilarating contrast to the sweetness she had observed earlier in his friend.

"Lizzy?"

"I beg your pardon?"

Mrs Gardiner smirked at her disconcertingly. "I asked whether you would play for us instead. Miss Darcy is a little shy."

Elizabeth regarded the young lady to assess *how* shy. "Shall we play together?" she ventured. "Your cousin is right. I am not very accomplished. You cannot fail to impress everybody by comparison."

They played, and they pleased everyone who wished to be

pleased, despite Elizabeth's making twice as many mistakes as even she expected. She could not seem to attend to the music. It had been a trying four-and-twenty hours, she was tired, and though she was determined not to look lest it put her off altogether, she felt Mr Darcy's eyes upon her from the moment she sat at the instrument to the moment her father announced it was time to leave.

"Has your evening turned out well after all?" she said quietly to Jane as they donned their coats in the hall.

"Better than I dared dream," her sister replied, smiling more broadly than was her wont.

"The perfect Christmas gift?"

"Absolutely! I shall have to think of something very special to give Mr Darcy next year to repay him."

Elizabeth screwed up her face in puzzlement. "I meant Mr Bingley."

"Oh yes! He was the gift. But Mr Darcy was the *giver*." After a quick glance over her shoulder to ensure they would not be overheard, Jane lowered her voice further still and said, "Mr Bingley has explained—or tried to explain, as far as he is able on so delicate a matter—that in essence, he left because he misjudged my affections, but he came back because Mr Darcy sent him an express on Christmas Eve, telling him that his hopes were not in vain or words to that effect. It sounds as though it may have been rather less sentimental than that. Either way, it worked, for he is here, and I have Mr Darcy to thank for it."

Elizabeth was not often speechless, but she had still not found the words to express her astonishment when the carriage was pronounced to be ready, and her family was ushered out into the night. When Mr Darcy stepped forward to say goodbye, she wished she could replicate her farewell smile from the previous day that had seemed to please him so well but found she was only capable of staring at him in wonder. He was a man too proud to marry, dance with, or ofttimes speak to anyone outside his own circle, yet he had reunited his oldest friend with a woman he considered wholly unsuitable because they were *in love*. What a wonderful thing to do! It made her question whether she knew him at all.

"Goodbye, Miss Elizabeth," he said with peculiar finality, then he bowed and walked into the house.

# CHAPTER

# 12

E lizabeth's delight for Jane increased further still when Mr Bingley called on them the very next day. It seemed he intended to make up for lost time, and he would receive no resistance from anyone at Longbourn.

"We had a wonderful time at dinner yesterday. I hope you will allow us to return the honour soon," said Mrs Bennet. "You are still quite in our debt when it comes to family dinners."

"I should like that very much, madam, though I am come with an invitation that might put me even more in debt. But you first. I should hate to offend," replied Mr Bingley.

"Well, if we must get in first, how are you fixed for tomorrow evening?"

"Done!" Mr Bingley exclaimed, clapping his hands together. "I say, Caroline always makes a mountain out of this entertaining business, but there is nothing to it. Right, now it is my turn. In an ideal world, I should be inviting you all to a lavish Twelfth Night ball."

Lydia and Kitty began cooing excitedly until he grimaced

apologetically and said, "Alas, I have not the time to arrange one at such short notice, and my sisters are engaged for other parties in London on the twelfth. But I thought it would be nice to have a smaller gathering the following day, when they are able to join us. I mean to invite the Lucases as well. What say you? Are you amenable to a Three Kings feast?"

The invitation was readily accepted for everyone but the Gardiners, who were due to return home on Tuesday. After that, Mr Bingley was drawn into a description of the sorts of balls and soirees he and his sisters usually attended when they were in London. Elizabeth wondered whether Mr Darcy's engagements were of a similar kind or whether he preferred quieter events. She fancied he might appreciate the theatre, though if he practised dancing with his sister, perhaps he enjoyed the *occasional* ball. It was a shame he was not there to tell them.

Indeed, it was a shame he was not there anyway, for it would have given Elizabeth somebody else to talk to whilst everyone vied for Mr Bingley's attention, and he vied solely for Jane's. She smiled to herself as she reflected that Mr Darcy probably would not have said very much anyway, but she had begun to rather enjoy his quiet attentiveness. She liked the consideration he gave to all that was said, even if he did not always remark on it. She supposed it was what Miss de Bourgh had meant by 'companionable silence.' Whatever it ought to be called, it was an improvement on her father's method of only joining a conversation to make sport. She contented herself with her aunt Gardiner's company, each of them stealing surreptitious glances at Jane to see how she fared throughout the remainder of the call.

"Until tomorrow evening, then," said Mr Bingley, donning his hat and coat.

"What time shall we expect you all? Shall we say seven?" enquired Mrs Bennet.

"Ah—no, not all of us! Darcy has left to take his cousin back to Kent. How dashed silly of me, I almost forgot to mention it! I do beg your pardon."

Jane assured him no harm was done, and Elizabeth stepped back, along with her mother, to afford them a more private farewell. It surprised her how greatly the news disheartened her. *Just as I was coming to dislike him less.*

At least she would not have to suffer Miss de Bourgh's insolence all evening. Though, a few trifling barbs seemed a price worth paying for a stimulating debate or two. The dinner promised to be a good deal less interesting now.

Elizabeth puffed out her cheeks, resigned to it—or as close to resigned as such fresh disappointment would allow. It was never expected that he would stay in Hertfordshire forever. She did, however, wish that she had said a proper goodbye the night before, instead of staring at him in such a stupid manner.

It mattered to her, she realised with a start, that his impression of her should be favourable. It had, perhaps, always mattered, for even at the beginning of their acquaintance when she had taken pains to debate most of what he said, it had gratified her to think that he should consider her clever. *Gormless* was most definitely not the look with which she would have chosen to fix herself in his memory.

Darcy awoke stiff and unrefreshed after too little sleep on a too-soft mattress. He detested staying at Rosings. Every item of furniture was either too old or too ostentatious for comfort, and the rooms were all either perishingly cold or perpetually sweltering. Of course, too many hours in the saddle had not helped, but that had been preferable to sitting in the carriage. Travelling with Mrs Jenkinson was about as interesting as travelling with a potato, and Anne had exhausted his every reserve of forbearance before they left Hertfordshire.

With Lady Catherine still away, they had arrived to an empty house. Eschewing any pleasantries, the ladies had removed directly upstairs, where they remained with dinner taken to them on trays. Darcy had done the same, more for the servants' sake than his own, but sleep eluded him long after he blew out his candle and capitulated to the incommodious bed.

Anne was obviously angry, though she could be in no doubt she was not alone in *that*. Their few words after dinner on Boxing Day had not been friendly, and they had said the absolute minimum to each other on the journey to Rosings. Darcy had not yet decided how many words he would spare her before he departed, though he could not avoid speaking to her at least a little, if only to ensure she comprehended that she must leave Elizabeth alone henceforth. He would not countenance a repeat of her behaviour at Netherfield, which had left him no less incensed than ashamed. For all his reservations about the Bennets, his own relation had betrayed a greater want of propriety, a shallower disposition, and a streak of malice that not one of them possessed. With what absurd prepossession had he held Elizabeth's family in such contempt?

Anne was not in the breakfast room when he arrived downstairs. Neither did she appear in the morning room afterwards. His temper simmered as the clock ticked towards midday. He was on the verge of sending a note, requesting that she bestir herself to come and speak to him, when the door opened, and Lady Catherine swept into the room.

"Darcy! It *is* you! Pratt said you were here, but I thought he must be mistaken. Whatever are you doing in Kent? Where is Anne?"

He stood to greet her, his expression carefully neutral as he bowed. This had not been part of his plan. "Anne is—"

"Here, Mother," said she, coming into the room behind Lady Catherine and sending Darcy an expressive look, though what she meant to express was beyond him. "We returned early. I wished to be home. I am glad I did now that you are returned also."

"Why did you wish to come home? Was your Christmas not enjoyable? Darcy, what happened in town that made Anne wish to leave so soon?"

"Nothing happened in town, Mother," Anne answered for him. "I only wished to be at home. How fares Mrs Fortescue?"

Darcy winced. He would have thought that after almost thirty years, Anne would have learnt such methods did not work on Lady Catherine.

His aunt's eyes narrowed, and she swivelled her head to peer penetratingly at her daughter. "Mrs Fortescue is dead. Thus, you will comprehend that I am in no humour to be put off with prevarication. Tell me this instant why you left London earlier than planned. Are you unwell?"

"We were not in London, madam," Darcy told her. Anne rolled her eyes and flounced dramatically in her chair. He ignored her. There was no avoiding the matter now. Better to get it over with. "We were in Hertfordshire."

"Hertfordshire? Why?" Her ladyship whipped her gaze back and forth between them, her generous girth adding momentum to the movement. She came to a quivering halt in front of Darcy. "Whatever made you go there? Have you taken leave of your senses, Nephew? You must know Anne is too frail to travel that far. What were you thinking?"

Darcy was unused to being spoken to in such a way, even by Lady Catherine, but he made an effort to swallow his affront. Anne was her daughter, after all, and she had a right to be concerned for her. His forbearance faltered when her ladyship sucked in an almighty breath and redoubled her attack.

"Clearly you were *not* thinking. This is not to be borne. I thought you intelligent! Or is it that you merely care so little for my daughter's well-being? Tell me what is so important in Hertfordshire that you would risk your cousin's life on poor roads and in icy weather to take her there?"

"I did not take her there," he said stiffly. "I went there to bring her home."

Darcy felt the enmity in Anne's glare and guessed she meant to punish him for divulging as much, as though she had not given him enough trouble already!

"What is your meaning?" demanded Lady Catherine. She did not give him time to answer. "What is his meaning, Anne? When did you go to Hertfordshire? And why have you lied to me about your plans? Tell me at once!"

"I went last week with Mr Collins. I did not tell you because I did not wish to obtrude on your time with Mrs Fortescue. And you will be grateful that I took the trouble when I tell you that my purpose was to prevent Darcy from marrying your parson's cousin."

Darcy ground his teeth. He had not doubted she would expose him, so he knew not why he was surprised she had presented it in as poor a light as possible.

Lady Catherine's countenance flooded crimson, and she fixed her hawkish eyes on him. "Pray, tell me my daughter is mistaken."

"I credit my cousin with knowing her own mind. If Anne claims that was her purpose, I shall not say she is wrong."

"Do not be clever. Tell me Anne was mistaken to suspect you *would* marry one of Mr Collins's cousins."

"I cannot answer that without knowing her reasons for thinking that I might." It was not an approach that held much promise of success, but Darcy would be damned if he was going to account for his decisions to his aunt. He wondered that she or his cousin thought it their right to influence him on the matter. He was painfully aware of the duty he had to his family, and he begrudged them thinking they had need to remind him.

"Come, then!" Lady Catherine demanded of her daughter. "What made you think he was marrying one of the Bennet girls?"

It was Anne's turn to blush. She lost some of her boldness and developed a sudden interest in the trim of a nearby cushion as she mumbled something unintelligible.

"Speak up, you silly, silly girl."

Darcy frowned. He had heard Mr Bennet call his girls silly many times—never with such a marked want of affection.

"Georgiana wrote that Darcy thought she was compassionate and—"

"Do not dare blame that dear girl," her ladyship interrupted. "Georgiana is too good, too sensible to do anything as reckless as you have done."

Darcy held himself still, gladder than ever to have concealed his sister's near-elopement from his aunt and undesirous of giving her away at this stage.

"Would that you could have turned out more like her, instead of this wretched, snivelling creature."

With deepening alarm, Darcy tilted his head, as though hearing his aunt's words from a different angle might mitigate their cruelty—a foolish act but one borne of disbelief.

"Is that it, then?" her ladyship went on. "You have no better reason for this preposterous behaviour? You have risked your health and your cousin's reputation because you heard it said that he thought a woman was *kind*?" When she received no answer, she demanded stridently, "Well, *child*?"

Anne folded her shoulders inwards and dipped her head, veritably cowering away from her mother. "Mr Collins said she was very pretty."

"Yes, and I can see why that would worry *you*, but if you think this sort of carry-on is going to make you any prettier, then you are even stupider than I thought. Fortunately, Darcy is more rational than to lose his head over a handsome face. You ought to give him more credit. He knows his duty to this family. It is about time you remembered yours."

"I am sorry, Mother."

"Your apologies are as worthless as you are. If you were a pleasanter, healthier, more accomplished woman, you would have been married by now, and your disappointing looks would be immaterial."

"Good Lord, that is enough, madam!" Only horrified incredulity had kept Darcy quiet *that* long. He stepped in front of his cousin, putting his back to his aunt. "Have your trunks packed, Anne. You are coming to London with me."

She looked at him plaintively but shook her head as her mother began railing at them both. "I cannot—"

"You can, and you will," he replied in a low voice that nevertheless brooked no argument. "I shall deal with your mother. Go now."

Darcy waited until Anne had left the room, then turned to face Lady Catherine. "I shall impute this reprehensible behaviour to grief and say no more on the matter, provided it is *never* repeated."

An unpleasant sneer deepened the lines about her ladyship's mouth and made her look older than she was. "Which one was it? The beautiful siren, put forth by the mother to capture unsuspecting heirs? The coquettish minors, out before their older sisters are wed? The bluestocking? Or the ungrateful fool who refused Mr Collins's offer of marriage?"

Darcy baulked. She could only mean Elizabeth. The thought of her marrying that dolt sickened him. Blast it, the thought of her marrying *anyone* sickened him. He had never allowed himself to consider it before. He knew why not now. The panic it induced made him feel winded.

"Oh yes, Nephew, I know *all* about the Bennet sisters. Mr Collins has told me everything. Take care. *He* managed to escape their greedy clutches. Make sure you do, too."

He stared at her. Had she always been so vicious? Or was it, as his conscience whispered, that four-and-twenty hours in the company of Elizabeth's family had fundamentally changed his expectations of his own? Whatever the answer, Darcy did not know this woman. And if her behaviour were any reflection of his—which, with profound dismay, he acknowledged it probably was—then he barely knew himself.

"Who said I have escaped?" He had not meant to say it, but now that he had, he did not wish it unsaid.

His aunt billowed with furious indignation. "Was Anne right, then? Is *this* your resolve?"

"I have nothing more to say to you, madam. I am leaving."

Darcy turned to go, but she stepped into his path, blocking his way. "Not so hasty, if you please! I demand to know. Are you engaged to one of these girls?"

He looked down at her with undisguised loathing. "Good-bye, Lady Catherine."

"Darcy, you have been drawn in! You cannot see it, but you have been worked on!" she implored, her tone insistent, yet her voice unsteady. "You will comprehend if you will only give it time. Promise me that you will stay away until you are able to see clearly once again. Promise me you will not go back to Hertfordshire."

"I could not promise you that, even if I wished to. I must return, for I have left something incredibly valuable there."

Elizabeth could not wholly justify the happiness she felt as she closed her eyes that night. It could have been Jane's increasing delight in Mr Bingley's attentions. It could have been that her family all behaved themselves impeccably at dinner, giving her sister no cause to be embarrassed. It could have been the delicious meal her mother devised for their honoured guest.

Yet, she could not deny the most likely reason was that Mr Bingley had not arrived at Longbourn alone. It transpired that, in the confusion of issuing various invitations the previous day, they had somehow all overlooked that Miss Darcy and her companion were still at Netherfield. Which, Mr Bingley explained, was because his friend had not gone for good. Mr Darcy was coming back.

Elizabeth refused to dwell on the reasons why this should

please her. His return was demonstrably unconnected to her, and his eventual departure would be equally independent of her inclinations. Once he arrived, his company would not be earmarked for her. She would, in all likelihood, see very little of him except for a few hours at Mr Bingley's feast. Better that she not attempt to account for it and only enjoy the sensation of being puzzlingly, delightfully, divertingly happy.

# CHAPTER 13

A night in his own bed meant Darcy was far better refreshed on Sunday morning, despite the hours he had lain awake furiously making plans for his suddenly vastly different future. He *ought* to be tired, for he was not convinced he had been asleep even when he dreamt, but fatigue could not trouble him. A potent medley of boyish excitement and exceedingly *un*childlike yearning coursed through his veins, igniting his spirits, urging him up, out of bed, and back to Hertfordshire.

He could scarcely wait until Monday to return. Already he had spent too many months battling with his reprehensible pride; too many miles travelling to visit, rescue, or cart his various relations about the country; and altogether too many years dancing to duty's tune. He would waste no more time. His trip to Kent had taught him a simple truth: there was no good reason not to marry Elizabeth. He owed his family nothing, and if those in his sphere could stomach Lady Catherine, then they could sure as the devil learn to tolerate Elizabeth, a woman ten times his aunt's worth. He could—he *would*—marry her. Understanding it had rendered him as close to giddy as anyone so naturally disposed to seriousness could get.

First, however, he must deal with Anne. For all his jubilant reflections, Darcy remained deeply troubled by what passed at Rosings. His aunt had always been difficult and was renowned for her imperious manner. Yet superiority was not the same as meanness, and never before yesterday had he thought her capable of outright cruelty.

Grief ought to be her excuse, except that Anne had not seemed surprised by the outburst. Darcy had grappled endlessly with his recollections of the encounter, attempting to discern whether he had misremembered what was said or misconstrued how it was received, but the effort had been fruitless. He had known the moment Anne agreed to come with him that it was not the first time she had been thus abused.

She had said very little in the carriage back to London, constrained by distress and the presence of her ineradicable companion. He knew not what she wished to happen next or what solution he ought to offer, but despite being still excessively angry with her, he would not abandon Anne to a repeat of Lady Catherine's derision. Thus, he awaited her in his library that morning, unsure what he meant to say but assured of a very different conversation than he had intended to have four-and-twenty hours ago.

At length, his cousin arrived and sat down opposite him without a word. He called for tea, which they awaited in silence. It arrived, and in silence they both took one sip, then set their cups aside to go cold.

"She is worse than Mrs Bennet, is she not?"

Darcy choked out a surprised laugh. "She certainly was yesterday. But be truthful. Is she always like that?"

Anne took a deep breath and let it out slowly. "She has grown more so, the longer you have procrastinated."

"The longer I have—"

She interrupted him with an exasperated huff. "Why did you have to tell her we were in Hertfordshire?"

"Come, Anne. She would have found out one way or another. And it was unreasonable to expect Mr Collins and Mrs Jenkinson to lie for you."

She made a noise of disgust. "You are always so incorrigibly *honest*. It is prodigiously tiresome."

Darcy wished he deserved her censure, but there were too many things he had been required to keep secret of late. He left her remark unchallenged, and the silence between them stretched long, until Anne shifted in her seat and fixed him with an expression that might have been defiance or apprehension.

"I have had something of an epiphany." She took a quick breath and tilted her chin. "I have decided I no longer wish to marry you."

Darcy held himself still. Many cogs whirred in his mind, all of them misaligning, none of them churning out a sensible interpretation of her statement. "I am afraid I do not take your meaning."

"I am not sure how else I might express myself to better convey it. It is not very complicated."

Indeed, it did not appear so. It also did not appear to make an iota of sense. "You *no longer* wish to marry me?"

"Do not pretend to be upset about it."

"I beg your pardon, Anne. I am not upset, but I *am* perplexed. I was not aware that you *ever* wished to marry me."

For the longest moment, she did nothing but stare at him. Then his cousin did something that reminded him so thoroughly of Elizabeth, it knocked the wind from him. She laughed. Indeed, she laughed so hard and for so long, he began to worry for her lucidity.

"Oh, I am sorry, Darcy. You will have to forgive me. Only, what an absolute joke!"

"Is it?" he replied, struggling to maintain a calm tone.

She made an observable effort to be serious, which had the effect of giving her laughter an edge of hysteria. "Answer me this. Have you *ever* taken seriously the pact our mothers made to unite our houses with an alliance between us?"

It was Darcy's turn to stare, only he did not laugh. Indeed, it was one of the least amusing remarks he had ever heard, for a multitude of reasons, none of them good. "I take it you have."

"Me, my mother, half the *ton*, the *whole* of Kent."

In the name of all that was holy! The *whole of Kent* believed that the fanciful whim of two sisters, conceived in the first flushes of motherhood almost thirty years ago, still held true? How was such a staggeringly stupid thing possible? How on *earth* had something so ridiculous, so entirely improbable, have remained *so* significant in the eyes of *so* many people for *so* many years *without his knowing*?

"I had no idea," he said through gritted teeth.

"I can see that. But why on earth do you think I gave a fig about Elizabeth Bennet if you did not consider yourself honour-bound to me?"

"I assumed your reasons were the same as my own. Family, duty, reputation."

Anne gave him a small, crooked smile. "When all along it was plain old jealousy."

Worse and worse. She had not only believed they would marry, she had desired it! He looked away to the fireplace, searching for something to say that would lessen the injury of the misunderstanding. Nothing occurred to him. There was nothing he could say that would mitigate the fact that he neither considered himself promised to her, nor had he any intention of becoming so. He adjusted his attitude in his seat and let out a sharp sigh.

"Cousin, I beg you would forgive me. It never occurred to me that you—"

"Oh, do not torture yourself, Darcy. You do it far too well. You will make me feel bad. You must understand, I was jealous because I have been brought up to believe you were mine by right. But my heart is not engaged. I am fond of you, of course, but only in the way one is fond of a favourite cushion." She shrugged. "You are nice to look at, and you are useful in an uncomfortable situation."

"Charmed, I am sure."

"I do not *mean* to be charming. I am attempting to break an engagement that apparently never existed. It is very difficult to do something unkind when everybody is so pleased with the result."

"Are you pleased?"

"I believe I am, yes. That is the point. I never questioned the arrangement because there was never anybody in my mind more worthy to be my husband than you. My mother taught me —taught both of us, I dare say—to think meanly of all the rest of the world. I have been encouraged to think you and I are superior to everyone who matters, and best suited for each other as a consequence.

"My short time in Hertfordshire opened my eyes to the possibility of there being better alternatives for me. I do not mean to say I now consider you *unworthy*. Far from it. You are one of the best men I have ever known, Darcy. Only, we have much less in common than I used to think. And, well, I certainly do not feel about you the way you feel about Miss Elizabeth."

He was too taken aback and too overcome with the exhilarating anticipation that accompanied every thought of Elizabeth to answer.

Anne nodded as though satisfying herself of something. "You love her, do you not?"

"Yes," he replied simply, eschewing any more syllables, for no quantity of words could ever convey the expansiveness of what he felt.

"I thought as much. I assumed at first it was a passing fascination. Georgiana made it sound more, but I could not believe you were serious—not considering her condition in life, which you must admit is *dire*, and her disposition, which even from your sister's bizarrely quixotic account left a good deal to be desired. But then I saw you with her."

Darcy had been about to vehemently defend Elizabeth's honour, but this last remark quite knocked him off balance.

Anne pulled a pitying face. "Dear Darcy, look at you, all bemused. But it is obvious to anyone who knows you. You are *only* happy when you are with her. At all other times, you are an awful object, impatient with everyone, angry at everything. But when you are with Miss Elizabeth, you smile—you *joke*, for heaven's sake. I never knew you could. She lightens you, some-how. It is quite touching now that I have ceased being vexed by it. And, of course, nobody could mistake your feelings after you left your sister there, so you had an excuse to go back."

Darcy did not smile, though not because he was unhappy. Rather, he felt too much to be light-hearted. "That was not my purpose for leaving Georgiana there, at least, not the one I avowed to myself. When I left, it was with a promise to Bingley that I would return for his feast a week on Monday, and a resolve to reason myself out of any irrational sentiments before I did. I hoped the trip to Rosings would remind me what I owed my family."

Anne laughed bitterly. "That worked tremendously, then."

"Quite. Your mother had not been in the house more than a few minutes before I realised I owed her nothing." He did not mention how significantly Anne's own performance over the last fortnight had aided him in his volte-face.

"So now, your *real* purpose in leaving Georgiana at Nether-field has come to fruition. Bravo! I only hope Miss Elizabeth will accept you."

Anne said it laughingly, but with just such a hint of sincerity as pierced Darcy's felicity like a hot knife. "What?"

"Well, she did not seem very pleased with you at dinner last Thursday."

Relief banished a measure of his alarm. "I am happy to report that was a misunderstanding. Bingley informed me that thanks to a letter from his sister and some of your choicer remarks at Lucas Lodge, the Bennets were all under the impression he had brought Georgiana there as his betrothed. It took most of the evening for the mistake to come to light."

"I see. I thought she must still dislike you for saying she was only tolerably handsome."

The knife cut a little deeper. "That is the second time you have made reference to that remark."

"Do not deny you said it."

"I shall not, but I should like to know how *you* know I said it. If Bingley told you, then he has been unusually indiscreet."

"Not as indiscreet as you saying it directly in front of her in the first place."

The knife was in up to the hilt now and being twisted. The memory of Mr Bennet's odd little smirk as he accused him of slighting one of his daughters made Darcy feel suddenly bilious.

"She *heard* me?"

"I thought it most unlike you, I must say. You are not usually so ungallant."

Again, Darcy found himself wishing he could contradict one of his cousin's opinions, but he could not. He had said it, he had meant it, at least in that moment, and it had been far from the first conceited judgment he had carelessly issued in a ballroom. And *that* total disdain for the feelings of others had been Elizabeth's first impression of him. *Dear God!*

He had spent the last months in agony that he could not be with her, then the last few hours in ecstasy because he had condescended to overlook his own deuced pride and offer for her. This was the first time it had *ever* occurred to him to doubt whether Elizabeth would have him. Agony and ecstasy both promptly abandoned him, leaving him feeling only searing alarm.

"Do you know," Anne said, "I think I should like you to take me back with you tomorrow."

Darcy regarded her in bewilderment, too caught up in his distress to make head or tail of her remark.

"To Netherfield? You must be joking."

"I do not see why. It was good of you to bring me to London, and I am grateful for the offer you made yesterday to take me to more parties while I am here. Especially now that I know you did not make the offer as a husband but rather as a friend hoping to help find me one. But I cannot leave Rosings indefinitely. We both know I am not well enough for London life. I shall have to go home and sooner than I should like. Will you not take me back to Meryton so I may enjoy one last week of freedom before I must face my mother again?"

"You cannot be serious. I am sorry, truly sorry, that your situation is so disagreeable, but you offended every acquaintance I have in Hertfordshire when you were there."

"None that you had not already offended yourself."

He could not defend himself there, so he did not pretend to, though he wished she would cease putting forth more reasons to fear that Elizabeth might despise him. He tried a different tack.

"I thought you disdained the society."

"I said it was inferior to what I am used to. That is not the same as disdaining it."

"It is exactly the same."

Anne exhaled petulantly, as though *he* were the one being unreasonable. "Pray do not demean me by telling me what pleases me. My mother does it too often, and I cannot stand it. I found the Meryton assembly vastly enjoyable. And even Christmas Day at Longbourn had its delights, buried *deep* beneath the chaos and vulgarity."

"You cannot believe, with opinions such as those, I shall ever agree to take you back there."

"No, I do not *believe* you will—I *know* you will."

"*Do* you?" he said heatedly, glad to give the truth to her earlier account of him by being angry with everything she said. "And why is that?"

"Because you are too generous for your own good. And because you need my help."

Darcy despised the way Anne smirked at him. "Your help to do what?"

"To correct the entire town's misapprehension that you and I are engaged."

He wanted to question her sincerity again, but he had already done so twice, and he did not wish to make himself appear addled. Instead, he stood up, stalked up and down in front of the fire a few times, swore aloud, and left the room.

&#8766;

"Have you been driving around in circles since Friday, Darcy?" enquired Bingley, laughing heartily when they arrived at Netherfield on Monday afternoon.

Darcy knew not how it was that after making it the study of his life to avoid those weaknesses that exposed a strong under-standing to ridicule, he had come to be an object of amusement to so many of his friends. "No. Why?"

"You seem to have forgotten why you left in the first place. Were you not supposed to take Miss de Bourgh home?"

"I did," he replied. "Give me a drink, and I shall tell you the story." He dropped into a chair. "Give me two, and I shall not object if you laugh at it. Give me three, and I might laugh, too."

"Gads, is it *that* bad?"

"Worse. Better make it four."

&#8766;

"I shall miss you very much, Lizzy. Are you quite sure you will not come with us to London? We could wait while you pack your trunks."

Elizabeth and Mrs Gardiner were both obliged to step backwards as two servants struggled to lift a large case onto the chaise.

Elizabeth ducked her head, feigning interest in a holly bush. She picked a sprig for good measure and was pricked for her trouble. "You are a saint to invite me, Aunt, but I shall not impose, no matter how many times you press me. You must have had enough 'Bennet' to last you until Easter, I am sure. And with Charlotte's invitation for me to visit her then, we do at least have a date to look forward to. Are you sure it will not be a nuisance for me to stay with you on my way there?"

"Of course I am sure," Mrs Gardiner replied. "Your uncle and I shall anticipate it most eagerly."

If Mrs Gardiner thought her frequent wary glances were subtle, Elizabeth had not the heart to announce otherwise, though she was, at least, forewarned when her aunt broached a more serious topic.

"If you are resolved to stay, I hope it is not with any unduly fanciful expectations for your own happiness."

"We ought to hope not," she replied, laughing, "otherwise, that speech might rob me of all optimism."

Mrs Gardiner's countenance clouded. "I do not wish to pain you, but it was obvious to me, if not to anyone else, that you were intrigued by Mr Darcy. And once the heart is intrigued—"

"I appreciate your concern," Elizabeth interrupted, "but you need not be under any alarm. Hill reports he has brought his cousin back with him after all. I believe we may be assured he is not here to involve himself in an affection with anyone else."

"That is unexpected," Mrs Gardiner replied, looking genuinely astonished.

"Is it? It was no secret that they had an understanding. I expect they have cemented their engagement on their travels. A week in Meryton no doubt confirmed all their worst fears of savage country manners and hastened them to their purpose."

Elizabeth was surprised by the bitterness in her voice—surprised and then diverted. "Goodness! How the tables have turned," she said with a laugh.

"In what way?"

Elizabeth was glad of the interruption of her young cousins being brought out to board the coach, for it excused her from satisfying her aunt's curiosity. Nevertheless, she could not help but be diverted by the complete about-turn that, after two weeks of the reverse being true, saw *her* now being jealous of Miss de Bourgh.

"Will you see him at Purvis Lodge this evening?" Mrs Gardiner whispered as her children were herded into the carriage.

"No, I do not believe so. It is a quiet affair. We are the only guests, I understand."

Mrs Gardiner nodded. "That is probably for the best, my dear." She leant closer, her expression earnest. "I would not see you be made a fool of by a man simply because he has too much money and a pretty face."

Fighting the absurd urge to cry, Elizabeth forced herself to grin. "We agree, then, that he has a pretty face."

"We could hardly disagree about that, could we? The whole purpose of this conversation being about facts, not fantasies. He is a beautiful man. And more fool him, he will never marry you, no matter how handsome or sensible or *worthy* you may be." She cupped Elizabeth's cheek with her hand and shook her head sadly. "My dearest Lizzy."

Nothing Mrs Gardiner said was untrue. Nevertheless, Elizabeth wished she had not felt the need to actually *say* any of it. It rather detracted from the holiday spirit to be reminded of one's utter lack of marriageability. She turned to peer into the carriage, resolved to concentrate on *her* cousins' departure, and spare not a thought for Mr Darcy or *his* cousin's return to Hertfordshire.

# CHAPTER
## 14

After a successful dinner on Saturday evening, it had been generally expected that Mr Bingley would become a regular visitor at Longbourn. Regrettably, his friend's return put paid to any calls on Monday, and the Gardiners' departure and dinner at Purvis Lodge occupied the Bennets on Tuesday. By Wednesday morning, Mrs Bennet had reached the limit of her patience. All five of her daughters were bustled out of the house and ordered to walk to Meryton to deliver a basket to their aunt and uncle Philips.

"And keep alert, Jane!" she cried after them from the front door. "Since you cannot seem to see Mr Bingley at home, you had better attempt to see him elsewhere."

Her direction was not to be fulfilled. It began to snow shortly after they set out, and Mary immediately petitioned to be allowed to return to the house. Jane, less fearful than her younger sister of Mrs Bennet's reproach but equally averse to getting cold, accompanied her. Lydia and Kitty would not be put off the chance of seeing some officers by anything so paltry as a bit of precipitation. Elizabeth was left to carry the basket as the pair of them walked ahead. She did not mind, for she always enjoyed snow. It altered everything, giving something new to discover in even the most familiar landscapes. She relished the beauty of it, despite how the cold burned her toes.

"There they are!" Lydia exclaimed excitedly, almost as soon as they turned into the bottom of the High Street. "Denny! Carter!"

Elizabeth did not reprimand her for the indelicate shriek, for there was something about snow that made one feel singularly festive, and she had not the heart to play the stern governess. Besides, the only people there to witness it were the several officers in the square, all of whom were engaged in a raucous snowball fight. She hardly thought they would care.

She followed her sisters to the water pump, behind which Captain Carter was taking refuge. "You look as though you are on the losing side, sir."

"'Tis not so much a matter of sides as every man to himself," he replied.

"Or girl!" Lydia said excitedly, already squatting to scoop up a handful of ammunition. She stood up to throw it but ducked down again directly as someone else's shot sailed over her head. She whooped with laughter and was soon dashing about the square with Kitty, hurling snow rather ineffectively at the swarm of red coats.

Elizabeth considered stopping them but decided it looked like too much fun to abstain and instead looked around for somewhere to perch her basket so she could join in. As she did, the door of the George and Crown opened, and Mr Darcy stepped out. Their eyes met, but there was no time for anything more, for at that moment, a snowball hit her on the back of the neck, and ice was wedged beneath her collar to tumble down her back. She dropped her basket and cried out in shock.

Behind her, Lydia and Kitty both fell into peals of laughter, and shouts of, "Bad form, Carter!" rang around the square, but the fight otherwise raged on, indifferent to her plight. Elizabeth bent, laughing, to gather up a retaliatory shot.

A movement by the inn door distracted her as she stood to discharge it, but she was mid-twist and did not see what it was. Captain Carter let out a loud grunt and staggered two steps backwards from the impact of the snowball that hit him hard on the side of his head, knocking his hat to the ground.

"Gads, my ear!" he bellowed. "Who threw that?"

Elizabeth regarded her own snowball, still in her hand. Then, as shouts went up accusing various officers, she peered over her shoulder at Mr Darcy. He looked as though he had never thrown a snowball in his life, standing tall and proper on the pavement, regarding the melee with a stern glower. And brushing something off his right glove.

Smiling to herself in wonder, Elizabeth knelt to gather up the scattered contents of the basket. She almost toppled over in amazement when Mr Darcy crouched next to her and took over the task. She stood up, flicking snow off her skirts, and thanked him when he handed her the refilled basket.

"That was a remarkable shot, Mr Darcy."

"Not really. I was not aiming for his ear."

She grinned, always appreciative to discover playfulness in people, and for some reason, particularly delighted to find a streak of it in Mr Darcy.

"What brings you to Meryton today?" She blushed a little, which was silly, for he could not have known that she had wished to ask whether his cousin was with him.

"I left my travel inkwell here when I stayed. My man would have collected it, but I was riding this way anyway. Bingley and I planned to call at Longbourn. In fact, he has gone ahead. I am to meet him there."

"Oh, Jane will be pleased. Could Mr Bingley not have waited for you, though?"

"It was too much of a delay for him, I am afraid."

Elizabeth was grateful to him for admitting as much. To her

mind, teasing his friend for his impatience to see Jane was as good as giving his approval of the match. She tried not to consider what his coming here first said about his own inclination to visit Longbourn.

"May I walk you and your sisters home?" he enquired.

"Certainly, if you do not mind waiting while I take this basket to my aunt."

"Of course," he replied and indicated for her to lead the way.

Though it felt a little traitorous, Elizabeth wished she could avoid a meeting between Mr Darcy and Mrs Philips. Her aunt was bound to do or say something—or many things—that would excite his sense of rank, and though she could not like his pride, this would be one of the last times she would be in company with him, and she felt again her new reluctance that he should recall her or her relations unkindly.

"You must not feel obliged to accompany me. 'Tis only on Gunners Street. I shall run there now and be back in a few minutes."

He only smiled and started walking. Unable to think of a reasonable excuse to put him off, Elizabeth called for Lydia and Kitty to come and then fell in beside him.

"My sister tells me she had a very pleasant evening on Saturday," he said.

"I am glad to hear it. Miss Darcy is a little shy, if I am not mistaken?" He nodded, thus she continued, "I was hopeful that, by the end of the evening, we had put her at ease."

"If the evening was as unrestrained as Christmas Day, I have no doubt you had." He gave her a half smile and added, "Your relations are all so comfortable with each other, it is difficult for guests to remain on ceremony."

"You mean you enjoyed my mother's nerves, my father's facetiousness, and my sisters' squabbling?"

"Would it surprise you if I said I did?"

"Yes!" she replied with an incredulous laugh.

He inclined his head. "That is fair. It surprised me, too."

They arrived, and Mr Philips answered the door, taking his basket of Christmas treats eagerly and waving away Elizabeth's apologies for those that had melting snow on their wrappings. Mrs Philips appeared behind him, Christmas wishes on her lips that dried up when she espied Elizabeth's companion.

"Good heavens. Look who is *tolerating* Lizzy today!" She laughed falsely and exaggeratedly to emphasise how humorous she found herself.

The ground did not swallow Elizabeth, despite the intensity with which she desired it. "We must be getting back," she said feebly and turned to go.

"Do not be daft," her aunt replied. "Come in out of the snow, and have some tea. Come."

Elizabeth looked back to refuse politely, only to see Mr Darcy remove his hat and step inside the house. "But, Jane and Mr Bingley—"

"They do not need either of us," Mr Darcy replied with impossible equanimity. "Let us leave them to it." With a startlingly winsome smile, he disappeared into the hall.

"Did I tell you, girls," said Mrs Philips as she poured the tea, "that your uncle's great- aunt Cicely was at his sister's on Christmas Day? And all these years we thought her dead! Mind you, she looked it—all bones and liver spots and her every other word four shades of nonsense. Though that might have been on account of her new teeth, which I should not be surprised to discover belonged to a horse before they were hers—ten times too big for her mouth, and Lord knows her mouth is ten times bigger than most people's…"

"Miss Bennet?"

Elizabeth glanced at Mr Darcy, who had leant close to address her quietly, but she could not long withstand his gaze. If her aunt continued in this manner, she felt she might wither so thoroughly with mortification that she would blink out of existence entirely. If only Mr Darcy had the courtesy to wait until she did, they would not be required to speak at all.

He was not that courteous, however. Indeed, he was positively persistent. "I beg you would forgive me for my ill-mannered words the first night we met."

She winced. "Pray, pay no heed to what my aunt says. *Any* of it."

Mrs Philips obligingly gave him something to ignore by making a remark about fat old ladies that made Lydia snort with laughter. Elizabeth closed her eyes.

"Did I hear you say Mr Bingley was at Longbourn, Lizzy?" asked her aunt.

"Yes, so I understand."

Mrs Philips nodded sagely. "That will cheer your mother."

"Do you think he will propose to Jane soon?"

"Kitty!" Elizabeth hissed, but it was no good. Her aunt had taken up the baton.

"I should consider him a scoundrel if he did not. To abandon her twice would be criminal!"

It was like watching a carriage accident that one could do nothing to prevent. Over the top of another impolitic remark from Lydia, Elizabeth said loudly, "Mr Darcy, did you enjoy your time in Kent?"

"Not especially. My aunt is newly bereaved and was not on her best form."

Mortification compounded mortification! "Oh, I am sorry to hear that."

He began to reply, but Mr Philips talked directly over him to enquire whether he and Mr Bingley would be at Colonel Forster's dinner that evening.

"We shall, sir," he replied with an impatient edge to his voice.

"Do you think Wickham will be there?" asked Kitty. "He was not in the square just now. Does anyone know when he means to come back?"

From the corner of her eye, Elizabeth observed Mr Darcy shift in his seat, and a surreptitious glance showed him with a heightened complexion. "He is not coming back," she said. "He has left the regiment."

"Never mind, Kitty," said Mrs Philips. "There is always Lieutenant Roberts."

Kitty and Lydia took this as a cue to regale their company with an account of every one of that young officer's virtues. Elizabeth sipped her tea, staring into her cup and wondering whether the leaves held any secrets as to how she might escape her present torment. If they did, she could not read them, thus she had not found a way out when Mr Darcy leant close to talk quietly to her a second time.

"I hope you will not think me too tiresome if I restate the warning I gave you about Mr Wickham during our dance at Netherfield. Should your paths ever cross again, it would be better if you and your sisters were not ignorant of the danger he presents."

Elizabeth had not understood that it *was* a warning at the time. She had been too blinded by prejudice to judge the matter properly. The thought made her grin, for she did enjoy a good bit of irony.

"It is not tiresome at all, and I thank you for your concern, but it is unnecessary. As you predicted, Mr Wickham has not managed to keep many of the friends he made here. Kitty is yet to be persuaded of his evils, but that will not take long, for she emulates Lydia in *all* things, and Lydia has quite forgotten him." Before she could think on it too long and decide against saying it, she added, "I was not so easily warned before. I owe you an apology for the way I harangued you about it at the time." The look this earnt her made her exceedingly pleased she *had* said it.

"No apology is necessary," he assured her. "As haranguings go, yours was one of the more pleasurable I have received of late."

"Do you mean that none of those other people who have dared to scold you danced an entire set with you while they did it? Nobody commits to anything properly these days, do they?"

He agreed they did not, and Elizabeth fancied he was amused despite his want of a smile, for there was something in his eyes that spoke of pleasure.

"I am in earnest about that other matter, too. I hope you can forgive me for what I said at the assembly. My behaviour that evening was abhorrent."

She dipped her head, feeling a flurry of anticipation for the chance to admit something she had never thought would come to light since he was soon to be married.

"Do not concern yourself too greatly. I shall not deny it was ill done, but that is not the only thing I have overheard you say about me." Hearing him suck in his breath, she raised her eyes to his, smiling encouragingly. "I had not left Lucas Lodge on Christmas Eve when you defended me to your cousin. I had only left the room because I did not wish to walk home with Mr Wickham." And then, because his continued gravity made her wonder if he had forgotten what he said in her defence, she added, "A commendation of one's character is a far greater compliment than praise of one's beauty. Even the best looks will fade, whereas good sense and disposition must last forever —or at least until one is so old that every other word is 'four shades of nonsense'."

They were interrupted again by Mrs Philips, who had several more pieces of imperative information to impart, including the full details of Miss King's new inheritance, hitherto kept private from the world for no good reason that she could see, and the receipt for a poultice for piles that she asked to be passed on to Mrs Bennet. Eventually, Elizabeth's family ran out of ways to embarrass her—or perhaps decided they ought to save *some* for her next visit—and it was agreed by all that they ought to go before the snow became too heavy.

Mr Darcy thanked Mr and Mrs Philips for their hospitality with a degree of civility that astounded Elizabeth. Her aunt and uncle were dear, well-meaning people, but refined they were not, and she doubted Mr Darcy had ever experienced a call quite like it. His kindness in not making them feel it meant a great deal to her and showed a generosity of which she had not suspected him capable a few weeks ago.

"Will you go directly to Netherfield?" she asked him once her aunt's front door was closed. "I doubt Mr Bingley will still be at Longbourn."

"Yes, I ought to. Colonel Forster likes to dine early. I must not make Bingley late in his first week back in the neighbourhood." He continued to look at her and made no move to begin walking. Snowflakes swirled between them, some settling on the brim of his hat, the collar of his coat, his lips. Elizabeth was almost surprised when he continued speaking.

"I would have you know that every word you heard me say in your favour at Lucas Lodge was true."

She smiled with genuine gratitude. It was a compliment she would treasure long after he was gone.

"Make haste, Lizzy, 'tis freezing!" Lydia complained.

There was no reason at all why Elizabeth should not do as her sister urged. Her feet simply did not move. And Mr Darcy's gaze simply would not relinquish her.

"And every word you heard me say at the assembly was rot. Nothing could be further from the truth."

She gave a little gasp that did no good, for it rendered her more breathless, not less. Since they were staring at each other, she took advantage of the opportunity to look at him closely—at his eyes, his nose, his mouth, his hair, his expression. It all felt so perfectly familiar, as though he were meant to be there, regarding her in his peculiarly intense way.

But there was something more than familiarity. She knew not when it had begun, but in that moment, Elizabeth understood her affection. It arose like a harmony, springing unexpectedly out of a melody that had been playing for so long it had gone unnoticed, and suddenly the thrum of life was grown richer for it. It flooded her with warmth, made her light with joy, and squeezed her heart with sorrow. What ill luck to fall in love with a man who was engaged to someone else.

"You are kind to say so," she whispered. "I shall remember it."

He might have frowned, but she could not tell, for they were both distracted by Lydia, now joined by Kitty, repeating her plea to leave.

"I had better go," she said, rolling her eyes and giving him a rueful smile.

Mr Darcy bowed but did not move, and when Elizabeth glanced back at him before she and her sisters went around the corner, there was no mistaking his frown. She was sorry for it, but it could hardly be helped. She could not have said more without bursting into tears.

# CHAPTER 15

It continued to snow intermittently overnight and all the next morning, resulting in an increasingly gloomy air at Longbourn as the prospect of Mr Bingley calling that day grew ever less likely. Elizabeth commiserated with Jane but could not decide whether she was unhappy or relieved for herself. She suspected it would be as painful as it was pleasurable to see Mr Darcy again if he accompanied his friend. His choosing not to come would present an entirely different source of misery.

All of them were surprised when a carriage was seen rolling into the drive, and none were so perturbed as Elizabeth when its door opened, and two bonneted figures stepped down from it. The ladies of Netherfield had called, and nobody but she could guess why.

"Mr Bingley and my brother are otherwise engaged at present," Miss Darcy explained once they were all settled in the parlour. "A part of the old stable roof has given way under the weight of snow, and they are organising the repairs. I am sure they will call as soon as they are able."

Jane observably took heart from the promise, but looking at the sky outside, Elizabeth rather doubted it would be fulfilled in the near future.

"I am surprised *you* both took the trouble to come in this weather," she said. "We are honoured, of course, but the snow is getting rather heavy."

"Our message could not be delayed, Miss Elizabeth," replied Miss de Bourgh.

Mrs Bennet launched into transports of gratitude for saving Jane from an afternoon of suspense while the gentlemen saw to the stable repairs. Elizabeth, suspecting the message to be something entirely other than the one already relayed, entered her own state of wretched suspense as she waited to hear it.

"I hope this snow will not prevent Mr Bingley's sisters from coming on Monday," Jane said. "It would be a great shame if they were not able to attend the feast he has planned. It sounds wonderful."

"Miss Bingley?" Miss de Bourgh enquired disdainfully, looking at her cousin. "The woman who has had her cap set for your brother since the turn of the century?"

Miss Darcy baulked and muttered a few inarticulate words, her hedging as good as a confirmation of the charge.

Miss de Bourgh sniffed contemptuously. "I should as soon pray for more snow, Miss Bennet. Any woman who has not yet worked out the difference between desire and delusion after eleven years cannot have much sensible to add to a party. I daresay she would not be missed."

Elizabeth might have been diverted were it not for an unbidden swell of empathy for Miss Bingley, one of the most unpleasant women of her acquaintance and the last person on earth with whom she would ever have expected to feel an affinity.

"Nevertheless, I hope she is not detained. Miss Bingley was exceedingly good to me last autumn when I was taken ill at her house," Jane insisted gently but firmly. "I shall be pleased to see her again."

"My cousin jests," Miss Darcy said with absolutely no conviction and looking increasingly bewildered. "The Bingleys are all good friends of our family."

Miss de Bourgh rolled her eyes but otherwise ignored her. "I understand you saw my cousin in Meryton yesterday."

"We did," Lydia answered. "He came with us for tea at my aunt Philips's house."

"Yes, he mentioned that." Miss de Bourgh fixed Elizabeth with a stare that was startlingly similar to her cousin's, if rather colder. "I trust you did not misunderstand his purpose."

"In accompanying us?" she answered. "No, I do not believe there was any misunderstanding."

"Indeed, none at all," cried Mrs Bennet. "Why Mr Darcy chose to show such *vast* condescension to the family who might soon boast a connexion of the *closest* kind to his *oldest* friend is his own business. We should never presume to draw any conclusions about it."

"That is well. Assumptions are clearly not your forte," Miss de Bourgh replied with a slightly bemused expression. With a sidelong glance at Elizabeth, she added, "So long as his attention was taken for what it was."

Elizabeth was careful to keep her expression neutral, despite how her stomach dropped. Here was her message then—a reminder of their conversation on Christmas Day. "Civility," she said, nodding. "I know."

"No," Miss de Bourgh replied with surprising energy. "No, he was *not* being civil."

"Cousin Anne, I cannot imagine my brother would have been impolite!" said Miss Darcy with alarm.

"That was not my meaning, dear. Of course he was *polite*. Darcy is unfailingly well-mannered, which is fortunate, given what he told me of the visit. But you cannot believe it was his design to call on Mr and Mrs Philips to exhibit his good breeding." She pierced Elizabeth with another glance. "He does not give such notice indiscriminately. I have said before that one should never mistake civility for attentions. I say it again now but with the opposite meaning."

Elizabeth made no reply, unsure she had understood properly. *Was it more than politeness that induced Mr Darcy to suffer that ridiculous visit?*

Her mother certainly took that as Miss de Bourgh's meaning. She preened and leant to clasp Jane's arm. "You see, Jane. In recognising our relations thus, Mr Darcy proves he knows what is coming between you and Mr Bingley."

"Mrs Bennet, you are a true wonder. How you managed to construe that hint as meant for you, I do not know," said Miss de Bourgh.

"Thank you," Mrs Bennet replied, puffing up with pride.

Elizabeth closed her eyes briefly, mortified by her mother's misplaced hubris, and dismayed by the confirmation that Miss de Bourgh's hint was meant for her. She replied with equanimity she did not feel.

"You have no cause to be uneasy, madam. *I* comprehend the importance of not taking things that are not meant for me. And I never would."

Miss de Bourgh replied in a flash. "I know. It is a disposition I find most tiresome."

"Lizzy, what are you running on about? Remember who you are speaking to, and do not vex our visitors so!" Mrs Bennet snapped, looking between them in frowning perplexity.

"We are talking about my cousin, Mr Darcy," replied Miss de Bourgh. "And the fact that he and your daughter share the same insufferable inclination to rectitude."

Elizabeth huffed in frustration. "In which case, you cannot believe him capable of ever showing...*civility* to more than one person at once."

"That is precisely my point. I am glad we have come to it at last."

The room fell silent as everybody else attempted to come to the *same* point and, judging by their bemused expressions, failed.

"Is *that* why he did not speak to Mrs Long at the assembly?" Mrs Bennet enquired dubiously.

"I am sure he did not mean to be rude to Mrs Long," Miss Darcy said breathlessly. "Or anybody."

Jane gave a mollifying tut. "Come now, Mama. Mr Darcy *did* speak to Mrs Long at the assembly. I have told you that."

"I find it difficult to know who to talk to when there are too many conversations happening at once," Kitty said, pouting. "Perhaps Mr Darcy is the same as me."

Miss de Bourgh pulled a disgusted face and turned her back on them all to address Elizabeth. "I heard it reported that you were clever. Please do me the honour of *attempting* to grasp what I am telling you."

"Perhaps I also struggle with more than one conversation," Elizabeth replied. "There are at least four going on here, and I am not sure I am following any of them properly."

"Then constrain yourself to just one, as my cousin is doing. And *his* conversation, I trust you comprehend, is *not* with me."

Elizabeth let out a sharp exhalation. Dismay and bitter disappointment herded her thoughts in the only direction they could now go.

Darcy had broken with his cousin. *How could he?*

"Oh, I detest it when men ignore me," said Mrs Bennet, determined to have her share of the conversation. "Mr Bennet does it all the time. You ought not to stand for it. But I am glad you came here today, for *we* shall not ignore you."

"Be fair, Mama. The gentlemen were obliged to see to the stable repairs. I am sure they did not mean to ignore anyone," Jane said.

"Mr Darcy might have meant to," Lydia argued. "Lizzy said he ignored her for a whole day when she was staying at Netherfield."

"I assure you my brother has not ignored either my cousin or me today. He is only helping his friend. He truly is exceptionally good," Miss Darcy said.

"Indeed," Miss de Bourgh added, still looking pointedly at Elizabeth. "Exceptionally good *and* unencumbered by honour."

Elizabeth could scarcely unclench her teeth enough to speak, so turbulent were her sentiments. Had Mr Darcy not seen the pain caused when he separated Jane and Mr Bingley? And they had known each other for but a few months. Miss de Bourgh and he had been engaged their entire lives.

For weeks now, Elizabeth had witnessed the desperate jealousy with which Miss de Bourgh sought to protect that connexion. Could he be ignorant of the strength of her feelings—or worse, indifferent to them? It mattered not how dearly she had come to think of him, Elizabeth would not, *could* not be party to Mr Darcy's callous abandonment. And neither could she forgive him for it, for despite all her good fortune to have evaded Mr Wickham's duplicity, she still found herself in the unenviable position of being in love with a scoundrel.

She looked Miss de Bourgh in the eye and nodded. "Entirely without it, it would seem."

"I hate to interrupt what looks like a scintillating exchange, my dear," said Mr Bennet, appearing in the doorway, "but unless Miss de Bourgh and Miss Darcy wish to stay for dinner, supper, and breakfast too, they might like to consider leaving us now. At this rate, the lane will be impassable within a quarter of an hour."

The ladies all turned in unison to look out of the window. The snow had indeed begun to settle at an alarming rate, but the horses had not been unhitched from the carriage for that very reason, and thus the business of departing took very little arranging. Less than five minutes after it was suggested that they leave, Miss Darcy and Miss de Bourgh had gone.

"Would that all your visitors were as efficient, Mrs Bennet," said her husband. "I confess I am surprised they came at all."

"I am not," she replied. "You can ignore all that nonsense about delivering the message of Mr Bingley being delayed. He could have sent a note with a servant to let us know that. They talked around the houses a bit, as these high and mighty folk often do, but it was as clear as day to me that they were here to discuss Mr Darcy."

Elizabeth kept her lips firmly closed, though she was grateful when Mary expressed the same doubts as to her mother's reasoning that she felt unequal to articulating herself.

"Oh Mary, you can be thick-headed!" Mrs Bennet replied. "Only consider it. First, Miss de Bourgh discredited Miss Bingley. That gives us leave to overlook *her* disapprobation. Then she talked about Mr Darcy's visit to my sister yesterday, and she was adamant that we should not mistake his intention in doing *that*. Then Miss Darcy and her cousin both gave a glowing account of Mr Darcy's character, assuring us that he is exceptionally good—particularly in his friendship towards his *friend*."

She paused to look at everybody and seemed disappointed when they did not instantly pounce upon the conclusion to which she had evidently meant to lead them. "It is obvious! As his cousin and sister, and therefore the best people to speak on his behalf, they came to let it be known that Mr Darcy commends the union between Jane and Mr Bingley!" She clapped her hands together and veritably wriggled with glee.

"Well then, Jane," said Mr Bennet after a pause of palpable astonishment, "if your mother is right, your Mr Bingley ought to appear at any moment through the snow to ask one or both of us a question. You may tell him I await his presence with bated breath in my library."

He departed to begin his vigil, leaving behind a clamour centred mostly around Mrs Bennet's anticipation for the imminent sound of wedding bells and Jane's attempts to moderate her expectations.

It allowed Elizabeth to escape unseen to her room, where she curled up on her bed and told herself repeatedly that it did not matter *why* Mr Darcy had broken his engagement. He was promised to Miss de Bourgh and ought never to have forsaken her. It was immaterial, therefore, that Elizabeth's heart yearned for him to have acted thus because he wished to marry her.

&.

Darcy stamped the snow off his boots and shrugged off his greatcoat into the hands of the waiting footman. Behind him, Bingley issued instructions for hot drinks to be sent out to the men still at work on the stable roof.

"Fancy a drop of something warming yourself, Darcy?" he enquired. "You have earnt it."

"Tea will suffice, thank you."

"Right ho," his friend replied, nodding at the footman to see to it. "You go ahead and find the ladies, then. I shall join you as soon as I have dashed off that report to the agent. Good advice, that. Thank you."

Darcy gave his best estimation of a smile. He did not begrudge helping his friend, but he was tired, cold, and bitterly disappointed to have lost the chance of seeing Elizabeth. He left to seek out his sister and cousin but found only Mrs Jenkinson in the parlour.

"Have you been abandoned, madam? That seems ungenerous."

"Mrs Annesley is resting, sir. And Miss Darcy and her cousin have gone out."

"Out? Where?"

"Longbourn."

Darcy kept his countenance carefully neutral so as not to alarm her with the extent of his consternation. "I did not realise they intended to go there. They said nothing of it."

The woman shrank into her seat. Perhaps he had not kept his countenance as blank as he had intended.

"I am afraid I cannot answer for that, sir."

"I can."

Darcy turned around slowly, undesirous of appearing unduly irate. Anne was walking calmly into the room with Georgiana behind her as though they had been nowhere more contentious than the drawing room. She lowered herself with exaggerated state into a chair and arranged her skirts before troubling herself to explain.

"The notion occurred to me when the carriages were all brought out of the stables. I thought it the perfect opportunity to visit my new friend, Miss Elizabeth."

Darcy bit back his words, clamping his mouth closed on a most ungentlemanlike outburst. He knew not why Anne had expressed surprise over his always being angry about things when she gave him such constant reason to be vexed. With forced composure, he asked Mrs Jenkinson to leave them.

"What have you done?" he enquired of Anne as soon as her companion was gone. She looked wholly unrepentant. His sister, on the other hand, looked petrified, and he regretted not asking her to leave also.

"We have not done anything, Brother," she said in the same, timorous tone she always used when she had done something she thought would displease him—which was *all the time* of late. "We only went to pay a call on Miss Elizabeth and her sisters."

"Through three feet of snow? What was it you wished to say to her that was so urgent it could not wait for more clement weather?"

She flinched and looked anxiously at Anne, who sighed affectedly. "It is not *three feet*. It is not even one! But I own, I did not think it would get so heavy. What does it matter? We are back safely."

"Which is why *that* is not what concerns me," he retorted. "Though I should have been a good deal less forbearing had any harm come to my sister. Or my coachman. Or my horses!" He took a deep breath to dispel the anger that stretched his composure tauter by the moment. "Do not prevaricate, Anne. Tell me what you said to Miss Elizabeth."

She seemed—finally—to comprehend the extent of his displeasure, for she lost some of her defiance and sank backwards a little into her chair, two spots of colour reddening her cheeks.

"I was only attempting to help you, Darcy."

"By telling her *what?*"

"That you and I are not engaged."

Darcy ignored Georgiana's gasp. That she, too, had been ignorant of the misapprehension was of little comfort at this stage.

"You did not consider me capable of imparting the details of my own marital status? Or deciding the best moment to do so?"

"I thought it would have more effect coming from me," Anne replied. "I have, after all, spent the last several weeks convincing her of the opposite. And it is only my affection for you that allows me to admit I may have been quite insistent on the matter. Rather too insistent, I fear."

"What do you mean?"

"Well, to be frank, I am not at all sure that my disclosure had the desired effect."

He glowered at her, too conflicted to speak, until she took the hint and continued. "One might have expected a *little* rejoicing. I suppose I ought to applaud Miss Elizabeth for not doing so, for it shows a more modest understanding of her situation than I had previously credited her with. She is right not to expect that she will receive an offer from such a man as you simply because she has learnt you are not engaged to me. Nevertheless, I did not expect her to be cross about it."

Darcy was still framing a sufficiently emphatic rejoinder when the door swung open, and a footman appeared, who took one look in his direction and seemed to change his mind about entering.

"What is it?" Darcy barked.

He mumbled that he had brought tea.

"Bring it in then," Anne said impatiently, "unless you would like us all to come and drink it in the lobby?"

Darcy turned away, disliking his cousin's manner of addressing servants—so like her mother's—and liking even less the fumbling incompetence of the man as he emptied the tray onto the table. The sound of teacups being set shakily in their saucers eventually ceased, and Darcy barely waited for the door to click closed behind the departing footman before turning to glare at Anne.

"Why was she cross?"

"How am I to know? Mayhap I was right the first time, and she does not like you."

"I am sure that is not the case," Georgiana interposed in a voice that was half reproach, half whisper, as though she were frightened by her own boldness. "Admittedly, a few of her relations seem to have a somewhat poor impression of you, Brother, but it can be nothing that will not improve on acquaintance."

Darcy fully comprehended that his previous complacency where Elizabeth was concerned had been egregiously misplaced. Yet, he simply could not believe she disliked him. No man who had been looked at the way Elizabeth gazed up at him in the snow yesterday could ever willingly give up hope of there being a warmer sentiment at play. It had felt as though, had he kissed her there in the street before all her relations, she would not have objected. How was it that Anne's admission had angered her so?

"What precisely did you say to her?"

"I cannot remember the exact words. I think...that your attentions were deliberate, not mere civilities, and that you were not being duplicitous in giving her such notice because you were not bound to *me* by honour."

"Did you say it exactly like that?"

"No, of course not. I am not completely devoid of self-respect, Darcy. I had no objection to enlightening Miss Elizabeth as to my mistake, but neither had I any intention of allowing Mrs Bennet to gloat about being right when she told me I was ill-suited to be your wife."

Georgiana let out a shaky breath that might have been an ill-concealed giggle. "She said that to you?"

"Oh, do be quiet," Anne retorted rudely.

Georgiana straightened her back, her expression as close to resentment as Darcy had ever seen it. "*I* remember what you said at Longbourn, Anne. You told them that Brother had no intention of being civil when he visited Mr and Mrs Philips, that he spent this morning ignoring you and me and that is what drove us to call at Longbourn, that Mrs Bennet was wondrous silly, and that you found Miss Elizabeth's disposition tiresome. I could not understand why you said any of it and hoped you had a kinder intention than was immediately apparent, but I am beginning to wonder whether that was the case, for you seem to take great pleasure in being *un*kind!"

"All done!" came a jubilant pronouncement from Bingley as he bounded into the room. "Ah, you have had tea already, I see. What else have I missed?"

Nobody answered. Darcy knew not what prevented the others, but for his part, he found panting with anger precluded much in the way of good-humoured conversation.

"Upon my word," Bingley said as he surveyed everyone's faces. "Who died?"

No one had, though Darcy knew who he would nominate if there were a ballot on who should. He ought never to have agreed to bring Anne back to Hertfordshire.

"My patience," he said darkly and then, though conscious that he had done it several times of late and risked beginning to look like a histrionic adolescent, he excused himself and stalked from the room, unable to trust himself to remain civil if he stayed.

# CHAPTER
## 16

Elizabeth's love of snow diminished considerably over the next day. The drifts that had accumulated on Thursday crystalised overnight into an icy blockade that kept them imprisoned at Longbourn and deprived of callers throughout the whole of Friday. It was a situation with which Jane appeared quite comfortable, but then, she had received word explaining her gentleman caller's absence, thereby allaying any doubts in his affection. For Elizabeth, it meant only that she was prevented from taking any exercise, leaving her at the mercy of her mother and younger sisters' inanity and denying her any reprieve from her own distressing reflections.

Matters had been much simpler a few months earlier when she had despised Darcy. Doing so had not caused her a moment's worry. She had reviled many less irksome men. When he left Hertfordshire, she had believed herself perfectly content never to think of him again, her enmity readily consigned to an unpleasant memory. Even after she had absolved him of any wrongdoing towards Wickham, recognised the prodigious care he took of all those he esteemed, better understood his self-averred resentfulness, learnt to admire his taciturnity, grown covetous of his rare smile and even rarer laughter, and become altogether too enraptured with his person—*still*, Elizabeth had been untroubled by doubts. For then, he had been engaged to somebody else, and her regard for him had been immaterial, an injury from which her heart would have eventually recovered.

It was all different now. Mr Darcy had broken with his cousin, and her feelings had assumed a portent of unbearable moment. Hope assuaged her at every turn, whispering that he might mean to propose to her, obliging her to constantly repress it, for it would be the worst form of evil to tempt him away from Miss de Bourgh. She could never live with herself for such a despicable act against another woman. Yet, therein lay her struggle, for Elizabeth grew increasingly unsure that she could easily live with a decision to refuse him if he *did* care for her. In such circumstances, she doubted her heart *would* ever recover.

Thus it was, despite all the reasons she ought not even to be contemplating it, Elizabeth could not prevent herself from endlessly speculating what it was that Darcy felt for her. By Friday morning, she had settled it that he could not possibly love her, for she knew he thought her too plain, her family too vulgar, and her situation too far beneath him. It was halfway through breakfast that she remembered his resolute disavowal of all he had ever said in censure of her beauty. Her resulting blush caused her mother to check her brow for a fever and instruct her to don an extra shawl.

By midday on Friday, she had recalled Darcy's request for a front row seat to watch the Gardiner children's Christmas play and decided that his disdain for her connexions was perhaps not quite so severe as she had assumed. By suppertime, she had decided that he *must* admire her, for nothing else justified his cousin's violent jealousy. By bedtime, she had recognised herself for the fool she was to presume such a man would ever notice her and despised herself for wishing that he would. By midnight, her reflections had turned to the way he listened, rapt, every time she spoke, and she despaired of ever finding another man who made her feel so precious.

Elizabeth woke early on Saturday, after too little repose. She tossed and turned in her bed long enough to make it certain sleep would not return, then pushed off her covers and crossed the room to open the curtains. Snow still blanketed everything. It was a little churned up at the gate and along the drive where the servants and farmers had traipsed through it, but the world was otherwise unchanged. She rested her head against the pane and sighed. There would be no visitors again today. There absolutely *must* be walking, though. If the servants had managed to get through the drifts, then so could she, and without some fresh air to clear her mind, she would go distracted long before anything thawed.

Something fluttered foolishly in Elizabeth's stomach at the thought of an accidental meeting out of doors with Darcy, but she quashed the silly notion and pushed herself away from the window to pull the cord for the maid. Hot water was presently provided, and in short order, Elizabeth was dressed in her warmest woollen stockings and thickest walking dress, ready to stomp out her agitation on the snow. She snatched up her bonnet and crept along the hall, navigating every loose floorboard and creaking stair, retrieving her coat, and digging out a pair of gloves without drawing any unwanted attention. Satisfied she had not roused anyone who would object to her going out, she pulled open the front door—only to stagger backwards two steps, shocked by a blast of icy air and a vastly unexpected sight.

"Mr Darcy!"

He lowered his hand from where it had evidently been poised to knock. "Miss Elizab—"

She gestured for him to be quiet. "You will wake everyone!"

she hissed, her heart hammering so violently that manners quite escaped her. "What are you doing here?"

He looked at her intently for a moment. Then he smiled very slightly but most effectively. "I came to see you."

His whispered voice was even more resonant than his usual one, an observation that vexed Elizabeth no end, for she had not previously been aware of its having any effect on her, never mind the absurd blushing breathlessness afflicting her at present.

"Well, I wish you had not!" she replied in an angry whisper.

The effect her words had upon his countenance tugged at her heart, though in too many directions to make it easy to know what else to say.

"I am excessively sorry to hear that," he said too loudly.

She pressed a finger expressively to her lips to silence him again. He obliged her, and they were both silent until a sharp gust of wind blew a flurry of snow into the house, and without thinking, Elizabeth gestured for him to come in so she could shut the door.

Then she wished fervently she had not, for inside, he was no longer silhouetted in the doorway but lit by the hall fire and standing awfully close to her, and she suddenly felt uncomfortably aware of how much larger he was than she. He removed his hat, which for some reason unnerved her further still.

"I was about to walk out," she whispered, as though it might make him put it back on again and go away. It did not.

"I would advise against it. It is freezing out there."

"That did not stop you."

"No. Not much would have."

The intensity of his gaze was—well, it was wonderful in truth, though it was hardly helping Elizabeth to remain impartial, and thus its effect was to make her angry. It was difficult to *sound* angry when one was attempting to be silent, however, which was perhaps why, when she told him again that he ought not to have come, he seemed less distressed by it than before.

"So you have said. Might I enquire why?"

Elizabeth gave a small, humourless laugh at the question, so simple in contrast to the complexity of her jumbled thoughts. She grew increasingly rattled the longer she struggled to frame a response, unable to answer that she dreaded the discovery he was an unprincipled scoundrel or that she had no wish to be tested on the strength of her own principles.

"Because it is snowy," she blurted at length.

Darcy—most unfairly—gave her another of his intoxicating little smiles. "Snowy?"

She nodded defiantly, incensed that he should be diverted—and handsome—when she was so miserable. Both put her at an insufferable disadvantage.

"Might I be so bold—"

"Hush! Pray, keep your voice down."

"Forgive me," he whispered. His deeper timbre seemed to hit a pitch that reverberated directly in her breastbone. "Might I be so bold as to enquire what is the significance of the weather?"

Abandoning all pretensions to composure, she replied in an agitated whisper. "Because the snow is knee-deep in places, which means you must have come on foot. And anyone who walks three miles *anywhere* in knee-deep snow must have a very particular reason for going there. And if that reason is me, which it is because you have said so, then it makes what I must say even harder."

"And what is it you must say?"

Elizabeth baulked and blushed deeply. "Obviously, I cannot say it until you have said what you came to say. And it would be better if you said nothing, for then so might I."

"That would make for a very dull conversation."

"This is not amusing! Why are you smiling?"

He stepped closer to her. "Because I do not believe you truly wish me to remain silent. Neither do I believe that you wish to say to me what you think you must."

"You presume a great deal, sir," she replied, desperate to shoo Darcy away from the truth that he had so readily and infuriatingly discerned. "Pray, what great penetration has convinced you of this?"

"Miss Elizabeth, I know enough of your disposition to be certain that, were you absolutely, irrevocably decided against me, you would acknowledge it to me frankly and openly, not seek to avoid speaking at all."

She inhaled sharply, taken aback for a fleeting moment, until her surprise was usurped by a tremble of pleasure that he should comprehend her so well. Her pleasure was just as quickly subsumed by resignation.

"That changes nothing," she replied bitterly.

"I beg to differ. I came here wholly uncertain of my reception, but you have given me hope that whatever other impediment to marrying me exists, it is not your sentiments."

A small noise escaped her—exasperation, perhaps, or maybe despair—that he had, despite her pleas, confirmed his intentions, thereby placing the responsibility of behaving honourably squarely at her door.

"Regrettably, we both know my sentiments are immaterial."

His smile vanished. "Elizabeth, no. Never think that. My insatiable need to *know* your sentiments is why I am here. Perhaps I ought to have paid you court for longer, to nurture your regard. A man who felt less might have, but I could go no longer without discovering whether I had any hope."

"You have twisted my meaning!" she cried in a voice more whimper than whisper, but he was making this so impossibly difficult, speaking of his hope while she was desperately attempting to quash her own. "But you are right—you have been entirely reckless in coming here in this manner. I thought you disdained precipitance."

"I do." His small smile returned. "This was not precipitance. If I had acted precipitately, I should have come to you in November instead of leaving Hertfordshire."

*November?* She stared at him, aghast to discover that his feelings were of such long duration. As though refusing him were not already the most painful thing she would ever have to do!

"You are the most provoking man I have ever met!" she exclaimed in a furious whisper. She jumped clear of the ground when the library door abruptly opened, and her father stepped into the hall.

"Is anything amiss, Lizzy? Mr Darcy? I heard you both talking out here and thought I might leave you to it, but matters do not appear to be progressing in the direction I anticipated."

"I was simply attempting to explain my position to Mr Darcy, but it is difficult to speak with conviction when one is whispering," Elizabeth replied.

With an annoyingly knowing look, Mr Bennet pushed his door open wider. "Should you like the use of my library? You ought to be able to raise your voices to suitably persuasive levels in there."

"Thank you, yes," Darcy answered at the same time as Elizabeth replied, "No!" in a voice she could no longer even pretend was quiet.

"Thank you. But I do not need to be in your library to tell Mr Darcy that I will not marry him."

Her father raised an eyebrow. "If that is what you mean to tell him, I suggest you not only go in but barricade the door, because if your mother should overhear you, I cannot vouch for your safety."

"That is easily resolved," Darcy replied, his eyes fixed on Elizabeth. "Do not refuse me." Then he turned on his heel and strode into the library, leaving her with no choice but to follow him.

He had lied.

It was, without a doubt, the most—possibly the *only*—

impetuous thing Darcy had ever done, but he could not have prevented it. Trapped at Netherfield, unable to go to Elizabeth to see what damage had been done, he had passed the whole of the previous day in torment as he pictured Anne abusing her so abominably to her face. He had attempted to assuage his disquiet by reminiscing about those precious few moments in Meryton on Wednesday, when they seemed to have made such a momentous advancement in their understanding.

Alas, by the evening, his recollection of that encounter had altered until Elizabeth appeared to look up at him with less admiration and more abhorrence. He had been reduced to stalking impatiently through Netherfield's rooms, reminded at every turn of the early days of his acquaintance with Elizabeth. Days when desire had flared hot and then, instead of dwindling as desire more commonly did, continued to burn, allowing deep and abiding admiration to creep in beneath the flames and catch him unawares.

Impatience to see her, to remedy whatever injury Anne had caused, to salvage whatever chance he had left of making Elizabeth love him, had kept him awake half the night listening for the sound of rain to wash away the snow. That same impatience had summoned a stream of curses from his lips when he opened his curtains at dawn to discover the landscape unchanged and brought him traipsing across fields of snow at an indecently early hour to present himself to a woman who, for all he knew, might not even like him.

Impatience was fast ceding to hope, and hope to exhilaration, however, as she inadvertently revealed more and more of her feelings, for they looked nothing akin to dislike.

"This is a wretched beginning," Elizabeth said once the door was closed.

"You concede it is a beginning, then?"

"That was not my meaning, as well you know. Mr Darcy, no matter how used you may be to getting your own way, you cannot *force* me to marry you against my will."

"And never would I attempt to. But I *can* discover your reasons for continuing so obstinately to insist that you do not wish to."

"That is not what I said. I said I *would* not marry you."

Darcy's heart turned over in his chest, though he did his best to conceal it from Elizabeth, lest she grow so vexed that she ended the interview. "Why not?" he enquired evenly.

She shook her head, and her brow creased with dissatisfaction. "It is frankly reprehensible that you should even need to ask. I am sorry if you do not wish to marry your cousin, and I can quite comprehend why you might not, for I have rarely met a more disagreeable woman, but you cannot forsake her after five-and-twenty or six-and-twenty years or whatever it is. *You* may be able to walk away unscathed and marry where you will, but as a woman, *she* will be ridiculed and scorned if you break with her now. Miss de Bourgh will not find it easy to secure another suitor at her age or with her indifferent health. Therefore, you will be abandoning her to a life of loneliness, with neither partner nor children to keep her company. And all this to say nothing of her feelings. It is simply not right!"

She was all but panting with indignation by the end of her speech and seemed braced for some sort of reprisal, but Darcy could scarcely keep the smile from his face.

"Do you have any idea how much I love you, Elizabeth Bennet?"

Her surprise was almost comical. "What did you say?"

"You are the most admirable, compassionate, *passionate*, and beautiful person I have ever met. And I love you."

She blinked at him a few times and appeared unable to catch her breath. He thought she was about to smile, but instead she exhaled heavily and shook her head.

"But you must still marry Miss de Bourgh. If not for her sake, then for mine, for how many years would it be otherwise before you came to resent me for the fortune you sacrificed to marry me? You are too much of a gentleman to mention it, but

Mr Wickham had no such qualms, and he told me that the engagement with your cousin was planned to enable your estates to be combined. Can you promise you would *never* come to regret forfeiting Rosings Park for my one-hundred pounds a year?"

Appalled, Darcy stared at her. "You would bring up things *George Wickham* has said at such a moment as this?"

"Yes, because it is true, is it not?"

"No! It—" He stopped and rubbed a hand over his face before reluctantly admitting, "There is some truth to it. My mother and aunt did speak of it at one time, when Anne and I were first born, but I never took it seriously, and neither did my mother or father. Lord knows they proposed enough alternatives in my formative years to remove all doubt of that. But—" He sighed deeply. "It seems Anne believed it."

Elizabeth did not respond straightaway. She only frowned as she considered this new information. He took heart from the fact that her eyes never left his for one moment of her deliberations.

"Believed?" she said at last. "In the past?"

"Yes! All misunderstanding between us has been well and truly resolved, and she led me to believe that she had clarified matters for you, also. Little though I liked the discovery that she had come here on Thursday, or how she spoke to you, I thought I understood that amongst all her insults, she did at least relay the information that she and I are not engaged."

"She did," Elizabeth replied, still frowning, "but she did not tell me that you never *were*. I thought you had broken the engagement. She seemed so very angry."

Darcy wanted to crow. Finally, he comprehended Elizabeth's reluctance! He constrained himself to a smile. "Anne *always* seems angry. It is a family trait, I am told." That earnt him a grin, though Elizabeth attempted to disguise it. "Do you see now? There never was any union planned for us. I have never aspired to combine our fortunes or our estates. Anne is neither angry nor distressed about it. She scarcely could be, considering it was she who attempted to break the blasted engagement."

Elizabeth raised an eyebrow in exactly the same manner her father had moments before.

"That is how we discovered our mutual misapprehension," Darcy explained, somewhat chagrined. "She told me on the way back from Kent that she no longer wished to marry me."

Elizabeth's eyes danced with mirth. She looked absolutely lovely. "That must have come as a bit of a surprise if you knew nothing about it."

"Just a bit. I understand it was something your mother said about our dispositions being ill-suited that decided her."

"Oh Lord, yes! On Christmas Day, Mama told her that you needed a wife who could teach you some liveliness, and Miss de Bourgh was not qualified. Goodness, I think you had better forgive your cousin her every injustice towards my family, for we seem to have matched her insult for insult."

"You *do* enliven me, Elizabeth," Darcy said with impassioned urgency, closing the gap between them and taking up her hands. "I have never known happiness such as I feel when I am with you. I have never laughed as much or worried as little. You lift my spirits merely by being in the same room. I cannot imagine my life without you, except that it must be the most miserable state of existence, and I have no desire to acquaint myself with it. What I *want* is for the chance to make you as happy as you make me. Every day, every hour, for the rest of my life. I want you to agree to marry me. Will you, Elizabeth?" He lifted her hands and kissed them, tenderly, reverently. "Will you agree to be my wife?"

Hope hammered out a desperate rhythm on his heart as he watched her. She continued to stare at him for what felt like an age until, to his vast confusion, she released a flurry of opposing sentiments at once. She nodded in the affirmative, and though she smiled, it was as tremulous as it was broad and largely eclipsed by the pitiful, shuddering breath she took, and the tear that spilled down her cheek.

"Yes, I will marry you." She nodded and wiped the tear away with the heel of her palm, only for another to drop over her lashes in its wake. "Nothing would make me happier."

The heartfelt delight this reply produced might have been such as he had never felt before, had it not been tempered by uncertainty. "Are you aware you are crying?"

Her smile broadened further still, and she gave a delicate sniff. "Yes, forgive me."

"I thought you said you laugh when you are happy."

"I do, usually. But I have never been this happy before."

She laughed then, and Darcy thought he had never been more in love with her. He gently wiped away her tear with his thumb. "Neither have I."

She beamed at him. "Then I must tell you, it becomes you very well."

That was a compliment he had not anticipated. It made him profoundly aware of how admiringly she was regarding him and how closely they were standing. He had not intended to kiss her, not here with her father on the other side of the door, but he could think of no other way to express what he felt. And he knew enough of the world to recognise desire when he saw it.

He heard it in her rapid breathing, saw it in the unblinking fervency of her stare, felt it in the heat of her breath on his lips. She held herself still, as though she ought to be ashamed of feeling it, yet it seemed that if he touched her, she would melt into his arms more readily than lamp oil soaks into a wick. He was not resilient enough to withstand it. And he wanted, with alarming intensity, to see how hot she would burn. He kept the kiss brief, for her sake. It was enough time to leave them both breathless and for him to correct his estimation from wick to touchpaper.

"That was quite the revelation," she whispered with a shy grin that did nothing to cool his ardour.

"*You* are the revelation, Elizabeth. When we have more time, I shall tell you all the lessons that loving you has taught me."

"Oh dear! You make it sound as though it has been rather hard work."

He held her gaze steadily and tried not to let his voice betray *all* his desire, lest he alarm her. "It has been torture from beginning to end."

She blushed but did not look away, and his heart soared, for he knew then that she comprehended him perfectly. He traced her cheekbone as he had envisaged doing more times than he cared to recount.

"Thank God you have relieved my suffering. I could not have survived another day keeping these feelings to myself."

"I wonder if we ought to keep them to ourselves a little while longer, though."

"Why? Pray tell me you have no doubts."

"Goodness, no! None at *all*. Please do not think that for a moment. It is Jane. She would never begrudge us our happiness, but she has been exposed to the world's derision for disappointed hopes once before. If we announce our news before she receives an offer from Mr Bingley—and I think it safe to assume he means to make one—it will raise eyebrows, and she will be embarrassed in front of all her friends a second time. I cannot do it to her."

Darcy looked away to grimace ruefully at the far wall. Miss Bennet's abandonment was as much his fault as Bingley's—something of which, he knew, Elizabeth was aware. It was not a request he was going to be able to refuse. He turned back when he felt Elizabeth take hold of his hand.

"Now this *is* a wretched beginning. You cannot be angry with me already."

What a sublime sensation, to have her touch him so boldly and regard him with such open affection. "I cannot presently think of a single thing you could do that would make me angry with you, Elizabeth. I am vexed at Bingley. As far as I know, he does mean to propose. I cannot fathom what the devil is taking him so long."

"Well, in fairness, he and Jane have not had much opportunity to see each other since he came back."

"Neither have you and I, and I still managed it."

She agreed with a delectable little humming sound that was almost a purr. "But not every man would walk through a snowdrift to propose."

Darcy wished to reply that not every woman was exceptional enough to warrant it, but he could not pay her the compliment without sounding as though he was insulting her sister. He settled for pressing a gentle kiss to her forehead.

"Very well. I shall remain silent a little longer. For *you.* Though if Bingley takes any more than a week, I may have to renege on my word. Disguise of every sort is my abhorrence, and *this* is the last thing in the world I would keep secret."

"If Mr Bingley takes anywhere *close* to a week, I may renege on it for you. Any longer and people will think I am gone mad, for I cannot keep from smiling."

Such an admission—pure ambrosia to Darcy's mind after so much anguish—kept *him* smiling all the way back to Netherfield. Mr Bennet's complicity in their concealment was attained as readily as was his consent, and all three parted company before the rest of Longbourn stirred.

Darcy arrived back before Bingley, Georgiana, or Anne were yet downstairs, and he spent the time before any of them appeared pacing the rooms of Netherfield, chasing the memories he had heretofore resented, every remembrance of Elizabeth now but a foreshadow of the bliss that was guaranteed to be his when they wed.

# CHAPTER 17

Were it not for Jane's sake that Elizabeth withheld her news, it would have been to her eldest sister she ran first. It felt strange keeping such momentous intelligence from her and stranger still to be engaged at all. Elizabeth could not help but think that an alteration of such magnitude ought to produce a more noticeable difference, but her reflection looked the same in the mirror, and though she felt positively incandescent on the inside, none of her sisters seemed to perceive anything different in her.

That everything *would* alter was indisputable, however. Consideration of what privileges and responsibilities might belong to the wife of Mr Darcy occupied Elizabeth's thoughts for the rest of the day, though it was only in the privacy of her bath that evening that she allowed herself to dwell on the way he had kissed her. The astonishing, enlightening, *sublime* way he had kissed her, the remembrance of which led her to reflect on what else Mr Darcy would wish to do to her once she was his wife and whether it would be equally sublime.

She was forced to sink beneath the water to conceal her furious blush from the maid. It might have been better not to do so whilst laughing at her own lovesick distraction, for she almost drowned on a lungful of soapy water.

§

It rained overnight, melting the snow enough to permit visiting at last. Most of the Netherfield party, sans only Mrs Annesley and Mrs Jenkinson, had joined all five Bennet sisters in braving a walk in the rather sodden lanes around Longbourn, though Elizabeth and Darcy were doing their best to outpace all the others.

"It is a miracle I have not been discovered. I am too happy to concentrate on anything. I keep dropping things and laughing at odd moments," Elizabeth told him. It delighted her to see how well this pleased him, his smile momentarily too broad to allow any response.

"Whereas I have been reproached for being even more ill-tempered than usual, though I hope I shall be forgiven once everybody learns it was only impatience to see you that made me so. I would have come back through the snow yesterday afternoon, had you not sworn me to secrecy."

"Yes, that might have raised a few suspicions." She indicated a fork in the lane along which she was certain the others would not follow. "You are very good to humour me."

"I wonder why Bingley did not suggest walking himself. He was equally annoyed to be away from Longbourn."

"Take pity. His legs are not as long as yours. Getting stuck in a drift might have seemed a far more plausible hazard to him than it did to you."

"Perhaps. But at least if he *had* got stuck and died of pneumonia, I would no longer have to wait for him."

Elizabeth espied a pheasant feather poking out of a bank of half-melted, muddied snow, which was fortunate timing, for her crouching to pick it up enabled her to conceal a smirk. "It must be very frustrating that he is not behaving as you would like," she said as she tucked it into her pocket. "He is usually far more obedient."

Darcy frowned. "If you mean when we left in the autumn—"

"I mean when he came back at Christmas after you wrote to him. That was exceedingly good of you. Though I wish you had told us on Christmas Day that you had done it. It would have cheered Jane immensely."

"It was because of your sister I said nothing. I do not have such influence over Bingley that I could be certain my letter would bring him back, and I did not wish to raise her hopes."

His modesty notwithstanding, Elizabeth was assured he possessed precisely that power, though since he had used it to such good purpose on that occasion, she would not tease him for it.

"Whatever has reunited them, they will be very happy together. But then, they are both of a disposition that makes discontent impossible. They were always assured of a happy marriage, whomever they wed."

"Indeed," Darcy replied absently. "Unlike me."

Before Elizabeth could decide whether she ought to be offended, he continued in a more serious tone. "It is true that I never intended to marry Anne. But I have, all my life, believed I must marry a woman of fortune. I have been brought up to view wealth, consequence, and connexions as the only markers of a match worth consideration." He cast her a wry glance. "Utter nonsense, of course, but it took a while for your lessons to sink in."

"It is not entirely nonsense," she replied, cautious, for she knew not to where his reflections tended. "There are few people who can afford such an imprudent marriage as the one upon which you are about to embark."

"You misunderstand me, Elizabeth. That was not my meaning. You talk of Bingley being happy in his marriage, and I am sure he will be, but his happiness can never be as great as mine, precisely because it was always assured and therefore, less worth the earning.

"I have never depended upon securing the same for myself. It was not a notion that ever gave me any distress. I always hoped I would be able to respect my wife, but ever since I was old enough to comprehend that I *must* marry, I presumed the arrangement would be formed of necessity, an alliance designed to benefit Pemberley and my family as much as myself."

He looked at her, his smile magnificent. "Never did I imagine I should love my wife as dearly as I love you. In truth, you make me feel such happiness when I am with you that everything I have previously done *without* you seems miserable in retrospect. Now, when I go home, I might choose to read a book in my library, as I have done a thousand times before, but with *you* reading yours next to me. I shall undoubtedly walk around the lake again, only this time arm in arm with *you*. If I sit quietly by the fire in my room, I shall enjoy the peace infinitely better than I ever have, for I shall have *you* in my arms. I shall continue to do all the things I have always done and more, only now I shall do them *with you*. I cannot express my anticipation to begin."

Elizabeth stopped walking and waited for him to face her. "You expressed it better than you think."

She had heard plenty of women boast of the parties and balls, jewels and gowns, houses and carriages their new husbands had promised to lavish upon them once they were wed. That Darcy spoke not of how he would embellish their marriage with trinkets but of how she would enrich his life merely by being in it proved what importance she was to him and made his affection every moment more valuable. She wished she could think of anything half so wonderful to say in return, but any eloquence she might ordinarily have claimed was presently lost beneath the powerful swell of warmth suffusing her entire person. She floundered briefly, but as she contemplated the man who would be her husband, her protector, her dearest friend, and her lover, the man presently regarding her as though she were the most precious creature in all the world, she found that words were easy to come by.

"I love you, Fitzwilliam."

His eyes widened slightly and then, endearingly, he frowned a little, as though in disbelief. Both were forgot when he kissed her. She was not quite as surprised and marginally better informed than the previous time, but no less affected by his embrace, which was heavenly, by his lips on hers, which were divine, and by his devotion, so apparent in the carefulness of his caresses and the unmistakable strength of his restraint.

She had worried there would persist an awkwardness between them until time and familiarity could overcome it. She need not have been concerned. The intensity of her sentiments was increased by the *rightness* of them, making his arms feel the most natural place for her to be in all the world. His closeness no more embarrassed her than his stares ever had, and she would happily admit now that she savoured both. If *he* felt any discomfort, he was doing an admirable job of disguising it.

"Where did you learn my name?" Darcy whispered, still so close that his lips brushed against hers when he spoke.

"I cannot remember now. I only recall thinking how well it suited you. Do you mind me using it?"

He gave her a rather devilish, lopsided grin. "Did it seem as though I objected?"

She hiccupped a little laugh and shook her head.

He inhaled deeply and let it out slowly, his smile fading as he exhaled. "On the subject of objections, I can go no further without mentioning to you that some of my relations may not be in favour of our marriage."

"If Miss de Bourgh's opinions are any indication of what the rest of your family will think, then we can safely assume none of them will approve," she replied, disagreeably sobered.

Regrettably, though she preferred not to be judged on it,

Elizabeth could not deny that the chasm between their stations in life did exist. It was a chasm that she sincerely doubted anyone related to an earl would be desirous of bridging.

"Some of them will approve very much," Darcy insisted. "My sister particularly. And Anne is less opposed than you might expect. But there are others on whose support we cannot depend."

"That is more likely to give you distress than me. I am exceedingly sorry that marrying me will bring discord between you and any of your family, but if you can bear it, then I most certainly can. They will not frighten me away, if that is what concerns you."

He gave her an extraordinary look, a mixture of pride and ardour that did something quite delightful to his features. "My object in broaching the matter was to assure you of my protection and constancy in the face of any unpleasantness, but I shall not deny that it is a relief to hear you say as much."

She reached for his hand and looked solemnly into his eyes. "And I hereby promise you the same protection." She grinned at his puzzled frown. "From my mother when she discovers you are to be her son. There is guaranteed to be a spectacle."

Oh, how she loved it when he laughed! It was always the most gratifying surprise.

"I have grown rather fond of your mother's theatricals." He tugged their joined hands so that she bumped gently into him, then he kissed her cheek. "I shall consider it a slight if she does not at least gasp when she hears the news."

"I have no notion what she will do. I am dreading it. I am beginning to wonder whether this is the real reason I asked you to wait to announce anything—because I harbour a deep, unacknowledged hope that she will exhaust all her raptures on Jane and Mr Bingley and have none left with which to mortify us."

He ran his thumb along her jaw. "I am as impervious to being frightened away as you, but if anything *were* to offend me, it would hardly be your mother's enthusiasm for our marriage. It is my aunt's resistance to it that will present the difficulty."

"Lady Catherine?"

He nodded, and with a heavy sigh, set them back off along the path. "It seems that she, too, has long believed I seriously intended to marry her daughter, a misapprehension I bitterly regret not comprehending sooner, but the damage is done, and it cannot be helped."

"I thought you said your cousin has decided against you anyway?"

"She has, but there was nothing to be gained by allowing my aunt to believe I would have married Anne even if she *had* desired it. Thus, she is furious with both of us."

Elizabeth let out a little squawk when her feet slipped on a patch of ice. She might have regretted choosing this path, had she not so gratifyingly benefited from its superior privacy already. She regretted it even less when Darcy took her arm and pinned her gently but solidly to his side to steady her. The intimacy was sublime, though it made keeping her tone even surprisingly difficult.

"She would be justified if she was confused by the fact that you brought Miss de Bourgh back with you. I confess I was."

"That was an unfortunate complication, but I could not have left Anne there. Lady Catherine was furious when she discovered we had been here over Christmas. I was shocked by her response. She was cruel—abusively so. Such she has continued to be in her letters to both of us this week—and this *before* she knows I mean to marry you. I do not anticipate a gracious response to the announcement. I am afraid she could make things very difficult for us."

"How horrid! My mother was angry when I refused Mr Collins, but she was never abusive. I certainly never felt unwelcome in my own home. What will Miss de Bourgh do? Will you bring her to stay with you and your sister?"

Darcy stopped walking and pierced her with an uncommonly

intense gaze, even for him. "You continue to amaze me, Elizabeth," he said at length. "Your only concern in all that I just told you is for my cousin, who has done nothing but abuse *you* for the past several weeks. Are you not concerned for yourself at all?"

"No, I am not. I have been the object of people's scorn before and survived it. Unless...can your aunt prevent us marrying?"

"No," he replied resolutely.

"Then let her rage. Disappointment is a uniquely painful and humiliating sentiment, but the injury will fade eventually. It is more pressing that you assist your cousin."

He raised her hand to his lips and kissed it. "And with your blessing, I shall."

They continued walking but had gone only a few yards before a shout from behind arrested them.

"Kitty?" Elizabeth called. "Is that you?"

Her sister arrived into view flushed and out of breath. "There you are, Lizzy!" she gasped, clutching at her side. "I knew you would come this way."

"How?" she replied defensively.

Kitty looked between her and Darcy with such a dubious expression that it brought heat to Elizabeth's cheeks. If she suspected their attachment, however, she did not mention it.

"You must come back. Miss de Bourgh says she can walk no farther. She got as far as the oak stump near the dairy and is refusing to move. Jane and Mr Bingley have gone to fetch the carriage. The rest of us were to wait with her, but she is in high dudgeon, so I said I would run on and find you."

Elizabeth heard Darcy's quiet sigh but did not draw attention to it. She only indicated for Kitty to lead the way and fell into step with him behind her.

"I did wonder whether it was a good idea when she said she would walk out with us. I have never seen her walk very far before." When Darcy did not reply, Elizabeth added, "Is the cause of her ill health known?"

"I can think of a few names for it," he muttered.

Elizabeth smiled sympathetically yet pressed the matter. "She could hardly be described as hale. She fainted after ten minutes of dancing at the assembly, and I do not think it was affected, for she was terribly embarrassed."

"No, it was likely genuine," he conceded. "Her affliction comprises a sorry mix of her mother's overindulgence and an inherent disposition to frailty. She is just ill enough that nobody can contest her needs but never quite ill enough to justify her behaviour. And she does not scruple to exaggerate her symptoms to get her way."

Elizabeth thought this was going a little far, but she did not cavil, for he knew her best.

"You seemed surprised that your sister discovered us on this path," Darcy said after a few minutes of silence and in a voice he obviously intended only she should hear.

"Yes, my sisters prefer the more direct route to Meryton. This path is more meandering and overgrown."

His countenance took on a decidedly complacent hue. "And did you come this way with any particular purpose in mind, other than to vex my manservant with my muddy boots?"

Elizabeth kept her eyes down and hoped her bonnet would conceal her burning ears from view. "If I did, embarrassing me in this manner will never induce me to admit it."

It did not help reduce her blush when she felt Darcy place his hand on her lower back and lean close to whisper in her ear. "You will like Pemberley very well, I think. It has plenty of paths on which we can get lost together."

Her head whipped up, and she laughed, delighted to be so easily rescued from discomfort by his teasing and vastly gratified by the look in his eyes that assured her his was not an empty promise.

They found Miss de Bourgh precisely where Kitty described,

seated on the broad oak stump with her arms crossed and her lips pursed. Everybody else was leaning against or swinging on a nearby gate, admiring the view. Kitty ran to join them, leaving Elizabeth and Darcy to speak to his cousin.

"The ramblers have returned, I see," said Miss de Bourgh as they approached.

"We were less than ten minutes ahead," Darcy replied brusquely. "What ails you?"

"I can walk no more today."

"Cannot or will not?"

"What does it matter?" she retorted angrily. "I only agreed to walk out so that I might begin to make amends to you both. If the pair of you are content to stride ahead and abandon me to —" She directed a disdainful look over her shoulder at the younger girls. "I struggle to see why I should trouble myself any further."

Darcy gave Elizabeth a look expressive of his exasperation, and stalked over to join his sister without another word.

Still unable to discern whether Miss de Bourgh's fatigue was feigned or not, Elizabeth opted to avoid the subject altogether. Instead, she pulled the feather from her pocket and held it out to her.

"I found this on the path just now. I recalled you like the iridescent ones."

Miss de Bourgh took it. After staring at it for a moment, she gave a terse grunt of acknowledgement. "I believe you will prove to be a tolerable cousin. More tolerable than some of my others at any rate."

"Mr Darcy told you we are engaged?"

Miss de Bourgh gave a bark of laughter. "Darcy does not tell anybody his business. It infuriates my mother."

"Then how did you know?"

"I did not, until you just told me."

Elizabeth swallowed the first response that sprang to mind. Never had she met a more contrary woman! "I see. Might I prevail upon you to keep the news to yourself for now? We were hoping to wait for Mr Bingley and Jane to come to an understanding before we announced it."

"That is a stupid scheme. The man spent almost half an hour deciding whether or not he wanted a cup of coffee at breakfast this morning. You could be grey-haired and barren by the time he decides to take a wife. But I suppose if that is your wish, I must play along."

Elizabeth thanked her and was inordinately relieved to espy the carriage come clattering around the head of the lane shortly afterwards. She was less pleased—though not as angry as Darcy —when it was reluctantly decided that the horses ought not to be sent hither and thither about the freezing countryside too many times in one afternoon, and the walk was curtailed with the entire Netherfield party conveyed home. Her only consolation was in the knowledge that, no matter how frequently her family might behave with a total want of propriety, Darcy's relations could be uniformly counted on to perform worse.

# CHAPTER
## 18

With all the tribulations of the past few weeks, the ugliness of his aunt's attacks, and the all-consuming euphoria of securing Elizabeth's hand, Darcy had forgotten the very particular torment of Miss Bingley. She arrived with Mr and Mrs Hurst just after noon on Monday with the evident resolve of refreshing his memory. There was little that would have given him more pleasure than to tell her of his engagement and put an end to her officious attentions, but Elizabeth was adamant—and Bingley *inexplicably* still single.

Tea was served in the parlour an hour before they were all required to dress for the feast. The room was crowded, noisy from the numerous conversations occurring, yet he was not surprised that Miss Bingley still managed to find herself a seat near him and to begin wittering in his ear. She took up precisely where she had left off in London, agreeing with his every passing remark and deferring every one of her own answers to him. Eventually, he took his cup to the window and stood with his back to the gathered company, staring out into the garden, willing the minutes away until Elizabeth arrived.

Miss Bingley did not take the hint. "Your tea must be cold by now," she said quietly, as she sidled up next to him. "Allow me to fetch you a fresh one."

"This one is still hot, thank you."

"I should have offered you coffee, for I know you prefer it, but Charles had already sent for refreshments before I came downstairs."

"I was offered coffee. I preferred tea."

"Quite so. Only tea will do when it is this cold. And this house is horribly draughty, do you not think?"

"I am not uncomfortable. Perhaps you are chilled from your journey."

"Perhaps I am. You are kind to be concerned for me. Still, I should have preferred to stay in London." When he made no answer, she continued. "Louisa and I saw Mr Pargeter at Lord Bertram's rout last night. He wished to know whether you would be back in town before his party at the end of the month. I took the liberty of telling him I thought it likely."

"That *was* a liberty, Miss Bingley," said Anne from her nearby seat. Darcy did not acknowledge her remark, though he objected far less to her eavesdropping on this exchange than he had when she obtruded on his conversation with Elizabeth on Christmas Day.

"I am sure Mr Darcy does not consider it so, madam," Miss Bingley replied. "After all, it was only a few weeks ago that he and I were discussing our intentions to remain in town for the rest of winter."

"My plans altered," Darcy said, then sipped his fast-cooling tea, indicating his disinclination to say any more on the matter.

Indeed, nothing more *was* said until a conversation struck up between those seated closest to them, at which point Miss Bingley shuffled closer to him and, in a hushed voice, carried her point.

"I must have misunderstood about my brother's plans. I thought we had agreed *they* should remain as they were."

"They *are* still as they were," Darcy replied impatiently. "Would that he make haste and do something to rectify the situation."

"By *rectify*, may I assume you mean *leave?*"

Darcy returned his cup to its saucer and spoke with studied composure, lest anyone else hear. "Madam, I was wrong about Miss Bennet with regards to both her feelings and her suitability, and I did your brother a disservice in advising him to forget her. I have made it clear that I will no longer involve myself in his private affairs unless it is his explicit wish. Whatever plans he makes, he will make them without my interference."

*Regrettably.* Given the choice, he would have counselled Bingley into action days ago, and they would both be celebrating something more than Epiphany at dinner that evening.

Miss Bingley peered at him questioningly. "You have always been good to him. I trust you will see him safely through this latest calamity, as you have seen him through all his previous ones."

It was not a question, and Darcy gave no reply.

"Speaking of calamities," she continued with an affected laugh, "I hear you were obliged to spend Christmas Day with the Bennets. What *must* that have been like? I dread to think!"

"That explains why you do it so infrequently."

Darcy's tea had gone distinctly tepid. He sipped it anyway and pretended not to have heard Anne's remark. Miss Bingley was doing the same, if her tight smile was any indication.

"We were made exceedingly welcome at Longbourn," he told her.

"Oh yes," Anne agreed, tenaciously inserting herself into their conversation. "It was a most enjoyable, most festive occasion. And Mrs Bennet's Christmas dinner was exceptional."

Darcy turned to level an incredulous glare at her that she did not deign to acknowledge.

"How nice for you, Miss de Bourgh," Miss Bingley replied, likewise turning to face her. "We had an enjoyable Christmas arranged ourselves, it being the first that Mr and Miss Darcy had agreed to spend with us. In the event, the day was quieter than expected, for half our company was required to rush off to Hertfordshire at the last moment."

"That must have been terribly disappointing. I expect you thought you were on the cusp as well. And now, all those years of planning gone to waste," said Anne.

"Hardly *years*, madam. A Christmas dinner can be planned in less than a week unless one is doing something *very* wrong."

"Christmas dinner? I beg your pardon. I thought we were talking about something else entirely."

"I am sorry our departure ruined your Christmas, Miss Bingley," Georgiana said meekly, her own conversation apparently over, her attention no doubt drawn to this one by Anne's dogged taunting. "I was eager to see my brother, but I ought to have considered—"

"Fie, do not let my sister make you feel bad," interposed Bingley, similarly interrupted from his chat with Hurst. "We offered to bring everyone with us."

"Pray do not feel bad at *all*," Miss Bingley cooed at Georgiana. "Of *course* you wished that your brother would not be alone at Christmas, just as your brother sacrificed his own happy Christmas to ensure that your cousin would not be on *her* own. You are both so very good, always thinking of others. Of course, I was obliged to remain with Louisa, so that when Mr Hurst inevitably drank himself to sleep, she would not be alone."

"Caroline, if you mean to make *me* feel bad, you will not succeed," said Bingley. "I was not about to stay in town and let Darcy have all the fun here without me."

"Really, Charles! Mr Darcy is a more rational creature than that implies. He does not chase about the country in pursuit of *fun*."

That might be true, but Darcy had nevertheless found it in the wilderness surrounding Longbourn yesterday. He turned back to the window to prevent anybody from guessing where his thoughts had gone and revelled in the memory of Elizabeth's gratifyingly passionate embrace. His reflections were entirely ruined when Miss Bingley stepped closer to him once again and spoke in a voice he presumed she thought alluring.

"Charles has an odd notion of what passes for entertainment. Perhaps you will allow me to delight you later this evening with the piece I was planning to play for you on Christmas Day."

"My tea has gone cold, madam. Pray excuse me."

Elizabeth was heartened by how rapidly Darcy came to her side upon her arrival at Netherfield. His evident pleasure in her company pleased her very well, though such was his determination to remain near her that she began to worry others might become suspicious. The thought was immediately followed by a rush of vexation. Would that there were no need for secrecy!

She observed Jane and Mr Bingley, hoping for an indication they might soon advance their understanding, but there was no hint of an imminent betrothal. For the first time in her memory, Elizabeth was displeased by her sister's composure of temper for, though obviously content in one another's company, Jane and Mr Bingley could as easily be discussing what was for dinner as declaring their eternal affection for one another.

She accepted a glass of wine from a footman and took a larger than advisable sip to quell her vexation. The idea to spare Jane's feelings had seemed noble and just when she thought of it, for Darcy's impetuous and quixotic proposal had given undesirable contrast to Mr Bingley's inconstant, lackadaisical attentions. In the face of her sister's glacial courtship, such generosity was losing its appeal.

Darcy, she knew, loathed the concealment even more than she, and it was not long before she comprehended there would be at least one very immediate benefit from him sharing the news soon. Until their engagement was made public, he would not be able to escape Miss Bingley's jealous attentions, which had apparently not diminished since the autumn.

"Miss Eliza," she said at a point early in the evening. "How delightful to see you looking so..." She left the remark unfinished, ending it instead with a disdainful appraisal of Elizabeth's person.

"How delightful to see you at all, Miss Bingley," Elizabeth replied. "You wrote in your letter to Jane that you would be staying in London for the whole winter."

"That was the arrangement upon which we all agreed. But then, none of us anticipated Miss de Bourgh's little expedition, nor that we should follow her here. Poor Mr Darcy," she said, turning to him with an exaggerated pout. "You were resolute in your plan to spend Christmas with us, were you not? And instead, you were obliged to spend it here, without any of your friends."

"I imagine there are few people who do not consider it an inconvenience when their plans are overthrown," Darcy replied, "but it would be wilfully obstinate to continue to disapprove merely because it was not what was originally intended. My time here has proved uncommonly agreeable, and I would not change a moment of it."

Elizabeth made no effort to disguise her delight with his answer. Miss Bingley made no effort to disguise her displeasure with it.

"And you, Miss Eliza? I do hope the presence of two such prominent guests did not interfere with your fascination with Mr Wickham."

How Miss Bingley could not perceive Darcy's furious incredulity was a mystery, but she seemed pleased with her attack, smirking as though she had scored a great victory.

"Not at all. Neither Miss de Bourgh nor Mr Darcy stayed at Longbourn. If there was any inconvenience, it belonged entirely to Lady Lucas. In any case, the neighbourhood had quite exhausted Mr Wickham's rather shallow reserves of charm long before that," Elizabeth replied.

"But not before my ball," Miss Bingley persisted. "You were asking a thousand questions about him then, I recall, and were quite determined to be pleased with him."

"I was determined to judge him fairly, a courtesy I wish I had extended to all my new acquaintances, but we live and learn." Elizabeth smiled warmly at Darcy, who returned the gesture with something more than warmth—an exchange that brought a spiteful sneer to Miss Bingley's countenance.

She turned slightly to dismiss Elizabeth and speak exclusively to Darcy.

"I meant to say when you came down earlier that your man has done a wonderful job of selecting a waistcoat in a shade so similar to my gown. What a pleasing coincidence."

Elizabeth struggled to contain her amusement as Darcy looked first at Miss Bingley, then between both garments with an expression of bewildered disdain. She shared his confusion. It would have been a curious non sequitur anyway, but it was rendered nonsensical by dint of his waistcoat being dark green and Miss Bingley's gown a dusky pink.

Perhaps seeing their puzzlement, Miss Bingley peered more closely at Darcy's waistcoat and then let out an affected and somewhat feverish titter. "A trick of the light. I thought before that your waistcoat was plum. It hardly signifies. I have never much cared for such fripperies as clothes anyway. You agree, I am sure, Mr Darcy?"

"No, I am quite fond of clothes." He betrayed no hint of amusement, which impressed Elizabeth no end.

Miss Bingley's eyes widened in alarm. "I did not mean that I do not *like* clothes. I only meant I do not care what I look like in them."

Miss de Bourgh joined them in time to give a tart hum of concurrence to this remark which, along with her contemptuous glance at the gown in question, threw Miss Bingley into ever more agitated spasms.

"That is, I meant that I am not vain."

"Then you are dishonest," Elizabeth said, tired of Miss Bingley's attempts to work on the man for whom she felt a new but formidable possessiveness. "Nobody is wholly without vanity."

"Nobody?" Darcy enquired.

He regarded her with that same burning attentiveness she adored, and she felt a thrill that he had so readily taken up the debate. She turned in the same way Miss Bingley had, excluding both other ladies and speaking for Darcy's pleasure alone.

"I never met anybody who did not care at least a little what others thought of them. People who boast of being unconcerned for other people's opinions, in truth, desire to be *perceived* as hard-hearted. Those who claim to be too modest to care how they are perceived are, by definition, concerned that others should *not* perceive them as self-interested."

"You are speaking of character, then, not appearance," he replied. "Not everybody is concerned about the latter."

"You speak from a position of luxury there, sir. It is all too easy to declare oneself indifferent to people's opinions when all opinions are guaranteed to be favourable." Elizabeth did not miss that Miss Bingley's eyes widened divertingly at this. Or that Darcy's darkened, his mouth lifting at one corner into a slight but captivating smile.

"Are you proposing that vanity is an immutable aspect of human nature—something to be accepted and not repressed? I seem to recall you telling me one night at Netherfield that vanity was a weakness."

"No, sir, *you* said it was a weakness. I merely pointed out that it was one from which you suffered."

Miss Bingley sucked in her breath. Even Miss de Bourgh raised an eyebrow. Elizabeth did not care. All she knew was that

Darcy was savouring the debate with palpable satisfaction, his gaze unblinking, his attention riveted. The thrusts and parries of the exchange reminded her, for reasons she dared not consider in Netherfield's drawing room, of their kiss the previous day. Her heart was certainly pounding with the same rapidity as it had then. She would happily have argued that vanity was second only to godliness if it meant she could continue the argument.

"You have not lost your penchant for turning everything into a debate, I see, Miss Eliza," said Miss Bingley.

"Better than turning everything into a blandishment," retorted Miss de Bourgh.

It was likely a good thing they were called into dinner at that moment—not only to avoid a more serious disagreement but to enable Elizabeth to eat something. She had drunk her wine too quickly, it seemed, for she was hot and breathless and unreasonably conscious of Darcy's unwavering stare.

# CHAPTER
# 19

"You must be relieved that Mr Collins was not kept away by the weather, Miss Lucas," said Mrs Hurst. "When is your wedding?"

"This Thursday," Mr Collins answered for her, spraying bits of pastry over the tablecloth as he said it. "I could not have waited a day longer or wished for a more lovely bride."

Darcy closed his eyes. The entire evening had been torture. For somebody who was determined to keep their engagement a secret, Elizabeth seemed perversely resolved on doing everything in her power to arouse him. Feigning indifference to her allurements had left him with little wit to counter Miss Bingley's unrelenting advances. He had long since run out of patience for the entire damnable charade, and he certainly had no desire to entertain a discussion about somebody *else's* wedding.

"It is fortunate Lizzy refused you, then."

He looked up sharply. He knew not who had said it—undoubtedly one of Elizabeth's younger sisters—but he could scarcely contain his indignation. The impropriety of such a remark notwithstanding, he absolutely could not listen to a conversation about somebody else's wedding *to Elizabeth!* He took a gulp of his wine and glanced in her direction. He ought not to have been surprised to discover she was laughing. Not aloud, of course, but her entire countenance was aglow with mirth. She lifted her glass to her lips and gave him an arch look over the rim. He remained utterly still, unwilling that any outward trace of the effect her expression had upon him should be visible.

"You are quite right, it is most fortunate. Had Eliza not had the courage to correct Mr Collins's erroneous belief that he *must* marry one of his cousins, he would never have had the opportunity to discover his perfect partner in Charlotte," replied Lady Lucas.

Miss Mary snorted at her dinner plate.

"But just think, Mary," said Miss Lydia in a whimsical manner, "if Mr Collins had not proposed to Charlotte, then Miss de Bourgh would never have come to Hertfordshire to make her acquaintance, Mr Darcy would never have come to fetch her, and Mr Bingley would never have returned for Jane."

"And had *none* of those events occurred, our present circumstances would still be exactly as they are, Lydia," muttered Mr Bennet with a weary glance at Bingley. "If your sister is Mr Bingley's perfect partner, he does not yet seem to have noticed."

Darcy took another sip of his wine in a private toast to that. Would that Bingley could pay as much attention to his courtship as he was to his present discussion with Sir William! Occupied with resenting his friend's lassitude, Darcy paid little attention to whatever Miss Lucas said in reply to her mother, but his attention was caught, as it always was, when Elizabeth began speaking.

"You once said to me that a woman ought not to be too guarded in her affections, Charlotte. That few people have heart enough to be really in love without encouragement, and she ought to show enough affection to help her admirer on. I laughed at you at the time, but I am beginning to think the theory has merit."

Darcy's stomach clenched to see Elizabeth's gaze fixed upon her eldest sister as she said this. It gave a slightly wild edge to his own impatience to know she was as anxious as he for Miss Bennet to get engaged.

"Why yes," Miss Lucas replied. "When one's acquaintance is limited to a few dinners or dance sets, it would be inadvisable to rely solely on the thin chance that one's wishes will be discovered by accident."

"Well, we all know *you* took no such chance," muttered Mrs Bennet.

Miss Bingley, with a pointed look at her brother, congratulated Miss Lucas for her insight. "By the same token, if a woman shows *no* signs of affection, it is probable that she does not feel any, and it would be better to give up on the attachment."

"I cannot agree," Anne replied. "There is something acutely vulgar about a woman who feels the need to advertise her availability by such means as flattery and deference. It would be far better to remain circumspect."

His gaze still fixed sullenly on Bingley, Darcy complained, "Subtlety is overrated. In some cases, particularly those where a gentleman might be uncertain of his reception, it is *imperative* that the lady gives some encouragement."

These were words he never thought to hear himself say, and he despaired when his friend paid them no heed. He did more than despair when he caught sight of Miss Bingley regarding him with an expression of hopeful delight.

*Damn!*

She leant towards him slightly with her elbow rested on the table and spoke in an irritatingly silky tone.

"Yes, in some cases, such inducements might be beneficial."

"Yet, in other cases, they are completely wasted, Miss Bingley," Anne said sharply, looking askance at Darcy even as she said it. He could hardly explain that he had been trying to provoke Bingley into action, thus he only drank his wine and said nothing.

"What are you talking about at that end of the table that has you all looking so gloomy?" Bingley enquired, taking an interest at last.

"Marriage," Mr Bennet replied. He put a forkful of food in his mouth and grinned around it. "It has that effect on people."

"We were discussing the relative advantages and disadvantages of marrying in haste," Mr Collins said. "The timing of my own happy celebrations was guided by my most estimable patroness, Lady Catherine de Bourgh, who desired that I marry as soon as possible. It is a matter of great honour to me that I have been able to accede to her wishes, and as my dear Miss Lucas assures me, there will be ample time after the ceremony for happiness to firmly establish itself."

"Fascinating as that is, Mr Collins, such an approach would not suit my brother," Miss Bingley said. "He is naturally more modest. The sort of person for whom something as momentous as securing a partner should *never* be hastily undertaken."

"Well, he can certainly learn from your example there," Anne snapped.

"Quite so! A precipitate arrangement does not suit everybody," Mr Collins replied. "The delightful Miss de Bourgh, for example, has enjoyed a life-long engagement to the noble Mr Darcy and without any need to rush into marriage." He somehow managed to bow to each of them whilst still in his seat.

Darcy had now reached the limit of his patience. Bingley, fully armed with all the facts of Anne's *rejection* in London, was openly laughing at him, though one hard glare was enough to curb his amusement. He promptly stopped grinning and suggested to his sisters it was a good time for the ladies to go through. It was with a vast sense of relief that Darcy stood to see them all file out.

"I look forward to playing for you in a short while," Miss Bingley said in a grossly coquettish manner as she passed him.

Elizabeth said nothing when she went by. Her countenance was a mask, her eyes, usually so expressive, were fixed blankly on the back of the lady in front of her, and her steps were quick as she walked around the table to the door.

It made Darcy's stomach clench. Never had he seen her thus, and he seriously disliked not knowing what had occasioned it. Yet, as the door swung closed, he ceased attempting to guess, for he saw quite clearly that Elizabeth had walked away from all the other ladies, in the opposite direction to the drawing room. Before the latch clicked home, he had made his excuses and gone in search of her.

"What are you doing in here?" he enquired upon finding her at the library window, peering out into the night. Despite telling himself he had not been concerned, he still felt awash with relief to see the pleasure with which she perceived him when she turned around.

"Escaping. I cannot bear another minute in that woman's presence."

He perched on the arm of the chair nearest to her. "Miss Bingley?" She nodded, at which he scoffed and replied, "You and I both."

He regretted his flippancy when it seemed to reanimate whatever ill-temper had afflicted her in the dining room.

"She is outrageous! She asked me just now whether it was true that you were engaged to your cousin. I would pity her the futility of all her aspirations, except that when I said you were not, she took it as some sort of licence to make that preposterous remark to you on the way out."

To Darcy's surprise, for he was used to her being more collected, Elizabeth then affected a mocking tone and parroted Miss Bingley's promise to play the pianoforte for him. Beginning to suspect the cause of her pique, he felt his pulse quicken and gave in to a small smile.

"Are you jealous, madam?"

"Yes!" she replied instantly, taking him by surprise. "You are to be *my* husband, and *you* did not require me to feed you a trail of promises before you would declare yourself. *You* had heart enough to love me without encouragement. And your regard means infinitely more to me for it. I love you, Fitzwilliam, and I would have the world know it. I am sick of this ridiculous concealment. It was a stupid idea, and I wish I had never suggested it."

That was more than acceptable to Darcy, though the announcement would have to wait a short while longer because before he let the future Mrs Darcy loose on every unsuspecting woman who ever set her cap for him, he meant to allow her to stake her claim upon him in whichever way she chose. He stood up, putting them toe-to-toe.

"I told you yesterday that I am impatient to read books with you in my library."

She blinked. "Yes, you did."

"I lied."

She did not answer. She only frowned, deepening the delicious crease at the bridge of her nose.

He kissed it. "I would get absolutely nothing read if I had you in my arms."

She let out a sharp, breathy exhalation, his ardour soared, and for a few heavenly moments they perused none of the library's shelves, opened none of its books, and read not a single word. Elizabeth kissed him in the way he would have liked to kiss her—hungrily, possessively, passionately. He dared not respond with equal fervour, not yet, but he savoured her exhilarating want of inhibition. Her absolute trust in him transformed what could have been perceived as an egregious transgression into an exquisitely poignant, perfectly natural beginning.

"Come," he whispered, "let us put an end to this nonsense. I have loved you for too long to keep it a secret anymore."

※

Elizabeth was not quite certain she was ready to be anywhere in company, but Darcy assured her she looked presentable. She took his proffered hand and, ignoring her thundering heart and thoroughly disarrayed thoughts, allowed him to lead her out of the library. With the agreement that they would make their announcement when the men re-joined the ladies, they parted ways in the hall. He returned to the dining room, and she walked on to the drawing room.

The door was slightly ajar, allowing Elizabeth to hear the altercation occurring just on the other side. The voices were not raised—neither much above a whisper—but they were strained, and they belonged to two of the most bellicose members of the group.

"I resent the insinuation, Miss de Bourgh."

"It was not an insinuation. It was an observation. You are attempting to captivate my cousin with your arts. But I would advise you to desist, Miss Bingley. You are making a fool of yourself."

"If that were true, he would not have agreed so openly with Miss Lucas's opinion that women ought to show their affection."

"If affection was what you felt, I might have more pity for you. But I am not without *any*, therefore, I shall repeat my advice. You must cease your flirtations for they will bring you nothing but mortification. Mr Darcy is engaged."

Elizabeth exhaled indignantly, though she knew not with which of them she was more cross.

"I know you are lying," Miss Bingley replied complacently, drawing a tut and an exasperated sigh from Miss de Bourgh.

"The engagement is of a peculiar kind."

"Yes, the kind that exists only in your head."

"He is not engaged to me, you fool. He is engaged to Miss Elizabeth. They have not announced it yet because, for some unfathomable reason, Miss Elizabeth has taken it into her head that it would be kinder to allow her sister to announce *her* engagement first."

"In that case," said a new voice. Jane had interrupted their bickering. "Allow me to put an end to everybody's distress and—"

"Miss Elizabeth? What are you doing out here? Has something happened?"

Elizabeth turned around to see Mr Bingley approaching, Darcy frowning in concern at his side, and the rest of the gentlemen following behind them. She looked at him archly, certain from what Jane had begun to say that something of great interest had, indeed, happened.

"I rather think you already know the answer to that." His expression confirmed it. Elizabeth pushed open the door, allowing all the gentlemen to hear Jane conclude her statement.

"—tell you that Mr Bingley and I are engaged."

"Are you?" cried both her parents, one on each side of the door.

Elizabeth felt a twinge of guilt for Jane's surprise at inadvertently announcing her news to far more people than just Miss Bingley and Miss de Bourgh, though she did not worry that it would last long beyond the start of everybody's congratulations, the commencement of which was heralded by a loud squeal of pleasure from her mother.

Elizabeth hugged her sister tightly, whispering how delighted she was by the news, then she clasped Mr Bingley's hands and honestly and heartily expressed her joy in the prospect of his being her brother. But as the celebrations quieted, she became aware of how still Darcy was standing, and how intensely incredulity emanated from his rigid frame.

"When did you become engaged?" he enquired stiffly.

"On our walk to fetch the carriage yesterday," Mr Bingley answered cheerfully. He leant around Jane to peer at Miss de Bourgh. "I must thank you for that, madam."

Miss de Bourgh inclined her head and smiled knowingly.

"Scheming wretch," Darcy muttered for Elizabeth's ears alone. Aloud to his friend, he said, "Why did you not say anything?"

"*You* decided we ought to come back after the walk to save the horses, if you recall. Had you not done that, I should have gone directly to speak to Mr Bennet." Mr Bingley nodded respectfully at his future father but otherwise looked so absurdly pleased with himself that Elizabeth began to question whether his engagement was his only present source of delight. "Why? What is the rush for me to tell anyone?" he added almost gleefully.

Elizabeth comprehended that they were discovered when she saw Jane bite her lips together against a smile. With a broadening grin of her own, she said quietly, "I asked him to wait until you were engaged before we said anything."

"Said anything about what, Darcy?" Mr Bingley pressed slyly.

With a brief glance seeking her consent, Darcy announced at last, "Elizabeth and I are engaged."

There *was* a gasp in the end, though it was not from Mrs Bennet. Miss Bingley, pale and frowning, fell heavily into the nearest chair and clamped her mouth closed. Nobody else made a sound.

"Well?" Elizabeth asked, looking around at her silent friends and family.

"We know," Jane said quietly.

"We *all* know, Eliza," Charlotte repeated. "It was not difficult to guess. A one-eyed partridge with a squint could see how dearly you both love each other."

"I own, I, too, guessed you had come to an understanding, for I have never seen you happier, Brother," Miss Darcy agreed.

"I would have guessed," said Miss de Bourgh, "had you not admitted it to me yourself."

Elizabeth looked at her father, who shrugged. "I thought it best to tell your mother in case something like this happened, and she made a scene."

Mrs Bennet winced contritely. "And I might have told your sisters. And *my* sisters."

"And me," said Lady Lucas.

Elizabeth began to laugh.

"You did not *need* to tell me," Kitty objected. "I guessed it would happen soon when Mr Darcy threw a snowball at Captain Carter for you. I nearly swooned when I saw it!"

"Mr Hurst and I guessed when Mr Darcy summoned Charles back to Hertfordshire," said Mrs Hurst, drawing a small cry of disbelief from her sister.

"I am sorry, old fruit," said Mr Bingley, chuckling. "You have been waiting all this time, and your big announcement was not much of an epiphany, after all."

Not for a moment did Elizabeth worry that Darcy might begrudge the loss of fanfare. She took heart from his expression of supreme contentment, for she comprehended what it signified. He did not require anybody's approval of their marriage, only that the world should know about it.

To be cherished in such a way, to be the object of such pride, was the most exquisite feeling. She almost laughed to consider how insufficient all her previous impressions of love had been. Until the moment Darcy had taken her heart into his keeping, she had never had the faintest notion what it truly meant.

"It has been for me," she replied, smiling up at him. She had an inkling that loving so deep and intricate a character meant her marriage would continue to be revelatory for many happy years to come.

*Darcy House*
*1 Arlington Street, London*
*June 1812*


*Dearest Anne,*
*I am delighted for you that your mother has been called away again. What a blessed relief that will bring until the time comes for you to join us in town. I hope you will not be too lonely there in the meantime. In your last letter, it seemed as though Mrs Collins was proving to be a stalwart companion. If you can both manage to avoid her husband long enough to get a word in, I am sure you will enjoy some sensible conversation with her.*

*My brother and sister do exceedingly well. They returned from Pemberley two weeks ago, and we are all settling in well together here. I cannot recall a time when Number One has heard so much laughter. It has gone from the most austere to the most joyful of places. There is only one thing I think could ever improve upon it, but it is a little soon to be wishing for such news. Still, I shall not pretend I do not greatly anticipate becoming an aunt.*

*Lizzy and Mrs Bingley have helped me choose all my gowns for the coming Season. I enclose some designs that we thought would suit you particularly well and that my brother has promised to have ordered for you as soon as you arrive in London, if you agree. Do not be shocked by our suggestions. Lizzy says she wishes you would cease dressing as though you expect to remain a spinster forever and begin dressing like the handsome, single, young heiress you are. Do not show Lady Catherine if you think she will disapprove. She does not need to know.*

*I have started to feel more excited about my first Season. With Mrs Annesley, you, and Elizabeth as my chaperons, I shall feel far less afraid. And Brother, Lizzy, and I all practise dancing so often together now that I have quite given up my old worry of tripping* over my own feet in front of a crowd of strangers. I hope you will enjoy yourself just as well. We shall make certain not to tire you, and you must only attend parties to which you feel equal, though I am afraid I must insist you attend my ball.

It might please you to know that Lizzy has invited Mr Conrad as well. You must have made quite an impression on him at dinner last month, for he asks after you every time we see him. Brother has not said whether he believes it is a good match, but I am not sure it matters, for Lizzy likes him, and that is often enough to make my brother approve of anything.

Do take care of yourself. I look forward to seeing you very soon,

Much love,
Georgiana

## THE END

# ACKNOWLEDGMENTS

I owe my sincere gratitude to my mother, husband, publishers, and editors for their contributions to this story and my sanity. Special thanks to my father who, having been shockingly neglected in previous acknowledgements, will now be duly recognised as the person responsible for every satirical bone in my body—my very own Mr Bennet. And as always, I thank Jane Austen. For her razor wit, stunning turns of phrase, and captivating characters. For the honour of incorporating some of her inimitable writing into this alternative journey for Darcy and Elizabeth, and for inspiring me to write.

# ABOUT THE AUTHOR

Jessie Lewis enjoys words far too much for her own good and was forced to take up writing them down in order to save her family and friends from having to listen to her saying so many of them. She dabbled in poetry during her teenage years, though it was her studies in Literature and Philosophy at university that firmly established her admiration for the potency of the English language. She has always been particularly in awe of Jane Austen's literary cunning and has delighted in exploring Austen's regency world in her own historical fiction writing. It is of no relevance whatsoever to her ability to string words together coherently that she lives in Hertfordshire with two tame cats, two feral children and a pet husband. She is also quite tall, in case you were wondering.

In addition to *Epiphany*, Jessie is the author of *Mistaken, Speechless*, and *Fallen*, and has contributed to *Rational Creatures: Stirrings of Feminism in the Hearts of Jane Austen's Fine Ladies*. You can check out her musings on the absurdities of language and life on her blog, **LifeinWords.blog**.

Subscribers to the Quills & Quartos mailing list receive bonus content, advance notice of sales and alerts to new releases by Jessie Lewis and other great authors.
Join our mailing list today at
www.QuillsandQuartos.com

# ALSO BY JESSIE LEWIS

### Fallen

*The air was all gone, and coldness overtook her, as though she had fallen into icy water and was sinking into the blackness. Her stomach churned, as it was wont to do these days. He would not marry her. She was ruined.*

THE ARRIVAL OF TWO ELIGIBLE GENTLEMEN at Netherfield Park sends ripples of excitement through nearby Meryton. But Mr Bingley and Mr Darcy are not the only additions to the neighbourhood raising eyebrows. An unremarkable cottage in the woods between Netherfield and Meryton also has new tenants. One of them—a lively little girl with an adventurous spirit, a love of the outdoors, and a past shrouded in mystery—draws the notice of more than one local.

ELIZABETH BENNET—YOUNG, INTELLIGENT, and UNFASHIONABLY INDEPENDENT—forms a poor first impression of the haughty Mr Darcy. On closer acquaintance, and against her better judgment, her disgust begins to give way to more tender feelings. Yet standing in the way of any potential romance is the closely guarded history of a certain little girl in a cottage in the woods. Elizabeth might be ready to disclose her hidden affections, but she is about to learn that some things are better kept secret, and some hearts are safer left untouched.

### Speechless

*Voted Austenesque Reviews Readers' Favourite 2019 and From Pemberley to Milton Favourite Book 2019*

Could anything be worse than to be trapped in a confined space with the woman you love?

Fitzwilliam Darcy knows his duty, and it does not involve succumbing to his fascination for a dark-eyed beauty from an unheard of family in Hertfordshire. He has run away from her once already. Yet fate has a wicked sense of humour and deals him a blow that not only throws him back into her path but quite literally puts him at Elizabeth Bennet's mercy. Stranded with her at a remote inn and seriously hampered by injury, Darcy very quickly loses the battle to conquer his feelings, but can he win the war to make himself better understood without the ability to speak?

Thus begins an intense journey to love and understanding that is at times harrowing, sometimes hilarious and at all times heartwarming.

Mistaken

*Voted Austenesque Reviews Readers' Favourite 2017 and Austenesque Reviews Favourite 2018*

A tempestuous acquaintance and disastrous marriage proposal make it unlikely Mr Darcy and Elizabeth Bennet will ever reconcile. Despairing of their own reunion, they attend with great energy to salvaging that of Darcy's friend Mr Bingley and Elizabeth's sister Jane. People are rarely so easily manoeuvred in and out of love, however, and there follows a series of misunderstandings, both wilful and unwitting, that complicates the path to happiness for all four star-crossed lovers more than ever before.

A witty and romantic novel that delights in the folly of human nature, Mistaken both honours Jane Austen's original *Pride and Prejudice* and holds appeal for readers of all genres.

MULTI-AUTHOR ANTHOLOGIES

Rational Creatures: Stirrings of Feminism in the Hearts of Jane Austen's Fine Ladies (The Quill Collective)

Made in United States
North Haven, CT
22 March 2022

17399060R00148

# The WAR for the
# COMMON SOLDIER

✝ ✝ ✝

## THE LITTLEFIELD HISTORY
## OF THE CIVIL WAR ERA

*Gary W. Gallagher and T. Michael Parrish, editors*

*This book was supported by
the Littlefield Fund for Southern History,
University of Texas Libraries*

This landmark sixteen-volume series, featuring books by
some of today's most respected Civil War historians, surveys
the conflict from the earliest rumblings of disunion through
the Reconstruction era. A joint project of UNC Press and
the Littlefield Fund for Southern History, University of Texas
Libraries, the series offers an unparalleled comprehensive
narrative of this defining era in U.S. history.

# the war for the Common Soldier

## How Men Thought, Fought, and Survived in Civil War Armies

—

PETER S. CARMICHAEL

THE UNIVERSITY OF NORTH CAROLINA PRESS

*Chapel Hill*

Designed by Jamison Cockerham
Set in Arno, Goudy Bookletter 1911, Dead Mans Hand, and Scala Sans
by Tseng Information Systems, Inc.

Cover illustration: *Return from Picket Duty, Green River, Kentucky, February 1862*, by
Adolph Metzner; courtesy Library of Congress Prints and Photographs Division.

*Manufactured in the United States of America*

The University of North Carolina Press has been a member
of the Green Press Initiative since 2003.

LIBRARY OF CONGRESS CATALOGING-IN-PUBLICATION DATA
Names: Carmichael, Peter S., author.
Title: The war for the common soldier : how men thought, fought,
and survived in Civil War armies / Peter S. Carmichael.
Other titles: Littlefield history of the Civil War era.
Description: Chapel Hill : The University of North Carolina Press, [2018] |
Series: The Littlefield history of the Civil War era
Identifiers: LCCN 2018010258 | ISBN 9781469643090 (cloth : alk. paper)
ISBN 9781469664033 (pbk. : alk. paper) | ISBN 9781469643106 (ebook)
Subjects: LCSH: United States. Army—Military life. | Confederate States
of America. Army—Military life. | United States—History—Civil War,
1861–1865—Personal narratives.
Classification: LCC E607 .C26 2018 | DDC 973.7/13—dc23
LC record available at https://lccn.loc.gov/2018010258

Portions of chapter 7 appeared in somewhat different form in
Joan E. Cashin, ed., *War Matters: Material Culture in the Civil War Era*
(Chapel Hill: University of North Carolina Press, 2018).

*For*

BETH

*Quand je ferme les yeux, c'est à toi que je pense,*
*si belle dans le jardin du Luxembourg*

———➤

# contents

*Introduction*   *1*

1   Comrades, Camp, and Community   *17*

2   Providence and Cheerfulness   *66*

3   Writing Home   *100*

4   Courage and Cowardice   *132*

5   Desertion and Military Justice   *174*

6   Facing the Enemy and Confronting Defeat   *230*

7   The Trophies of Victory and the Relics of Defeat   *266*

*Epilogue*   *303*

*Acknowledgments*   *317*

*Notes*   *325*

*Bibliography*   *357*

*Index*   *381*

# figures

John H. Pardington  4

*In Front of Yorktown,* by Winslow Homer  19

"Transformation into a Veteran"  24

Charles B. Haydon  29

Charles T. Bowen  34

*Pay-Day in the Army of the Potomac,* by Winslow Homer  51

"Rebel Deserters Coming with Union Lines"  80

William Shepherd and the Kenoshans in Taylor's Battery  89

William Shepherd's copy of *Words for Men at Arms*  92

David E. Beem  105

Sunken Lane at Antietam, Maryland  108

Adolph Metzner watercolor  117

*Playing Old Soldier,* by Winslow Homer  147

Trajectory of a minie ball  150

Attack in front of Marye's Heights at Fredericksburg  156

Francis A. Donaldson    *157*

Charge of Creighton's Brigade, Battle of Ringgold    *167*

Ambrose Henry Hayward    *168*

Henry Fithian    *169*

Fort Stedman    *188*

"Execution at Beverly Ford," September 26, 1863, by Alfred Waud    *198*

John Futch letter, July 19, 1863    *216*

Modern-day site of crossing near the James River    *219*

Political cartoon of Union soldiers in *Harper's Weekly*, 1864    *243*

Pickets trading between the lines, by Edwin Forbes    *248*

Alfred Waud sketch of Union and Confederate soldiers
cutting up apple tree at Appomattox    *274*

Stump of tree cut down by bullets on Spotsylvania battlefield    *298*

Oliver Wendell Holmes Jr.    *308*

Oliver Wendell Holmes cap with Twentieth Massachusetts and bugle    *312*

Remnant of the Twelfth U.S. Regulars battle flag    *315*

# The WAR for the
# COMMON SOLDIER

# Introduction

—

Michigan's John Pardington slept among the dead and the dying at Antietam. The slim, full-bearded twenty-three-year-old awoke to smells and sights that exceeded his worst expectations of war. The battered landscape aroused Pardington's curiosity as he left camp to get a closer view of the destruction. Pardington was understandably intrigued, given that his regiment had missed the fighting on September 17, 1862. Just two months earlier, in response to Abraham Lincoln's call for three hundred thousand Union volunteers, John had quit his job as a store clerk, enlisted in the Twenty-Fourth Michigan Infantry, and said goodbye to his wife, Sarah, and their infant daughter in Trenton, Michigan. The mighty conflict that Pardington could only imagine as something on a distant horizon was suddenly upon him.

Pardington only had to walk "a stone throw of our camp" to see bodies mangled by war. Hundreds of Confederate wounded lay sprawled before him, barely holding on to life without an attending nurse or doctor. "The awfulest sight you ever see Sarah," a shaken Pardington scribbled in a letter to his wife. "Some Dying some legs off and arms and they are as lousey as they can be. They are lying in Barns and sheds just as they can get shelter." "I go down and see them every day," he added. "There is one or two die every day. It is an awful sight." His outpouring of sympathy, though deeply felt, did not soften his hatred for the Southern cause or temper his desire to kill a Confederate. "Dear Sarah," he wrote, "I must now close for I must clean my gun and keep in good fighting trim so I can Pop a Rebel every time."[1]

Pardington's bravado could not mask his struggles in deciphering God's intentions in such human suffering. He felt deeply for the Confederates wasting away in makeshift hospitals, even though he despised their rebellious cause and believed the fight to preserve the Union was a sacred one. Pardington never countenanced the idea that God might abandon the North, yet he could not help but wonder about providential intentions after so much killing when the prospect of peace appeared so distant. Was anything gained or lost from the slaughter of nearly twenty-three thousand men in a single day at Antietam? "God grant it there has been enough lives sacrificed in this unholy war," he pleaded. "Now I should think if the head men would see the suffering it [has] caused they would close it at once." Yet Pardington was not sure if anyone could rein in this seemingly unstoppable conflict until both nations were drained of blood. "But I hope for myself if it is ever settled it will be done satisfactory to Both Parties. If it aint let it go on till ether side or the other is Anihilated. It is very strong talk but it must be so. But things somtime look dark. But the darkest Hour is just befor day. We are on the Right and god will Help us and favor our arms."[2] Despite his confident words, Pardington worried that God's ways were not discernible. As with most Americans, John expected the war to follow a predictable cause-and-effect equation in which divine favor would reward his people with victory. He discovered, as all soldiers did, that God ruled over man in ways that existed beyond human comprehension and control.[3]

The terrible images of Antietam stayed with Pardington, but they never fully possessed his thoughts or owned his emotions. He rarely dwelled on the evils of war when writing home, always striving to be cheerful, believing that if he cultivated the right feelings, he would uplift his wife and protect her from the dangers of despair. Keeping spirits up throughout the war would be no easy task when his wife Sarah lived on the brink of destitution. She boarded with relatives out of financial necessity, often finding herself in the crosshairs of family squabbles, and at one point she considered cutting her hair for extra cash. All the while Pardington scraped by on the army's irregular and paltry pay. When the financial demands became so severe Sarah considered going outside the home and taking a job, John flew into a rage. If she ever suggested working again, he would desert and she would be responsible for his crime that would dishonor the family for generations to come. The incident passed and Sarah remained at home, fulfilling John's idealized vision of their marriage as a partnership in war. By all accounts, Sarah played the part, encouraging her husband to do his duty, to be a good Christian, and to know that their letters kept them emotionally connected. "Dear Sarah," John wrote in a typical letter, "God and your Prayers give me strength and courage to Pass through whatever may be my lot. . . . I have Put a little Pocket in that Blue flannel shirt right By my heart and there you and Baby lays night and day (that is the locket) the one you sent me last. I keep it in the Bible and I carry that in my Breast Pocket. So you see dear I have you By me all the time and through every danger. I will try and not get you hurt."[4]

As soon as Pardington buttoned his blue sack coat and shouldered a musket, he turned to Sarah as his spiritual comrade in war. He beseeched her to pray for him in almost every letter. Her words soothed his emotions and inspired him to live a godly life. He put down the bottle and picked up a Bible, showing himself and Sarah his deep desire to live and fight like a Christian warrior. His high aspirations reflected the society that had sent him off to war. The North, like the South, looked to war as a moral purifier for men who would, through a disciplined and religious life in the ranks, achieve character. Pardington promised to return home a different man. The shame of having surrendered to drink in his past clearly haunted him; there were too many memories of coming home full of whiskey and rage. What transpired during their late-night altercations is impossible to say from John's letters, but in admitting his sin Pardington found hope in the Lord's eternal promise of redemption. He also sought forgiveness from his wife: "Sarah," Pardington pleaded, "if I could recall those nights I would sacrifice my right hand But you will forgive me wont you dear and I make a faithful Promise before God if ever I get back to you I will live a different life."[5] Like so many Northern and Southern men, Pardington underwent a conversion experience in the ranks, believing that fighting made the man and that courage and piety were the pillars of a dutiful soldier sacrificing for the nation by leaving his beloved wife and family behind.

If the scenes from Antietam had caused Pardington to wonder if God directed the war, then the disaster at Fredericksburg shattered his belief that wartime conduct would lead to predictable results. The useless slaughter of Union soldiers on December 13, 1862, showed Pardington that acts of supreme courage, even when inspired by a just cause, could not defeat impregnable Confederate works or overcome bungling Union generalship. The deaths were indiscriminate, impersonal, and gruesome. Shell fragments tore into the bodies of comrades while he stood unharmed, leading him to think that God must have shielded him. And yet Pardington walked away from his first battle feeling "out of spirits." He did not care "how quick they comprise this thing." Only a week later he regained his emotional equilibrium when he reflected upon his own survival. Only Providence, he reasoned, could have protected him from death.

John H. Pardington left his Michigan home in the summer of 1862 with the Twenty-Fourth Michigan Infantry. Once in the field, he struggled to find the hand of Providence in human affairs, but he never doubted that the Union cause was a righteous one and that military service purified his love for his wife, Sarah.
(Photo courtesy of Tod Davis and Gettysburg National Military Park)

"Thank God," Pardington wrote, "I have come out safe though our foarces suffered teberall and lucky enough for us that we left as we did for had we staid there another day they would completely destroyed our army."[6] Pardington's gratitude to Providence has to be placed side by side with his acknowledgment that luck and military field position determined who lived and who won. Pardington composed a letter full of trepidation to Sarah on January 18: "But I tell you Sarah I don't like much to cross that river in the same Place as we did before. I wold not care so much if we only had them on equal footing. But to take them w[h]ere they are behind such entrenchment and Barricade it dont seem fair."[7]

*Introduction*

In the weeks that followed the Battle of Fredericksburg, Pardington tried to avoid any talk of the dismal war situation. His letters were devotionals to Sarah, for in their love he generally found peace and contentment in the ranks. As was with any soldier, however, emotions could master the man to the point that a longing for home could descend to the blues. On Christmas Eve John felt his spirits sinking after seeing a close hometown friend who, "when ever I look at him," he wrote to Sarah, "I think of you more." "No one knows the feeling of a Husband and Father away from home," John confided, "and everything looks so discouring and dark that I am almost sick and tired of it." Pardington was edging toward a dark place in his letter, even though he knew, like most Civil War soldiers, that keeping one's spirits up demonstrated character, proved one's faith, and testified to the power of loving a woman. "I Pray for you and Baby every night as I lay down for God to keep you Both in health and spirits. Sarah I did not think a man could love a woman so as I love you today.... O that the time was come when I could clasp them once more to my breast but keep up spirits dear for your John sake."[8]

The bottom nearly fell out for Pardington and the entire Army of the Potomac after Burnside's failed offensive at the end of January, which was derisively called the "Mud March." Union morale plunged and desertion skyrocketed, but Pardington would not budge from the ranks. Nothing could induce him to abandon the army; his reputation as a fighting man was too precious to risk. "I would sooner be brought home in my coffin to you as bad as I want to see you dear I never could desert. Sarah I never could Bring such disgrace to you and my little darling."[9] Pardington remained committed to military victory, but in his letters following Fredericksburg he focused more on the hardships of soldiering than the idealism of the Union cause. After describing a trying rotation on picket duty, where he stood in the blowing snow for more than twenty-four hours without a fire, Pardington reminded his wife that the trials of a soldier could not be imagined but only experienced: "Sarah I never knew before what a man could stand.... Talk about hardships here is where you will find them."[10]

Just before the opening of the Gettysburg Campaign, Pardington sent a cautionary letter to Sarah, reminding her that luck might bring victory to the enemy once again. He expected the Rebels to maneuver toward Manassas, where Union armies had suffered a humiliating defeat in July 1861 and again in August 1862. Pardington judged the Manassas battleground a favorite Confederate hunting ground for Yankees. "That is a lucky Battle feild for the Rebels," John opined. "If we should have one there I hope it will Prove lucky for us this time."[11] At the same time, Pardington could not imagine that God's hand would not direct military affairs. His lack of certitude about providential intentions is telling. Pardington was likely reassuring himself as much as he was Sarah when he wrote, "God Prosper Our arms if we do for we are on the *Right Side* and (Right is might) we all know," and yet he still suggested in the same letter that the campaign's outcome might hinge on luck. His confusion should not be interpreted as a loss of faith. He was only coming to terms with a war that was not easy to read. Even if misfortune struck, and the Army of the Potomac blundered into another death trap like Fredericksburg, Pardington remained confident of one thing—he and his comrades would follow any order with unhesitating obedience. He could, as a result, look to the future with a measure of confidence, given that he would "bare up with soldiers fortitude."[12]

Pardington's belief in "soldiers fortitude" illustrates how much he had changed in less than a year of service. During those times he struggled to find certainty about God and his will, John always knew in doing the job of the soldier he found the truth of his existence. He and his comrades had endured brutal marches in the field, punishing discipline in camp, and gut-wrenching fear in battle. No one who had not endured the same experiences could possibly question their standing as men of moral courage. His sense of duty drew its strength from relationships forged by experience in the ranks, and religious or patriotic rhetoric receded to descriptions of men suffering and sacrificing. Pardington explained it very simply to Sarah: "For I don't think it is hardly Possible for me to come home this summer," he wrote on June 5, "for they need every man they got, and I don't think its my duty to leave now when we are needed the most."

If there were any doubts about his standing as a soldier, Pardington could also point to the bullet-riddled flag of the Twenty-Fourth Michigan as indisputable evidence of his regiment's valor for the cause of Union. The banner actually guided Pardington's thoughts and actions, keeping him from applying for a furlough in early June even though he wanted to see Sarah as much as he ever did. Military necessity demanded that every man shoulder a musket when there was a whiff of a coming campaign. He explained to his wife that when he saw the flag he felt an overpowering love for her and his country. "Not [that] I love you less than the good old flag." "But," he added, "I love that next to you and will stick by it as long as she waves for it is the only flag of the free." Pardington predicted that preservation of the flag depended on the will of the individual soldier, who would have to keep killing until the national banner would "triumph over all other *rags* that are afloat against us now and ever."[13]

John Pardington's account is not *the* story of the common soldier of the Civil War, but his personal history shows how members of the rank and file learned to be flexible in thought and in action. It did not take long for Union and Confederate volunteers to appreciate how they were conditioned by the world they inhabited. Circumstances controlled army life, and adaptability, more than any other trait, best describes how Union and Confederate soldiers navigated their world on a daily basis. A Minnesota soldier captured this perspective when he outlined the qualities most valued by the rank and file. "We want a man of greater flexibility of character, a man of rough and ready energy, who knows how to adapt himself to circumstances and men in all conditions of life."[14]

Ideas never lost their importance to Civil War soldiers, but beliefs did not always lead to a predictable cause-and-effect pattern of rewards and punishments during a tumultuous armed conflict. Even as soldiers insisted that the war had a higher moral and political purpose, they struggled to find moral certitude in the waging of war. Acts deemed criminal in the civilian world suddenly seemed just, necessary, and essential to survival. The randomness with which men died in camp or were indiscriminately shot down on the battlefield was especially troubling, for it suggested the absence of an orderly universe based on divine selection. Soldiers could not help but wonder—as Pardington did—if maybe it was every man for himself. A Mississippi soldier echoed this point shortly after his enlistment. "We cannot rely upon any one with certainty. The distress everywhere prevailing . . . [has] thrown every individual upon his own resources for a support and have had the effect to isolate, it seems, every human being."[15] Yet their probing questions about the war's destiny and human nature rarely caused a crisis of faith or led to widespread disillusionment. Union and Confederate soldiers kept going, even when all seemed lost, relentlessly driven by a strong desire to live up to the expectations of home and their desire to preserve male honor in pursuit of military victory. Pardington cherished his standing in the ranks as a man of courage, and any loss of reputation would have called into question a deeply felt and robust love that bound him to his wife, his comrades, and his nation. Duty became Pardington's watchword, as it did with most Civil War veterans, because it made the job of soldiering sacred while also offering men a degree of latitude in dealing with the dilemmas of army life. The concept of duty proved malleable, rarely triggering a mechanical or predictable course of action among veteran soldiers who knew that they did not have a prayer of surviving unless one assumed a situational view of life.

In *The War for the Common Soldier* I argue that Union and Confederate soldiers navigated the war with a spontaneous philosophy that can best be described as a hard-nosed pragmatism. Louis Menand was among the first historians to show the importance of pragmatism in his exceedingly important study of Union officer and Supreme Court Justice Oliver Wendell Holmes in *The Metaphysical Club: A Story of Ideas in America*. According to Menand, Holmes's pragmatism overshadowed his idealism by 1864, when Holmes came to distrust ideology and to value duty, experience, and professionalism above all else. Plenty of soldiers on both sides shared Holmes's veteran outlook, but their pragmatism did not compete with their idealism as Menand's argument would suggest. Rather, I believe that pragmatism gave them the flexibility to act in ways that actually helped them preserve their faith in ideas. Adaptability, the hallmark of pragmatism, empowered soldiers to shape themselves to the ground conditions of war, thus the ideas themselves could bend. As Joseph Glatthaar has shown in his pioneering study of Sherman's army, the reworking of codes of appropriate conduct did not drain Union soldiers of their idealism.[16] In fact, the rampant foraging and destruction of Southern property rarely descended into plundering. The men saw themselves as acting out of military necessity and legitimate retribution in order to restore the Union. Sherman's men might have been the most pragmatic in their approach to war, but they were far from alone. Adhering to a strict code of conduct proved unsustainable in the field on both sides and in all armies. To most men's shock, well-established binaries of duty or disobedience, morality or immorality, loyalty or disloyalty, and bravery or cowardice were blurred by war. Situational thinking prevailed but never occurred in isolation from soldiers' relationships to their households, families, and wives. The fluid ways in which soldiers read and reacted to daily life in the ranks largely drew from their hard experiences and lessons learned on the ground, making it possible for Union and Confederate soldiers to live with the contradictory elements of their violent and volatile existence in the ranks.[17]

Pragmatism also helped affirm Civil War soldiers' sense of being independent-minded citizen-soldiers. This ethos drew from the example of George Washington, whose civic virtue and high-minded service set a standard Northern and Southern volunteers sought to emulate. They fashioned themselves as selfless defenders of liberty, having set aside the mundane matters of life to achieve immortal fame by defending the nation. When the crisis passed, Northern and Southern men intended to return to their civilian pursuits just as Washington had done after the American Revolution. Life would resume after the war, but people would see them differently. They were war heroes deserving of eternal gratitude and remembered as patriots.[18]

Sentimentalism proved incapable of reconciling the inherent tensions in the model of the citizen-soldier. Wartime sentimentalists put their faith in the individual soldier's ability to rise above the dehumanizing aspects of military life through physical and moral discipline. Living with a pure heart was supposed to instill moral courage in men so that they might face battle without fear.

The individualized sentimental soldier (who was always imagined as white) would fight courageously, pray fervently, and suffer silently for the national cause. If a soldier cultivated the "right" feelings, sentimentalists predicted that he would show himself as a man of character whose sacrifices would demonstrate the power of willed behavior over the impersonal forces of mass organized warfare.[19]

Although sentimentalism never lost it potency in making the bodily sacrifice of the citizen-soldiers sacred, it could not accommodate the extremes of the military world, where days could oscillate between sheer boredom and uncontrollable terror, between a feeling of safety and a sudden fear of death. To conclude that war's horrors kept soldiers from following an idealized cultural script is a prosaic point. The challenge is to understand how the ideas of the citizen-soldier—imbued with the feelings of sentimentalism—intermeshed with the daily practices of soldiering. Northern and Southern volunteers reinterpreted the idea of the citizen-soldier in ways that countered its intended meaning of strict obedience. Necessity compelled them to pursue alternatives that simultaneously deepened the hold of the citizen-soldier as a practice and offered opportunities for subversion. Citizen-soldiers were expected to be dutiful, yet absolute submission to authority was unthinkable to American men steeped in the idea of white liberty. Professional officers had no choice but to compromise, since volunteers insisted on having a say as to who ruled over them and under what terms. Even generous concessions could not placate volunteers, who often mistrusted their officers. Veterans came to realize that blind obedience could lead to needless death in camp or battle. As historian Kathryn Meier shows in her pathbreaking work, enlisted men thought by the seat of their pants in the field, always trying to adapt to the natural environment without regard to regulation or authority. Their spontaneous acts likely enhanced their chances of surviving, but they often put them in the crosshairs of their superiors, who dismissed self-care tactics as the mischievous shenanigans of undisciplined volunteers.[20]

The whirlwind of conflicting obligations of military life reminds us that a "soldier" was never a state of being but always a process of becoming. *The War for the Common Soldier* considers the totality of the Civil War military experience—the idealism, the camaraderie, the boredom, the marching, the sinning, the sickness, the stink, the filth, the drilling, the punishments, the hunger, the exhaustion, the frustrations of being away from their families, the mental fatigue, and the grinding poverty that caused men to forget who they were, what they looked like, and even what they used to be—all punctuated by the horrible violence that in an instant turned beloved comrades into unrecognizable corpses. To persevere, soldiers were continually remaking themselves as circumstances dictated. The fortunate managed to find themselves as men, husbands, and soldiers. They passed through the eye of the storm because of a pragmatic "come what may" outlook that kept them going until either they were played out or the war was over.

Ideas had the power to rescue Civil War soldiers during the darkest moments of military service. Thanks to historians Joseph Glatthaar, Earl Hess, Reid Mitchell, James McPherson, Chandra Manning, Aaron Sheehan-Dean, Frances Clarke, Stephen Berry, Susannah Ural, Lorien Foote, and many others, we understand why men fought and why their reasons changed over time. We know that the defense of slavery mattered to Confederate soldiers; we have discovered that antislavery sentiments gained strength in Northern armies without submerging the primary commitment to Union; and we have reconstructed the dialogue between soldiers and the home front, with all of its tensions, contradictions, and expressions of mutual support.[21] Virtually all historians agree that Civil War soldiers were not apolitical defenders of home and hearth, but complicated political beings who were deeply ideological, articulate, and driven to fight and die for high ideals. We also know how Civil War soldiers could act with incredible political solidarity at one moment and, in the next instance, turn against their government, the people back home, and each other. Both North and South, goes an established argument, also shared a political culture of republicanism, a similar national history, a deep faith in Christianity, and a universal commitment to manly honor and duty, which instilled in Northern and Southern soldiers the fortitude to endure incredible suffering as they strove to live out their sentimental ideals about manliness, religion, and national duty. Much of this scholarship pivots around an immensely important question: What motivated Union and Confederate soldiers?[22] We have, as a result, a deeper appreciation and understanding of the reasons why men fought and why their reasons for fighting changed over time. I did not write *The War for the Common Soldier* as a rebuttal to the work on soldier motivation, but I do not believe that this body of scholarship has fully recovered the life of the rank and file as it was lived. Too often historians invest ideology and identity with an all-encompassing explanatory power. This creates the impression that soldiers acted in reflexive ways to abstractions like sentimentalism, the ideal of the citizen-soldier, nationalism, and duty. In many cases, the connections between soldiers' thought and action appear mechanical and static because they fail to adequately account for the ways that beliefs and actions rose spontaneously out of particular conditions. The contingencies of soldiering, above all else, are often lost when ideological comments are extracted as transparent statements as to why men fought.

Above all else, this book seeks to reconstruct the totality of the military experience by pursuing three broad questions.[23] First, what were the cultural and ideological boundaries that framed the world as Civil War soldiers imagined it? Second, how did soldiers respond to those moments when they felt hemmed in by the sentimental expectations of society, the military's need for discipline, and the pleas for help from those at home while also facing the pressing practical demands of trying to survive in the ranks? Third, how did soldiers intellectually and practically navigate moments of doubt, when the nature of knowledge and its relationship to truth and belief seemed incongruous with a war that overturned the idea of an orderly universe under God's direction? I respond to these questions by shifting the axis of investigation from *what* Union and Confederate soldiers thought to *how* they thought.[24]

Examining how soldiers thought is fraught with challenges, given that so much of the existing Civil War correspondence can be catalogued as terse tales that never pierce the inner world of the writer. The internalization of the war among veterans, as pervasive as it was, does not mean that any inquiry into how these men thought is beyond reach. Moving the inquiry below the content of wartime writings uncovers cultural orientations that shape, color, and organize the way people see, comprehend, and represent the world around them.[25] My understanding of the act of writing is closely aligned with my belief that soldier letters are neither transparent windows into the workings of the author's mind nor unmediated statements that reveal why men fought.[26] The act of writing registers an expression of reality filtered through cultural lenses and the idiosyncratic tendencies of the writer. When less emphasis is placed on the truthfulness of a soldier's writings, it is possible to see letter writing as a creative act. Historian Arlette Farge correctly observes that greater attention should be given "to understanding how a narrative came to be articulated in the way that it was. How was it shaped by the authority that compelled it to be given, the speaker's desire to convince, and his or her pattern of speech?"[27] Farge reminds us of the importance of situating the words of Civil War soldiers within the cultural and rhetorical models of the time. It is then possible to identify the circumstances that helped create them. My approach is not an exercise in intellectual history or a study of rhetoric. Rather, analyzing the act of writing serves as a bridge between intellectual, social, and cultural history. To create a fuller contextual picture of the soldier experience, I have incorporated material and visual culture as well as sensory and emotional history. From these varied sources and methodologies emerge the many dramas of soldiering, where men heard the diverse, confusing, and often contradictory voices—both private and public—that framed their everyday perceptions of a world fraught by turmoil.

*The War for the Common Soldier* relies heavily on case studies of men of all backgrounds. Using a case-study approach minimizes the cherry-picking of quotes from soldier writings, a persistent problem in the historiography that has led to a static view of Civil War soldiers as men of duty who acted on a set of beliefs in predictable and unchanging ways. I have tried to minimize this standard approach by positioning the words of soldiers within the flow of events over an extended period of time, capturing in the process the fluid nature of thought and action while also revealing the tensions embedded in this dialectic. Above all else, a case-study approach illustrates that no one man can stand for all the experiences in the ranks and that no single individual can possibly represent the approximately 2.7 million men who served in the Union forces and the 1.2 to 1.4 million men who stood in the ranks of the Confederate military. There was no common soldier in the Civil War.[28]

The case studies reflect a wide spectrum of social, racial, class, and regional backgrounds and men who fought in the Eastern and Western Theaters. Some soldiers came from privilege, while others were dirt poor. Most of the men were well educated, but others were barely literate, including two Confederates who dictated letters to their comrades. All of the men were reflective about their place in the ranks, but they made meaning of their experiences in radically different ways. A few deserted, but most remained in the army, including some battlefield shirkers and medical malingerers. The majority of these men were motivated, dutiful, and committed to using the violence of war as a redemptive power for the individual and the nation. At other moments, these same men were depressed and apathetic about the war. The patriotism of some soldiers cracked under the economic pressures of army life, while other men persevered even when they and their families were destitute. The link between household and soldiers plays a critical role in almost every soldier case study. It was rare when a man did not feel the emotional pull of family and sought the approval of loved ones on the home front. There was no boundary between the home front and the army, as the examples in *The War for the Common Soldier* illustrate.

Ultimately, I chose the soldiers who serve as case studies here because their letters are sufficiently rich to tell a man's story over an extended period of time. Rather than poll soldier opinion in the search of representative enlisted men, I have relied heavily on deeply contextualized stories that resemble what cinematographers call deep focus. This visual framework keeps the lens on the main figure without blotting out or blurring the background. The consequence is a narrative of greater depth, for it keeps a variety of people, institutions, and forces on center stage, enabling us to see how a soldier interacted with a cast of characters as he sized up his choices in the field. This technique helps recapture the spontaneity of the historical moment so that we may get to the ground level of war as it looked from the ranks. Some might question my reliance on men who deserted or openly contested military authority, since the vast majority of Civil War soldiers remained at their posts and rarely felt estranged from their respective causes. Such a criticism misses the value of studying soldiers seen as the army's outliers. Case studies of shirkers and deserters mark the permissible boundaries of expression and action in Civil War armies. While each man had his own conception of the world, putting a spotlight on deserters and malingerers is crucial to understanding the experience of the majority. The words and deeds of dissenters reveal how military and cultural authority functioned, getting us closer to what Union and Confederate soldiers imagined as available alternatives of political action. Deserters and shirkers, by their very exceptionalism, help us to understand the strategies of the "dutiful" who had to make their own accommodations to military power.

A final note about methodology is in order. Every page in a book has margins, and I, like any author, had to stay within them. I decided to focus on the soldiers who experienced combat in the ranks of mainline Civil War armies. As a result, I did not include soldiers who were assigned to garrison duty, veterans who served in the invalid corps, prisoners of war, Native Americans who aligned themselves with the Union or Confederate armies, and women who passed as men to fight in the ranks. I also did not incorporate guerrillas or partisan rangers into my narrative. My omissions should not be interpreted as dismissiveness. Scholars such as Dan Sutherland, Kenneth Noe, LeeAnn Whites, Barton Myer, Brian D. McKnight, Matthew Hulbert, and others have produced valuable work on the ways that guerrillas shaped broader military operations while working within and on household networks. The field of irregular warfare contains some of the most exciting and engaging scholarship coming out in the field of Civil War history, but unfortunately its inclusion would have diverted attention away from my primary focus on conventional armies.[29]

I have divided *The War for the Common Soldier* into seven chapters. Each chapter addresses key aspects of the soldier experience. All are tied together by a common inquiry: How did soldiering trigger shifts in attitudes, beliefs, and emotional dispositions? Chapter 1, "Comrades, Camp, and Community," explores the "job" of being a soldier and how soldiers bent their bodies and minds to the circumstances of camp. They came to embrace a pragmatic or flexible understanding of what it meant to be a citizen-soldier. Their challenges in the ranks were inseparable from the household, despite their geographical distance from home. How civilians and soldiers forged support networks of survival is at the heart of this chapter. Chapter 2, "Providence and Cheerfulness," explores the ways that providential pragmatism and the emotion of cheerfulness served Northern and Southern soldiers when God's intentions appeared indecipherable. Special attention is given to the coping strategies of soldiers seeking guidance from above while also trying to read the practical situation on the ground. Men on both sides struggled to describe these moments of crisis when the war weakened their bodies and wore down their minds. The composition of letters to family and friends and its connections to the act of soldiering are detailed in chapter 3, "Writing Home." So much of what we know of the wartime experiences of Civil War soldiers comes from their writing, but in the evaluation of *what* soldiers wrote, it is easy to miss the equally important question of *how* the men wrote their stories. The manner of language, aesthetics, and writing style can tell us much about how they interacted with the sentimental culture that was so prevalent in the Civil War era. Social class and educational background proved crucial in shaping different writing aesthetics.

Chapter 4, "Courage and Cowardice," offers a fresh perspective on what propelled men to fight and how survivors dealt with the ghastly results of combat. The important linkages between ideas and motivation are crucial to understanding the violence of combat, but what is missing from the literature is a greater sensitivity to the forces of compulsion—physical coercion, medical knowledge, male honor, and sentimentalism—that pushed men to attack and kill in battle. As the war progressed, there was a growing awareness that willed behavior and human endurance had its limits, that a soldier's body could stand only so much punishment before his morale wavered and his body collapsed. When this occurred, soldiers referred to themselves as being "broken down" or "used up," as if they were draft animals driven past the point of usefulness. Chapter 5, "Desertion and Military Justice," examines those soldiers who risked their reputations to escape battle or to flee the army for good. The causes and consequences of desertion have been well chronicled and analyzed by scholars, but the voice of the runaway is rarely heard, especially if the man was caught and condemned to death. The intent of this chapter is to see the world through the eyes of a soldier at that moment when he decided to risk his life for the freedom of home. This chapter reveals that desertion was situational and usually a defensive measure animated by the desire to survive.

How did soldiers respond to a military loss? Chapter 6, "Facing the Enemy and Confronting Defeat," suggests that members of the Union rank and file had the capacity to stand outside themselves and recognize the paradoxical effects of their own behavior on the world around them, even in the wake of a defeat. They were also disposed to confess both privately and publicly how they were at least partially responsible for the unintended consequences of their individual actions, rather than assigning blame to the impersonal forces of war or the mysteries of Providence. This kind of critical distance was much more difficult for white Southerners, whose need for reputation and whose desire for mastery kept them from deep self-criticism. Even when the material foundations of their slave system started crumbling around them, exposing the most jarring ideological contradictions of their world, Confederates, particularly of the slaveholding class, tended to frame the demise of their nation as a tragedy outside their control and beyond their responsibility.

How soldiers came to terms with the end of the war is the focus of the final chapter, "The Trophies of Victory and the Relics of Defeat." A discussion of veterans transitioning to civilian life does not appear in these pages, though the reader will find references to a rich body of scholarship on this important subject.[30] Rather, much of this chapter explores how soldiers dealt with the war's end through their collections of relics. Attention to the common practice of gathering artifacts reveals that Southern soldiers, though shamed by defeat at Appomattox, recovered their reputations through mementos associated with the last days of the Army of Northern Virginia's existence. Union soldiers, on the other hand, treasured any relic associated with the war's final campaign as a way to commemorate their individual role in saving the Union. The lively trading of mementos that occurred between the former combatants also speaks to the astonishing degree of political moderation that characterized the breakup of Rebel armies. The chapter concludes by following Union soldiers across Virginia to the Grand Review in Washington, D.C. During the journey William Sherman's men became tourists for a day, visiting the famous battlefields around Fredericksburg, Virginia. The sight of shallow burial pits and a ravaged landscape was a poignant reminder of a violent world that they were finally leaving behind.

Any study of the American Civil War is both blessed and cursed by a primary source base that one could describe as oceanic. *The War for the Common Soldier* is based on extensive research in letters, diaries, newspapers, and official documents that other scholars have utilized. I come to the sources at a slightly different angle. In every soldier letter that I read, I looked for the collision between official and unofficial stories. It is here that we can locate the dialogue that takes place between an individual and society, and this is where the tension resides between how a soldier identified with the self and how he was identified by others. Exploring the tensions between collective solidarities—such as a man's family, community, regiment, army, and nation—and his understanding of himself is of central importance. A close examination of these pressure points exposes the many forms of power that bore down on every enlisted man through the duration of the war.

John Pardington again serves as a useful illustration in this regard; throughout the course of his service he wrote about life in the army with a distinct ambiguity. There were plenty of inconsistencies in soldiering that proved to be troubling for Pardington. He had expected the army to pay him regularly, to issue him a livable ration, and to provide sufficient shelter from hostile conditions. In return, he would always stand by his comrades and would never turn his back to the enemy. The military, however, routinely violated this covenant, as was frequently the case on both sides during the Civil War. Therefore, there were times when Pardington described a soldier's life as a world of honor, duty, and bravery and other moments when he could not stand in the ranks without feeling empty, embittered, and alone.

The ever-pressing demands of home and nation led Pardington to question his place in the war and nearly pushed him to the brink of desertion. He harbored a deep resentment toward tyrannical officers; he was disgusted by the wretchedness of army life; and he was appalled by the slaughter of the battlefield. At the same time, he imagined that all of the death and destruction was necessary to defeat a traitorous rebellion for the cause of Union. In having to discipline and subordinate his self while in the army, Pardington assured his wife that he was becoming a decent and God-fearing man who was finally worthy of her love and respect.

Unfortunately, Pardington never had the chance to make amends to Sarah for all of those drunken nights back in Michigan. In a fierce melee at Gettysburg on July 1, Confederates from North Carolina shot him down; his body was lost somewhere in the carnage of McPherson's Woods. Months passed before Sarah received confirmation that her husband had been killed. A comrade from the burial party wrote that he could not find John because "those I buried on the field were so changed that I should not have known his body had it been there."[31] Pardington's corpse was likely removed to an anonymous grave on Cemetery Hill, not far from where Lincoln gave his famous oration on November 19. The power of the president's address not only resided in the words themselves, but also stemmed from the field of action where soldiers like Pardington discovered the truth of their conviction in the blood sacrifices of their comrades.

# 1

# Comrades, Camp, and Community

—

INTRIGUE HANGS IN THE AIR OVER FIVE UNION SOLDIERS manning an isolated picket post in Winslow Homer's painting *In Front of Yorktown*. A gloomy backdrop of impenetrable woods deepens the sense of the unknown. The men are not sentinels stationed along the army's edge, dodging enemy sharpshooters that could steal life with one well-aimed shot. They are far enough behind the lines to build a fire and rest under a shanty, yet they remain at a distance from the main camp of the Army of the Potomac. The men appear relaxed, even comfortable, and Homer conveys their sense of security by placing their muskets near the border of the painting, barely visible and, more importantly, beyond the quick reach of the men. Cartridge belts, scabbards, and belts dangle from some pine logs under which two men sleep soundly. The three other figures are carefully positioned around a campfire. Three trees dominate the painting's foreground, dividing the men into two distinct groups. On the left are two enlisted men, sitting close together at the edge of the fire and conversing privately while trying to stay warm. To the right of the campfire and physically separated from the two enlisted men sits an officer, upright and authoritarian in posture, wearing a double-breasted overcoat and a kepi sewn with the insignia of rank. Only the officer's facial features are discernible; his emotions are unknowable. He stares blankly into the flames, seemingly lost in thought.

Trying to visualize the world from his vantage point is the challenge that Homer presents to his audiences. What is the man contemplating? What are his calculations? Homer offers few clues. The officer is clearly preoccupied, but what thoughts engage him? Is he lost in a nostalgic dream for home? Or is he looking at the two other soldiers, whose clean uniforms suggest their newness to war? Maybe he feels the weight of an uncertain future with men that he will lead to the front. How will they respond when the shooting begins?[1]

Tensions abound in *In Front of Yorktown*. Isolation and conflict have a strong presence, as do physical closeness and emotional intimacy, but the question of unity remains somewhat open. The contradictions and ambiguities that emerge from Homer's work point to a significant question: How did the psychological and physical demands of being a soldier in the field simultaneously unite and divide Civil War soldiers of various temperaments and class backgrounds as they tried to live out sentimental aspirations within a world that was as uncharitable as it was unpredictable? This chapter answers this broad question by examining how volunteers learned the many jobs of being a soldier, which provides a window into ways that enlisted men adapted to the everyday challenges of living in the ranks. Pragmatism figured prominently into soldier coping strategies, but pragmatism did not lead to moral relativism, the abandonment of objective truth, or the loss of patriotic ideas among members of the rank and file. Until the end of the war they clung stubbornly to the sentimental vision of war as a moment to demonstrate the power of heroic individualism as proof of manliness and Christian character. Yet veterans came to see the limits of willed behavior within highly disciplined and hierarchical armies where the failure to conform to military authority often resulted in a loss of pay, and sometimes in corporal punishment.

This chapter opens with an overview of soldier and civilian expectations of war as filtered through the cultural lens of sentimentalism and through the ideologies of their respective causes. It then considers how the organization of Civil War companies and regiments could simultaneously foster consensus and conflict among comrades. The volunteer soldiers' struggle to harness their individualism and conform to the ways of professional military men shows how surviving camp and comrades required flexibility in thought and action. The military's promotion of discipline, moral restraint, and bellicosity caught citizen-soldiers off guard, for they had never contended with such radically different demands in their prewar lives. The heart of this chapter is devoted

Winslow Homer's *In Front of Yorktown* counters the romantic view of soldiering as an adventure among a band of brothers. Through the two privates huddled together and engaged in private conversation, Homer acknowledges that enlisted men could forge intimate relationships in the field. Yet the atmosphere is thick with suspicion and marked by division. The soldiers and the officer are separated by the fire, rather than sharing the warmth of the flames as trusted comrades. (Yale University Art Gallery)

to fleshing out this major theme through five case studies — three Union and two Confederate. This approach provides a variety of personal voices that are expansive enough to offer insight into the broader strategic considerations of Civil War soldiers as they tried to muster a degree of control in an army where autonomy was circumscribed.

In the wake of Fort Sumter, every Northern and Southern man who rushed to enlist knew that the eye of the crowd was on him. Any misstep could ruin reputations, bring shame down on oneself, and forever blacken a family's name, especially if the man remained at home while others did the fighting. A Louisiana soldier who served in the Trans-Mississippi Theater described the moment that he headed out the door for the army. He confided to his diary that he "could not refrain from weeping" when he said good-bye to his "beloved companion & our four little infants." His reputation demanded action. He could not stay back while others fought without risking dishonor. "I *will* not be a reproach to the name I bear" while an invading enemy was threatening "to tyrannize over us."[2] The close association between manliness and the cause also unleashed a spirit of rage militaire among Northern men who rushed off to war with romantic dreams of glory. Shortly after his regiment was mustered into service, Pennsylvanian Amos Judson marched down the streets of Pittsburgh imagining what the cheering crowd might be saying: "'There goes a splendid officer,' 'He's a brave fellow,' '*He'll* face the cannon's mouth,' and '*He'll* dash into the enemy's ranks and come out with his sword reeking with the blood of traitors.'" Their expectations, Judson admitted, would likely endanger his "personal safety," something that "I have always nursed with the greatest care"—but at that moment, he was carried away by the exhortations of the crowd, their cheers appealing to his "vanity" as well as stirring his patriotism. In that instant, with flags flying overhead, martial music filling the air, and his comrades following in perfect military order, Judson felt he would not have hesitated "to be blown up to glory from the jaws of a ten-inch Columbiad."[3] Similar visions of battlefield immortality filled the heads of Union and Confederate volunteers who breathed in the heavy air of sentimentalism. Everyone wanted to return home as a conquering hero, his bayonet and sword crimsoned with the enemy's blood. The initiation into the military was the beginning of the transformation in how citizen-soldiers saw themselves as men.[4]

To Northern and Southern families who sent their men off to war in 1861, it must have seemed as if their loved ones became soldiers overnight. As soon as a volunteer put on a uniform, his physical appearance showed that he had left the ranks of the civilian world for a distinct military fraternity. The coat, hat, and accoutrements were a visible connection to other soldiers, conveying a spirit of martial masculinity that imbued Northern and Southern recruits with a sense of manly pride that encouraged feelings of superiority. Even though a man's understanding of himself changed on entering the army, departing for war did not divorce the citizen-soldier from his home. As historian Reid Mitchell notes, "To be a good son, a good brother, a good husband and father, and to be a good citizen meant trying to be a good soldier."[5] In fact, men on both sides looked to articles sewn by wives and sweethearts, especially homespun uniforms and battle flags, as tangible links to homefolks. These material items served as a constant reminder that they were defending their homes and local communities for a national cause dedicated to different conceptions of liberty.[6]

The first letters to arrive from camp often included images of recruits looking determined and stern. They wore immaculate uniforms, with shoulders touching, arms interlocked, and usually a pistol or Bowie knife in hand.

*Comrades, Camp, and Community*

The physical intimacy of these pictures conveyed a powerful sense of solidarity with men posing as brothers-in-arms who were willing to die for each other in defense of family, comrades, and nation. For those at home, the "likeness" captured the sentimental expression of the "bold soldier boy," an image idealized as the quintessence of a Civil War volunteer.[7] He was to be brave but not reckless, pious but not a zealot, disciplined but not authoritarian, and dutiful but not obsequious. These early war images complemented the popular romantic stories of war, told since childhood, that helped create the illusion of "bold soldier boys" embarking on an adventure in which selflessness, physical strength, and pure courage would sweep away a dastardly enemy from the field of battle.[8]

Mothers and fathers helped foster sentimental fantasies among men, imploring their sons to win the love of women and the respect of the public. In letter after letter, soldiers on both sides described themselves as dutiful sons to family and to country, an idea that never lost its emotional and political resonance even among hard-bitten veterans. Even as soldiers proclaimed that they personally felt morally rejuvenated upon entering the ranks, they quickly discovered that the army could transform an innocent choirboy into a debauched and slovenly soldier overnight. A North Carolina soldier revealed to his cousin on January 1, 1862, that "camp is any thing but a place to improve a man's moral & religious feelings. It seems as if most men soon forget in camp that they have to be accountable for their words at least & a great many for their actions."[9] Such complaints were understandable, but soldiers and civilians drew comfort in knowing that the moral conscience of the community followed every enlistee into his company. Those at home kept close tabs on their companies through newspaper reports, letters received from the ranks, and stories from soldiers returning home on furlough.

The seeds of the communication grapevine sprouted from the company, the smallest but most important unit in Civil War armies. The company was composed of men who were brothers, fathers, cousins, and childhood friends, typically from the same hometown or surrounding area.[10] Enlisted men served under familiar and respected figures of authority. The lawyer in town, the neighboring planter, and the local businessman usually organized companies, composed of a hundred men who came from all social classes. Ten companies made up a regiment that almost always reflected a broad cross section of a particular region, town, or city. Class and social tensions did not immediately disappear once units were mustered into service, but at the same time soldiers did not divide themselves into competing factions based on economic status, but archaeology surveys of Civil War camps reveal that officers enjoyed more luxury items and possessed more physical comforts in their quarters than enlisted men did.[11] For the most part, however, a fluidity existed within the command structure of Civil War regiments. Resignations, battlefield death, sickness, and promotion offered men of modest backgrounds positions of leadership that were beyond reach in the civilian world. In the Twentieth Massachusetts Infantry, nicknamed the Harvard Regiment for its large contingent of volunteers from Cambridge, a dearth of commissioned officers after the Battle of Antietam necessitated the promotion of sergeants who came from modest backgrounds outside the environs of Boston. Those promoted included a whaler, a carpenter, a currier, a Scottish-born ironworker, a laborer, and a bootmaker. Many of the bluebloods grumbled about the rise of the plebeians, but at least in this instance, the distinguished battle record of the latter trumped class elitism.[12]

Within these tight-knit ensembles of men, soldiers discovered that their every move was under the surveillance of communities that possessed the power to level damning judgments against its own. Soldiers who had been intensely guarded about their personal lives before the war were shocked to find little separation between their private and public lives in the army. A Pennsylvania soldier reminded his mother to "keep me posted" on what his furloughed comrades "says about us."[13] A grapevine of letters and rumor could entangle a soldier in ruinous gossip or promote his reputation in public as a valorous fighter. Michigan's John Pardington reported on a court-martial of six comrades for running at Fredericksburg. "First our Bragrade," he explained to his wife, "was drawn up in [a] solid square. The Prisners were in the center. They then had their heads shaved and were drummed out before the whole of us and were disgracefully decharged from the service of uncle Sam." One of the convicted, John noted, came from their county and was an acquaintance. "So if any of them around there should see him," Pardington ordered, "let them Point the finger of scornd at him."[14] When a member of the Army of Tennessee fled for home after receiving a desperate letter from his wife, the congregation of his Baptist church called him before the parishioners. He admitted to his "sin" and promised to return to the ranks.[15] Though the fear of being ostracized weighed heavy on the Civil War rank and file, they also did their duty to prove their worthiness as men—not just because of peer pressure, but also because they believed the cause was deserving of their lives.

Idealism could easily surrender to regimental ambitions and politics, combustible ingredients that caused some units to explode into partisan fragments—particularly in relation to military promotions. In Union armies, Republican and Democratic soldiers formed secret alliances to advance their own candidates at the expense of a political rival. The Confederates, by contrast, had plenty of political intrigue, but the central government in Richmond, not the individual states, approved commissions. The Confederacy also lacked a two-party system, further discouraging political animosities from shackling the promotion process. In the North, the Republicans and Democrats blunted the fighting edge of their armies through a shameless use of patronage. Republican George W. Watson, for example, a lieutenant in the Ninetieth Pennsylvania, led his men with distinction throughout the summer of 1862 after his captain fell. Protocol and merit justified Watson's promotion, but as historian Timothy Orr discovered, when Governor Andrew Curtin forwarded a captain's commission, the documentation mysteriously disappeared. The regimental colonel, Peter Lyle, put up fourteen officers for promotion—all Democrats—and Watson was bypassed for a Democrat who had been absent for months and only fought in one battle.[16]

Such partisan differences, personal grudges, and long-standing feuds were quickly forgotten on the battlefield, where Civil War soldiers displayed a powerful solidarity. The armies' organizational structure fostered devotion to the unit, ensuring that blood would be shed among men who came from the same clan and community, standing shoulder-to-shoulder on the battlefield not as strangers but as intimate companions who had known each other. At the same time, the very localism of Civil War regiments could also be an impediment to unity and professionalism. Men from their local neighborhoods ruled over volunteers with varying styles. Their long histories and personal relationships afforded soldiers an opportunity to settle old scores. The election of officers in particular injected community politics into regimental governance. Subordinating oneself to peers, especially a rival who had won a popularity contest, was difficult to swallow for American men who treasured their inflated sense of equality. Shortly after arriving in the Army of the Potomac, New York's Charles Biddlecom promised to live as an independent man of honor, telling those at home that as long as his officers showed him sufficient respect, he did not mind having nothing but "our little dog tents to crawl into," adding, "We are well smoked up, look very greasy and dirty, besides we have got a few graybacks." "Even my company officers says I am as capable of an office as any man they have got, but my ever lasting temper keeps me from it. They know I don't care a darn for many of them. Even if I do look kindly dirty and rough, I think myself as good as they."[17]

Biddlecom, like a number of Union and Confederate soldiers, never fully reconciled himself to losing his precious independence to West Point—trained officers. These professionals approached warfare as a military science: they believed that discipline was largely based on teaching skills to the rank and file. Learning how to properly handle a weapon or march in formation were among

Uniforms made the man, as can be seen in this "Transformation into a Veteran" sketch. For enlisted men on both sides, what a soldier wore and the accoutrements he carried revealed his status in the army and his emotional outlook toward war. Jettisoning unnecessary equipment and excessive baggage marked the passage into veteranhood.
(Image reprinted from *Corporal Si Klegg and His "Pard"*)

the many tasks that the army considered critical to a soldier becoming disciplined and combat-ready, but a soldier was also seen as part of a machine that needed to behave in a predictable and orderly way. In other words, a disciplined soldier must display habits of deference and obedience to his officers at all times. His manners, body language, word choice, and even his physical appearance must convey a spirit of submissiveness. At the same time, there are plenty of accounts, particularly on the Southern side, in which dress and comportment retained a high degree of individualism. Soldiers, moreover, showed their pragmatism in the ways they altered their uniforms to adapt to the environment and the demands of active campaigning. In his reflections on the war, Ohio's Wilbur F. Hinman, a veteran of the fighting in Tennessee and Georgia, opened his book about a soldier named Si with an illustration that shows how changes in a man's outward appearance reflected his move to veteran status. Under the drawing of a man loaded down with a backpack, a coffee can, a kettle, hatchet, and extra boots is the line "How Si started in." In the adjoining illustration, Si has—because of active campaigning—discarded all of his superfluous

*Comrades, Camp, and Community*

belongings. He now carries only a blanket roll, canteen, and accoutrements, and the caption below reads, "How Si came out."[18]

Professional soldiers discovered that the American volunteer was not so easy to subdue. Repeated roll calls, relentless drilling, and the routine of practicing the manual of arms imparted discipline, but the desire to survive often kept soldiers from fulfilling the military's demand for order and fighting efficiency. The goals of both sides intersected and diverged on a daily basis, falling in and out of alignment and creating a tense and tumultuous relationship among privates and the army's hierarchy. Some armies enforced training with greater discipline than others. Union and Confederate armies in the Western Theater were often perceived as more lax than their Eastern Theater counterparts. The commanding general often made the difference, and Confederate Braxton Bragg, for instance, subjected the volunteers in the Army of Tennessee to a strict regimen. A Mississippi artillerist observed that "there has been a great improvement in regard to discipline and drill. Three hours every day (except Sunday) each regiment, battalion and battery is required to drill upon the field. Discipline is rigid, army movements are kept close, and Gen. Bragg is fast bringing this volunteer army to approximate the standard of regulars."[19]

Even when a professional officer presided over an army like Bragg, whom many damned as a martinet, neither a mass rebellion nor an uprising ever occurred. With so much at stake for both sides, men could see past slights and grievances for the good of the cause. In fact, the transition from new soldier to veteran usually witnessed an acceptance of, and even an appreciation for, the strict military professionalism that was ultimately seen as crucial to their own survival. The following five narratives of Charles Haydon, William Walker, Charles Bowen, Joshua Callaway, and Christian Epperly intersect at many points, even though these men were very different in background as well as in personality. The thread that ties this chapter together is the connection between the business of being a soldier and its relationship among pragmatism and patriotic ideas. To their surprise, Northern and Southern volunteers found themselves beholden to the conditions of military life, a world where life-and-death choices were made but certitude was in short supply. This was disorienting to Americans who came from a world where clear-cut laws under providential direction supposedly governed life. In war, soldiers leaned toward valuing beliefs and actions that proved through experience to be good for the cause or beneficial to one's survival.

Except for William Walker, who was executed for mutiny, all of these soldiers showed remarkable adaptability in thought and action in an attempt to cope with the insecurities of soldiering. These case studies also show how the daily demands of the military could simultaneously knit men together as well as pull them apart. While remaining sensitive to the different ways that individuals interacted with the surrounding landscape, and recognizing the importance of ideology and the values of sentimentalism, the portraits of Haydon, Walker, Bowen, Callaway, and Epperly reveal how the common struggles in Civil War armies centered over the control of scarce resources and soldier labor. These conflicts are situated within larger economic, military, and social structures as a way to see how the soldiers themselves imagined their options as they tried to meet the confusing and conflicting obligations to home, comrades, and army. The diverse roads taken did not follow ideological guideposts, nor were members of the rank and file culturally hardwired in uniform ways. Civil War soldiers were always improvising in a world where the driving needs of survival could easily overwhelm established rules and practices.

### Charles Haydon
*Michigan Lawyer*
### Second Michigan Infantry

As soon as Michigan's Charles Haydon manned the picket line outside the Washington, D.C., defenses in 1861, the gap between the sentimental expectation of war as an adventure of heroic individualism and the hard reality of doing the job of a private came into focus with startling clarity. Haydon quickly learned, as all recruits did, that war was laborious work, that survival depended on steady training and obeying orders, and that simple misfortune often defeated individual heroism. These realizations did not go down well for vast numbers of Civil War soldiers on both sides, since they wanted the public to see them as independent and heroic fighters. This was Haydon's expectation when he entered the army in 1861 as a twenty-seven-year-old lawyer and graduate of the University of Michigan. He trusted in the power of individual action and was confident that God would never relinquish his people against a vile slaveocracy. He recorded his thoughts in small memorandum notebooks that measured five and three-eighths inches, making them easy to carry in the field. Every few months his brother and father would receive a package in the mail containing one of Haydon's journals. Writing to a male audience freed Haydon to disclose the sordid as well as the inspiring exploits of military campaigns in Virginia and the Western Theater.

During his first assignment at the front, Haydon saw plenty of questionable behavior among his men. He watched in mortification while his green soldiers fled their posts at the first hint of danger: "Some of them showed the white feather badly," he scribbled in his diary. "I would get them together in part & while looking for the rest some of the first were sure to sly off & hide themselves." Twelve days later all order was lost on the picket line when some of his fellow officers went on a drunken spree. Whiskey-induced negligence at the top clouded the judgment of those on the ground, and Haydon was stunned to see enlisted men initiating truces along the front to swap goods and stories with the enemy. The staggering violation of military law resulted in curious interactions among adversaries. Haydon looked on as one Confederate handed "the name of his mistress in Charleston" to one of his soldiers and "urged" him "to call on her if he ever went there."[20]

It did not take long for Haydon to wash out war's romances from his journal. Unlike his Manassas entries in 1861, which were largely narratives of adventure, Haydon wrote only one dramatic account of his exploits from the front during the advance on Richmond in 1862. Forced marches and constant picket duty drove Haydon and his comrades to the point of utter exhaustion. They were jittery and emotionally ragged, and their bodies were broken down as if they had been driven like draft animals. When his detachment was relieved from the front on June 14, 1862, his body was covered with "sores & blotches," and his clothes crawled with lice. Haydon pulled out his diary and wrote of his filthy uniform as a material thing more powerful than words to convey his condition and suffering. "We are compelled to be on the alert so constantly," he wrote, "that I have ventured to sleep with pants off but once or twice since we left Ft. Monroe."[21] Rumors, he wrote, blew in "fitful gusts" across the front, convincing him that nothing he heard could be trusted, even when the information came from those who were staring at the enemy. Armies in motion full of sleepless men grinding back and forth were bound to commit reckless acts out of fear and exhaustion. On the evening of June 19, three men in Haydon's regiment were shot down by friendly fire while at their outposts. Haydon was so disgusted by these incidents and so appalled by other acts that had transpired that evening that he decided to omit any references to the tragedy in his diary. "I was along the lines several times last night," he wrote, "& saw some things which although they did not much surprise me were anything but pleasant."[22]

By the summer of 1862, Haydon no longer imagined the picket line as a stage for acting out sentimental fantasies of adventure, nor did he sensationalize his experiences on paper as a dramatic narrative. The sentry post, above all else, had become an assignment to dread, given that the army's perimeter was an erratic place of killing. If soldiers were to survive, they had to obey orders and master the practical skills of war. Haydon came to appreciate war as a regulated business with its own rules and protocols that could be valued only through routine experience in the field. Obeying military strictures, however, did not crush sentimental aspirations entirely.

As was the case with most veterans, Haydon tempered his expectations of soldiering as a moment of individual heroism, but he never altered his self-portrait as a fearless fighter who deserved admiration from those at home. Haydon's reflections on the poem "The Picket Guard," better known as "All Quiet along the Potomac Tonight," shows how he straddled two worlds—one regulated by the mandates of being a professional soldier and the other of an idealistic volunteer driven by the emotional forces of sentimentalism and individual valor. Haydon was so moved by the poem that he pinned a copy to the inside cover of his diary. The piece tells the story of a lone picket stealthily moving along the rocky banks of the Potomac. On stopping under a moonlit sky, he says a prayer for his family, causing a tear to fall from his eye just as a concealed rifleman guns him down. The man was left to die an isolated death for his nation.[23]

It is significant that when Haydon turned to his diary for reflection, his commentary focused almost exclusively on the technical components of soldiering. The pressing and overwhelming tasks of survival—not the sentimental death of the soldier in the verse—are what claimed his attention. The poem, according to Haydon's interpretation, was significant in offering practical instruction as to how a man might save himself from getting needlessly killed. "The only safety for pickets in such cases lies in frequently & noiselessly shifting his position," he observed in his diary. "In this way a lurking enemy while looking for him in one place is pretty sure to be seen by him from another. It needs a keen witted fearless wide awake man for a good picket guard on a dangerous post."[24] The notion that physical bravery and cunning distinguished men on the picket line surely appealed to Haydon's sentimental desire for individual heroism, but he also looked to the army's perimeter as a crucial testing ground where green recruits remade themselves into professionals. Harnessing individualism through the army's bureaucratic structures was necessary, he concluded, if recruits were to fight efficiently and effectively. Those seeking personal adventure would likely get themselves or others needlessly killed.

Haydon might have understood his own transformation into a soldier better than most men, yet he never lost his high ideals or questioned the political cause for which he was suffering. In late 1862, he occupied a dangerous post in Kentucky, where Confederate guerrillas arbitrarily shot down Union pickets. The pages of his journal show no trace of a sentimental rush, just grim entries of death, drudgery, and despair. Haydon's war had become a cold struggle of survival. "All one can hope for here at present," Haydon observed on April 18, 1863, "is merely to preserve life, i.e. to stay along from day to day. We wander

*Comrades, Camp, and Community*

Michigan's Charles B. Haydon strove to become a professional soldier as soon as he joined the picket line in 1861, but his men routinely flaunted orders and regulations. Haydon came to appreciate war as a regulated business that had to be learned in the field, yet he never gave up on the sentimental promise of war as a moment to achieve character through duty, discipline, and individual bravery.
(Bentley Historical Library, University of Michigan)

around with overcoat & gloves on or sit shivering around a smoky fire from m'g till night & then sleep cold till m'g & then repeat the same performance." When Haydon looked across the river and watched the Confederate pickets walking their beat, he did not aspire for individual laurels or imagine daring raids against the enemy. The sentimental impulse barely flickered as he wondered if "they have as dull times as we."[25] Haydon, who would die in a military hospital of pneumonia in 1864, had seen too much and lost too many friends to abandon the cause. "Alas how many unpleasant things we have learned in the dear school of experience," he wrote in his diary on April 18, 1863. "Our Regt. & the whole army will fight well," he wrote, "but it is with the dogged obstinacy of veteran troops having prescribed duty to perform & not with the hilarity & confidence which used to characterize our movements."[26] Haydon was not becoming disillusioned. He knew that the Union cause was right and worthy of his life, but at the same time, he found a higher purpose in his ability to do his duty as a man who now saw himself not as a volunteer but as a veteran soldier.

## CHARLES BOWEN
### *New York Farm Laborer*
### Twelfth United States Regular Infantry

In the weeks that followed the disastrous Union defeat at the Battle of Fredericksburg on December 13, 1862, New Yorker Charles Bowen awoke every morning feeling weary and foul, greeted by a panoramic view of Marye's Heights, a place he damned as "Burnside's slaughter house." Bowen had spent the night on the battlefield, taking cover behind a corpse whose "whole top of his head [was] carried off by a shell, the eyes were open & stared at me whenever I looked at him." The next morning, when the Union army began its retreat, Bowen slipped into town, where he joined his comrades in a looting frenzy. Bowen stole food, booze, and books. In one abandoned house, he listened to a drunken comrade, whom he mockingly called a *bold soldier boy*, play "Root Hog or Die" on a piano. To his wife he admitted, "I got *considerably up on my bottle of wine* & felt as good as Gen. Burnside or any other man."[27]

Bowen's brazen disregard of military law and authority is startling, but his example shows how Civil War soldiers, when weighed down by extreme mental and physical stress, reworked notions of duty to meet the exigencies of the moment. Bowen, like so many other Americans, could never have imagined that he and the "soldier boys" of 1861 would have embarked on a rampage with such a wild and fierce joy. Since the battle, he had felt sad and lonely, missing his wife, Kate, who was caring for their infant daughter in Utica. Christmas did not bring him any cheer. No treats or delicacies could be procured from the sutler, and no packages had arrived from home, though his captain did bring some joy by brewing "five gallons of community whiskey." The bacchanal broke the tedium, but it could not permanently distract Bowen from the grim situation facing his army and nation. He looked for any chance to flee, believing that the entire Northern nation had abandoned him and his army. "But how are they (Union soldiers) used by their government," he wrote:

> Not paid in months when many have families to support who are
> starving for the money which is so basely held back by red tape.
> All their good generals taken from them & left to be butchered by
> the blunders of some "*nincome poop*" of a man whose only forte is
> serving under a general who can *order* him what to do. Marched &
> countermarched all winter with no shelter but a dirty little shelter tent
> so called, & to no purpose but to kill the men by exposure & fatigue,
> & useless battles. It is more than human strength & patience can bear
> in silence, & I tell you that it finds vent in expressions now, but the time
> is not far distant if this way of carrying on the war is held too when acts
> will take the place of expletives & then the war will be finished because
> Jeff (Davis) will have no one to fight.[28]

Bowen's outcry against the war was tied into an ugly knot of grievances and disappointments, ranging from poor conditions to poor generalship, a callous bureaucracy, and an indifferent home front. "I did once *blame* deserters," he wrote his wife on January 27, "but as time passes away & shows more & more plainly the corruption of some of our chief officials I can blame no man for leaving the *rotten old hulk & worse than drunken crew* who man it."[29] His cynicism even darkened his view of providential intervention, believing that God had delivered them from the Rebels by unleashing a massive rainstorm in January that sunk the army in roads of bottomless mud. "And I do think that we have Providence on our side, for had not this opportune rain come on when it did, we would have been taken across the river to what the boys call another 'Burnside slaughter house' & many of us today would be laying beneath *Virginia Mud*, while others would have been groaning in a hospital bunk." All things considered, Bowen should have headed to Canada as he had promised to do on numerous occasions, but understanding why he stayed requires us to follow in Bowen's tracks, to see his strategic options within the military system, a soldier's economy, and a sentimental culture that constrained choices without silencing the voice of duty. Ironically, it was the daily acts of being a soldier, which Bowen and other men endlessly groused about, that forged solidarities in the ranks that no man could easily break, even when the war news was desperate and gloomy.

When Bowen surveyed his camp, he stood in awe of the heroic endurance of his comrades. For in their hardship there was no gray area, no mystifying rumor, and no trickery of confidence men and malingerers, but an indisputable display of Union soldiers realizing the sentimental dream of soldiers coming in touch with gentle emotions like sympathy when confronting suffering. While writing home from Fredericksburg, Bowen was drawn to the plight of a poor comrade who took on extra laundry work for a few "shillings" to support his impoverished wife and five children in Minnesota. "How hard it is for some who have large families to support to be kept out of their pay for six months more at a time & keep receiving letters from home begging for money to buy bread & meat for their starving little ones," Bowen observed. "This man I speak of is one of those unfortunates. He cannot read writing & always brings me his letters to read to him, & many a one I have read that would bring tears from stone. Such is war, cruel heartless *bloody*, war, that starves the innocent & enriches the guilty."[30] Even as a hardened veteran, Bowen was like so many other soldiers who never lost their ability to feel for all men who were subjected to the cruelties of war.[31]

It was easy for Bowen to empathize with his impoverished comrade: he too was in a precarious situation after Fredericksburg, walking around camp nearly barefoot, with his shoes and socks in tatters, and his hands freezing, because he could not afford a new a pair of gloves made of "common sheep skin." They cost $1.50 from the sutler, an exorbitant price, he complained to his wife, when he could have purchased the same pair for fifty cents at home. Boots were as high as eight dollars a pair — an outrageous sum, Bowen thought, given that the workmanship was of "a very poor twenty-shilling sort." "I would wear the government shoes until doomsday before paying such prices," he promised.[32] Every day Bowen eagerly awaited the mail, desperate for a package of clothing and foodstuffs, because he could not subsist off the army's ration and its uniform allowance. At the same time, his family depended on his wages, but his pay was never regular and always insufficient. He supplemented his income through gambling, and although he had seen many "foolish" men squander their money in rigged games, Bowen boasted to his wife that he had bested a notorious card sharp. Even when he was on a hot streak, the New Yorker complained of living on the brink of poverty.[33] Bowen's problem was a universal one for members of the rank and file, who were always vulnerable to a cycle of debt. Too often, cash-hungry soldiers secured credit from regimental and brigade sutlers to buy necessities at grossly inflated prices while also having to pay

*Comrades, Camp, and Community*

the army for lost or destroyed equipment. When the paymaster made one of his infrequent visits to camp, soldiers, especially new recruits, were astonished by how little cash was received in hand.

Empty pockets did not just affect material wants; they also constrained political options, especially for poor men who could not afford to desert without casting their families into a state of destitution. On reaching Canada, a Union soldier who deserted after Fredericksburg received a frantic cry for help from his penniless wife, who was stranded in New York. "I can not live in this old shanty," she wrote, "this little bit of a hole of 6 little ons and my self. I canot stand it. I shall not live a Month."[34] There were scores of poor Confederate soldiers who confronted similar financial considerations when deciding whether or not to desert. A North Carolinian after Gettysburg spelled out the financial realities of deserting when he wrote: "We are all out of money here. . . . I think as soon as they get money a lot of them will leave [as] that is all that has kept them here this long."[35] In the same vein, Bowen likely never imagined that in the army he would have to turn to gambling in order to survive. He appears to have been fairly successful, but his letter likely did not reveal to his wife the days when fortune had turned against him.

In time, Bowen's living situation stabilized in his Fredericksburg camp, but his anger toward the army and the government did not fade. Yet he still refused to defy the military by deserting, even as he called for peace. "The army is only anxious for one thing to occur & that is the *termination of the war*, for they argue that in the way things are going on there is no prospect of conquering a peace," Bowen explained on February 23. The words "conquering a peace" are critical, for they affirm his faith in the Northern armies to subdue the South as long as the soldiers were given the necessary support. "We want peace or we want *a draft of every ably bodied man in the north from 18 to 45 & with McClellan at our head we'll sweep the south clean of every root & branch of both treason & slavery*."[36] It is tempting to see the dismissal of the popular George B. McClellan, a conservative War Democrat, as the cause of Bowen's disillusionment, but that overlooks the simple fact that Bowen had enjoyed battlefield victories under McClellan and no other officer. His faith in "Little Mac" was a realistic and practical response to a war that, at that particular moment, appeared to be sinking to defeat. In Bowen's estimation, only a tested military man could rise above the political factionalism and rescue the army and the nation.

As important as generals were to battlefield success, Bowen knew that men made the army, and it was the act of soldiering, which he had been performing for nearly two years, that firmly convinced him that only disciplined troops could suppress the rebellion. A confrontation with a drunken comrade in his

Charles T. Bowen imagined himself as a "soldier boy" who was "very blood thirsty" when he volunteered in 1861; like other men on both sides, he lost his innocence but not his sense of devotion to a higher cause. After the Confederates had mauled his army at Fredericksburg, Bowen got drunk and plundered the town with the rest of his comrades, but weeks later he could mock the failed Union war effort without losing his high ideas for fighting, because of the sacrifices he had made in the field and also because of the love he felt for his wife.
(Gettysburg National Military Park)

Fredericksburg camp reinforced his belief in the power of discipline. In the aftermath of the incident, Bowen noticed how he had changed from an idealistic and naive recruit into a professional soldier. As part of his February 23 letter, Bowen described his role in enforcing an order against an intoxicated soldier who refused to move wood in camp. The rebellious soldier lunged at Bowen, who then laid the drunkard out with a spade, nearly crushing his skull with a single well-directed blow. Once the man regained his senses, he was ordered to carry a forty-pound log around the sentry post—a light punishment, Bowen believed, for a full court-martial would have occurred if a commissioned officer had witnessed the fight. Even though Bowen thought he had been easy on the man, he expected the soldier to carry the resentment with him for the foreseeable future, looking for "a good chance to give a fellow a sly shot in battle." Bowen did not fear his vengeful comrades as much as he worried about his family thinking he was too severe in knocking a man senseless for a minor infraction; Bowen explained to them that "a wholesom[e] dread of infringement of known rules has to be instilled into the minds of ignorant & brutal men who will always be found in the army."

This ugly incident moved Bowen to reflect on how much he had changed since 1861, when he left his job as a laborer on his uncle's farm near Utica, New York, and enlisted in the U.S. Regulars, looking the part of an innocent "soldier boy" with his smooth beardless face and his blue kepi hat. When he reflected upon those early days of war, it felt "like a dream through which I have passed, but it is so indelibly impressed on memory that I shall never forget it while life shall be mine." "Now I was just one of the *greenest* specimens of the *genis* homo that ever started on his travels—no self reliance—knew nothing of the ways of the world but of my own sphere—in fact was a perfect know-nothing." He admitted that his "school master has been none of the tenderest," but Bowen could now appreciate the military "holding strong control" over enlisted men like himself, for he felt "more self-reliant & confident in his plans & purposes." "It is wonderful to see," he concluded, "what a change will take place in a man's disposition" once in the army.[37]

Although Bowen knew that the war had changed him into a tough-minded professional, he still imbibed from the cultural font of sentimentalism. Even when conditions turned harsh and the military situation was bleak as it had been at Fredericksburg, Bowen never lost his faith in willed behavior or the emotional power of individual sympathy. Although the New Yorker used the language of "bold soldier boy" to mock himself and challenge civilian notions of war as all glory and little realism, he still derived immense fulfillment from popular sentimental literature because it idealized military service as a heroic adventure.

Bowen was especially drawn to the cultural message that military sacrifice purified the love between man and wife. The war tested his marriage to Kate, who was answering to many masters while her husband was away. Bowen tried to control the family's finances from afar by giving money to other relatives to dispose as an allowance. Kate resented these intrusions into her household, but she put aside family squabbles to write loving letters of support. Bowen responded with unrestrained expressions of love for his wife and child, telling Kate that she always *"had my heart in your power."*[38] During one exchange, Bowen complimented his wife for sending a letter filled with passionate sentiments of love as well as some extracts of published poetry extolling Northern women for giving their husbands to the national cause. Bowen was touched both by the verse and by the knowledge that Kate was prepared to make the greatest sacrifice she possibly could for the Union. His idealization of his marriage served as an emotional refuge from the awfulness of war, an imaginative sphere of domestic harmony that existed outside the grim physical world that he inhabited in the army. He treasured his correspondence with his wife because it moved the war from political abstractions to reminders of their past lives at home, where pure feelings of sympathy, compassion, and familial love made life sacred and worth dying for. Kate's words did more than comfort Bowen during times of trial. They affirmed life during times he was surrounded by bleeding corpses and burnt-out buildings. "When will these long weary months of service be passed," Bowen wrote on the cusp of the 1864 spring campaign, "that I may once again clasp my darling to my loving heart & tell her of the sleepless nights I have passed thinking of *her,* tell her of the *form* which seems to walk by my side in the battle where death reigns supreme, bidding me to be of heart, tell her of the undying love which has been my shield & protection from many dangers, & tell her that love is all for her, my chosen wife, my adored Katie."[39] Bowen's marriage, above all else, filled him with an idealism grounded in love for home, family, and nation, giving him an emotional resilience that kept him from deserting the cause or descending into the darkness of organized killing.

## JOSHUA CALLAWAY
### *Alabama Teacher*
### Twenty-Eighth Alabama Infantry

For all his Confederate patriotism, Alabama's Joshua Callaway could not bring himself to enlist during the furious call to arms in 1861. The thought of leaving behind a wife and two young children at home harnessed his raging ambitions, but he broke loose in the spring of 1862, when the Confederacy rolled out conscription. Callaway answered the call rather than suffer the indignity of being drafted. He was twenty-eight years old when he signed up for three years or the duration of the war, and had spent almost all of his previous adult years in the classroom as either a student or a teacher. Now he could shed the image of an effete academic and remake himself into a warrior straight out of the romances of Homer or Sir Walter Scott. Instead of disciplining rambunctious Southern boys in the classroom, he was off to slay godless black Republicans for the sanctity of Southern womanhood and the preservation of slavery.[40] The state of Alabama helped finance Callaway's romantic venture into the ranks. Not only did he receive a fifty-dollar bounty, but he was also guaranteed public assistance if his family needed clothes or food. Within days of his March 1862 enlistment, Callaway was bumped up in rank to orderly sergeant and given orders to leave for the Confederate camps surrounding Corinth, Mississippi.[41]

As soon as Callaway and his comrades reached their destination, their officers tested their bodily discipline by ordering them to fell trees for fuel and huts and to dig latrines and wells in what must have been exhaustive work, especially after a long march. Few volunteers could have imagined that soldiering demanded long hours of such grinding labor that pitted them in a continuous struggle against the natural world.[42] The physical desolation left by Civil War armies crushed any fanciful idea of warfare as a tidy affair played out on the field of honor. "You have no idea how much timber it takes to build huts and cook a soldier's beef and beans," a New York soldier informed his wife. "Within a week this regiment has stripped at least fifteen acres of heavy timber. The sound of the ax is heard from early dawn 'til late at night."[43] When Civil War armies returned to the field for active campaigning, enlisted men often slept wherever they could find a piece of ground, without regard for regulations. When there was a lull, officers cracked open their manuals and used a measured grid to lay out their camps, but the land often outranked regulations, requiring men to align their camps around streams and ravines.[44] The tents of the enlisted men were aligned into two tight rows with only two paces separating each tent. The police guard was strategically posted at the center of the formation with the company officers just twenty paces behind the men. Stationed at the head of the encampment, and just forty paces from the men, were the tents of the regiment's colonel, lieutenant colonels, and majors. This layout segregated officers from their men while also ensuring visual mastery over their units during daylight hours.[45] Once tattoo sounded, signaling that it was time to settle in for the night, regimental officers demanded silence.

Officers' attempts at visual and aural mastery of camp left enlisted men with little space that they could call their own. This extended to the latrines, which were intentionally dug within the perimeter of the sentinel line and always within the visual range of walking guards. If the winds were blowing in the wrong direction, the nauseating smells enveloped camp. A putrid gust of noxious air sickened a gagging Louisiana soldier, who scribbled in his diary that "about ¾ of the regiment are affected with camp diarrhea, & after a little detention at the guard line, many cannot get much farther. The consequence is filth in the extreme. A breeze from that direction renders breathing an unpleasant exercise."[46] Even worse and much more serious was the widespread practice of men urinating or defecating wherever they pleased. This confounded officers, who ordered patrols to regularly sweep through camp and arrest any man caught with his pants down and not at the sinks.

The stench of human waste was a symptom of a larger health crisis that eviscerated Civil War armies.[47] The situation for the troops was especially dire at the beginning of the war, when soldiers, military surgeons, and officers were largely ignorant of the environmental causes of disease and sickness. At Corinth, Mississippi, for instance, Callaway's regiment staked its tents on the site of a former camp, once occupied by a Confederate regiment apparently filled with careless men and negligent officers. Thanks to inadequate policing, the ground was covered with debris and the water supply was polluted. As soon as Callaway arrived, he knew he was entering a death trap. "Corinth is a very disagreeable place," he wrote with fear and apprehension to his wife on May 5, 1862, "& so is all the country about here. It is shoe mouth deep in the nastiest mud I ever saw, & the water is mean enough to kill an alligator." Although Callaway could not have possibly known that the water contained dangerous microbes, its foul smell necessitated resourcefulness. Green soldiers quickly discovered that passive resignation to any situation almost always committed a soldier to a torturous, disease-ridden death. Civil War soldiers often had to push back against regulations and the dictates of their officers. This was not a streak of manly rebelliousness, but an act of independence for the cause of survival. Callaway was fortunate to have the financial wherewithal to purchase goods from civilians, fellow soldiers, and merchants, but he discovered—as most men did—that hucksters were always on the prowl for naive soldiers. When Callaway tried to avoid the poisonous waters at Corinth, a deceptive camp vendor sold him a "canteen full of butter milk made sour of chalk & water made sour with cream of Tarter."[48]

Although Callaway managed to escape illness at the Twenty-Eighth Alabama's first camp, his foreboding thoughts proved frighteningly accurate. Corinth was a fiendish place where some eighteen thousand Confederates were placed on the sick list for measles, typhoid, and dysentery. The hellhole

*Comrades, Camp, and Community*

at Corinth nearly swallowed Callaway's entire company. "The boys are puny, some real sick," he wrote from his tent under a "gloomy" rain on May 24, 1862. "Our Company can muster only 21 men for duty. Thirty of our men are absent sick."[49] Relocating the camp to Tupelo, Mississippi, stopped the hemorrhaging of men from the able list, but even as the company recuperated its health, the sounds of sickness and death echoed in Callaway's head. In the middle of August, nearly three months after evacuating Corinth, he admitted to his wife, "I shudder when I think of the suffering and death that I witnessed while at Corinth." "I seldom heard an animated conversation or saw a soldier smile, but my ears were constantly saluted by the groans of the sick & dying."[50] The very uniforms that Callaway and all Civil War soldiers put on with such pride when they enlisted became something to fear. Modern scientific research shows that the porous nature of cloth was likely to capture infective agents that had the potential to spread disease. Although the Civil War medical community was divided over the spread of disease, historian Sarah Jones Weicksel shows that soldiers came to believe that their garments, especially those stained with the blood and pus of the sick, carried the contagions that could infect the healthy with a deadly illness. In the transition to becoming a veteran, a private discovered that his uniform, which was supposed to be a statement of independent manliness, possessed a power over him, and in some cases was to be feared, especially when the clothing had been stripped from the dead.[51]

Callaway's point also highlights the importance of soundscapes in camp — that while a soldier could avert his eyes to sickly comrades, his ears were always exposed to the pitiful cries of the dying. The death tones of camp shattered the sentimental image of the good death, in which men at the end of their lives were calm and reserved, resting in the knowledge that God's heavenly kingdom awaited His followers. The sounds of men puking in the company street, moaning helplessly from their tents, and jabbering insanely from fever reminded every soldier that death was random and ruthless.[52] At the same time, for Callaway and many other men on both sides, the sounds of suffering did not deaden their political idealism or diminish their sentimental aspiration to die with Christian dignity. The religious instruction of all Americans framed this sentimentalized moment of suffering as an opportunity to demonstrate character through faith. A brief scripture from Romans conveys this message: "We also boast in our sufferings, knowing that suffering produces endurance, and endurance produces character, and character produces hope, and hope does not disappoint us, because God's love has been poured into our hearts through the Holy Spirit that has been given to us."[53]

Even the most devout struggled to find spiritual peace among their fellow soldiers. It was not unusual for religious men to complain about the remorseless sinning of their comrades, but as men of faith they were taught to worship as part of a Christian community. Many of these same men, realizing that there was little Christian fellowship in the ranks, sought solitude in nature as a way to commune with the Lord. Philip Hamlin, a pious farmer from Minnesota, had looked to the military as a means of converting nonbelievers into an army of Christians, but the "circumstances" of active campaigning left men too "exhausted" to build a relationship with Christ. Hamlin felt he had no choice but to turn inward to practice his faith, and in effect he abandoned the traditional aspiration of being part of a larger Christian community. He would essentially have to become a loner if he were to practice his faith in his regiment. "I find great comfort and profit in the Bible and in meditating on its glorious truths," he informed his friends on December 5, 1862. "While here in camp it is my custom to rise early and in silence give myself to reflection and prayer. I find these hours of seclusion among the happiest of the day."[54]

Indeed, the soundscape of camp proved crucial in shaping a professional military consciousness among volunteers who were, at least initially, overwhelmed by the unfamiliar noises in camp. In time, veterans adjusted to the ceaseless drumming and bugling marking the fast pace of military life, and some men, such as Callaway, came to appreciate how every part of the day was scheduled to occupy the minds and train the bodies of the soldiers. At first light, the drum sounded morning roll call, which was followed by a quick breakfast, the cleaning of camp streets, and sick call. Callaway then inspected weapons before making assignments for guard and fatigue duty. At nine o'clock Callaway lined the men up for a second roll call, drilled them for two hours, and then returned to camp for lunch. As an orderly sergeant, Callaway spent the middle of the day immersed in regimental paperwork, writing requisitions and reports and responding to the repeated requests of the officer of the day. The "lazy life" of the soldier was unknown to him, he explained to his wife with a great deal of pride. To impress on her the exacting demands of his important post, he included a portion of the morning roll call in a letter home with a detailed explanation. "I am called a hundred times by the officer of the day," Callaway added, "to do something about the camp — bury a dead horse, or a man, to fill up some hole, or *something*."[55] Of course, Civil War camps could be extraordinarily dull and monotonous places, and Callaway's duties as a sergeant probably kept him busier than most, but the job of being a soldier was difficult for most men to adjust to, especially those from the country who were not accustomed to a day in which they did not control their own time.

The incessant use of the roll call was an effective way to keep tabs on the men and to ensure that they had not slipped away from camp. Callaway's regimental officers never missed an opportunity to assemble the men. The sound of the drums must have lost their martial luster to volunteers who associated the sounds of the long roll with surveillance and more training, but the reactions of Callaway's comrades when they reported at three o'clock for two hours of battalion drill are unknown. Afterward there was a brief respite for dinner and then free time before a final roll call where Callaway read any general orders or Articles of War pertaining to the soldiers. The substance and intent of these announcements were the same in Union and Confederate armies throughout the war. They sought to tighten discipline, instill greater respect for military authority, and exert as much control as possible over the time and labor of the rank and file, whether in camp or in the field. The soldiers then headed to their tents, reminded a final time of the rules and regulations that subordinated the self to the will of the army's high command.[56]

Civil War soldiers were notorious for straying from quarters, even on the watch of the most vigilant of officers and responsible guards. Too often pickets were willing accomplices, looking the other way as long as the offending party promised to bring back provisions from their foraging expedition. A rare order book from an Alabama brigade in Lee's army, covering the years from 1861 to 1863, attests to the illegal collaboration of comrades who turned sentinel lines into sieves. An 1861 order prohibited guards from speaking to anyone except "authorized officers." Violations called for punishments intended to hurt the soldier financially and physically as well as to injure his pride. One Alabama soldier who "absented" himself for two days was sentenced by a "drum head" court-martial "to forfeit one month's pay, to be bucked one hour each morning and evening for ten days and to be confined each night to the Guard Quarters."[57] This example might constitute an unusually severe enforcement of the Articles of War and general orders, but it illustrates some of the penalties soldiers could have faced. Even where laxness prevailed in individual regiments, professional officers were always at the helm of Civil War armies, projecting authority through state-sanctioned violence and military law. West Point–trained officers like Confederate Braxton Bragg, under whom Callaway served for most of the war, used all of their resources to subjugate the independent spirit of volunteers. "We are nothing more than the subjects of a military despotism now," a dispirited Callaway wrote to his wife on July 20, 1862, "and have no right to think, and are hardly allowed to sigh at the fall of our friends and relatives: and if we do happen to shed a tear secretly, it is soon dried up to make room for one for some one else."[58]

Callaway's outburst against military authority would seem to suggest a growing disillusionment with the army, but his remarks were made in the moment, and his intense feelings on the subject settled down in time as he came to see the value in organization and discipline. The Alabamian quickly discovered, as did virtually every other soldier during the war, that enlisted men needed to organize their own messes for emotional support and to meet material needs, given that shortages inevitably swept through the army. Messes formed an extended military family in which daily physical contact bred emotional intimacy. In fact, soldiers replicated familial-like relationships in the ranks, and they called the winter quarters they occupied their homes. Callaway joined a mess with three other men, which was typical among Civil War soldiers who needed to pool their resources together as well as their labor if they were to subsist in the field. He was fortunate that one of his messmates brought his slave to camp to do the onerous chores of cooking, sewing, and cleaning. Callaway said nothing more about the slave in his letters home, a typical reaction of Confederates, who reduced the "camp servant" to a tireless instrument of labor to be exploited for the comfort of the mess without regard to the fact that their slave had also been removed from his loved ones back in the slave quarters.

Confederate slaves were in the unusual and remarkable position of watching their masters submit to a higher authority, a truly shocking display of humility that they must have secretly and thoroughly enjoyed watching. The constraints on white supervision, moreover, allowed slaves to become roving entrepreneurs in camp—to build their own customer base and cook, clean, and sew for a profit. In some instances, they were allowed to retain a portion of their earnings. Such an arrangement enriched Confederate General William Dorsey Pender's slave for a while, but the good times came to an abrupt end when he walked into camp wearing clothing that was the envy of every white soldier. "The rascal seems to have plenty of money," Pender informed his wife, "but I have ordered him to allow me to be his treasurer. He has managed to dress himself in a nice gray uniform, French bosom linen shirt—for which he paid $4—has two pairs [of] new shoes."[59]

The presence of slaves in camp could remind men of all classes that their struggle would decide the fate of white liberty, and at the same time it could foster deep resentment between Confederate officers and private soldiers. It could not have been easy for a poor white soldier to watch a slave leave a marching column and forage for his master or to see slaves strip the Union dead of shoes, blankets, and equipment while having to remain in the ranks and under fire during the midst of a battle. A Louisiana soldier, forced to clean up the "entrails of fowls" covered with maggots and left in his captain's tent, could barely contain his rage while the "buck negroes of [the] officers stood around and grinned."

"The picture needs no varnish," he wrote, "and my comment is what could be more humiliating."[60] A Virginia artillerist also thought that slaves in the Confederate army enjoyed a privileged position, writing in his diary, "I wish I were an *army* nigger until 'this cruel war is over.' They are the happiest dogs I ever saw."[61] These resentments never boiled over into an attack against slaveholders, and the compliance of nonslaveholding whites cannot be fully explained as an expression of white solidarity. The privileges of slaveholding often intertwined with the advantages of rank, bestowing material benefits to members of the rank and file. On the one hand, it must have been galling to see slaves coming and going from the army without having to receive permission through the chain of command. Furloughs were as scarce as good shoes in the Confederacy, but slaves need not apply for leave, since their masters only had to sign a pass to secure a journey home. In this way, the slave functioned in a role that Confederate soldiers deemed the responsibility of a white patriarch, keeping lines of communication open with their communities while also carrying precious necessities to the front. Enlisted men knew better than to harm another man's slave property, especially if that property in some small way made life better in the ranks and for those back home.[62]

Messmates formed an extended military family in all armies that built intimate physical and emotional relationships. Their survival depended on their mutual cooperation and support to endure difficult times of privation. Messmates borrowed clothing, shared boxes of food from loved ones, and often bedded together under the same blanket. The physical closeness in camp often continued on the battlefield, where messmates were shoulder to shoulder, linked together as a band of brothers who overcame fear through their collective demonstrations of strength. If a man fell, he often died in the arms of a messmate who felt the loss of his comrade as if he were a family member. The death of one of his messmates devastated Charles Bowen, who felt free to open up in his diary and divulge emotions for a man that he could have never possibly felt in the civilian world. "I suffered a great loss in the person of a poor fellow whom I loved as well as a brother," Bowen wrote after a failed attack at Spotsylvania. "Poor George Neeger, my best friend in the army was shot through the head by my side. He never spoke but drank some water as though he still has sense. His troubles are over & I may soon meet him again in another world."[63]

The extended family created within the ranks originated within community-based networks of support. They were usually more attenuated for Union soldiers than they were for Southerners, especially for troops in the Western Theater, where deep advances could isolate soldiers for long periods of time, making it extremely difficult for individual family members and community leaders to travel to the army and offer direct aid to the rank and file.[64] As long as a soldier's home was within the orbit of military operations, relatives and friends, commissioned officers, and slaves brought vital necessities and welcome news from home. Only on a few occasions did Callaway complain of being stranded in the Confederate army, since he enjoyed reliable links to his hometown of Summerfield, Alabama. Food, clothing, and letters flowed back and forth with little interruption. Of the seventy-four letters written by Callaway during his service, at least nineteen were hand-carried to Summerfield. On ten other occasions, someone visiting the army carried a letter or package from his wife. At a bare minimum, 37 percent of all letters or parcels that reached Callaway were personally delivered from home. The number is likely higher, since Callaway did not always record who carried the goods and correspondence to and from camp.[65] Plenty of Callaway's letters went astray in the mail, even when he occupied a permanent camp at Corinth, but his friend Dr. Vaughan, who served as an unofficial courier, certainly lightened Callaway's anxiety over the welfare of his household. Dr. Vaughan also hand-delivered a portion of Callaway's pay to his wife, Dulcinea, with the instructions "If you got it you can [buy] anything you want." In return Callaway only wanted a shirt and one pair of socks, sewn with his initials to replace "my Yankee socks."[66]

Material conveniences from home enhanced comfort and the odds of surviving for all Civil War soldiers, but they were also tangible acknowledgments of the justness of a soldier suffering for his nation. Physical objects, however, only partially satisfied Civil War soldiers, who desired a fulfilling connection with their loved ones through the cultivation of uplifting emotions. Feeling the warm sympathy of a caring mother or the tenderness of a compassionate wife assured men of their value as son or husband as well as their standing as fighting soldiers. In some instances, couples essentially renewed their vows during the war, promising each other to elevate the sorrows of separation into a higher expression of romantic love based on a foundation of sacrifice and patriotism.[67]

The expressions of personal sentiments were not just private matters, but also a form of political participation, as evident in the Callaways' efforts to cultivate "pure" emotions for the cause of the Confederacy. Callaway repeatedly praised his wife for her cheerful writings, which lent him the necessary resolve to give himself physically to the nation. After comparing Dulcinea's letters to those written by the wives of other soldiers (when Callaway became a lieutenant he read his men's letters without their permission, not for the benefit of illiterate enlisted men, but to verify their political leanings), he determined that she stood as an exemplary Confederate woman. "I have seen & am constantly seeing the most desponding & patriotism killing letters imaginable written by women to their husbands in this co. or Reg. generally," he gushed with praise on June 16, 1862. "Indeed," he added, "I almost grumble, sometimes, at my own want of courage when I read your letters."[68] In this letter, as in others, Callaway sought his wife's sympathy as well as her approval. His sense of self-worth clearly depended on his wife's adulation.

Callaway's emotional openness with his wife was far from unusual, and in confiding to their wives Northern and Southern men showed their emotional vulnerability. Such admissions would have been unthinkable before the war, but the duress of soldiering forced men to adjust how they related to the women. In other words, they became emotional pragmatists out of necessity to cope with a military world that at times left them feeling lonesome and isolated. Yet no man wanted to appear weak and utterly helpless to those at home, especially to his wife. The language of "poor soldier" offered soldiers a way to preserve their sense of manliness by stressing how the everyday miseries of life were borne with heroic suffering while also acknowledging that there were uncontrollable forces of war that acted on them. Callaway could, like so many other men on both sides, elevate himself as a man of duty while still admitting that he was lost in the maelstrom of war, struggling to get by and unable to control or predict what might happen to him next. On June 22, 1862, Callaway popped the sentimental bubble of war, confessing to his wife that "the poor soldier knows nothing of the object of these moves, all he knows is that the order is issued & if he complains he is insulted if not punished."[69]

The "poor soldier" language did not completely undo the sentimental ideal of the "bold soldier boy." Rather, the words "poor soldier" offered Union and Confederate veterans a more realistic descriptor of the daily ordeals of army life, for it exemplified the nature of their suffering in the field. Suffering in silence did not trump battlefield courage in either army, but for the scores of soldiers like Callaway who only saw the distant smoke of battle and never smelled it, the gnawing hunger felt in camp and the bruising pain of a long march offered indisputable evidence of his fortitude and his devotion to the cause. After the 1862 Kentucky Campaign, where there was little fighting for Callaway's regiment but plenty of marching, Callaway did not have to invent battlefield exploits to prove that he and his men had risked everything for the Confederacy. "We are now naked, bare footed, dirty, filthy and lousy (with body lice only) beyond description. We have never been paid off yet. My little old blanket has long since failed & but for the kindness of my messmates who let me sleep with them I should long since 'have gone under,'" he wrote with unsparing honesty on October 27. "[It all feels] really that we are 'naked, poor, despised, forsaken.'" Only God's mercies could explain why only a few of his men perished, reasoned Callaway, who pronounced at the end of his letter: "I wonder that *any* could endure so much but we have endured it cheerfully and are still resolved by the grace of God, to be free."[70]

In conquering such hardships Callaway saw himself as a veteran, but his hardening to war's rigors did not deplete his idealism. He battled war weariness for much of the remainder of his service, but even during his darkest moments, when he was sick of this "abominable war," he told his wife that "starvation is much better than subjugation."[71] Fighting the Yankees was all he wanted, and his opportunity finally came at Chickamauga on September 19, 1863. The Confederates scored a smashing victory, but the murderous results of the fighting dashed Callaway's dreams of glory, and he was no different than men on both sides who struggled to convey the magnitude of battle. Most men shied away from frank assessments when writing home, worried that their reputations might suffer if they were too candid. Callaway, however, did not feel like he needed to hide anything from his wife. To his embarrassment, his men had skulked "behind trees [and] under the hill," even as a frightened enemy skedaddled from the field. Callaway could not find any peace that night, even though the battlefield was securely in Confederate hands. All he could think about was the falsity of the histories of Napoleon's campaigns that had enthralled him as a youth. The "sleep of a victorious army on field won is not very sweet when we are haunted all night long with the groans and cries of the wounded dying," Callaway wrote with a deep sadness. Everything around him had been obliterated. Shells and bullets had ripped open the ground and shredded the trees. Callaway sought consolation in being on the right side of the sod, but he wondered if he had fully acquitted himself under fire. His letter to his wife suggests a tinge of doubt: "I am proud to say that I don't think I did anything of which you or I or any of my friends need be ashamed."[72] His subdued tone and the blasé assessment of his performance hardly recalled the accolades lavished upon military heroes. Callaway was somewhat unusual in this regard, given that Civil War soldiers were prone to romantic exaggerations in reporting their battle exploits to those at home, especially during the war's first two years. The absence of male bravado in Callaway's Chickamauga letter reveals how a man troubled by the experience of combat did not necessarily shake him out of his belief in the cause and his desire to keep killing for it.

The heat of battle had cooled Callaway's ambitions in the army, but under no terms would he countenance submission to the Yankee foe. War had humbled Callaway, and survival without surrender was enough for him. A little more than a month after Chickamauga, while standing atop Missionary Ridge, surrounded by "the golden leaves of autumn" and looking over the spectacular

Tennessee River valley—a natural environment unadulterated by the armies—Callaway could not help but think of the "blessed quiet of home and *peace*." "I am sick of war as any man who ever deserted. But do not you think I have any notion of a similar course. No never," he promised his wife on November 1.[73] Twenty-four days later, standing on the same ground where he longed for home, Callaway fell with a wound through his bowels during a Union assault up Missionary Ridge. As he was carried off the field, Callaway begged his comrades to put him down so that they would not be captured. They placed him under a tree, where he died alone. His body, left to an enemy that buried him in an unmarked grave, was never to be recovered. W. F. Aycock, a comrade of Callaway's, informed Dulcinea of her husband's passing. "Never can his place in the Co. be filled," he wrote. "I feel at a loss without him as we started out in a mess together and remained together till he was wounded."

The bulk of Aycock's letter, however, did not memorialize Callaway, but was devoted instead to calculating the cost of dying in the Confederate army. Aycock, who was a second lieutenant, promised to return Callaway's clothes and other personal items, but he advised Dulcinea to sell her husband's bedding, "which will demand a good price here." The selling of the bedding seemed unavoidable, he counseled, since "he (Callaway) had left one months pay account wich [*sic*] it will take to pay the debts he owes in the Regt wich [*sic*] I shall collect and pay." In his final remarks, Aycock offered some comforting lines to Dulcinea, reminding her that Callaway was now in a place without war and what "is your and our loss is his Eternal gain."[74]

CHRISTIAN MARION EPPERLY
*Nonslaveholding Virginia Farmer*
Fifty-Fourth Virginia Infantry

From the moment that Christian Marion Epperly stepped into a Confederate camp in the spring of 1862, he looked to the Almighty to end the mighty cataclysm of war. Wherever he turned, he saw a stunning disregard for God's laws. As a passionate and devout Lutheran, Epperly was both baffled and disgusted by his comrades' "devil-may-care attitude," a term used by soldiers to describe men who lived for the moment and nothing else. Unless people started living by scripture, this "time of trouble" would turn apocalyptic, in Epperly's judgment. By 1863, he had given up on this simple solution to ending a war that increasingly confounded him. His prayers shifted away from appeals for people to exert themselves as Christians to end the war, and centered more on his personal survival and the safety of his family. As Epperly struggled to see a higher purpose in God's wrath, he came to accept that he was beholden to the authority of man in a war that he came to see as a material and spiritual struggle for individual survival.

Epperly never filtered his suffering through the lens of sentimentalism. His sense of isolation in the ranks stemmed more from his religious opposition to war's inhumanity than from his political hostility to the Confederacy. No sense of camaraderie overcame Epperly, unlike most Civil War soldiers, whose devotion to each other was nearly indestructible.[75] Epperly tried to draw a line between himself and his boisterous comrades, vainly searching for a quiet place in camp where he could commune with God and avert his eyes, but the sounds of sin were raucous and irrepressible. If the wind carried a whiff of drunken laughter, Epperly felt "lonsom and desolate."

Although Epperly was prodded into Confederate service under the threat of conscription, he was no less ideological than Civil War soldiers who were part of the patriotic surge of 1861.[76] Epperly initially thought secession was just, but he came to express his vision of peace with increasing conviction, and by 1864, while in the ranks of the Army of Tennessee, Epperly turned into a closet Unionist. It is tempting to attribute his antiwar sentiments to his civilian life in Floyd County, Virginia—an area of the state renowned for its hostility to the Confederacy—where Epperly lived before the war with his wife, two children, and widowed mother-in-law. The mountains and wooded coves offered a perfect hideout for deserters to bushwhack home guard units and Confederate forces.[77] Reports of Floyd County descending into guerrilla warfare were always on Epperly's mind. He worried incessantly about his family, but the presence of a fifth column did not cause an instantaneous conversion to Unionism.[78] The calculations of soldier loyalty were far more complex than knitting together ideological statements, motivational factors, and morale into an expression of identity or nationalism. The variables were endless, and make any attempt at modeling soldier behavior difficult to predict. Epperly's example is a case in point. On the surface, he seemed to resemble the class of nonslaveholders who condemned the Confederacy for spilling the blood of poor people for a bunch of arrogant slaveholders. It is true that Epperly had little love for the rich, and he thought Confederate impressment policies gutted Virginia farms at the expense of the needy. Yet he remained politically neutral for much of the war, even as he wrote antiwar declarations imploring humankind to live in peace as God desired for all of his people. His moral reservations against the inhumanity of war, more than anything else, fueled Epperly's political dissidence.

Homesickness was a universal condition in Civil War armies, and some men were more vulnerable to fits of loneliness than others. Living in close physical proximity in camp could lead to emotional seclusion for men like Epperly, who showed no interest in soldier diversions around the campfire. Epperly's sense of estrangement from his comrades was acute, but it is hard to imagine that he did not find someone in the ranks who shared his enthusiasm for reading the Bible, praying, and going to hear a sermon. Epperly could not have persevered through so many hardships without forming a relationship with a comrade, but his letters say little about the men in his company. Military authorities had little patience for melancholic soldiers like Epperly, insisting that men of character possessed the power to defeat depression and demoralization if they were sufficiently trained and better disciplined.[79] The culture of sentimentalism reinforced the military's notion that a man of true character could overcome the physical separation of home and find emotional resolve by simply drawing on memories of mothers and wives. This message propped up scores of men during trying times, but for Union and Confederate soldiers who were on the economic and cultural margins of their armies, dreaming about home could lay bare the indignities of army life, leaving them more restless and desperate to go home. "I dream of being at home every night and kissing the children," Epperly wrote on April 24, 1863, "but when I wake up in the morning I am still here in this distressing situation."[80]

Epperly found refuge in writing to his wife, Mary, and when he put pen to paper he delivered his words as if he were speaking directly to her. His letters, though pulsating with raw emotions, were strikingly different from the ones Bowen and Callaway sent to their wives. The Virginian felt free to bare his soul of all his tormented emotions and worries. His confessions were put forth without any pretenses of protecting public honor or any fear of being unmasked as cowardly. In one desperate letter, Epperly admitted that "it would be a pleasure to me to die . . . if we could go together." However, he recanted in the next line. "But the Idy of never Seeing you and the children on urth again I cannot bear."[81] Bowen and Callaway never wrote home without reminding their wives that womanly love propelled them to fight for their nation and that their political cause depended on shared sacrifice. Epperly, on the other hand, expressed his version of sentimentalism in images of domestic bliss without regard to the outcome of the war or his reputation in the ranks. In one exchange of letters during August 1863, Epperly wrote his wife about the orchards on their Floyd County home, which he imagined were blooming and "getting good by this time."

The thought of ripe fruit could not be divorced from the army's monotonous rations of meat and bread that left him in a half-starving condition.[82] It was a diet of deprivation, and it could cause Civil War soldiers to question whether their lives mattered to the army. Apples reminded Epperly of what he had had before the war — of the land he had farmed, of the crops he had raised, and of the food he had put on the family table for his wife and children to enjoy. His wife was of the same mind. She wrote in response: "Dear Husban you wrote in your leter that you wished you was at home to get som aples to eat. . . . I never eat a apel without thinking about you and wish you had some and when I set down to eat and think about that you have nothing but meats and bread and sometimes . . . I can hardly stand it. I would be willing to live on bread and water if I could just give you what I have to eat but I hope the day is not fare distant when we can share with each other." She would not let her dreams induce him to leave. In letter after letter she warned her husband that runaway soldiers were being hunted down in Floyd County.[83]

A few months after expressing his desire to eat apples at home, Epperly defied his wife and deserted his regiment at Knoxville, Tennessee, some 270 miles from his home in Floyd County. Though the choice to flee was his most momentous decision of the war, Epperly never spelled out his reasons. His wife must have been surprised when her husband walked through the front door in early September 1863. Up to that point, Epperly had reminded Mary that he had no choice but to remain in the ranks. Too many guns surrounded him inside the army, and there were plenty of muskets blazing away in Floyd County. He knew that there were a "heap of men at hom," but he was not inspired by their boldness. Their exodus, he predicted just eight days before taking flight himself, would turn Floyd County into a killing ground. "I fear ther will be Blooddy times yet by men Running away," he predicted on August 27, given that Confederates forces would inevitably hunt down deserters. Epperly did not doubt that "it will go hard with them for they wont have much pitty on them."[84] His reasoning undoubtedly kept scores of Southern soldiers fixed in the ranks.

Why Epperly suddenly changed his mind and bolted for home is a difficult question to answer, but it cannot be read as an act of revolt against the Confederacy. Epperly left, it appears, for self-preservation. He offers a few clues as to his motivation. In late August, he reported to his wife that a "ganerl movement [would] be made befor long." If he stayed put, Epperly knew that he would likely find himself in the midst of another horrible battle, writing, "I fear ther will be Blooddy times yet," and he knew that his chances of getting killed by the Yankees were just as good as, maybe even better than, falling into the hands of Confederate guards while trying to get home.[85] The odds of surviving as a deserter significantly improved once Jefferson Davis granted amnesty to all deserters on August 1. This was only supposed to apply to men who were away from their posts, but scores of Confederates like Epperly, who were still in the army, decided that Davis had essentially granted them an "authorized" furlough

Winslow Homer's *Pay-Day in the Army of the Potomac* shows men in a spending frenzy after the elusive paymaster has finally arrived in camp. Readers of *Harper's Weekly* must have felt they were in the midst of a mob of soldiers consumed by an uncontrollable urge to buy items at the sutler store. Homer's decision to place two smaller portraits of soldiers sending money home comes across as a rebuke of the spend-free habits of most enlisted men. Poor soldiers like Christian Epperly rarely had the extra funds to buy from the sutler or to send to his wife and children. His financial situation turned dire after Chickamauga, when the army docked his monthly pay for desertion.
(Wilson Library, University of North Carolina)

home. This was not the president's intention, but that made no difference to Epperly, who in early September left his gun behind in camp, dodged the regimental guards, and started the journey that eventually brought him home to Floyd County. He stayed at home for two months, and when he returned to camp in late December his regiment was considerably smaller, its ranks having been thinned by the vicious fighting at Chickamauga.

As soon as he reached the Army of Tennessee, Epperly was put under arrest and escorted to a guardhouse, where he remained for ten days until he returned to the ranks without having to face additional charges of misconduct. "I am very thankful that wee got off so well as wee did," he informed his wife on January 4, 1864. "Wee will have our guns to pay for but I will give tenn times that to be at home a month any time tho wee had a long walk to get their."[86] Epperly likely wrote this without knowing that the army would charge him $58.58 for replacing his weapon and accoutrements, a financial penalty that consumed his monthly pay of eleven dollars for a little more than five months. Epperly was suddenly destitute, and the scarcity of money hit his household hard.

Like so many others across the South and North, the household collapsed without wages coming from the ranks. In the four letters that survive from Epperly's wife, three written in August 1863 and one in March 1865, she explained to her "Dear and Absent Husban" that deserters found a safe haven in Floyd County, since the home guard showed no interest in tracking down runaways, while at the same time speculators preyed on poor people by inflating the prices of produce.[87] Epperly and other Confederate soldiers could do little from the ranks. Only state and local governments could provide relief, and as early as 1862, a group of Floyd County citizens complained to Richmond authorities that many of the soldiers' wives and families were starving and without shoes. Whether Mary Epperly was one of those women is difficult to say, but her status as a soldier's wife gave her the power to make claims upon local courts for relief, and she likely sought some public assistance, but government support did little to quell the internal conflicts of Floyd County. It is also important to note that Mary Epperly, like so many Confederate women, did not exist in a world absent of men, even though she was the head of her own household. Her role and responsibilities certainly expanded on this unfamiliar ground, but women could call on the elders of the community or disabled soldiers on permanent leave if necessary. In poorer rural households in the North, a similar situation existed where lower-class women lived on a marginal existence, dependent on neighborly support and often some form of government assistance while their husbands were away in the army. The result, as historian Judith Giesberg has shown, was that Northern women heading a household faced a precarious situation, given that the loss of male labor and income kept women "in constant motion, doubling up the work of caring for children with taking over work on the farm."[88] Although Northern soldiers did not have to worry about their communities engulfed in guerrilla warfare as Epperly did, plenty of men who wore the Union blue heard similar messages of deprivation and hardship from wives who refused to frame their suffering as a sacrifice for the nation.

Fragile household economies were inseparable from a perilous soldier economy that kept enlisted men hanging on by a gossamer thread. Irregular mail, overdrawn clothing allowances, inadequate rations, and, above all else, an inept pay system continually made daily life exceedingly challenging for the rank and file. The army also routinely fined soldiers for misbehavior or charged for replacement items, including lost cartridges, caps, buckles, and bayonets.

In the Army of Tennessee during the summer of 1863, soldiers were charged twenty-five cents for a lost cartridge and five cents for missing percussion caps. Any travel expenses incurred when going home on furlough also came from a Confederate or Union soldier's wallet, not from their government. A wrong box checked or a misfiled form came at the soldier's expense as well. "There is one boy in our Co that has bin charge 24 dollars for transportation and he never went anywheirs," a Wisconsin soldier wrote home. "You see he was at the hospitol and he applied for the furlow, and they went to work and got out his papers of transportation and charge it to him and he did not go home but was sent rite to the frunt."[89] Even in death, as with Callaway, officers subtracted unpaid debts and other charges from the deceased's pay.

A soldier economy played a critical role in framing the alternatives of resistance as perceived by the rank and file. In Epperly's case, his Fifty-Fourth Virginia had one of the highest desertion rates in the Army of Tennessee, even though officers exercised an astonishing degree of control over the daily movements of their men. A rare regimental order book from the National Archives, for instance, reveals that the Fifty-Fourth Virginia's officers were desperate to stop the flow of deserters. In one instance, they tightened the camp perimeter from two miles to a half mile, called roll call three times a day, and instructed "any man caught without a pass to be shot without the formality of a trial."[90] In the face of such overwhelming authority, Epperly and his comrades could not form but the frailest of alliances. In the spring of 1864 the officers of the Fifty-Fourth Virginia tried to put flour barrels on delinquent men, but Epperly's comrades stepped in and "busted them [barrels] to peases and wold not let it be done." The fracas ended when an unnamed colonel ordered another regiment to fire into the mob. Shots were exchanged, and scores of men were killed and wounded, but Epperly claimed victory once the smoke cleared. He saw that "they di[d] not get they Barles on atoll."[91]

For the remainder of 1864 and until the surrender of Confederate forces in the spring of 1865, Epperly expressed with increasing candor his hope for a Union victory without regard for the possible political consequences of the South's collapse. He made no mention of possible racial wars, nor did he seem to envision African Americans let loose on white women once Confederate armies disbanded. What to make of this silence is difficult to say, when it is clear that Southern soldiers of all classes were enraged when they confronted black troops.

Ending the inhumanity of war, even if it resulted in racial upheaval, mattered above all else: "I hope God will have murcey on us and bring this cruel war to an end that wee ma meet on urth again to live in peas Union and harmony to goeth as Christians ought to live."[92] When his feelings gave way to despair, Epperly pulled himself up with the knowledge that God "has always been my friend and brough me safe throo maney daingerous and gloomey plases." He wrote with gratitude on November 8, 1864: "Blest with good Health and doing as well as a Por souldier could exspect being so far from our soplis [supplies]."[93] Epperly must have been living off the land, since the Confederate commissary was virtually barren at this late stage of the war and he could not afford civilian prices for produce. "Wee have getting Sweet Potatoes for 10 and 12 dollars a bushel sins wee cam to this plase but they wont last long," he reported to his wife. "Money is verry scearce here[.] I haven't drawd but 44 dollars sins I have been with the Regt[.] they owe me now seven month wiages and 45 dollar clothing money for last year."[94]

Poor finances, a long distance to home, and a military regime determined to break up soldier solidarity kept Epperly hemmed in within the ranks of the Confederate army. This largely explains why he did not desert during the great Confederate exodus of 1865, but asking how Epperly endured gets us deeper into his coping strategies. His Lutheran faith, above all else, gave him the strength to live with tyrannical officers, depraved comrades, physical exhaustion, and the awful loneliness of being away from his family. Always looking down on him was a forgiving and compassionate God, whom Epperly trusted to save the world from committing self-annihilation by bringing this "time of trouble" to an end. Epperly's spirituality was his most potent weapon of survival, opening up his imagination so that he could dream of an alternative world, far removed from the confines of military life, and allowing him to soar above the daily miseries and sins of soldiering to a future place where peace and reunion reigned. With the help of his wife, Epperly continued to feel the presence of God as a guiding and protective force. As he walked home to Floyd County after Joseph Johnston's surrender, the words from his last letter were fulfilled just as he knew they would be: "You need not be much surpised to see me at hom some time this spring if my life is spared. . . . I feel ashurd god will not for sake [me]."[95]

## WILLIAM WALKER
### Former Slave
### Third South Carolina Colored Infantry

On March 1, 1864, Sergeant William Walker of the Third South Carolina Colored Infantry waited at the base of a hollow square composed of black soldiers for the order that would ultimately take his life. His eyes were bandaged and his hands and feet were bound together; sweat streaked down his face under a Florida sun when the command to fire finally broke the horrible silence. A ragged volley followed, but just a single bullet struck Walker in what can only be explained as a bold act of defiance by the firing squad. White officers immediately rushed a reserve company of black soldiers forward, halting them at point-blank range, where they unloaded their weapons into Walker's writhing body.[96] Walker's life ended with such violence because he demanded the rights accorded to white soldiers, including equal pay, the resumption of government support to black soldier families, and an end to the exploitation of men as if they were common field hands; this sparked a mutiny in his regiment that Walker had helped to foment. If he had ever imagined himself a casualty for the cause of freedom, Walker probably thought he would be slain on the battlefield, fighting the Rebels to the bitter end, and not before a firing squad of his own comrades.

Walker was one of fourteen African Americans condemned to death for the crime of mutiny during the Civil War. Only five white soldiers were executed for the same offense. The racial disparity in justice, though hardly surprising, underscores the gross inequities between black and white troops during the Civil War. Walker's example is also valuable in illustrating how the day-to-day acts of being a black soldier were intertwined with family histories, local economies, and the military's overriding power to determine who worked where and under what terms. Unequal pay, abusive officers, and endless work details embittered scores of black soldiers.[97] Similar complaints came from whites serving in Union and Confederate armies, but in no way does this suggest that conditions were even remotely the same for the two races. They were not, but the circumstances surrounding Walker's arrest raise related inquiries into the nature and range of soldier grievances and the subversive will of Civil War soldiers. Their acts of protest, ranging from acts of trickery to conspiratorial plots of violence, show that Civil War soldiers simultaneously saw themselves as disposable pieces of property—used and persecuted by authoritarian officers and an unthinking army bureaucracy—while still feeling an incredible attachment to their comrades and the very units that were partially responsible for their exploitation.

Walker did not have to enlist in the Third South Carolina Infantry. He thought he was exempt from conscription because he had been working as a civilian gunboat pilot since running away from a South Carolina plantation in 1861. Two years later, while ashore on leave, recruiters persuaded Walker to enlist with the "solemn promise" that he would receive $13 a month and a clothing allowance of $3.50. This was a drastic pay cut from his pilot's salary, which ranged between $30 and $40 month. Instead of heading to the drilling fields to master the science of soldiering, Walker and his comrades were ordered to the docks to perform gang labor on coaling ships. The army had wasted no time in asserting its legal right to master the bodies of black soldiers by reducing them to mere "hands." Day in and day out, Walker and his comrades labored under the constant surveillance of officers who did nothing to stop passing white soldiers from spewing racial insults at the toiling black soldiers. The white officers appeared impotent to do anything that might even remotely improve the confidence of the rank and file. Willful negligence partially explains the ineffectiveness of the white officers. For days at a time, the regiment's lieutenants and captains disappeared from camp, essentially abandoning their men, who were eager for proper military training. Some of the white officers were downright corrupt, as they were caught stealing the men's rations. By the middle of June twenty members of Walker's company decided that they had had enough of the soldiering charade and deserted.[98]

A crisis could overtake Civil War regiments where officers either were slipshod or ruled with iron fists over enlisted men who felt that the covenant they had made with the army had been violated. The men's sense of injustice did not originate from the notion of male independence or the belief in the prerogatives of the citizen-soldier. While these cultural ideas mattered a great deal, it was the material realities of their situation and the power relations of a particular unit that gave rise to a soldier's assertion that he should control his time and body—a claim that should be understood as a survival strategy. At the end of a long and grueling march or while enduring the tedium of a permanent camp, sergeants and corporals had the daily task of assigning fatigue duties. These chores were both loathsome and demoralizing to veterans, especially when they were at their physical and emotional limits after a grueling day in the field. Cutting firewood, carrying buckets of water, setting up an officer's tent, performing guard duty, and digging latrines required that commissioned and noncommissioned officers make additional demands.

These repeated tasks could create the perception that officers were acting arbitrarily by always protecting their pets while picking on those soldiers who had seemingly fallen into perpetual disfavor. Enlisted men had a long memory, and over time an accumulation of resentments could lead to a minor incident exploding into a violent exchange. In Battery G of the First Pennsylvania Artillery, for instance, Sergeant Thomas D. Fields ordered the men to fall into the ranks under a cold February rain. From his tent, Private William Wolf yelled: "God damn you, are you going to have us out to roll call again?" Fields insisted that Wolf join the company, telling him that he was only carrying out the orders of the lieutenant. Wolf did not care who was responsible, calling Fields a "damn loafer; son of a bitch, [and] a bummer." Months later, during a subsequent court-martial, Fields recalled that Wolf then shouted, "If it was not for my [Fields's] stripes, he [Wolf] would knock shit out of me." When Fields called for assistance from the corporal-of-guard, Wolf tackled Fields, grabbing his throat and hitting him repeatedly in the face until they were eventually separated and the fiery Wolf was escorted to the guardhouse.[99]

Civil War soldiers of all backgrounds jumped into these free-for-alls, but in writing their official reports both Union and Confederate officers often removed themselves from these brawls by blaming "undesirables" as devious instigators. The poor, immigrants, African Americans, conscripts, and substitutes were popular scapegoats. They were portrayed as an inferior class of men whose perceived deficiencies in morals and in manliness made it impossible for them to become "good soldiers."[100] That citizen-soldiers were too proud to submit to military authority offers only a surface reading of these ugly episodes between enlisted men and officers who clashed over control of labor and access to limited resources.

The examples of William Wolf and William Walker are telling. Weary from being in the field and doing the job of the soldier, Wolf wanted to stay in his tent, seeing no reason why he should expose himself to the elements and endanger his health. Although it is likely that Wolf did not appreciate any man telling him what to do, he did not respond to authority in a culturally mechanical way, nor did he see his superior as part of an elite and adversarial class. Rather, it is telling that Wolf called Fields a "loafer" and "bummer," implying that he was not doing his share of the work. This had little to do with rank and everything to do with his frustration of existing in a military system that determined who worked and under what terms.

Every day William Walker and the men of the Third South Carolina Colored Infantry marched to the docks without their muskets or accoutrements. Their blue uniforms essentially mocked them, as the heavy lifting nullified male dignity in a world where soldiers were men only when they killed on the battlefield. The men of the Third South Carolina Colored Infantry were little better than slaves, and their emasculation was complete when the jeers of white soldiers came raining down on them. In fact, everything was closing down on the camp of the Third South Carolina Colored Infantry and an internal battle was clearly brewing. The first "skirmish" occurred on August 23 when Walker refused Lieutenant George W. Wood's order to leave the docks immediately. The two men must have exchanged words, likely over the issue of pay and the excessive hours spent on fatigue duty. As soon as Walker returned to camp, he grabbed a musket, waved it in the air, and yelled, "I will shoot him [Lt. Wood]!" A captain tried to arrest Walker, but the sergeant could not be restrained. He told his superior that he had better call the provost guard if he had any intentions of shackling him. These bold words, according to one white observer, sparked a "mutinous and noisy" rage among the black enlisted men. Eventually the soldiers were quieted and they returned to their tents. It is not clear how they were placated; nor do we know whether the provost guard subdued Walker, who was eventually confined to his tent rather than the guardhouse, which was no small victory for Walker and his comrades.[101] The duration of Walker's arrest is difficult to determine, but for the most part he lay low for the remainder of the summer and through the early fall while his regiment continued its slow and depressing spiral downward. Every day, as the soldiers carried themselves back to the docks, they likely combined their hopes for equal pay and improved working conditions with preparations to take matters into their own hands.

The tipping point for the Third South Carolina Colored Infantry came in early November when the army stopped distributing rations for the families of black soldiers. The unthinking callousness behind this order was not the handiwork of the unit's white officers. Army headquarters in nearby Beaufort justified the move because of rising black "dependence upon the Government for food and clothing." "Even at the risk of some suffering," the officers in Beaufort insisted that the families should not be regarded as "'destitute'" even though their husbands in the army "are receiving seven dollars a month."[102] The Third South Carolina Colored Infantry had come face-to-face with a hard truth about Civil War soldiering. Military policies reached behind the lines, shaping, limiting, and even controlling the lives of loved ones who were contending with shortages in food, manpower, and cash. Very little could be done from the ranks to maneuver around this destructive regulation from Beaufort that had the effect of pressing black soldiers and their families down below the subsistence level.

As if intolerable conditions and destitution in the ranks were not enough, Walker and his comrades watched with indignation as newly arrived freed people secured lucrative positions in the quartermaster and commissary departments — the very positions that black soldiers like Walker had relinquished in order to fight the Rebels. In a petition sent to Beaufort, every white commissioned officer in the Third South Carolina Colored Infantry agreed that "the cause of much grievance to the colored Troops of this Command arises mainly from the partiality shown to men of their own Nationality employed in the Several Departments [quartermaster and commissary]." Their appeal turned this injustice into a black problem that left them off the hook for their malfeasances and general negligence.[103]

The November 19, 1863, mutiny in the unit was grounded in long-standing grievances over unequal pay and working conditions and expressed through nonviolent collaboration and conspiratorial planning. The day began with the drummer Ranty Pope announcing that he would not "beat the fatigue call" because "it was no day for work." A white superior demanded that he play on the spot or risk being tied up. Sergeant Walker happened to be standing nearby, and he quickly interceded, warning the white officer that if he tied Ranty Pope up, then he better have enough muscle to shackle Walker as well. In front of the court-martial that assembled on January 1864, the judge advocate asked the white officer how he responded to Walker's brazen act of insubordination. The officer showed remarkable candor in his answer: "The camp was in a state of excitement and I did not like the looks of Ser[g]t. Walker at the time. . . . I was actually afraid of him." He apparently did not try to "shackle" Walker, because moments later Walker marched his company to the tent of Lieutenant Colonel A. G. Bennett, where they stacked rifles and hung their accoutrements on their bayonets. The men made such a racket that Bennett emerged from his quarters to see the stunning display of rebelliousness. "What does all this mean?" he demanded, but silence greeted the colonel, even after repeated inquiries. Walker eventually stepped forward and announced that they would no longer serve for seven dollars a month. The colonel commanded the men to take their weapons and return to duty or he would report them all to the "Post Commander, who would certainly have them all shot down." No one budged, thanks in part to Walker, who kept telling "the men not to take their arms." Walker's company obeyed their sergeant, and they walked away from the colonel, leaving their weapons to stand as a silent protest against the injustices perpetuated against them by their own army and government.[104]

On January 9, 1864, Walker stood before a general court-martial to answer for his role in the mutiny (which coincidentally took place on the same day that President Abraham Lincoln delivered his Gettysburg Address). Despite an aggressive legal defense from a lieutenant of a New York regiment, Walker was convicted of mutinous behavior, a crime that he was certainly guilty of committing. Yet there were justifiable grounds for acquittal. In his affidavit, signed with his mark, Walker stated under oath: "Never, since the organization of the company have the 'Articles of War' been read to us nor any part of the 'Regulations' even." Such an oversight resulted in the acquittal of scores of white soldiers, but Walker, an illiterate black man and former slave, was denied the prerogatives of white citizen-soldiers and was executed less than two months later.

For the crime of mutiny there could be no ending for the condemned except a firing squad. Outright rebellion was plain foolishness for even the most desperate and aggrieved soldiers. The pragmatics of survival demanded that the men be risk averse when venting their frustrations. Cursing, silence, mocking, malingering, practical jokes, taunting, and jeering were ways of managing anger and controlling aggression while still asserting their dignity and making a point without risking harsh retaliation from superiors. Individual cries of injustice needed to be lost in the cacophony of the crowd. Under the veil of darkness, for instance, it was common for packs of soldiers to let loose with savage barking. A seemingly pointless march in February 1864 unleashed a thunderstorm of howls that rolled across the Army of the Potomac. "Such shouting I never heard in my life [and] they kept [it] up initially they got into camp," a New York soldier reported home. "Then they took a turn and swore nearly as loud as they had cheered. I do not know of anything that will enrage volunteers so much as tramping through the mud without having some definite good come out of it," he added caustically.[105] The anonymity of a vast camp, especially at dusk, offered enlisted men an opportunity to violate the sanctity of rank. They took well-aimed shots of ridicule at certain officers for an abusive order or for some past transgression. "A stout-lunged soldier," a veteran of the Army of the Cumberland recalled, would begin the ritual by shouting "at the top of his voice a question touching upon some foible or peccadillo of an officer. Another stentorian patriot, perhaps at some distant point in the regiment, would answer by yelling out the name of the officer in a tone that could be heard half a mile." The same veteran of the Army of the Cumberland recounted the details of a typical "colloquial exercise":

> "Who stole the ham?" shouted an anxious inquirer.
> "Captain Smith!" was the answer, loud and clear.
> "Who got behind a tree at Stone River?"—from another voice.
> "Lef-tenant Brown!"
> "Who gobbled the lone widow's chickens?"
> "Who drank too much applejack?"
> "Major Robinson!"
> "Who got sick at Mission Ridge?"
> "Lieutenant Johnsing!"
> "Who tried to run from the guards and got nabbed?"
> "Colonel Williams!"
> "Who stole the black bottle from the sutler?"
> "Lieutenant Druzenberry!"
> "Who played off to ride in the ambulance?"
> "Captain Smart!"[106]

The night jeering of soldiers, though offering a much-needed release of pent-up emotion, actually points to the relatively weak position from which the rank and file could effect meaningful change in the army. Every morning when soldiers awoke, the physical space of camp remained firmly in the control of officers. The latter almost always exerted complete domination over the structure of the workday. The round-the-clock surveillance, the incessant fatigue duty, and the intrusive inspections created frustration that could boil over into unrest, but black soldiers discovered that they had to be circumspect given a military court system that held them to a more severe code of justice.[107]

The narratives of Haydon, Walker, Bowen, Epperly, and Callaway follow similar plot lines in crucial ways. All of these men endured a process of military professionalization backed by physical violence and aimed at transforming the individual into obedient soldiers for their nation. They all resented and resisted the authoritarian ways of their officers; they all felt abandoned at some point by their army and their governments for leaving them broke, hungry, and half-starved; they all were trapped in a predatory economy; and they all were inextricably connected, both financially and emotionally, to loved ones behind the lines. These overlapping experiences would seem to argue for a common soldier identity, but such a sweeping claim is unsustainable when one considers race, class, gender, and ethnicity. Other critical differences emerge when accounting for the very specific circumstances in which men soldiered. The intersection between the physical demands of soldiering and the landscape, where fierce collisions between soldiers and military authorities occurred, varied based on a soldier's background and place in the ranks.[108]

The words and actions of Haydon, Bowen, Walker, Epperly, and Callaway suggest that in the ranks soldiers interacted with their comrades and related to those at home in new ways that suspended traditional understandings of manhood. The physical separation from home and the perils of surviving in the ranks unleashed powerful feelings that surprised the men themselves. The intensity of their emotions challenged soldiers to rein in such strong feelings as they had been instructed to do before the war. Rather than weakening masculinity, the war made it more malleable. The flexibility of their emotional dispositions, as historian James Broomall correctly points out, calls into question the idea that Civil War soldiers aspired to uphold a single model of martial manhood.[109] The pliability of manliness arose out of the desire to endure, and as a form of resistance to a military regime that tried to strip the soldier of his individualism.

The military's uncompromising demand of soldiers to give their labor triggered pragmatic responses from the ranks on two levels. Men improvised in how they actually performed their various duties, and they also altered their ideas about what they considered acceptable practices in waging war. Of all the tasks, soldiers on both sides showed the greatest ingenuity and situational thinking in how they lived off the land. The inevitable privations of soldiering coupled with irregular and inadequate pay spurred men to adapt or unnecessarily risk their lives. A soldier could not simply act on a pragmatic impulse. Circumstances as well as his racial background, class standing as well as his physical proximity to his household and community largely shaped what choices were seen as possible. A fairly privileged soldier like Callaway, who was almost always in communication with family and friends, could usually tap a steady stream of goods and clothing that flowed from his Alabama home. Even Callaway came to appreciate the necessity of adaptability. He turned into an expert forager, using his rank as a lieutenant to slip away from his regiment without fear of serious punishment or fines. The Alabamian almost always returned with fruits and vegetables for his company, but not before stopping at a local farmhouse to enjoy a home-cooked meal. In a June 21, 1863, letter to his wife, he described a foraging expedition across a rainy countryside in the middle of the night, portraying it as a test of individual will: "When [I] got in I found all my mess uneasy about me, afraid I would undertake to come across there in the night. They say it was almost a superhuman feat. I hope, My darling, that this account of my adventure will be some relief from the dull monotony of my letters."[110] In turning his scavenging mission into high drama Callaway stayed true to the sentimentalist impulses that beat strongly inside him, and in his mind and on paper he reworked his understanding of the bold soldier to accommodate the unexpected but inescapable monotony of scraping by in the army. In the end Callaway showed himself to be a pragmatist by justifying the means by the ends. His indiscriminate foraging challenged early war expectations of proper conduct toward civilians. In less than a year of service he gave license to stealing in order to meet practical needs, which in turn helped foster a bond of brotherhood in his company that likely eased class tensions and soothed resentments that enlisted men may have harbored toward their officers, as evident in the Winslow Homer painting *In Front of Yorktown*.

To suggest that deprivation produced soldier solidarities, however, demands qualification. Empty stomachs and ragged clothes did not lay the material groundwork for a collaborative spirit in the ranks. Scores of desperate men took to stealing—a crime commonly reported in Civil War regiments, where the scramble for the same resources eviscerated any mystical feeling of comradeship. Pay lost or stolen in letters home was not infrequent, and when it occurred it was devastating to soldiers and their families.[111] Civil War soldier

*Comrades, Camp, and Community*

memoirist Wilbur F. Hinman, in his underappreciated but immensely important fictional account *Corporal Si Klegg and His "Pard,"* conveyed the survivalist mentality that overtook many veterans. When the naive and inexperienced Si hesitates to accept a stolen blanket from the battle-tested and pragmatic Shorty, the latter offers him a quick lesson in army ethics: "Now, pard, never you mind the buts. Ther' aint't nothin' ter be said 'bout it. Ye've got a good blanket 'n' ye wants ter freeze to it. Ye'll have ter larn ter look out fer yerself, same's all the rest on 'em does."[112]

Household relationships also proved crucial in shaping how soldiers imagined the range of viable political options from their place in the ranks. The collapse of Walker's South Carolina household is a particularly powerful example, since the termination of support to black soldiers' families factored into his decision to organize a mutiny. In the face of similar perils, it is curious that more Civil War soldiers did not engage in acts of mutiny like Walker. Screaming out loud against imperious officers could earn a man a few days in the guardhouse, but a direct and open subversion of military authority could get a man killed. Ritual executions in both armies reminded members of the rank and file to stay away from comrades who spoke of plots and rebellion.

Deep fissures existed in the ranks of both Northern and Southern armies. With the Confederate draft in 1862, followed by the Union's conscription act the next year, veterans on both sides did not give conscripts and bounty men an easy initiation into the band of brothers. Racism, nativism, and classism fueled hostility to all soldiers, not just new recruits. The incessant quarrelling in Civil War regiments cannot, however, be reduced to a class battle between the privileged elite on one side and the hard-drinking roughs on the other. Their internal battles occurred over the control of their bodies, their labor, and their access to very limited resources. Soldier tricks might appear as harmless shenanigans, but they were often violent acts of intimidation with the intent of pushing back on an officer's authority. A Michigan corporal, for instance, was walking through his regiment's winter quarters when he fell into the hands of two soldiers who lunged at him with "a red hot poker" and "a red hot shovel." They demanded that he do a jig while holding up his right hand and swearing "eternal fidelity to his squad." The corporal initially refused, until the hot weapons were moved "in close proximity" to his "bare legs." Once he finished his dance the two soldiers demanded an encore, insisting that the corporal "stand on his head." The man tried to resist, but "the hot pokers & bayonets had by this time so multiplied around him that there was no escape." After this last feat was performed, an observer noted, the humbled corporal "was allowed to retire to his bunk."[113] That humiliating corporals and other noncommissioned officers became a popular sport in Civil War armies suggests how difficult it was for enlisted men to declare open opposition against higher military authority without risking their necks.

Yet even on those rare occasions when soldiers collectively organized and protested, their aims were not intended to overturn the military hierarchy or to alter the ideological or political goals of the war. Open defiance was almost always confined to soldier outrage over the army's failure to provide for and to protect the men in the ranks. The Eighty-Seventh New York Infantry, for instance, staged a mutiny when the unit was amalgamated into the Fortieth New York. The possibility of being absorbed into a new regiment decimated unit pride and often led to lost promotions in both armies. The men of the Eighty-Seventh reluctantly formed into line, grumbling that they "would not submit" to any consolidation. They faced toward the veterans of the Fortieth New York, who stood at "shoulder arms and fixed bayonets." When the order came for Company A to be transferred, not a single man moved. An officer in the Fortieth New York ordered his men to load at will. He repeated it a dozen times, but "a great many," according to Jonathan Sproul of the Fortieth New York, "put nothing but powder in their pieces and threw the ball away. Others would not put anything in but only go through the motions of loading." The officers were "furious," and in the face of such united opposition they decided to call out the names of each soldier in every company. As soon as each man stepped forward, two guards surrounded him, and Sproul was certain that "we were going to the stake for execution." Instead, each man was escorted to his new quarters until the consolidation was complete. The entire episode left the veterans of the Eighty-Seventh New York embittered, but they were extremely fortunate, for their white skin likely saved them from a court-martial and a possible firing squad.[114]

Yet even as comrades directed violence against each other, they came to express a soldier consciousness—though not a solidarity—through the language of "poor soldier," which captured how veterans came to see themselves as things for the army to exploit or as victims of uncontrollable forces. To those at home, "poor soldier" communicated the soldier's sense of victimization in a world where living was hard and unforgiving. Even in trying times, officers and men forged a sense of fraternity through drinking, gambling, and pornography. Although there were plenty of soldiers like Epperly who tried to shelter himself

*Comrades, Camp, and Community*

from the sins of camp, plenty of men, as historian Judith Giesberg writes, created a fraternity where the initiation centered on the "exchanging and sharing [of] erotic words and images" as "part of the sexual culture of the camps." The loss of male restraint, though a flagrant violation of domesticity, did not necessarily turn a man into a "bad soldier" in the eyes of his comrades.[115]

Early in their military careers, Haydon, Bowen, Epperly, and Callaway trimmed the romantic excesses away from the idea of the bold soldier boy, and with this change came a more transparent critique of the inhumanities of war and the unavoidable injustices that arise when nations demand bodies to fill up armies. Yet like the vast majority of Civil War soldiers, they did not separate themselves from civilian society, create an oppositional culture, or pursue an alternative political perspective. There was never even a whiff of a grand revolutionary proclamation calling for the emancipation of the "poor soldier" coming from mainline Civil War armies. The darkness of war never drained the world of its meaning, even for an antiwar soldier like Epperly. Rather, men of various backgrounds came together in the face of unforgiving conditions, and despite incredible physical and emotional suffering they managed to express a shared devotion for cause, comrades, and family. Such idealism, however, could not always stabilize soldier thinking or steer men toward a predictable course of action in a war where immutable laws did not govern life. Survival and military victory, as men on both sides quickly discovered, depended upon situational thinking and pragmatic action. Enlisted men did not discard high ideas but judged their value based on experiences in the field. In this way, they determined their own truths of soldiering.

# 2

## Providence and Cheerfulness

———

FROM HIS PERCH BEHIND A MASSIVE TRENCH, North Carolinian Alexander Keever stared across a barren swath of land stretching between opposing Union and Confederate siege lines. A day rarely passed in the winter of 1865 when Keever did not spot squads of Confederates running toward the enemy without rifles, their hands in the air, and begging to be taken prisoner. The sight of Lee's veterans deserting in droves caused him to wonder if their safe escape was a sign from above. Maybe Keever should also act on his own free will and make a run for the enemy's lines. Or should he refuse to take his chances with God or man, since every sign seemed to suggest that the war's end was near? Yet when the North Carolinian considered the enormous scale of military operations and the frightening collapse of moral boundaries inside and outside the army, he did not know what to think about the cause or the course of the conflict. Was he a pawn of impersonal forces, an agent of Providence, or a man who could control his own future? Was everyone being persecuted for individual sins, or was the South facing God's wrath alone? Civil War soldiers struggled to find consistent answers to these questions, and the vast majority looked to the heavens for guidance, including Keever, who found comfort in resigning himself to Providence. "For it is better for a man to trust in the Lord than to run a risk to desert," he wrote to his wife, "for there was a man left our company last week and he was taken up and brought back and put in the guardhouse and he may be shot."[1] Keever had observed that a grave often awaited the rebellious, and he did not want to stand in the execution line with other unfortunate men.

That Keever and countless other Union and Confederate soldiers made sense of military service through a providential trope, using stock phrases about trusting the Lord, is far from contrived, given that an aggressive Christian millennial discourse held sway over both societies. Simply put, the war did not undermine faith or lead people to stray from the idea that they had a direct and personal relationship with God. Letters full of certitude abound from both sides as a result, but even soldiers who wrote with blinding clarity could not always paper over the metaphysical confusion that drifted into their thinking. Even the pious struggled to reconcile their belief in truth and willed behavior with a war that called into question whether God's relationship to his people was truly knowable or whether matters were situational and open to revision. The war did not trigger a crisis in Christianity in either the Union or the Confederacy, but soldiers did have to modify their thinking about religious life — their emotional and physical survival demanded it. Recruits on both sides quickly learned that they could not afford to rely on God absolutely and unconditionally if they hoped to make it in the ranks. They needed to find a way to trust in themselves, to render their own judgments, and to modify beliefs for their own safety and the security of their families. Soldiers navigated their perilous journey in the ranks via many different paths, of course, but their various strategies were united by a spontaneous philosophy best described as providential pragmatism, which enabled a soldier to think in the moment without giving up on God. Moral codes became more malleable as the war progressed, but this move toward pragmatism in the ranks did not cause men to stop fighting for what they thought was right.

Historians have not fully appreciated the role of pragmatism in the religious life of Civil War soldiers.[2] They have focused instead on the ways that religion invested battlefield victory and defeat with providential significance. Historian Mark A. Noll has persuasively argued that Northern and Southern ministers rarely questioned their ability to predict and understand the workings of Providence and that they looked to the military situation as a reflection of God's will.[3] Yet Noll and other historians have overlooked how direct and simple answers coming from the clergy and theologians did not always resonate with soldiers, particularly in the moments when providential frameworks collapsed (predicaments that were not always caused by battlefield defeat).

Soldiers struggled to reconcile difficult choices of survival with the notion that God ultimately directed the world according to fixed truths on behalf of his people. Plenty of soldiers avoided spiritual crises by accepting God's inscrutable ways, but a more complicated story resides beneath declarations of providential consolation.[4]

The Christian belief that God controlled all events and that humans had the capacity to read and interpret the ways of Providence was foundational to how the vast majority of Americans thought on the eve of the Civil War. Organized warfare forced people of all denominations and classes to think deeply about their ability to understand the workings of divine Providence. Scholars such as Mark A. Noll, James H. Moorhead, and George C. Rable have done a brilliant job of investigating how theologians, both Northern and Southern, showed unshakeable confidence in their abilities to read providential purpose and meaning. While those in the pulpit never lost their certitude about how providential rule would grant victory for their respective sides, those on the front ranks did not see the future with such clarity, especially during those moments of spiritual crisis that were an unavoidable consequence of living in a world immersed in violence. The clergy's direct and simple answers to explain the war did not always stabilize soldier thinking. Plenty of men felt as if they had lost the ability to fathom providential actions and were shaken by their inability to discern the future, since what could be seen could not always be controlled or explained during a time of war.

The loss of certitude among the rank and file was fleeting, seldom leading to a permanent condition of doubt, resulting in an identity crisis, or pushing men to reject Christianity's fundamental tenets. While historians such as Noll and, more recently, Rable have acknowledged that only a few people relinquished the certainties of the Christian Enlightenment, other scholars such as Steven Woodworth have been concerned about the depth and meaning of religious sentiment and whether it expanded or was altered during the war. Trying to establish the strength of faith misses the critical question: How did soldiers navigate those moments when providential frameworks collapsed, when they could not reconcile difficult choices of survival with the notion that God ultimately directed the world according to fixed truths? Statements of divine vindication or prophecies of future redemption after the war reflect a certitude that reasserted itself after Appomattox. Only focusing on the interplay between thought and daily action enables us to see how Northern and Southern soldiers often became pragmatic when interpreting divine will. Noll convincingly argues that religious thinkers in Europe were breaking from the evangelical-Enlightenment synthesis, while American theologians remained fixed in defending a worldview based on providential causation, but he underestimates how providential mystery enveloped the ranks, causing soldiers on both sides — except for Confederate die-hards — to move from absolutism to pragmatism. If Noll had canvassed soldier correspondence, he would have found that Northern and Southern soldiers were not far behind the avant-garde across the Atlantic.

This chapter has three aims. First, it defines providential thinking on the cusp of the Civil War and the ways the concept mutually reinforced sentimental assumptions about free will and the importance of being cheerful. The chapter will then home in on the ways that life in the military and the war in general upset perceived notions about the nature of truth, human volition, and religion. Many facets of soldiering, including the subsuming of the self in the ranks and the prevalence of rumors, muddled providential thinking for the survivors of battle. The chapter then concludes with three narratives focusing on Louisianan Reuben A. Pierson, North Carolinian Alexander Keever, and Illinois artillerist William Shepherd. Their lives and letters home offer insights into the moments when the randomness of death, both on the battlefield and in camp, struck hard at the foundation of providential causation. Pious soldiers reached out to God during these times of trouble, praying fervently for God's grace, but they could not patiently wait for a sign from above if they hoped to survive. As veteran soldiers, all three men became less inclined to unravel the mysterious ways of Providence, and they found a degree of certitude from what they saw with their own eyes, rather than from theological or political abstractions. Soldiers came to believe that they were verifying Christian principles and the power of male honor by killing and dying for their respective causes. Even though the nature of combat defied providential calculations, no other arena offered a sterner test to a soldier's sense of honor and faith in God than facing the enemy's murderous bullets. As battlefield survivors, Pierson, Keever, and Shepherd felt entitled to the moral high ground, from which they reminded their loved ones that only they had the right to judge how they fought the war. No sermon or political tract could sway them from their self-proclaimed position of truth makers. All three men found truth in their experiences in a world where the circumstances — not the absolute laws of God and man — determined life and death. Finally, I will offer some conclusions as to the effectiveness of providential pragmatism in keeping minds sound and bodies whole as soldiers tried to cope with the physical, emotional, and mental stresses of war.

Northerners and Southerners headed to the battlefield in 1861 believing that Providence would crown a redeemer nation through the fire of war. Imagining

God as the final arbiter of this conflict rested on the well-accepted assumption that personal and collective behavior ultimately determined the course of public events. Regardless of denominational or political perspective, nineteenth-century Americans were virtually unanimous in this belief, and there was widespread agreement that individual will and collective character mattered to an omnipotent and omniscient higher power, whose ways were always mysterious but ultimately just. Thus, in putting their faith in the heavenly Father, they assured themselves that justice would come through military victory to those who were truly God's chosen people.[5] Americans quickly discovered that the war did not follow the sort of providential plan they had envisioned. "A providential view of history carried disturbing ambiguities because mere mortals could hardly discern the Lord's will with any great certainty," observes George Rable. "How could either side be sure that they had secured God's favor?"[6]

The belief in God's unlimited sovereignty, as pervasive as it was in antebellum America, did not dissuade Northerners and Southerners from acquiring verifiable information through hard empirical evidence and direct observation. They generally agreed that truth consisted in the facts of life, inspiring, to varying degrees, a shared quest for realism in their intellectual pursuits.[7] Men could be certain about the justness of their cause, love the Union or the nascent Southern nation, respect their comrades, and still be baffled as to why information was so unreliable, so broken, and so utterly irreconcilable in the field. The fragmentation of knowledge kept Civil War soldiers in a perpetual state of confusion spun by word of mouth, broadsides, military orders, gossip, newspaper accounts, and letters from home. It did not take long for a Civil War soldier to discover that the eye, ear, and nose rarely offered a "true" reading of his situation. Military operations by their very nature devoured certitude and splintered knowledge.[8] The vast territory occupied by Civil War armies and the scale of military operations exceeded one's line of sight. To find meaning in the strange world they now inhabited, Civil War soldiers would have to use all of their senses to navigate their surroundings. Noises reached farther than the eye could see. Shots from distant picket lines, the long roll of drums, the calls of bugles, the cheers of men, and the clattering of horses' hooves reached men's ears without mediation.[9] The bustle and confusion created distinct sounds that imparted particular meanings that the men trusted almost instinctively, but these noises spoke of vague movements into the unknown, where danger was almost always a certainty. Nobody seemed to know whether they were coming or going, and those who purported to know were almost always full of themselves and not full of reliable information. No matter where they turned, Civil War soldiers were always encircled by speculation, conjecture, and rumor. They frequently complained that their officers let them hang in a constant state of anxiety and suspense just for the sport of it. Few veterans on either side would have disagreed with the crude assessment of Union soldier William Berrier, who threw up his hands in exasperation and exclaimed: "Shit we can't believe a damn word that we hear anymore."[10]

The endless challenge of trying to separate fact from fiction reminded soldiers that the war was a colossal phenomenon, at times incomprehensible and resistant to any grand claims of truth even as men insisted that their cause possessed a clear and moral purpose. There was no relief from the tidal waves of rumor that repeatedly washed over the ranks and gradually eroded the men's confidence in ascertaining the facts of military life. They grew weary in trying to sort out conflicting and fragmented reports, feeling manipulated by unforeseen forces and unfamiliar people. As the war progressed, Union and Confederate soldiers turned deeply suspicious of anything they could not see with their own eyes, but even then they could not bring life into focus. Civil War soldiers learned the tough lesson that seeing and knowing were not always possible.[11] Men went to great lengths in an effort to confirm reality, given their suspicions of any news that could not be confirmed by observation. Sometimes this could lead to needless killing. North Carolinian Henry Biggs, for instance, stood in a quiet zone at Petersburg where an empty soundscape suggested safety and security, where there was no sharpshooting, shelling, or senseless killing. The situation suddenly changed, he explained in a letter home, when a rumor passed through the ranks that African American soldiers stood opposite his regiment. Under no circumstances would Confederates follow the soldier's informal code of "live and let live" when black troops held the opposing picket line. Biggs and his comrades strained their eyes, looking across no-man's-land with the intent of getting a black soldier behind their rifle sights. Their hatred for African Americans was so overpowering and their wariness of outside reporting so great that his Tar Heel regiment sallied forward to discover the "reality" of the situation. "They thought they would find out the truth of the report," Biggs recounted in a letter home, "and one morning attacked their skirmish line and found out they were regular 'blue coats,'" not black troops.[12] As a consequence of this pointless fact-finding expedition, thirty of Biggs's comrades lay sprawled across the ground in agony, wounded or killed by white Federal soldiers.

Northern soldiers were also deeply suspicious of any report involving black troops that countered established notions of racial inferiority. The prevailing racial stereotypes disposed white veterans to dismiss African Americans as soldiers because they lacked the "natural" qualities of manliness to stand up in battle. In fact, many held on to this opinion even after black blood had been spilled effusively in successful military actions in Louisiana, Mississippi, and South Carolina during the summer of 1863. Newspaper accounts of these actions did not settle the debate among Union soldiers, some of whom remained deniers of black heroism even in the face of overwhelming evidence. Like much of the Army of the Potomac, the men of the Twelfth United States Regulars had not witnessed black soldiers fighting in Virginia, so the accounts of the Fifty-Fourth Massachusetts Infantry's heroics at Fort Wagner did not sway the deniers. "They did not believe a word of it," reported one member of the Regulars. When black soldiers acquitted themselves during the opening attacks against Petersburg in early June 1864, there was "a change in tune" among his comrades, the soldier noted, but only after his fellow soldiers "went over the ground afterwards & talked with men who did see the whole thing." The Regulars studied the deep ditches encircling the massive walls of the Rebel redoubt, taking special note of the enemy's clear field of fire that extended for two hundred yards over which the black troops charged. In this particular instance the professional expertise of being a veteran soldier trumped abstract racial beliefs of black inferiority, and the men reworked their opinions based on what they witnessed on the ground. These same Union soldiers were told that the black soldiers were yelling "Remember Fort Pillow!" the entire way, as bullets and shells shredded their dense ranks. Despite the heavy losses, the black soldiers pushed forward, surging over the enemy's lines and then slaying a number of Confederates as they tried to escape capture. This dramatic episode received wide newspaper coverage, but journalists had long lost their credibility with the Regulars. When the Twelfth U.S. Infantry visited the actual battlefield — where they could closely examine the point of attack and converse with soldier eye-witnesses — they were finally convinced that "colored troops are an honor" to the Army of the Potomac.[13]

Volunteers on both sides tried to fit combat within their preconceived notion of war as a heroic moment in which God shielded the brave and granted victory for the virtuous. A simple cause-and-effect equation, in which people were either rewarded or punished by the Almighty in a rational and predictable manner, was an expectation that crossed sectional and sectarian lines.

The first volley of musket fire exposed the illusion. Bullets ripping into bodies, the smell of blood filling the air, and wounded comrades shrieking in pain awakened men to a world where actions did not always appear to be controlled by divine will. As the war progressed, Providence became something to hold on to for security, for consolation, and for spiritual restoration. Even as the experience of combat drew men closer to the Lord, members of the rank and file could not run from a metaphysical battle that pitted the impersonal forces of war against the powers of Providence.[14] This was a troubling conclusion for Americans who had dreamed of war as a morality play directed by the hand of the Almighty, but the magnitude of the carnage, as Drew Gilpin Faust correctly observes, raised "uncertainties of God's benevolence" and forced both sides to face "profound questions not just about God but about life's meaning and the very foundation of both belief and knowledge."[15]

Faust's keen insight affirms the importance of faith and ideas for those in the ranks (*what* soldiers believed), but she pivots in a new direction: rather than continuing to focus on ideology, she begins to probe the interior world of emotion, spirituality, and knowledge creation (*how* they thought). To generalize about how soldiers thought raises the inevitable question of representativeness, given that soldiers' backgrounds were so varied and their personalities so idiosyncratic. This is an unnecessary roadblock keeping us from fully appreciating how the reconstruction of one person's perspective cracks open the broader cultural world that all soldiers inhabited. Louisiana's Reuben Pierson, North Carolina's Alexander Keever, and Illinoisan William Shepherd were very different people, but they shared a similar struggle in the ranks: they were constantly seeking and rarely finding coherence and consistency in the mysterious ways of Providence. None of these men abandoned their faith over this metaphysical dilemma, but since entering a military world where the prewar belief in a predictable universe — governed by immutable laws and watched over by a benevolent God — was often indiscernible, they all wondered if they really knew the Lord at all. This was very unsettling to Americans inculcated in the idea that fixed truths ruled all aspects of life. Soldiering destabilized treasured assumptions of a world steeped in the culture of sentimentalism and Christianity.

The examples of Pierson, Keever, and Shepherd are overlapping but not interlocking. None of them followed a fixed or predictable course of action because they were beholden to some identity, ideology, or class interest. Their words and behavior were always evolving and were often out of alignment with or in opposition to each other, but the contradictions reflect the turbulent nature of Civil War soldiering and the struggles of men trying to survive in the ranks while simultaneously remaining true to God, family, and nation.

### Reuben Allen Pierson
*Louisiana Slaveholder and Teacher*
Ninth Louisiana Infantry

The simple act of putting on the Confederate uniform unleashed Reuben Pierson's ambitions, awakened his sense of honor, and heightened his spiritual awareness to such a great extent that he felt himself becoming a different person. On the battlefield the transformation was made complete in his mind. In a letter intended for women in his parish to read, Pierson described himself as a warrior fighting for all that he held dear at home. Killing intensified his feelings for the Confederate cause, and he made bold promises about avenging the deaths of his beloved comrades. Even in these fiery letters, however, Pierson could not hide the troubling prospect that Providence did not rule over the battlefield. The loss of certitude was not crippling for Pierson, or for most soldiers for that matter, because the tactical realities of war in the 1860s were largely compatible with the desire to be seen as a war hero. After his first campaign in 1862, Pierson wrote of battle with a strong emphasis on his individual experience: "I have seen the cannons flashing in battle at night till the light lit up the whole surrounding country. I have seen men fall in battle like trees before the hurricane. I have listened to the balls whistle like bees around a flower pot. I have walked over the dead bodies of men, and listened to the pitiful cries of the wounded after the battle was over."[16] Pierson continued to stress the role of the individual soldier as the prime actor in the war in his letters from 1862 to his death in the summer of 1864. Investing the soldiers with such power and importance did not easily fit into the established idea of providential agency. No matter how hard he tried to bring order to his combat letters, the battlefield showed Pierson that the world was uncertain and far from absolute, that luck often decided who lived or died, and that in war there was no single chain of causation that could be clearly attributed to a higher power.

Pierson came from a strongly Unionist family of slaveholders living in Bienville Parish. He left his position as a teacher as soon as he could, enlisting on July 7, 1861, in the Ninth Louisiana Infantry as a sergeant. His regiment headed straight to Virginia, arriving too late to see action at Manassas. Pierson and his comrades had to wait until the following spring for their battle baptism. They were assigned to Stonewall Jackson's command and served in his Valley Campaign before participating in the Seven Days' Campaign outside Richmond. In all of these engagements, Pierson felt the divine presence of God thanks to the petitions of his relatives. He believed that his "many miraculous escapes" under fire were attributable to the power of prayer, but he could not walk away from the battlefield without wondering why "others fall around on the right and left and are momentarily hurried into eternity." "The question naturally arises," he asked after Second Manassas, "what protects me from a similar fate? . . . The only answer being one," he averred. "Who gives life and Who alone can take it away."[17]

But in the same Second Manassas letter proclaiming God's omnipotence,

Pierson seems to be scouring his memories for evidence of providential intervention. He pointed out to his brother that from "what I saw I am certain that the enemies['] loss was four times that of ours," and that his "little brigade" killed and wounded "their full number" while his company suffered the fewest losses in the entire regiment. Yet he wondered why the Almighty had not protected his cousin John Williams from an enemy shell. Near the end of the battle, a Union case shot slammed into John's head, "tearing out his brains." Pierson struggled to explain why this had happened when John "has been nearly always [ready] for duty and participated in every battle."[18] John's death raised difficult questions about providential favor, but even in this tragedy, Pierson could find the hand of God in the experience of killing. He called attention to his cousin having lived just long enough to see the rout of the enemy and to "rejoice at our success."[19] It would appear that Pierson had invented a deathbed scene on the battlefield to comfort his grieving family. How could he have possibly known his relative's final thoughts, when John was unconscious, barely breathing, and had brains oozing out of his cracked skull?

Yet Pierson was neither delusional nor dishonest in his letter home. Like the vast majority of Civil War Americans, Pierson thought he could read the spiritual state of the dying, even if the latter was convulsed in pain and unable to speak. When Pierson looked at his cousin's lifeless body, he imagined the passing of a Confederate hero who would live forever in the memories of families and friends. A powerful antebellum death culture explains why Pierson idealized battlefield deaths as a transcendent moment of religious and political significance. He lived by this creed: "If I fall (which I fear but little) and my life is sacrificed upon the altar of liberty I hope I shall die happy for no one could die in a holier or more noble cause."[20] Pierson's words were not unique; Americans of all backgrounds entertained similar ideas about death. They were, as a result, uniquely prepared for the devastation of war, and it should come as no surprise that Union and Confederate soldiers were so willing to lay down their lives with such reckless abandon. Mark Schantz argued this point when he concluded, "Americans came to fight the Civil War in the midst of a wider cultural world that sent them messages about death that made it easier to kill and to be killed."[21]

When the grisly photographs of Alexander Gardner and Timothy O'Sullivan showed the grotesque nature of battlefield deaths to Americans North and South, people were shocked by the violence inflicted on the bodies and the utter disregard that armies had for the enemy's fallen. The revulsion Americans felt was understandable, but civilians and soldiers alike never doubted that a heavenly reunion awaited Christians who fell in battle.[22] The strength of this conviction is indisputable, and the confidence in which it was held can obscure a shift in providential thinking in the ranks. Veteran soldiers never stopped acknowledging the mysterious ways of Providence, but this belief could not always satisfy what soldiers wanted from war—to survive and achieve victory. When soldiers walked away from the killing fields feeling dazed and confused and wondering if God was with them, they still knew that the acts of soldiers and the plans of generals ultimately determined battlefield outcomes. War remained an individual experience, even during the final two years of the war, when armies on both sides had largely succeeded in disciplining the volunteer to the demands of vast, bureaucratic armies that resembled impersonal killing machines.

Minnesota's Philip Hamlin, who saw himself as a Christian warrior for the cause of Union, pushed Providence to the side when he explained Union defeat at First Manassas. Although he assured his family that he could feel the Lord's comforting presence throughout the fight, Hamlin resisted the idea that God's hand was responsible for leading the Confederates to victory—though he likely would have reversed this position if Union forces had been victorious. (Conversely, the Confederates did not have their collective reckoning with providential assumptions until their spring defeats in 1862.)[23] When the result on the battlefield was not what Hamlin wanted, he became pragmatic, distancing himself from providential explanations and dissecting the defeat with empirical precision as a veteran soldier. If his comrades had followed their training and stayed in their ranks, if the Confederates had not been protected by woods and supported by abundant reinforcements, and if his own officers had not expected too much of the men, then victory would have been theirs.

Not all hope was lost for Hamlin, who called attention to individual acts of courage as cause for optimism, given his core assumption that final victory would ultimately come to those who showed themselves to be the bravest. As the war progressed and both sides showed themselves to be tenacious fighters, Hamlin must have realized that his principle had to be reworked. Neither side appeared to have the monopoly on bravery. Like veterans on both sides, Hamlin came to the conclusion that discipline and training were indispensable, but early in the war he would not let a rout like Bull Run overthrow his faith in the power of individual gallantry as a force of change. "I cannot close this letter without speaking of the coolness and bravery of Lieutenant Col. Miller," Hamlin wrote. "When our ranks were broken and our men retreating, he went to the front of the storm of bullets, caused our flag to be hoisted and called on our men to rally around their flag. This he did twice or more, though once was enough to cover him with glory and honor this state."[24]

Over time veteran soldiers grew critical of men whose reckless bravery needlessly compromised the lives others, but they never lost their admiration for soldiers like Hamlin's colonel. Combat simultaneously affirmed values of male honor while also leaving men feeling gloomy and depressed. Soldiers on both sides knew that they would never be the same after leaving the killing fields of war and that those at home could never understand how they had changed (this subject receives greater attention in chapter 4). The fraying of relations between civilians and veteran soldiers is well documented in letters from an assortment of perspectives. Some historians believe this contributed to wide-spread disillusionment in both armies, but the evidence does not support this extreme interpretation.[25] It is true that over time soldiers showed less and less patience for those who remained lost in war's romances, but feelings of isolation in the ranks did not gut ideological convictions that had been made sacred on the killing fields of battle. In fact, the sense of isolation actually strengthened the bonds among comrades as they came to believe that they no longer needed the moral oversight of those at home.

Reuben Pierson rarely let an opportunity pass to remind those at home that soldiering was beyond their comprehension. While his family learned of the conflict from dubious newspaper accounts, Pierson felt the war through sound, smell, and touch, an immersion of his entire body and soul that only a fellow veteran could understand. By 1863, Pierson was not shy in lecturing his loved ones, including his father, about the "realities" of soldiering. Propping up civilian morale also spurred Pierson's didacticism. After the cataclysmic defeat at Gettysburg, for example, Pierson went on the offensive in his letters home, reminding family members that he had seen too many brave men die to countenance, even for a heartbeat, the notion that Providence had turned on the Confederacy. His experience as a veteran had taught him that the outcome of any military operation arose within a complex set of circumstances that were not beholden to any laws of providential causation. Pierson seemed untroubled by this conclusion, having grown skeptical of any grand theory of war. The previous spring he had essentially mocked the idea of Providence intervening in military affairs, given that the armies were plainly visible to each other but neither side would take the first step into the ring of battle. "It seems as if the divine Ruler of the Universe was procrastinating the great battle which appears to be so imminent between the forces of Gen. Hooker & those of Gen. Lee," he wrote. It made no sense to Pierson that two "great and powerful armies which was fighting nearly all the time last year has been lying in plain view and striking distance of each other for near five months" as if it were a time of peace.[26]

Pierson was incredulous not just toward Providence but also toward his own generals, whose passivity did not make any sense when the power to wage war resided with those at the helm. But his frustrations could not overtake his faith in the soldiers to do their duty under any conditions. The Battle of Gettysburg reinforced his thinking, even though the Confederates suffered a spectacular failure. An unconquerable spirit showed itself in Pennsylvania, where hardships were endured and gallant charges executed, but the repulse begged an explanation. Pierson lavished praise on his comrades, but no amount of courage, in his estimation, could have overcome the enemy's impregnable position at Gettysburg. Discounting the resolve of the Union army speaks to his fear of shame that in the wake of defeat led him to distortion. On August 22, 1863, when the Army of Northern Virginia was in shambles, Pierson wrote of war as if it were 1861, when male bravado filled the air. He promised those at home that he and his company of twenty men could "whip twice their number of Yankees any day." In sharp contrast to his Second Manassas letter, in which he tried to find traces of providential intervention, Pierson made no attempt to locate the hand of God on the Gettysburg battlefield.[27] All of the Louisianan's boasting about the invincibility of Lee's army could not paper over Pierson's nagging concern that God had become distant while his comrades died in droves against an enemy that he condemned as spawn of the devil. His demonization of the enemy kept him believing that God was on the Confederacy's side, and his very survival at Gettysburg also assured him that Providence still had a presence in his life. Yet even though Pierson felt lost on his spiritual path and in need of direction, he refused guidance from those at home. "I shall be governed by my conscience," he affirmed, "for everything is all mystery and darkness with me. I pray God will right me, and I may once be brought to see light for my case is a terrible one."[28] The following March, Pierson made a similar confession to his father: "I intend to be guided by the dictates of conscience as my whole mind is now bent on complying with what I deem my duty."[29]

Pierson's assertion "I shall be governed by my conscience for everything" is a revealing affirmation of soldier pragmatism. Pierson granted himself the authority to adjust his moral code and thinking as he saw fit. The authority of his claims drew its emotional and intellectual power from his experiences as a veteran soldier. Pierson's words and deeds have many parallels on both sides. Massachusetts's Oliver Wendell Holmes Jr. informed his father in 1864, "I have laboriously and with much suffering of mind and body earned the right . . . to decide for myself how I can best do my duty to myself to the country and, if you choose, to God."[30] The two men were radically different in personality and politics, but they underwent a similar transformation in becoming veterans. The truth of their existence was not grounded in abstract thinking or anchored by providential predictions. Veterans used the word *duty*, which could be capacious but conveyed the concrete and unique experiences of being a soldier. On the eve of the 1864 Overland Campaign, Pierson predicted military triumph based entirely on his experiences in the field and what he saw in camp. God was present, but command decisions and hard fighting would determine outcomes. "The general health and spirits of this army are altogether unsurpassed by any band of soldiers that history either modern or ancient gives an account of and all are eager for the opening of the spring campaign," he boasted in March 1864, concluding, "We will be blessed with some grand and glorious victories." Pierson was grateful to God not because he expected Providence to bestow victory on white Southerners, but because God had given him the strength "to perform my duties no difference how hard or patience trying they may be."[31]

Pierson's elevation of the soldier as the pivot on which the war turned illustrates the malleability of providential thinking, even among soldiers who were fiercely committed to cause and country. In fact, it was the pragmatism of Pierson's faith that helped him retain his high ideas, keeping him and hundreds of thousands of men on both sides from succumbing to practicing a savage war where the soldier saw himself as a soulless killing machine. The widespread refusal of Civil War soldiers to retreat to a position of doubt saved them from becoming bitter and cynical. Yet in reaching this important and largely satisfying conclusion, historians have been deterministic in drawing lines between soldier thought and action in the field. Men on both sides did not simply consult principles and sentiments and think and act accordingly. Their decisions were grounded in the circumstances of the moment and based on knowledge gained in becoming a veteran soldier—and in the process beliefs became inseparable from the act of soldiering itself.[32]

### ALEXANDER KEEVER
*North Carolina Nonslaveholder*
Thirty-Fourth North Carolina

By the spring of 1865, Alexander Keever's dream of a ruined Confederacy was materializing into reality, but his emotionally laden letters reveal his continued sense of mental and physical entrapment behind the trenches. No patriotic proclamation from his officers could dispute what he saw with his own eyes. The sight of Lee's veteran soldiers abandoning their posts in droves filled Keever's mind with subversive fantasies of ranks reduced to officers without private soldiers to command. The killing would stop out of necessity, Keever assumed. Vacillating over what to do, Keever decided to get on his knees and look

Though published in *Harper's Weekly* on July 16, 1864, this image titled "Rebel Deserters Coming with Union Lines" foreshadows the scene that Alexander Keever witnessed from his Petersburg trench during the final months of the war. Seeing comrades run for enemy lines proved too much for Keever, who showed himself to be a providential pragmatist when he finally deserted just weeks before Appomattox.
(Wilson Library, University of North Carolina)

to the heavens for guidance, but when he opened his eyes he still did not know whether he should stay or make a run for Union lines. If only he could discern God's controlling hand in this earthly catastrophe, then he could decide on a course of action. Keever's dilemma raises a fundamental question of Civil War military service: How did soldiers reconcile difficult choices of individual survival with their obligations to their families and their duties to the army within an all-consuming war where God's intentions were indecipherable and the factual basis of life appeared fractured? There was no easy answer to this practical and metaphysical quandary, and providential predictions and explanations—though always expressed with incredible certitude from the pulpit—proved inadequate to some members of the rank and file. In becoming veterans, Civil War soldiers understood that they needed to find ways to trust in themselves, to reach their own judgments, and to pursue their own course of action without losing their religion or running afoul of the military establishment.

One might argue that Keever's displeasure with the Confederacy grew out

*Providence and Cheerfulness*

of his material situation at home and in the army as well as his ideological dissatisfaction with the Confederacy. This cause-and-effect equation, however, is too deterministic in its outcomes and overlooks the private sphere, where emotions actually clarified political options for men plagued by ambiguity. It is important to acknowledge that members of the rank and file did not fully understand their world: they did have some free choice, and when feeling confused and vulnerable Northern and Southern soldiers sought shelter and direction from the very dominant culture and power structure that they decried as unjust. This could blunt the radical tendencies imagined in the private realm. Keever's status as a Confederate outlier is especially important in this regard, for his experience shows how a dominant culture had the power to reach a soldier who was far removed from elite circles. Feeling cheerful and content took an extraordinary emotional effort for all soldiers, particularly during times of duress, but even hardened veterans considered emotional management indispensable to their own survival.

As Civil War armies became more professional, more orderly, and more committed to organizational hierarchy, members of the rank and file came to accept their loss of control in the ranks. Yet Northern and Southern soldiers refused to give up the idea of free will, insisting that a man still possessed the individual power to shape his circumstances through emotional management. People understood their feelings as sentiments, both natural and constructed, that held the power to purify souls, to stir virtuous thoughts, and to inspire heroic action regardless of the circumstances. On the wide spectrum of emotions, cheerfulness was preeminently valued as a wellspring of moral and physical strength. Happiness, light-heartedness, joyfulness, and gaiety were particularly prized because they were understood as inseparable from personal health, piety, individualism, and national loyalty.

Until the end of the Civil War, Union and Confederate soldiers believed that a man should put up a good front if for no other reason than that it enhanced his chances of survival. Crises could actually heighten a cheerful feeling, as they spurred a desperation to live, but striving to be cheerful could also lead to censorship: that is, soldiers sometimes chose to repress emotions or engage in subterfuge when writing home in order to present a more sanguine facade. Union soldier John Willey, for example, routinely suffered from night terrors caused by what he called the "cussed war." Although Willey told his wife of these dreadful episodes, he never speculated about the cause of his nightmares, nor did he try to describe the dreams that possessed him with such a fierce hold. "I get so worked up," he confided to her, that "grate drops of swett roled of from me." Willey thought he could eventually master his nightmares by preserving a spirit of cheerfulness. Willey admitted as much to his wife, allowing that his emotional stability depended on his ability to block out the gloom of army life and to compose cheerful letters. "I thought I would not writ until I felt in better sperrits," he concluded in the same letter, but "you can not hav[e] any idea to be placed as I am whare death is starring in our faces."[33] He hoped that pushing aside the dark thoughts when writing home might free him from the oppressive dreams and give him peace at night.

Willey's letters home, like those of all Civil War soldiers, were not simply designed to transmit the reality of military life; they were also structured to inspire, protect, and control.[34] A filter of moral optimism helped to clarify what information to include and what to emphasize in letters home. Maybe that is why Keever abruptly ended his 1863 commentary on the Christmas rampage against army sutlers, worried that the news of a mass looting might burden those at home with images of Lee's soldiers fighting among themselves like common thugs. While Keever disclosed many details of army life to his wife, he still remained guarded, refusing to dwell on his hunger, the lack of a furlough, and his thieving comrades. Too much bad news might darken his family's spirits and cause irreparable harm to their bodies. Along with all the practical suggestions that Keever offered his wife, Ruth, during the final days of the war—and there were many—he urged her to become more cheerful, believing that an optimistic bearing would fortify her body and mind from the potentially deadly effects of the "blues." "I want you to cherish [cheer] up yourself," he instructed on January 15, 1865, "and quit grieving for me for I want you to look well and hearty when I come [home]."[35]

Keever's prescription of cheerfulness was not a soldier-brewed remedy for homesickness, but an established idea based on prevailing nineteenth-century medical knowledge.[36] Northern and Southern physicians agreed that good spirits preserved bodily health, enlightened the mind, and uplifted the soul. In theory, a cheerful temperament could ward off disease or inspire a soldier to overcome any situation, no matter how desperate or dangerous. Civil War Americans typically believed that a loss of optimism could have fatal consequences, and Keever certainly thought this was the case. He never stopped evaluating his moods when putting pen to paper, reminding his wife that they must shut out dark thoughts and strive to be cheerful—even when conditions in the army and at home looked bleak. "If you do not quite your studying," he warned his wife, "you will be a nocount when I do get home—[you] will be nothing but a skeleton."[37] Keever's cultural and medical understanding of cheerfulness originated not in middle-class tracts on morality, but in the Bible. Verse after verse from Proverbs instilled the idea that physical health, good cheer, and faith were interdependent: Proverbs 15:30, "A Cheerful look brings joy to the heart, and good news gives health to the bones"; Proverbs 15:13, "A glad heart makes a cheerful face, but by sorrow of heart, the spirit is crushed"; and Proverbs 15:15, "All the days of the afflicted are evil, but the cheerful heart has a continual feast."[38] These biblical messages of cheerfulness simultaneously implored men to trust in God and acknowledged the individual as an agent of change. Men who adopted or at least feigned a cheerful attitude did so because they trusted in God and in themselves to keep them from sliding into the dark waters of despondency, where all they could see was a man headed toward doom.

Emotional management meant something quite different to enlisted men than it did to those at the helm of military power. To prove their loyalty to the cause and willingness to fight, enlisted men needed to demonstrate emotional obedience to their officers. Orderly and disciplined men appeared happy and content in the eyes of officers on both sides. A typical Confederate inspection report reveals the linkage between emotion and discipline: "The discipline is, I venture to report," the inspector reported, "as good as any in the Army, and state of feeling all things considered, cheerful."[39] Soldiers who brimmed with cheerfulness were also viewed as fearless fighters. During the 1862 Peninsula Campaign, Pennsylvania's Amos Judson knew his comrades were ready for a fight by their carefree attitude and cheerful spirit. "But there are no fears, no anxieties, no doubts among our soldiers," he wrote without equivocation. "There is as much cheerfulness among them as if they were attending a country dance at home," he continued. "All goes with them as merry as a marriage bell. A Rebel bomb bursting among them produces as great an explosion of laughter and merriment as the roar of the shell it-self."[40] There was no need to probe any deeper to find the truth. Judson, like millions of other Civil War Americans, thought exterior appearances were windows into the hearts of men.

Not all soldiers were deemed manly enough to be cheerful in times of duress. Some officers thought ethnic, black, and poor soldiers lacked the inner will to make themselves cheerful, and they used this belief to deny them the full status accorded to middle- and upper-class white soldiers. Linking "emotional appearances" to popular notions about race and class marginalized these groups. High rates of black mortality—though actually a direct consequence of unsanitary conditions in camp and negligent white leadership—led some Union doctors to conclude that African Americans were more susceptible to disease and low spirits because they lacked "heart, hope, and mental activity."[41] These supposed inherent defects, conveyed through the language of biological racism, offered a popular explanation as to why African Americans were not suited for the fatigues of soldiering or the dangers of battle. Officers also deemed lower-class whites emotionally unfit for army life. They were thought to lack the essential qualities of manliness — restraint, coolness, purity, and cheerfulness — that appeared "naturally" among men who possessed the holy grail of sentimental culture — moral character.[42]

Regardless of the troops' racial or class background, officers on both sides grasped for any display of optimism from the ranks, especially when the war turned furious and unforgiving in the trenches, where soldier laughter was rarely heard over the sniping of sharpshooters and the explosions of mortar shells. When desertion in Lee's army reached an unprecedented level in early 1865, scores of officers at the regimental and brigade levels published petitions proclaiming the troops' allegiance. These proclamations purportedly represented the voice of the rank and file, but it is clear that they were almost entirely manufactured by the officers to portray a united front. The mendacity of the resolutions is a serious question and worth deeper investigation, but *how* the officers lied is just as important. Almost every resolution extolled the cheerful spirit of their men as the ultimate proof of loyalty to the cause. From the camp of the Fifty-Sixth Virginia Infantry, "the men" wrote the following to the editors of the *Richmond Enquirer* on February 18, 1865: "Resolved, That in the ability and skill of our Commander in Chief, Robert E. Lee, we repose the most implicit and unreserved confidence, that firmly believed in the justness and holiness of our cause for final success, disdaining all of the privations, hardships and perils of war, we will promptly and cheerfully respond to every call of duty and patriotism and press forward with zeal, confidence and vigor to the glorious prize before us."[43] Such statements tapped the public's faith in cheerfulness as a feeling that united people while obfuscating dissent. The power of the claim resided in its subjectivity. Lee's officers knew they would lose a soldier referendum on the war.[44]

Although significant numbers of white Southerners were fanatically devoted to Lee, the political declarations coming from the ranks cannot be read as unconditional statements of affection. The voices of Confederate dissenters were too often suppressed or ignored. It is possible, however, to see how Southern officers misread their men. Cheerfulness appealed to soldiers as a means of survival; it was not necessarily a political statement of allegiance. When officers insisted that their men were in good spirits, they rarely penetrated the emotional exterior of the rank and file. Whether officers were sincere in their claims is beside the point. Their assessments of army morale kept the public focused on soldier will as the preeminent force in war and thus shifted attention away from any difficult and potentially subversive issues that resided in the men's hearts and minds.

This difference in emotional management between enlisted men and their officers points to a problem in the historiography. Scholarly assessments of army morale is too descriptive, too subjective, and too focused on emotions as a state of being, rather than recognizing emotion as having agency in shaping perceptions and actions.[45] Conventional scholarly thinking reflects this approach, given that it still focuses on exterior displays of emotions without fully accounting for the ways that inner feelings possessed contradictory implications in soldier thought and action.[46] Alexander Keever's conscious effort to fill his letters with the language of cheerfulness actually speaks to his internal confusion, but his daily appearance in camp could have sent a message of confidence and hope to his officers, especially those men higher in the command chain who had no personal relationship with Keever. Any man who knew Keever well would have quickly deduced that he wanted out of the war, yet the North Carolinian struggled to disavow the Confederacy publicly outside his letters. Even though every indication from the ranks pointed to desertion as the obvious best choice in 1865, Keever and most other soldiers often struggled to comprehend their situation. Furthermore, running away from the army was not a straightforward issue of national allegiance or a simple matter of what was practicable (desertion as a matter of loyalty is explored in greater detail in chapter 5). For Keever, to desert was to call into question his entire moral and ethical universe, a step that was particularly difficult from the front lines, where it was problematic to see God's hand in the world. So while most soldiers never truly contemplated desertion, Keever's example remains instructive for understanding soldier thought and behavior because he was in knots over how to act — not from a crisis in identity or weak national loyalty, but because the official providential framework lacked the complex scaffolding necessary to hold the contradictions that arose when the practical challenges of survival exceeded what the men could grasp.

The official message of the Confederacy implored ordinary soldiers to trust in God for their own salvation, for their personal safety, and ultimately for the preservation of the nation. Scores of soldiers embraced this perspective, assuring themselves and their loved ones that their destiny was in the hands of a just and loving God. The pervasiveness of this sentiment at the end of the war attests to the durability of wartime Christianity in both the North and South, but even the most fervent expressions of faith cannot be read as blanket statements of providential resignation. Words of devotion and comfort could not always mask conflicting voices heard by men who were not sure how they should act as men of faith. Keever himself acknowledged how men could deliver the final blow to the Confederacy by deserting, but he held back, waiting to see how things might unfold under providential design. "I can say to you my dear wife, that the soldiers is a running away going to the yankeys and going home by hundreds every night and I think that will stop this cruel war shortly." In this admission Keever revealed a coil of tensions intertwined around human agency and God's will. The upheaval in his mind and the chaos on the front did not stop him from questioning the power of those in charge of the Confederacy. Keever went back and forth, but ultimately he put his trust in man, rather than the hand of Providence, to stop the killing: "For the war will continue as long as the soldiers will stay here and fight," he concluded, without the slightest acknowledgment that he was part of the problem.[47]

Keever's contemplations were not simply exercises in abstract thought, but concrete deliberations that spoke to the collapse of Lee's army during its worst crisis of the war. He was especially mindful of how the breakdown in the army's machinery of discipline suddenly opened up new strategies of survival and resistance. In letter after letter, Keever demonstrates an awareness of the institutional powers arrayed against him while always seeking a pragmatic balance between Christian faith and willed behavior in calculating his odds of surviving. While he never doubted that God governed from above in ways that defied comprehension, there was also no mystery about coercion as the ruler of military life. Every recruit—whether Northern or Southern—knew that even a slight infraction might bring violence against his body and that the military possessed the ultimate power to take life away. The possibility of lethal force was never far from the thoughts of Civil War soldiers. Just a few months after his 1863 enlistment, Keever stood in a three-sided formation, watching as men convicted of desertion were shot down before a firing squad of their peers. "I have saw one case of that kind," he wrote to his wife, "and expect to see more next Saturday. It's the awfullest sight I ever witness." He then ordered his wife to "quit commenting about me coming home." Keever never forgot the grisly execution, reminding Ruth that any soldier who left the ranks might face a firing squad. "My dear friend do you not know that it is out of the questions for me to go home without leave," he wrote on February 4, 1865. "If I would run away they would take me and send me back again and then they would shoot me—and that would be worse on you than for me to stay out here."

Keever could make a clear argument in favor of desertion: he had a long list of grievances against the Confederacy. But having an enemy to the front and a firing squad in the rear kept him fixed in place—not out of consent but out of necessity. Waiting out the war worried Keever, for he knew that military service was killing him by degrees. "My flour is all done that you and Mother sent me," he wrote, "and now I will have to go on rashens I draw and I dread it."[48] By the end of February 1865, Keever was desperate, and he began mapping out his escape from the army, telling his wife to expect him home in the spring, in time to help with the plowing and planting of the fields. She should see him soon, he wrote, since the army was "all out of heart." Even though he was cheered by the prospect of coming home, Keever reminded her that nothing was certain in the army. "So I think you may look for me some time this spring," he hoped, "if I live and I have a good hope of getting home this spring—at least I will try and see how migh[t] I can get there."[49]

Four days later, after studying the situation with some of his comrades, Keever decided that the risks of running were too great and that remaining in the army offered his best chance of survival. Deserting, as he explained again to his wife, could unexpectedly turn into a self-inflicted isolation and even death sentence. "It is too far to walk for and dangerous also . . . [and] if I go home I could not stay there unless I would hide out and that would be worse than to stay here. And if the officers would find me they would send me back here and I would be shot to death and that would be worse than to stay now."[50] Keever's reasons for remaining in the ranks were sound, pragmatic, and devoid of abstractions. Had he somehow forgotten that his chances in the army were hopelessly bleak? Tipping the scales against desertion—at least for the moment— was the arrival of a box from his brother, a lifeline from home filled with food, clothing, and other necessities. "I am proud to say to you that I think I have enough to do me till the war ends," he informed his wife, "or at least enough to do me as long as I will stay in the war." When the supplies from his brother had been exhausted, Keever promised his wife that he would reevaluate his options: "You need not send a box to me as I have the notion not to stay here long. I shall go one way or the other before long certain."[51] Ruth Keever must have wondered what might have been if her brother-in-law had not sent her husband a care package. Whether Keever would have fled or not without supplies from home is impossible to say, but it is clear that his survivalist calculations were always under revision, always rooted in the actualities of his situation, and always realistic.

In his last letter written from the front, Keever had seemingly reached a final decision for his wife: only God could deliver him safely from the army. The odds were too steep, the dangers too great, and Providence's ways too mysterious for him to assert his will. "Dear wife, I do hope and trust in the Lord that this cruel war will soon end so us poor soldiers will get home to see our beloved families," he wrote on March 5, 1865, but "I do not know how to wait any longer but I will have to wait till it pleases the Lord for me to be loosed from this cruel yoke of bondage. If it is his will, then I will get to come home and see you all one more time and if it is his will for me to die here, it is all right with me." This statement of submission has a sense of finality to it, a resolution to accept whatever might come next that Keever conveyed in a poignant farewell to his wife: "He [God] knows best what to do, but I still put my trust in him and if it should be my lot not to return home again, I hope the Lord will take me to a better world than this where I and you and our dear little children will all meet to part no more." Three days later, Keever suddenly decided that he was his own master and that his destiny resided in his own hands, not in God's. With four other men he slipped past Confederate pickets. As he ran across no-man's-land toward the enemy lines, he was undoubtedly hoping for providential protection to guide him to freedom. Whether the Lord looked down on Keever and his comrades did not matter in the end, since Keever had acted on his own instincts as a soldier and his practical reading of conditions on the front. Prayers were answered when all five men were "captured" by Union soldiers. Sent to Washington, D.C., by train, Keever was imprisoned for a few months until he took the Oath of Allegiance. Released as a United States citizen, Keever headed home to North Carolina knowing that his act of individualism had defeated a vast machine of war and that willed action, not providential intervention, had bought his freedom.[52]

## WILLIAM T. SHEPHERD
### *Chicago Clerk*
### First Illinois Light Artillery

Standing among twelve thousand rabid Republicans in 1861 at Chicago's famous Wigwam, the air filled with raucous cheers for Abraham Lincoln and songs praising the nobility of the Union cause, William T. Shepherd felt himself becoming a different man. In the days that followed, when thinking about "the great question of the day," his "heart jumps—sending a chill through my veins, inspiring my soul with courage to do anything in the cause of my country & liberty. *I have never had such feelings before.* It seems as though I must do something to rescue my Native land from destruction and ruin." Shepherd's Christian upbringing had taught him to trust his emotions as a moral guide, but he admitted to his mother that "my head runs wild almost with excitement."[53] Every day after the firing on Fort Sumter he could barely concentrate on his job as a bookkeeper for a printing office. He wanted to bolt from his desk and enlist,

*Providence and Cheerfulness*

William Shepherd (upper right) is pictured here surrounded by his high school classmates from Kenosha, Wisconsin, who served together in Taylor's Battery. Their presence was a source of comfort, and when Shepherd's dear friend Charles Dana (upper left) was medically discharged from the service, Shepherd did not hide his strong feelings of loss to his father, writing: "I'm really glad he is out of the service for he is unable to endure the privations and hardships of a life in the field. But you don't know how much I miss him! And how much I would like to be with him too—now that he is with our dear friends at home." (Archives of the Kenosha County Historical Society)

but the nineteen-year-old from Wisconsin—who, with his smooth, unshaven face and wavy brown hair, barely looked his age—desired the approval of his parents. "What do you think of my joining?" Shepherd asked on April 21, 1861. "Just consider the question and say *yes or no*. Be assured that if I go," Shepherd reminded them, "the Christian's armour covers all the rest."[54]

Shepherd's words did not dent the protective shield that his parents still wielded over him, and William found himself stuck at his desk, struggling to concentrate, knowing that his dreams of glory were slipping away while all of Chicago was preparing for war. Out his window Shepherd could see soldiers on the march and children scurrying up and down the streets waving American flags. At the height of his frustration, Shepherd pulled out a letter from his father and read the concluding paragraph: "Pray on, my son, and when the necessitous call for action comes, meet it like a true Christian & a patriot."[55]

Young men did not always hear words of patience over the beating of the war drums, but disobeying a parent would be a serious transgression, since scrupulous obedience demonstrated familial love and parental respect. When the moment arrived for action, Shepherd immediately wrote to his father, assuring him that he did not reach his decision in a lightning flash of emotion. "I am not hasty or have not been unthoughtful in regard to the terrors of a battle scene and the duties attendant upon a soldier," he explained with delicacy, "but am calmly settled in my own mind—My Country needs my services." "I am stronger you know than I look to be," Shepherd concluded, "& the divine aid of God—power will come."[56] Nearly two weeks passed before he received his father's blessings, but as soon as he did, Shepherd joined the First Illinois Light Artillery.

Shepherd's emotional introspection is a telling reminder that the rage militaire that prevailed over the North and the South in 1861 cannot be easily reduced to blood lust or romanticism. He did not succumb to his feelings, even noble ones such as courage and duty, without careful thought and reflection. He shared with other Americans the nineteenth-century faith in the individual as the master of his own destiny and the belief that emotional expressions were an extension of a man's willpower and a demonstration of self-control.[57] Emotional expressions were also keyholes into a soldier's inner world, where the struggles between the public and external self played out within the broader physical world of soldiering.

Shepherd was no different than most Northern and Southern volunteers who discovered raw emotions that had been locked away in the routine predictability of their antebellum lives. Shame, hatred, fear, pity, melancholy, love, and rage erupted in war, and these emotions possessed the power to transform soldiers in ways that they could never have imagined before 1861. When Shepherd enlisted, he firmly believed in self-mastery as foundational to Christian manhood, but the training, marching, deprivations, and killing in the army turned life in the ranks into a struggle for bodily as well as emotional control. Ideas and political commitments resonated with Shepherd, but they did not dictate his choices in the field. His feelings were so jumbled, intense, and powerful that it was impossible for Shepherd to emulate the citizen-soldier as he understood it in 1861. His experience at Shiloh in 1862 forever changed him, forcing him to rethink his understanding of Providence's relationship to the war, his view of himself as a man, and his concept of duty—without ever calling into question his core belief in the Union cause as one that was deserving of his life.

The prospect of military service, with its promise to rejuvenate souls and improve morals, exhilarated Shepherd. Disappointment came instead and it hit immediately. On reaching the training camp in Cairo, Illinois, Shepherd sought a brotherhood of Christian soldiers, but he quickly discovered how difficult it was to practice his faith in the army, where there was an alarming lack of restraining influences on men. Work details and drill allowed little time for spiritual contemplation. Officers rarely insisted on church attendance, and prayer meetings were never a priority. Shepherd's fellow soldiers preferred the convivial but sinful pursuits of drinking and gambling. The nights felt lonely, especially when the curses and raucous laughter of drunken men reached every corner of camp. "There is so much noise and worldly strife among the boys," Shepherd lamented. "How I should like to . . . be free."[58] The sounds of iniquity hung over camp like a stubborn smoky haze, and Shepherd could no longer see the possibility of a great Christian awakening in which "every man who shoulders a gun for the battle, knew the God of peace, and felt the *Christians* strength for the struggle. How surely then would the victory be ours."[59]

Shepherd and other Christian soldiers came to realize that no amount of proselytizing could convert comrades to live morally when temptations abounded in camp. This was never easy for a religious man to accept, knowing that God was always watching and judging and that all men would suffer the Almighty's wrath as a result. The lack of Christian fellowship in Shepherd's company triggered bouts of loneliness that only led him further away from his comrades as he searched for a place of solitude for communion with his Heavenly Father. He found quietude in his long, meditative strolls along the banks of the Mississippi River. At night when he was alone and walking the sentry post, he would stop and gaze at the sky, taken in by "the clouds" passing over the "pale face" of the moon. For a moment, when enshrouded by darkness, he felt lonesome and sad, but when the winds cleared the skies and the moon was shining brightly, Shepherd thought that everything appeared "bright and happy again and purer and more beautiful than before."[60] During these spontaneous moments, when Shepherd turned meditative, he was careful not to give in to extreme emotions, fearing that he might slide into nostalgia and become one of those soldiers who moped around camp, always grumbling and pining for home. "I must stop my day dreaming and write or I may get homesick." He closed his letter to his cousin by reminding her that he needed her prayers, since a "soldier [is] under many evil influences," but he assured her that "I shall endeavor to do my duty to God as well as our country."[61]

A connection between courage and godliness was an established fact for Shepherd and his fellow Christian soldiers. Shepherd's opportunity to prove himself to his Maker and his country came on October 17, 1861, at Fredericktown, Missouri. The affair was nothing more than a minor skirmish, but it had

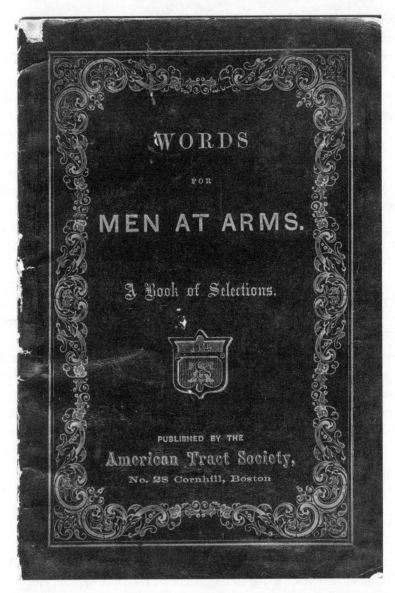

William Shepherd's copy of *Words for Men at Arms*, a popular religious book advertised with the following proclamation: "Let them [the religious tracts contained inside] be scattered by the thousand. Such seed sown in faith may yield an abundant harvest." Shepherd likely turned to this small volume for solace when he sought a spiritual light in a military world that he thought was enshrouded in sin. As was the case with many Civil War soldiers, his religious musing stirred a deep longing for home. "Every Sabbath I long for home," he wrote his father from the Shiloh battlefield, "and the holy privileges of the day—I often picture myself walking into the old church at service, and Sabbath school, and at home enjoying a good dinner in the place of hard bread and salt bacon."
(Archives of the Kenosha County Historical Society)

a profound impact on Shepherd, who considered the incident "a grand victory for the cause of Union and liberty." Even though some of the men had been raucous sinners in camp, their gallant charge "showed their true character," while the enemy "proved themselves [to be] perfect cowards." Shepherd subsequently wrote home about the daring deeds of his comrades as if warfare was an adventure of great drama and pathos. Every anecdote he shared celebrated the triumph of Union masculinity over the timidity and backwardness of the Southern soldier. Never mind that Shepherd could not verify these stories with his own eyes. He had no qualms about passing along questionable tales of highly visible and individualized acts of bravery. "One of our Colonels," Shepherd wrote with a flair for the dramatic, "charged up the hill eating an apple," followed by a soldier unconcerned about his safety and carrying "a tin cup of honey." When a ragged Confederate volley "rattled" another Union regiment, the officer in charge ordered his men to perform the manual of arms in full view of the enemy until "their nerves became steady." All of this occurred, according to Shepherd, because the Rebels hid in the bush and refused to "show their heads." When the enemy scattered from the field, Shepherd hunted for relics, only to find that the Confederates fought with "the old flintlock rifles" and "homemade knives, pouches, and chargers of every description." The primitive nature of these weapons confirmed his antislavery perception of the South as a savage and backward land.

Shepherd returned for more war trophies the following day, but his mood became somber as he surveyed the field. The men who had fallen appeared as though they were asleep, with their "hands folded across the breast," looking "cold and rigid in the embrace of the Great destroyer." Another soldier "had been eaten by the hogs—till the face was but a mass of bones." Before Shepherd returned to camp, he stumbled upon a Confederate soldier who had been shot in the head but was still alive, gasping for air, his brains running "out on the grass." "Oh I shudder at the thoughts occasioned; much more the sight of such a living death," he wrote to his parents.[62]

Although Shepherd was sickened by the bloodshed, his political and religious convictions steadied him when facing such chilling sights. His traumatization was real and expressed with unusual candor, but his example shows that while the stress of combat delivered a terrible blow to the body and mind, it did not usually incapacitate a man.

Shepherd found a way to function in the ranks after each battle, even deriving a sense of pride in the artifacts of killing that he collected and sent home, as he struggled to keep the horrid memories at bay. Just one day after the skirmish, he watched in approval as billows of black smoke rose above homes set ablaze in Fredericktown. In 1861 citizen-soldiers considered the battlefield the only arena where armies should wage war, but Shepherd surprisingly broke ranks with the vast majority of Northern and Southern soldiers who denounced the violation of civilian property in Missouri. He never explained his willingness to strike at the slaveholding class, but one can speculate. Perhaps Shepherd was, like most Union soldiers, a pragmatist in his relations with Confederate civilians. Throughout the war, their behavior against civilians could be simultaneously harsh and forgiving, rather than following a rising trajectory of escalation from conciliation to hard war.[63] Shepherd's views after Fredericktown contain the same logic later used by Sherman's men in Georgia and Sheridan's troopers in the Shenandoah Valley, who were convinced, as historian D. H. Dilbeck writes, "that the most humane and just course of action . . . was to do *nearly* whatever was necessary to win their war against the Confederacy as quickly as possible."[64]

A little more than two weeks after the Fredericktown affair, Shepherd witnessed heavier fighting at Belmont, Missouri, on November 7. More than six hundred Union soldiers fell in the fight, and in the days that followed, Shepherd noticed that his comrades were initially full of a nervous energy, but that as the "excitement passes away," everyone felt more comfortable "to reflect calmly" on the battle. A random crack of a rifle shot from afar would startle the artillerists. Shepherd immediately felt jittery, his body tightening in anxiety. "The sound of a musket makes me shudder," he confided to his parents—apparently without fear of being seen as weak—"and the discharge of a cannon seems unfinished, without the whizzing of a shell immediately after." The sounding of tattoo sent the soldiers to their tents and brought the day to an official close, but it did not stop the awfulness of war from reappearing in the night. "My rest at night is often troubled with a visionary battle," Shepherd wrote. Grotesque images of the "dead and the dying" populated his frightening dreamscape.[65] He awoke every morning feeling restless, unable to avoid an unanswerable issue: "We wonder more than ever that we are yet alive and unharmed."

This case study of William Shepherd illustrates how Christian soldiers adjusted their providential thinking depending on what was happening around them. During the first two years of the war, Shepherd trusted his ability to discern the ways of the Lord. His confidence largely came from the battlefield, particularly the Fort Donelson siege, which was important in convincing Shepherd that Providence recognized Northern soldiers for their righteousness and rewarded their armies with victory. He felt God's comforting presence at every moment, shielding him from danger and carrying him safely out of the fight. "My heart overflows with the gratitude to our Heavenly Father," Shepherd wrote on February 23, 1862, "that he so kindly spared my life. It does seem as though He had an especial care over our battery for, during the whole siege — but one was killed and four slightly wounded." A close call with a Confederate sharpshooter offered further evidence that God answered the prayers of the faithful. "Many times during the daily battles did I have occasion to thank God for the trust I had in His all powerful hand," concluded a grateful Shepherd, "and doubly so when selected as a mark by a Rebel sharpshooter whose whistling ball almost stirred my hair."[66]

Fort Donelson did little to test Shepherd's intricate understanding of courage and Providence. He stood by the conviction that only a Christian soldier possessed the necessary moral and physical strength to defeat the Rebels. Shepherd was in the religious mainstream when he wrote that "God's faithful promises" imparted special courage to the believers.[67] This providential expression had a practical effect on the battlefield, where piety reinforced discipline to propel men against the enemy with spectacular fury. Some pious soldiers on both sides leaned toward zealotry, such as Confederate William Pegram, who walked away from the fighting at Cedar Mountain on August 9, 1862, with four bullet holes in the skirt of his tunic. One sharpshooter, who was not particularly skilled at his craft, "took deliberate aim at me eight or ten times, and missed me," Pegram reported in a matter-of-fact tone, his close calls with death filling him with a sense of invincibility, for his escape was proof that divine Providence worked through him for God's good and higher purposes. Pegram saw no reason why his family in Richmond should flinch about his safety as long as everyone trusted the Lord. "What have I to fear from Yankee bullets and shells," he wrote, "as long as I am under His protection?" He closed his letter by reminding his sisters and mother that they should "cheer up," since they were all under God's protection.[68]

Although Shepherd shared Pegram's belief in godliness as a protective mantle, he could not find his emotional equilibrium after witnessing a full battle, an intense display of man's awesome capacity to destroy and kill. Shepherd wanted no more of war after enduring two hellish days of fighting at Shiloh on April 6–7, 1862.[69] Although the Confederates ultimately abandoned the field, the young artillerist did not consider Shiloh a providential gift, like his previous Union victories. As soon as Shepherd put pen to paper, the dark memories took control, pulling his thoughts back to the battlefield and the terrifying screams of men dying in agony. One week later he described the sounds of battle to his sister: "The roar of cannon — the rattle of musketry — the flying hiss of bullets and bursting shell — with the deafening yells of a bayonet charge, the cries and death groans of thousands of human beings rent the air in wild confusion."[70] At that moment, Shepherd could not hide his troubled and distracted mind from his family.

Shepherd's Shiloh letters demonstrate how the writings of Civil War soldiers could both sanitize war and speak of its dehumanizing effects.[71] His words paint a picture of a man in an emotional free fall after Shiloh, but a more complex picture emerges when the full evolution of Shepherd's views is considered. To be sure, Shepherd never stopped battling the memories of those two dreadful days in April. Paradoxically, his direct experience in combat confirmed his prewar ideas about Providence and the sacredness of the Union cause. To retreat completely into the darkness would have betrayed his deepest religious convictions, keeping him from praising God for keeping him safe through Shiloh and for Union victory on the Tennessee River. Shepherd could not allow himself to fall into a depression and become forlorn; he had to repair himself or risk losing God's favor. In no way should Shepherd's providential expression be construed as a cynical ploy of self-preservation. His faith gave him inestimable strength and resolve to show his family, comrades, and, most of all, God that he possessed emotional and physical control over his body. In the end, Shepherd largely succeeded in managing the horrid thoughts of war, but the brutalizing effects would always remain. He likely also wondered whether supernatural forces could suddenly restore peace. Men clearly possessed at least some power in controlling the destiny of human events, and Shepherd would not relinquish the belief that an individual could affect the war's outcome. From the wreckage of the Shiloh battlefield, a subdued Shepherd wrote: "I am quite well—and though not eager for a fight (if one should come) am quite confident of a safe issue. God is still very kind to me and in Him I trust."[72]

After the Battle of Shiloh, Shepherd must have felt that his prayers had been answered. He never again stood on a battlefield drenched in blood. During the summer of 1862, his battery resided in the quiet confines of Memphis, Tennessee. A few excursions were launched into Mississippi, but Shepherd and his comrades idled most of their time away in camp. In these environs Shepherd grew weary of the monotonous days, which oscillated between uncontained excitement and ruthless boredom. For his sister he attempted to record the unsettled tedium of his daily existence: "A call to arms at the hour that brings the first grey streaks of light from the eastern horizon—opens our military day. A picket skirmish soon follows and every man prepares to meet the enemy should he advance, and then in breathless anxiety and excitement, wears away the morning till 9 o'clock." The state of not knowing was an inescapable condition for those in the ranks, and Shepherd impressed upon his sister the difficulty of sifting through the deluge of wild reports to uncover the truth.

"Then our camp is full of flying rumors," he added, "of an attack from the rear, of a reverse of our arms in some other part of our great drama, or a cheering report of some brilliant victory, that fills our cup almost full, but to be dashed from our lips by the next camp story which contradicts all." Throughout the afternoon, the "dull booming" of heavy artillery echoed in the distance, startling the men's "partially quieted nerves." Heavy skirmishing almost always followed, and this, according to Shepherd, further aggravated their "unpleasant state of mind."[73]

The curious mixture of stability and uncertainty tried the patience of any man in the ranks, and every soldier had his own breaking point. For Shepherd it came on July 22, 1862, when he unleashed a furious condemnation against the military. A batch of letters from home sent him flying into a rage. "I had a genuine fit of homesickness and became doubly disgusted with this war—from morning till night and night till morning—nothing but war." This statement as a free-standing quote would suggest that Shepherd's war weariness had won out, that the flame of his idealism had been snuffed out, and that he was marking time until he could return to Wisconsin. There is no question that he had lost his enthusiasm for military life as a vehicle of moral and physical uplift, which was a common trend among veterans on both sides. At the end of the same angry July letter, Shepherd reined in his temper and reminded himself that God would give him the power to endure. "Yet our nation and flag must be restored to its former unsullied name—May God grant me strength and grace to bear up under every duty and trial."[74] Yet over time there was a profound shift in how Shepherd understood the workings of the war as it related to the hand of Providence. He never lamented again, as he did in an 1861 letter to his cousin: "Would that all who fight for their country could also be Soldiers of the Cross and obey the teachings of Him Who died to save. How surely, then, would the victory be ours."[75] After the Battle of Shiloh, Shepherd never pinned the fate of the Union on the moral state of Northern soldiers. To be sure, Shepherd still believed that he was fighting for a historic national mission to preserve a republican form of government against a traitorous rebellion of Southerners. However, no more of his wartime letters meditated on the place of soldier piety, patriotism, or courage in gaining providential favor so that the North might secure victory.

Shepherd would not leave his life to the capricious forces of the battlefield. In the fall of 1862, he transferred from his battery and accepted a clerk's position in the ordnance office. The transfer came with higher pay and the promise of promotion, and, above all else, it offered him safety from the front. For the remainder of the war, Shepherd made no special effort to return to the battery. The practical advantages of his situation were a godsend. Even so, when the time came to reenlist during the summer of 1864, Shepherd was not moved by either profit or patriotism to return to the artillery. "I shall not be with the Battery any more while in the Army, and shall take good care not to get shot elsewhere," he informed his sister. "Two years and a half, I've survived the trials & danger & hardships of a soldier's life, and I feel confident that I am able to stand five more months."[76] In a subsequent letter he exclaimed: "My heart's desire is to return home and live among those whose society I can enjoy, and where I can be a man and not a Thing."[77] In stating his unequivocal intention of coming home, Shepherd had renounced neither the army nor the cause. In fact, before returning to Wisconsin, he shipped home a package with his "old coat—that I wore at Shiloh" and books that "were a source of much comfort through the toils and perils of the siege of Corinth."[78] These sacred relics—though connected to some of Shepherd's most painful memories of war—would forever remind him that God chose to see him through a war for Union and liberty. We will never know whether Shepherd sent these items to the family so that they might have a "glimpse" of war or whether he saw them more as heirlooms for future generations to display as evidence of his war record. Maybe he locked the relics away and pulled them out in private. What feelings welled up inside him when he picked up his old sack coat or piece of shell is difficult to say, but these things likely spoke to him in a concrete language that testified to the suffering and sacrifice of being a soldier—an experience that proved so difficult to translate to those at home.

The theory of providential causation had promised nineteenth-century Americans a direct and simple explanation of the war as soon as shots were fired at Fort Sumter, but the message from the pulpit did not always clear a path for Civil War soldiers. Rather, providential thinking assumed various iterations in the ranks based on one's experiences in the field. Its remarkable adaptability accommodated the personal desire for survival and for military victory, enabling individuals to follow God's purposes as they saw them as well as to take matters into their own hands when deemed necessary. William Shepherd, Alexander Keever, and Reuben Pierson showed flexibility in thought and action based on their individual circumstances. Like all soldiers who were sick of the blood and battered and worn down by war, they found ways to adjust when Providence seemed to be orchestrating the action yet inescapable moments of confusion arose. They had little choice but to put their trust in willed behavior without relinquishing the idea of God as a protector of his people. Above all else, the stories of Keever, Pierson, and Shepherd show the contradictory ways in which soldiers navigated a world immersed in violence without ever following a fixed or predictable course of action determined by some identity, ideology, or class

*Providence and Cheerfulness*

interest. Their words and behavior were always evolving, often out of alignment with or in opposition to each other, but the contradictions reflect the turbulent nature of Civil War soldiering and the struggles of men trying to survive in the ranks while simultaneously remaining true to God, family, and nation.

The distinct experience of waking up each day in the army was an intellectually and theologically humbling experience for common Civil War soldiers. The religious and intellectual foundation of their prewar world lacked stability, and soldiers freely admitted that it was a struggle to discover what was knowable and true. The loss of certitude was far from intellectually or spiritually crippling, as the case studies of Keever, Pierson, and Shepherd demonstrate. These men were frustrated and confused from time to time, but they never relinquished their belief in themselves as largely in charge of their own destinies. They all remained faithful and prayed fervently, but they also became more pragmatic in their reading of the world. They took in life from a situational perspective—above all else, their experiences in the field became the ultimate arbitrator of the value and meaning of their political and religious beliefs. Civil War soldiers agreed that the war had upset the rules of life, and volunteers on both sides undoubtedly felt alienated from everything familiar at some point during their military careers. Some, like Keever, endured a prolonged upheaval. Others may have been more like Shepherd, who experienced a fleeting moment in which he mended himself through prayer and highly confessional letters to his family. When Pierson fell into a spiritual funk, he was more guarded than Shepherd and Keever, worried that he might appear weak. He sought to defend his sense of male honor at all costs, which in turn buttressed his Christian faith. This was not an exercise in abstract thinking for Pierson. He looked to the exertions of his comrades, whose sacrifices verified his belief in a Confederate nation under divine stewardship.[79]

Out of necessity, they reaffirmed the power of willed behavior and pragmatism, believing that an elastic nature was crucial to survival. While the political and ideological floodwaters that had swept Americans into war never fully receded after Fort Sumter, the volume of high ideas rose and fell with great unpredictability in Civil War armies until Lee's surrender at Appomattox. Nevertheless, the erratic currents of idealism, even when drained dangerously low by a seemingly purposeless war, never left Northern or Southern soldiers standing on the barren ground of nihilism.

# 3

# Writing Home

———

WITH THE PULL OF A TRIGGER, Reuben Pierson's heroic fantasies of war came to life. As his Louisiana regiment charged the Yankees at the Battle of Port Republic on June 9, 1862, the faces of the "young ladies" appeared to him, and in that instant he felt unconquerable. "Tell them," Pierson asked his sister-in-law, "that for them the soldier grasps his musket, faces the enemy, and risks life with all its comforts for their liberty and freedom."[1] Just days after he described the battlefield as a place of gallantry and glory, he composed a very different, more emotionally conflicted letter to his father. Fighting, he admitted, was not the stuff of boyhood dreams: "I have seen the dead and wounded lying in piles, the ground literally covered with blood. I have heard the groans of the dying, pitifully crying for help in the last agony of death." The images of brutal death overwhelmed him, and Pierson admitted to his father, "Everything is very different from what I had imagined it to be." His own loss of emotional control troubled him, and he could not suppress the memory of surrendering to the most savage instincts of war. "A man can rush heedlessly on through battle over the dead and dying with as little remorse of conscience as he could shoot a wild beast," he added with a hint of guilt. "The excitement it is true is great and nothing can picture it so well to one[']s mind as the witnessing [of] it with one[']s own eyes."[2]

The contradictions between Pierson's two letters are startling, causing one to wonder if the Louisianan was even capable of telling a "true" war story. Such a question is understandable, but in the evaluation of the accuracy of *what* soldiers wrote, one might miss the equally important question of *how* the men composed their stories. The language, aesthetics, and writing style can tell us much about the cultural context that structured how they thought and why they expressed themselves on paper. Paying careful attention to how soldiers' words came to be articulated reveals the cultural screens through which Civil War Americans perceived and interpreted their experiences, then projected them onto paper. Keeping the focus on how they wrote offers a window into the contradictory consciousness of soldiers whose self-described actions were not always in alignment with their stated beliefs and values. In other words, members of the rank and file might extol the bravery and suffering of their comrades in the field and in the same letter express apathy and frustration about the very purpose and direction of the war. In these contradictions reside the ambiguities of soldiering. The complexity of consciousness can be difficult to retrieve in Civil War letters, yet plenty of men revealed their interior world to those at home, especially to the wives and sweethearts who served as an outlet for their most private thoughts.[3]

It was not uncommon for Northern and Southern men to write with remarkable transparency, but as Pierson's letters show, a soldier never put pen to paper without considering how he might be perceived by his loved ones. Soldiers admitted that when they tried to describe the indescribable, words often fell short. Even as they struggled to communicate with those at home, Union and Confederate veterans still demanded that the home folks accept their view of the war as they depicted it. When the reactions to their letters did not meet soldiers' expectations, they dismissed civilians as being helplessly naive or acting with callous indifference. Ironically, it was the soldiers themselves who contributed to their own sense of alienation from their loved ones. Their letters often reinforced civilian naïveté because of their need to be seen as men of bravery who proved their character through noble acts of suffering. As a result, their writings generally framed military service as a moment of individual heroism and manly redemption. To conclude that soldiers simply invented war stories avoids a critical question. What choices did the soldiers in the ranks feel they had to make as writers? Even hardened veterans on both sides dwelled on aspects of military service that reminded themselves and their audiences that the war had not turned them into uncivilized brutes. The overall effect of their writing, consciously or not, kept the flame of sentimentalism flickering, even during the darkest days of military service.

Three soldier narratives — the stories of Indiana's David Beem, South Carolina's John Crawford Anderson, and Georgia's Wright Vinson — are at the heart of this chapter, and they were selected because they have little in common. The men came from very different social and educational backgrounds, held different political positions on the war, and expressed different attitudes toward military life. Above all else, these men were chosen because their letters are incredibly rich. They thus offer a glimpse into how the act of writing home was a mix of words heard, said, and read as well as sights, sounds, and smells absorbed — all brewing together in a man's mind. When spilled on paper, a soldier's words did more than recount events or tally casualties. His stories home show how members of the rank and file interacted on a daily basis with a sentimental and nationalist culture that was preeminent in both the Union and the Confederacy.

## David Beem
### *Indiana Lawyer*
### Fourteenth Indiana Infantry

Captain David Enoch Beem needed his wife, Mahala, to embrace the war for Union if he were to live out his idealized view of himself as a selfless soldier sacrificing for the noble cause. He sent her carefully crafted letters imbued with the sentimentalist belief in individual action as the great determiner of events. Beem kept her eyes on the ground level of war, where he depicted his fellow soldiers as always facing forward, steadfast, and fearless because of their overpowering patriotism. Beem invested tremendous emotional energy in his realistic stories of battle because he had lived them. Some of the most violent assaults in the history of the Army of the Potomac had ripped the Fourteenth Indiana apart. The killing and mangling of his comrades had stripped war of its romance for Beem, but at the same time, battlefield heroics unleashed powerful emotions that sentimentalists prized for their capacity to inspire audiences to feel sympathy for the soldiers' bodily sacrifices in the field.[4]

Beem was like veterans on both sides: because veterans assumed that a man at the front should be recognized as a legitimate truth maker regarding the war, they expected people to accept their war stories without criticism.[5] Unfortunately for Beem, Mahala (or Hala, as he called her) was an incorrigible critic of the Union war effort who felt little sympathy for her husband and never missed an opportunity to lecture him about why he was needed at home, not far away fighting a war that was questionable in her eyes.

After graduating from Indiana University in 1860, Beem had devoted himself to building a law practice and promoting the Republican Party in his hometown of Spencer. When shots were fired on Fort Sumter, he showed no indecision as to what he should do next. On April 19, 1861, Beem organized the first military company in Owen County as a first sergeant in what would become Company H, Fourteenth Indiana Infantry. By the following year, he had risen to the rank of captain and was no longer a single man. On April 10, 1862, he married Mahala Joslin, who was also from Owen County.[6]

The Beems' failure to achieve the ideal wartime relationship, where romantic love and patriotism mutually reinforced each other, exasperated Beem until he left military service in the summer of 1864. It was rare when a soldier did not demand that members of his household fall in line with his own politics, especially during wartime, when having a wife, mother, daughter, or sweetheart was seen as essential to keeping a soldier going in the field. As historian Alice Fahs argues, sentimentalism bound women and men together through emotional expressions that included "feminized" elements, making it appropriate for soldiers to show emotion, to weep over a slain comrade, and even to shed a tear for wives and sweethearts who were far away.[7] David and Mahala Beem never achieved this exalted emotional state in which their love for each other and the nation melded together in a pure and ennobling expression of mutual affection. As with many soldiers, Beem never stopped trying to exert power over those at home through emotion, but his wife's intransigence pushed Beem to look inward to his band of brothers for sympathy and understanding.

Just three months after their marriage, on July 25, 1862, Hala let her husband know that the time had come for Beem to get himself right with God, given the precariousness of army life and the sinful nature of the world. "How encouraging is it to me my dear husband, to know that you are still trying to discharge[e] your religious duties," she wrote. "Yes, how often does this encourage my sad heart. When I feel discouraged, almost ready to give up, how pleasant the thought, that you are living so, that if should you be called to meet God, you would be prepared. . . . I fear you spend many *dark hours*, look to God, my dear, in every trieing hour. He will never forsake you, No never, but will ever give you grace sufficient for every day and trial."[8] Hala, who was devoted to her religion and taught Sunday school at her Methodist church, could invert their marital roles by assuming authority as his moral counselor, reminding Beem that through prayer they would come together in looking for God to protect and direct them through a precarious war. The sincerity of her words touched Beem's soul, and he committed himself to following the ways of Christ, reading his Bible, and praying every day. He even complained about finding few comrades of faith in camp. Hala weakened her own domestic influence, however, because she only played the part of the spiritual counselor, refusing to even pretend to be the dutiful patriotic wife who felt sympathy for her husband's suffering in the field. By the end of her letter, she could no longer hold back her true emotions. "You seemed very anxious to know how I am getting a long, Well, just as well as could be expected. I can't say that I get along at all well. I am all the time uneasy. Not in very good spirits."[9]

While Mahala's letter was in transit from Indiana, Beem was finishing a letter to her, dated July 27 and sent from Harrison's Landing, where the Army of the Potomac's failed Peninsula Campaign came to an end. Beem launched a moral counterattack against his wife for sending depressing letters suggesting that he quit the army and come home. He responded in a calm and reasoned tone, never even hinting that she was forgetting her place as his wife. However, he did shame Mahala by pointing out that she was violating the religious principles that she had been preaching to him. "I think I haven't got a letter from you without your saying in it that you couldn't stand it to be separated from me so long, that it is so hard for women to be so far from their husbands, and so forth," he wrote. Beem understood her position, but nevertheless reminded her that Christians suffer and sacrifice for what God deems as just and right. "Well, of course it is, or ought to be, and I am glad you say you will stand it the best you can, but you must remember that this world makes us experience a great many things disagreeable to us, and that the more cheerfully we endure hardships and disappointments the better it is for us," he declared.[10] Beem concluded his case with a powerful closing statement aimed at both the head and the heart. "Besides, your situation is favorable compared to that of many other women, and if you think that your case is hard, many others have reason to despair. How is it with Lizzie Archer, Capt. McNaughts wife, Col. Alexander's wife, and the wives of at least a hundred other men in Owen County, who have large families to take care of? If they can stand it, as they have to do, most certainly you can do the same."[11]

In case Hala was not moved by his comparison to the wives of other Owen County soldiers, Beem reminded her that their reputations as honorable, self-respecting, Christian people required that they sacrifice together for the nation that protected all they held dear. In the same letter, he explained his feelings about that nation:

A good government is the best thing on earth. Property is nothing without it, because it is not protected; a family is nothing without it, because they cannot be educated. . . . I thank God for the impulse that

Like many other Civil War soldiers, Indiana's David E. Beem wanted his wife to be his spiritual confidant and partner in war, but Mahala never embraced the Union war effort: she questioned her husband's political position and ultimately refused to enshrine their separation as a sacred act for the nation. After he received a letter full of complaints from Mahala, Beem sent her a sharp rebuke on July 27, 1862. "How is it with Lizzie Archer, Capt. McNaughts wife, Col. Alexander's wife, and the wives of at least a hundred other men in Owen County, who have large families to take care of? If they can stand it, as they have to do, most certainly you can do the same. Were I a woman, I would be ashamed of a husband who would not fight for his country when it was in peril."
(Indiana Historical Society, Mo841)

caused me to take up arms at the commencement of the war. Had I not done so then, I would certainly feel it to be my duty to do it now; and if I were too big a coward to shoulder a musket under the last call, I would hide my head from the face of men, and pray for rocks and mountains to fall on me to cover up my disgrace.

The moral currents zigzagging between the Beems followed the sentimentalist vision of war, but they did not always produce the desired results for the couple. These communications were supposed to unite families politically and spiritually, bringing them to an elevated emotional state.[12] Many soldiers experienced a revival of romantic love and patriotic feeling within their marriages, but the Beems struggled as a couple at war, unable to find renewal in the suffering and sacrifice despite the conventional platitudes they penned. Beem concluded his July 27 letter by appealing to his wife's faith: "All I ask of you is to be patient and cheerful like a good Christian ought. For my part I have no doubt I am a great deal happier than I would be at home; and lie down at night with a much lighter and more grateful heart than many a big, lazy pup at home who is too cowardly to come out and defend the old flag of Freedom."[13]

The emotional distance between Beem and Mahala grew after the Battle of Antietam on September 17. The Fourteenth Indiana led one of the first attacks against the Confederate center along the Sunken Lane. The ground afforded the charging Hoosiers little cover, and the Southern infantrymen delivered volleys that eviscerated their ranks. The Rebels accelerated their rate of fire by having men in the second ranks load weapons and then pass them to the front to blast at the Yankees. Over the din of the battle Beem's brigade commander was overheard saying, "God, save my poor boys!"[14] The Union offensive eventually captured the Sunken Lane, but not before 1,750 fell in the Fourteenth Indiana's division.[15]

On September 18 Beem wrote the first of seven letters that he composed over the course of the following month. His sustained coverage affords a unique opportunity to explore how his feelings about and perceptions of Antietam were multifaceted and always evolving. In his first note, Beem jotted down a few lines, informing Hala that he was unhurt but that the company had suffered severely. "My dear wife," he hastily wrote, "Yesterday we fought a terrible battle. I came out safe, after being engaged from Sunrise till dark. Lt. Lundy is killed — Nineteen are wounded; several mortally. Last night we laid on the battle-field, and still hold it." In the last line he admitted that his own survival had left him bewildered and questioning whether a higher power had any presence in the helter-skelter chaos of battle. In a single blunt sentence, Beem hinted at the metaphysical confusion that could follow a combat experience: "It was a horrible battle, providence strangely protected me."[16] Beem's use of "strangely" is noteworthy, suggesting a degree of doubt as to whether the Almighty or good fortune decided who died and who lived. The casualty figures, however, offered Beem the solid ground from which to prove his unit's courage. Counting the dead was the surest way for Civil War soldiers to convey the battlefield's terrors as well as to substantiate the men's sacrifice.[17]

The second day after the battle afforded Beem more time to write a longer piece that included the names of the wounded from Owen County, presumably so that Mahala could spread the sad news to friends and neighbors. Beem worried about the families of his men, "knowing they are all full of anxiety for their fate." He was still pressed for time and would have to cut his second note short, but he managed to squeeze out a very brief description of the fighting in a passage that did not resemble his typically smooth prose: "The battle of the 17th was a hard contested one, and the loss on both sides frightful. It lasted from 8 AM till 12½ o'clock, with furious carnage, and fighting more or less continuous from sunrise till dark." He apparently put the letter down and picked it up again to write a postscript that must have been chilling for Mahala to read: "Oh! The rush and roar of the battle! I wonder if the dreadful sounds will ever get out of my ears!"

On September 20 Beem pulled out paper and pen to write to Mahala again, his mind feeling more settled and his hand less jittery as evident by the writing, which is more legible and more carefully composed than in the previous letters. Beem shifted his attention away from the counting of the dead and turned to the injured, visiting a nearby field hospital, where he attended to the needs of the wounded. When he looked at their broken bodies and their pained faces, Beem was overcome by a deep sympathy for men he described as "poor fellows." Oppressive sorrow enveloped him, and all he could do was mourn their loss. He certainly considered their sacrifice sacred. Yet in that moment, he could not convert the "deathbed" scenes of Union soldiers into an idealized sentimental moment for Mahala. "Poor fellow, many of them are badly hurt, some of them will doubtless die, and they are suffering much. But all that can be done by us to render them comfortable has been done, and we will continue to do our best," he informed his wife.

After describing the hospital, Beem tried to give Mahala an overview of the battle, but he struggled to create a coherent narrative of events from the ghastly images lodged in his mind. The movements and decisions of generals and men seemed inconsequential when compared to the blood sacrifice of his comrades in the Army of the Potomac. "The ground presents a scene of honor, that can-

A day after the fighting at Antietam, David Beem walked over the field where his regiment had fought, shocked by the vast destruction of human life. He likely saw the tangled knot of corpses in this Alexander Gardner image of the Sunken Lane and identified by the photographer as Confederates shot and killed by the men in Beem's brigade. The sights and sounds of September 17, 1862, never left Beem, hunting him down for the next month. At that point he felt compelled to leave his unit and recuperate in a private home near Harpers Ferry. Like so many soldiers, Beem could not expel the traumatic memories of battle, but he could manage them when he reflected on the cause itself. "In all my past life," he wrote on October 19, 1862, "I never had events and circumstances so strongly and vividly impressed upon my mind as everything pertaining to that battle seems to be, and I can scarcely realize that a month and more has slipped by since then. Let the days pass as swiftly as they will—I would not detain a single one, for I want to see an end to this wicked, cruel war, believing as firmly as ever that God is on our side."
(Library of Congress Prints and Photographs Division, Washington, D.C.)

not be well imagined," he said, unless the eye took in the thousands of graves dotting the blighted field. This scene did not inspire lofty sentiment or intense feelings. Beem seems emotionally flat in this letter, even when he looked at the ground where he made so many miraculous escapes. He could not help but wonder if war was not utterly random and without a grand design. "When I reflect what a terrible ordeal we have passed through, and how many have fallen around me, I feel very thankful that I have been so remarkably preserved. I presume that at least a half-dozen men were killed within six yards of me, and some of them fell at my feet."[18]

The revulsion Beem felt for the battlefield did not dam his emotions or unleash uncontrollable feelings of despair. When he returned to his tent to write the condolence letter to the widow of Lieutenant Potter Lundy, he admitted to Mahala, "I scarcely know in what terms to convey the dreadful news to her and her two little children."[19] To Beem's surprise, the words flowed from his pen in a finely crafted letter that transformed Lundy into a heroic martyr. "On the morning of the 17th he [Lundy] was cheerful and bore himself gallantly for three hours in that terrible battle. Much of the time he was by my side. He was near me when he fell. Struck in the back of the head by what is supposed to have been the fragment of a shell, he never spoke afterwards. I laid his head on a blanket, stooped over him and asked him if he could speak, but he was unconscious and breathed his last." Through a detailed recounting of Lundy's last moments, Beem had assured Lundy's wife that he had died without suffering and that when he took his last breath he was among friends. Alas, there were no final words of Lundy's to record that might reveal the state of his soul or his feelings for his family or country. Beem's decision to describe Lundy as cheerful must have been of great consolation to his widow, for it demonstrated that the fallen officer possessed emotional control, fought with determined bravery, and trusted in the Lord, since the faithful had no reason to fear the future.[20]

Beem's words were still not enough to turn Lundy's passing into the highly idealized good death. Neither the regimental nor the brigade commander could facilitate the transportation of his body to Indiana, and the staggering number of dead exceeded the capacity of the "facilities for embalming." Lundy's comrades would not dispose of his corpse in an anonymous trench. "It may be a satisfaction to you," Beem wrote with great delicacy, "to know that we buried him decently in a country cemetery under a beautiful tree, and have placed a suitable head board at his grave, so that his resting place can be identified in after years." If the widow Lundy and her two children never made it to Maryland, they would at least have "his sword, pistol, belt & all that he had," thanks to Beem, who had it shipped to Lundy's family by express. When the box of personal effects reached Indiana, the family would have a tangible link between the artifacts of war and the glowing tribute by Beem, whose words immortalized his dear friend and comrade as a noble hero of the Union cause. "Although nothing can repair the terrible loss which you sustain in the death of your affectionate companion, yet it may to some extent soften your sorrow to know that your husband died the death of a brave soldier in defense of his country, rights, and in the full performance of a most sacred duty," Beem concluded. With the relics of her husband's service, Beem hoped that the widow Lundy would "tell his children that their father died a glorious death; when they arrive at mature years, they will know they lost an affectionate parent in the great struggle for a priceless government."[21]

Beem's ability to express and manage a wide range of emotions in his letter to Lundy's widow speaks to a general ambivalence he felt toward the battlefield, but not for his comrades or the cause for which so much blood had been shed. Beem felt the unmistakable tragedy of war deeply, yet the killing and death drew him closer to his men, deepening his sense of devotion to them as trusted brothers who would selflessly face together the unforgiving judgment of the battlefield that had taken so many of their comrades down.

Despite his devotion, the emotional ups and downs continued for Beem even after the regiment left the Antietam battlefield. At their new camp, the empty places around the fire pit reminded Beem and his comrades of the horrible losses they had suffered. "Since so many of the boys have been compelled to part with us," Beem wrote on September 24, "it seems like everything has changed. Many of the most cheerful and light hearted of the boys are now absent from us suffering from their wounds in the hospital, and we miss their jovial spirits continually. Our camp seems stiller and less animated than a few short weeks ago found it."[22] To fill the emotional emptiness, Beem directed his thoughts toward a "merciful Providence" who "spared so many of us. Hereafter, we can say with truth we have seen all the horrors of war."[23]

The sights and sounds of combat would not leave his head, his body was giving out, and Beem confided to his wife that he could feel his strength decline. Worst of all, he wrote, was that his head was "too full of *bumblebees* to write much."[24] Beem's headaches worsened, and fever followed, symptoms that most likely indicate a form of battle fatigue. It appears, however, that Beem did not connect his deteriorating health to the violence of Antietam. By the first of October, he had obtained leave from his unit to convalesce at a boardinghouse. He spent his days trying to read and write, but confessed, "My aching head will not allow of that." He only managed to write one letter a day. For much of the time, he sat alone thinking "about the war, what and when will finally be the end of it."[25] No high idea or call to manly honor could keep him from sinking further, and he felt no shame in telling his wife of his desperation. He could not write long letters, he explained to Mahala, because "I am still quite weak, my nerves are all unstrung, and it requires an effort to make my pen go right."[26]

Beem nearly came undone after his experience at Antietam, and his health had not been fully restored when he returned to the ranks in early October without explanation. He could do little in camp, and going out on picket duty was out of the question. When his company tramped out of camp without him, Beem discovered how deeply connected he had become to his comrades, telling his wife, "This is the first time that the Regt. Ever left camp without me, and I tell you I wanted to go this time, but thought I had better not. They may have a skirmish but I think nothing more, and I will look for them back tonight. It rained last night, and while I lay in my tent I could not sleep for thinking of the boys."[27] Without question, Beem wanted to share the dangers with his men. His sense of isolation is telling, and he did not hide his need for their emotional communion from Mahala. Their camaraderie was not a fellowship founded on aggression and violence as much as one based on affection and a mutual understanding that arose out of their shared experiences in the field and extolled as the purest and most powerful emotion of sympathy.

Beem's willingness to tell his wife that he missed and needed his comrades' physical presence in his life counters historian Gerald Linderman's claim that war emotionally hardened idealistic volunteers. Without question, veterans became accustomed to the horrors of the battlefield, but adaptation was the hallmark of pragmatism, and flexible understandings of manliness enabled soldiers to form tight-knit communities of mutual support when confronting the dehumanizing aspects of war.[28]

The bonds of comradeship did not isolate men from the home front, as Civil War regiments almost always replicated the local communities that sent them off to war. Tensions certainly abounded, and labor shortages and physical dislocation frequently destabilized households, but the Beems suffered no such crisis. They did not have children and lived within an extensive network of kin. Their troubles centered on a fundamental disagreement over whether the Union cause justified their separation and suffering. No sacrifice could sway Mahala from her emotional indifference to David's suffering in the field. Beem sent her mixed messages, given that many of his letters offered stark revelations about his twisted emotional state. Beem showed no emotional ambiguity to the public, publishing only a highly sentimentalized battle account of the Fourteenth Indiana in an Indianapolis paper. A few weeks after its publication, a letter arrived in camp from a reader who was so moved by his Antietam article that "a quiet tear stole down my cheek." The reader congratulated Beem and his "Spartan Band" for passing through the "fiery ordeal" with "fidelity." "We all feel proud of your conduct," he wrote, "and want stock in the glory" of the regiment.[29] This is exactly the response that Beem had long desired but could never elicit from his wife: an imagined identification between those at home and the soldiers sacrificing in the field, and sharing in the same powerful emotions felt in the ranks.

Veteran soldiers on both sides, even those who felt a strong sense of partnership with those at home, could not help but feel that their world was beyond civilian understanding. Beem, for instance, was stunned by Mahala's refusal to acknowledge the restraints of army life that kept soldiers from even moving freely inside their own camps.

> I'll tell you what I would have to do to get a leave of absence. I would in the first place have to get a certificate signed by *two* Surgeons that my disability was permanent and that I could never get well here; and then I would have to get the signatures of at least four Generals, who know nothing about me personally, to my application for a leave, before I could get it. So you see it's a hard matter to get off, and your saying "please come home" don't have much to do with it, and if you were to write a thousand such letters it would come as near getting me home as the cow come to jumping over the moon, and not a whit nearer. However, if my dear, anxious wife will only have a little patience, and try to understand that her husband, unworthy though he be, has some duties to perform, and solemn oaths to fulfill to the country.[30]

Mahala did not give up her lobbying campaign to get Beem home, and with every letter from home he became more intransigent in asserting his right to define duty as he understood it. The failures of the Army of the Potomac made him even more sensitive and suspicious of civilian critics than of soldiers who were under more successful commands. The bloodletting of Fredericksburg, followed by the harsh condemnations of the war by the Northern public, embittered Beem against anyone opposing the war and more broadly estranged him from all civilians. Any Northern or Southern soldier who came from communities divided by the war — as Beem's Indiana community was — were likely to see themselves in an adversarial relationship with the civilians back at home. After Gettysburg, for instance, Beem did not mince words with his wife, whose political stripes contained shades of Copperheadism. "I cannot say too much in praise of the two brave men who fell, nor have I time to say what I would like,"

Beem wrote two days after the battle. "None ever fell more nobly, none were ever mourned more by surviving comrades," and, he added with an underline for emphasis, *"They were buried by their friends."* [31] Only his fellow veterans, he felt, could adequately mourn for his fallen comrades with the sympathy and respect deserving of their sacrifice.

The bond of comradeship forged through the emotional ordeal of killing locked men together. Powerful emotions were not enough to get men to follow orders under fire, and the need for mass discipline as the foundation to individual bravery lodged in Beem's mind during the Fredericksburg Campaign of 1862. He was in awe of his fellow soldiers for attacking with daring heroism. Antietam helped convince Beem that the organizational structure of the army provided the discipline that channeled raw courage into a transcendent personal moment on behalf of the nation. The calm courage of Lieutenant Lundy at Antietam stuck with Beem. At the same time, pragmatism fueled a veteran's sense of entitlement, empowering him to determine his sense of duty based on individual conscience and not on others' judgment.

Beem's decision not to reenlist in the summer of 1864 reveals how his sense of duty had taken a pragmatic turn, in which he decided his own course of action. A rumor circulated at home alleging that he had given a patriotic speech to his company, imploring them to reenlist for an additional three years. When Beem got wind of the rumor, he denied the report, lecturing Mahala that no one had a right to impose their sense of duty on any veteran: "I thought then and still think that I could persuade several to re-enlist," he wrote, "but as I am not going with them, and as they have already faithfully served three years, I shall not try to persuade them to serve longer — but leave every one to judge for himself as I do for myself." [32]

Four months later, Beem returned to Indiana believing that he was his own man and that his departure from the army had been not only on his terms, but also entirely justified by a battlefield record of personal valor and courageous leadership. If the couple's personal history remained true to form, then Mahala was likely not moved one way or the other by her husband's reasoning for coming home. Not once had she shrunk before his passionate arguments about why they needed to suffer as a couple for the Northern war effort. Her uncompromising stance had prevented Beem from fully realizing his sentimental aspirations of military service, but falling short became almost an afterthought for the captain of the Fourteenth Indiana, who had discovered during his service that his beloved comrades had shown themselves to be men of character in sacrificing for the divinely sanctioned cause of Union.

## WRIGHT VINSON
### *Georgia Farmer*
### Fifty-Seventh Georgia Infantry

Wright Vinson did not write letters—he spoke them. To understand him, we must read his words out loud, hear his voice, follow the jagged rhythm of his sentences, pausing in unexpected places, working through the inconsistent spelling for what amounts to an oral recording of the past. His unfamiliarity with the pen did not seal off his emotional interior to his wife, nor did he contain his feelings when dictating his letters to a comrade, which he did on a few occasions. Regardless of whether Vinson wrote his own letters or a comrade transcribed his words, a wide range of emotions washed across his correspondence with his wife. These documents are a remarkable act of written and oral expression at a time when Southern men were to appear emotionally reserved when facing the world and controlled and moderate in their private interactions with social intimates.[33] Vinson shows that soldiers could assume many roles when their pens did the talking. His letters pick up in the spring of 1862, but Vinson had enlisted in the Second Georgia state troops in the fall of 1861 and was assigned to the coastal defenses near Savannah. He was twenty years old when he entered military service and married with one child, but he was not listed as a head of household in the 1860 census. He was probably working a portion of his father's farm without the assistance of any slave labor. It is impossible to ascertain why he enlisted, but it is plausible that Vinson sought a post on the Georgia coast with the hope of remaining close to home while fulfilling his obligations to the state.

Everything changed for Vinson with the Confederate Conscription Act on April 16, 1862, when Vinson's unit became the Fifty-Seventh Georgia, Vinson was promoted to third sergeant, and his regiment was reassigned to Braxton Bragg's command, which would ultimately be named the Army of Tennessee. Vinson's letters do not cover this crucial period of transition, but the transfer from the Georgia coast kept him from making quick and probably unauthorized trips home, testing the emotional resolve of Vinson and his wife, Christiana, who was expecting a child. Traversing the physical distance through letter writing created barriers for a man who was barely literate and came from an oral culture. As with many soldiers of limited educational background, the act of writing felt unnatural to Vinson, and the frustrations fueled a desire to go home and talk to Christiana face-to-face. Trying to forge a spiritual and emotional bond through hastily written letters of fragmented prose was not the idealized portrait in popular literature of a couple joining together through letters that expressed their yearning and affection for each other as an act of suffering for the higher cause of nation.[34]

Vinson opened one of his first letters from the camp of the Fifty-Seventh Georgia with a standard salutation, suggesting that he had some familiarity with the accepted writing decorum of the day—though in all of his correspondence, including this letter, it is difficult to determine which came directly from Vinson's own hand. "My Dear loving Wife and Child I have taken my penn in hand to day to let you heare where I have got to Darling thes lines leaves mee and harty and I hope when they Come to hand they will find you all the Same good blessing Darling a Sunday when I left there." His opening acknowledged the unpredictability of life in the army, followed by a quick assurance that he felt "harty." He barely acknowledged the military situation before turning his attention to the restrictions of a military regime. "Darling my letter will bee short for I hant heard the nuse yet I hant heard now war nuse to write to you Sow you must look over this short letter if you please Darling it dident Cost mee but 55 Cts to Come down here I run the blackade from macon to Savannah I got here Safe as a buck Darling I eat a good diner with you lost." Vinson felt no shame in comparing himself to a runaway slave when he slipped into Savannah to buy a decent dinner. The hastiness of the composition conveys the stress of the moment, of financial pressures, and of his powerlessness to come help his pregnant wife at their Crawford County farm. Nothing in this letter suggests that Vinson found emotional gratification in the ranks, where at times he felt like a slave rather than a citizen-soldier inspired by the purer emotions of being part of a band of brothers fighting in the defense of the nation.[35]

The next day, Vinson sent off an urgent letter home, informing his wife that he had fallen ill. "My Dear Wife I will write you a few more lines to let you now how I am this morning I dont fell as well as I did yesterday wee hant Got nothing to eat but Bread and molasses and Coffee and it nearley Kills mee to eat it it makes mee bad off in my bowels I have got the headache this morning verry Bad Darling wee hant got our bounty yet but wee will get it this weak." The immediate health danger did not lend itself to a reflective moment for Vinson, in which he referenced the typical Christian refrain of having to bear life's tribulations as a test of faith. When words failed him and his body was doubled over in physical pain, Vinson was in no condition to elevate his suffering in the ranks as evidence of Christian character. Instead Vinson wrote of his vulnerability and fears, hoping that he could find comfort from his wife, seemingly without any concern that she would see him as weak and unmanly. "Sow I must Close for this time write soon your Dear loveing husband untill Death Darling they is one things that I Dont wont you to forget and that thing is I dont wont you to forget to pray and think of one that is gone from you how good by to you both."[36]

Vinson could not keep the melancholy thoughts of missing home from intruding into his mind, and by summer he could barely think of his wife and infant child without feeling overwhelmed by lonesomeness. His isolation brought him to a point where he confessed to his wife that he could not control his emotions — an admission that would have been unthinkable before the war. "Darling you spoke to me to pray and pray in forth Darling it comes from my heart you dont now how it makes mee feell when I get down you and the baby is on my mine all the time and it hurts mee to think that I cant bee with you and the baby."[37] This passage offers a glimpse into Christiana's role as a spiritual caretaker. While she likely had performed this duty before the war as well, the call to prayer now functioned as a conduit of affection for Vinson, who most certainly felt the "presence" of his wife when he looked up to the heavens and prayed for God's mercies.

For the remainder of his service, Vinson continued to turn to his wife for comfort and religious guidance when he felt overwhelmed by the physical and mental demands of war. Although her letters have not survived, it appears that she imagined a universe where Providence controlled life in all matters big and small. What can be pieced together from their correspondence resembles a private journey toward salvation and survival without any thought about whether or not God sided with the Confederacy. Vinson's tepid enthusiasm for the war effort likely had many sources, but if he were influenced by the sentimental promise of war, he did not articulate it. Practical matters pressed down on the couple, and Christiana was largely on her own, though Vinson's father offered labor and advice on the farm. Nevertheless, from where Vinson marked time in the world, they were not positioned to imagine the war as a moment of moral uplift for a political cause when the struggle to live consumed daily life.

Wherever Vinson looked, he saw men sinning with impunity in camp. Unlike most soldiers, who shielded their families from the dark side of army life, Vinson pulled back the curtains on the sordid world of soldiering for his wife to see that war was not a civilized business. "Darling dont you beleive all that you heare from Camps," he wrote on June 26,

> and I will tell you the reason of it they is some folks in Camps that
> takes a delight in it for they now that the women will bee on easy a bout
> it till they heare better Dont Beliave a word of it for it ant sow. Darling
> you write to archy long a nought for him to get the letter before you
> gow for I dont want you to bee chought there [Macon] by your self for

*Writing Home*

Indiana's Adolph Metzner's watercolor of Union cavalrymen watching a black woman give birth offers a rare glimpse into the sexual voyeurism of Civil War soldiers. Evidence of sexual desires and behavior is difficult to unearth in letters and reminiscences because of self-censorship in the ranks. Wright Vinson was unusual in speaking about acts of sexual violence against women. In contrast to formulaic narratives written by educated soldiers, the conversational style or "writing by the ear" from illiterate and semiliterate men like Vinson enabled him to strip away the gloss of war and reveal a darker side of soldiering that remained beyond the reach of most civilians on the home front.
(Adolph Metzner American Civil War Collection, Library of Congress)

> they is solgers passing there ever day and some of them is getting sow
> bad they take the woman down anny where it was done up here the
> other day and the woman Coldent help here self dont think nothing
> of this I am just telling you how they will doo Darling when you gow
> down to Archy tell him to get a subtute for mee.[38]

The rambling and disjointed nature of this passage pulls the reader into Vinson's troubled mind and his rapidly fluctuating emotions and thoughts. The troublesome camp rumors were more than an annoyance to Vinson, who could not combat such stories through letter writing given his difficulties with the pen. Rapidly firing off his dictation, he spouted out his grievances, the infectious army gossip, the likely raping of women in Macon by men who were nothing more than savages, and the impossibility of finding an honorable way out of the army through a substitute.

Vinson tried to maintain an intimate emotional connection with his wife, but no expression of sympathy and compassion could possible stabilize Vinson's life when only his physical presence at home could restore his desired place as the head of household. In a subsequent letter, when Vinson wanted revenge after it was rumored that a neighbor's slave had stolen a pig and his impotency to do anything about it enraged him, he spewed out his thoughts with a disorienting fury:

> Dear you said that Some body had stole one of our hogs pa sais he
> think that it was hightower nigers I wish I Cold Just get their I wold
> give him one killing sertain pa sais they is a nother one missing he dont
> where any body had stole it or Dear you said that Mr Davis wonts to
> By Some of your g hogs Dear you had Better keep them what ant stole
> Dear you needent to by any corn till I Come home pa sais I have yet
> plenty to faten you hogs.[39]

For the remainder of the summer, Vinson's letters spoke mostly about the poor conditions in camp, the financial strains of war, advice on managing the farm, and his desire to find an honorable way out of military service by purchasing a substitute. The frustrations of being an absent husband mounted, but he drew from the sentimentalist idea that the emotional and moral state of a person could leap across space to their home and bring a degree of contentment to a couple. "I wish that I knowed something to write that wold keep you in good hart for I now that you Cant Bee in good hart if you are like my self for it ant mush Satisfactions that I see when I heare something that sturs up my feelings it ant long Before I heare Something wright the other way and then it is worst than ever."[40] Emotional power was one of the few options that Civil War soldiers possessed as absent patriarchs. In this instance, Vinson was similar to a sentimentalist of a higher social and educational class. They valued letters for their emotional didacticism, believing that health and happiness resided in the individual, that one could cultivate uplifting emotions as a way to maintain control of one's life regardless of the circumstances. Despite his best efforts to rally the spirits of his household, Vinson could not lift himself up from his own despondency and find grace in his family's suffering. To interpret his estrangement from sentimentalism as a cultural and political matter alone overlooks the religious dimensions of this problem. As a Christian, he had been instructed since his youth to embrace the trials of life as an opportunity to show God and the world that he was a true believer.

In the fall of 1862, Vinson accompanied Braxton Bragg's Confederate forces into Kentucky, but the military possibilities for the South of this Northern invasion did not register in the Georgian's letters. He knew that every step north would likely disrupt mail lines and further isolate him from his wife. The ensuing campaign culminated with the October 8 battle at Perryville, but Vinson's unit did not see any action—just plenty of hard marching and some skirmishing. As he feared, Vinson lost regular touch with his wife while the army was in constant motion. When there was a break, he turned to an identified comrade and dictated a letter. The November 6 letter is not in Vinson's own hand, and its style differs from previous correspondence, but the words flow in a conversational tone—unstructured, full of feeling, and transmitted as they were pronounced. "If I could see you I could tell a heep," it reads.

> I could tell you more than I could write in a week and do nothing else, and I hope the time is speedally comeing when I shall be with you again as I wd ~~day~~ in days that are past an gone if peace was made now I wuld be one of the happyest Boys you ever saw in your life I long to see the day when I can go home an stay ~~When~~ If these lines you eve see Cast a thought once more on me Although we be many miles apart We are still joined in hand an heart Wright Vinson.[41]

The longing to see his wife took on an added sense of urgency when Vinson's regiment had a run-in with the enemy. It was a minor affair, but the sight of blood did not stir feelings of martial manliness in Vinson.

> Dear if I just Cold See you I Cold tell you a heap dear when wee got in kentucky wee ran right in a monks the yankees and they shot at some of our Brigeade but dident hurt now body wee kill 6 of them and left them lying there Dear I have walk over the battle feild it was fught beetween Richmond and Lexington our men whip them bad what they dident kill they taken prison Darling that was a sight to look at the wounded Dear I went in the housepittle where they was it was the worst Sight I ever Saw in my life some with there arms off and some with their legs off and other plases.[42]

Once again Vinson's conversational style freed his letters from formulaic narrative structures that channeled the war's ugliness into inspiring narratives of heroism. He spoke unselfconsciously about the impact that violence had on the bodies of the dead and the minds of the survivors. After one brief encounter with the enemy, he spoke of his exploits as if he were at home conversing with his wife after a long day in the fields: "Darling wee taken some prisonrs and kill Some I Saw one man lying in the gam of the fence killed he was shot right through the heart I walk up to him and look at him good I saw the hole that he was shot turn over."[43] Maybe Vinson could have translated this experience into a heroic moment if he possessed the language and composition training of the majority of Civil War soldiers. His own actions after the battle were non-heroic, given that he desecrated a dead body. His rough and very brief combat description illustrates just how far removed he was from the cultural core of a wartime culture of sentimentalism. The highly idealistic and popular rendering of a fighting man as an innocent soldier boy was not even a shadowy figure in Vinson's world. In fact, the Georgian did not hesitate to tell his wife of the horrid things he saw and did, including his decision to poke at the bullet hole of a fallen Yankee. Admitting to desecrating a corpse was a remarkable confession on Vinson's part, but we are left to imagine how Christiana reacted to her husband's morbid fascination with the dead.

During the fall of 1863, Vinson spent much of his time in camp, struggling every day to cope with the hardships and homesickness of a life in the army that sometimes left him emotionally drained. Only the thought of his wife kept him going, and he would not let propriety keep him from telling his wife that he missed the touch of her body at night: "I wis that I Cold hug up with you though I Cant doo it but I hope the time ant far off [when I can] Sleep with you all the time." Vinson's dreams brought his wife into his arms, but when he awakened, Vinson would "bee hugging the Boys [in his tent] and then I would bee mad."[44] This incident did not follow the script of Victorian manhood, and his inability to see humor in cuddling with his comrades is telling. Vinson had lost his ability to stand back and find any emotional release in the absurdities of war.

In November Vinson's emotional state bottomed out. He broke down in a dictated letter to his wife, telling her that he could no longer face this cursed life and that the only way out was the sweet release of death: "My life ant now Satisfaction to mee," he wrote from a pit of emotional darkness. A life without her and their child was not worth living for Vinson. As awful as it was, she must know the truth: "I had just as soon die as to live."[45] Christiana's reaction is unknown, but one can imagine her own personal agony when reading her husband's words of despair, knowing that he needed her physical presence more than ever at a time when a cheerful letter or a call to prayer would not lift her husband out of his desperate mood.

The decline of Vinson's physical health might explain the mental downward spiral that subsequently intensified his sense of urgency to escape a situation he saw as unalterable. Without the funds to supplement the army's meager rations by buying fresh produce from nearby farms, Vinson had no choice but to eat putrid meat, even though he was certain that "it will kill all of us in our Bowels if wee don't get some [fresh food] soon." When his stomach was not churning from spoiled beef, Vinson was furiously scratching all over. Lice covered his body and uniform, which was hardly surprising since he had not taken a bath for more than a month; he was so poor that he could not even buy a scrap of soap. After some time in the field, he eventually borrowed a mirror. When he looked at his reflection, he felt as if he had lost his true self. Feelings of shame overcame him, and in that moment he felt broken down, a man without dignity scavenging for survival as if he were a pauper.

> I hant wash my Close in a month and Shant tell I get Soap ever thing is that I have got is Black as the Back Sow I dont recond you wont to see mee Bad with my fine Suit on Darling I am a Shame to tell you that I am lousey it is the Body louse I have done my Best to keep them off but god in heaven nows they ant now Chance to doo it Sow if I was to get the chance to Come home you wold hate to tech mee for you wold get them on you and I woldent have that done for 50 Dollars Dear I Cant keep them off unless I Cold get Soap to wash my Cloas.

To conclude this letter, he wrote in the upper margin, "Kiss Charley for mee and tell him he has a Father But a sorry one."[46]

In seeing himself as an unworthy father and a failed soldier, Vinson disclosed how his sense of suffering had resulted in an abjection of the self—which was common among poor and semiliterate people—and how far removed he was from the cultural pull of sentimentalism.[47] There was nothing thrilling in his descriptions of army life, nothing picturesque in his depiction of war, no claim of moral superiority for serving his nation, and no trace of militarized manliness. The wasted bodies, the depravity of soldiering, and the physical destruction wrought by the armies drove Vinson's depiction of events. He wanted those at home to know the filth, the hunger, the exposure, the loneliness, and the punishing violence that was, as the Georgian feared, pushing him toward the grave.

Indeed, the end for Vinson came suddenly, when he died an antisentimental death in a Jackson, Mississippi, hospital on June 18, 1863. On a soiled cot, his body covered with blisters and his skin charred from internal bleeding, Vinson succumbed to the ravages of smallpox in less than one week. All he could do was look at the photograph of his wife that felt so lifelike that "it ought to Speke" to him.[48] Inside the hospital, he had no choice but to break off communication with her. Touching the paper, envelopes, or stamps that she would receive might contaminate his entire family with the dreaded disease. A hospital attendant, who himself was barely literate, copied the dying soldier's final words into a short note. He explained that Vinson "was afraid to write to you him Self for fear he might have the Small pox him Self and Send it to you in a letter."[49] In a bitter and final irony, to protect his family while an absent father, Wright Vinson had to cut off the one tie he had been able to maintain with the ones he loved the most.

## JOHN CRAWFORD ANDERSON
*South Carolina Student and Slaveholder*
Citadel Cadet

Stuck behind a desk in a Citadel classroom and lost in daydreams about future battlefield glories, South Carolina's John Crawford Anderson felt the war pulsate around him. Everyone else was in action, including his sisters, pulling together for the military effort while he remained confined in his quarters, likely feeling imprisoned by the very books that promised military glory to those who would rally against the rapacious invader.[50] Frustrations mounted with every letter he received from home. Anderson's father, a prominent slaveholder from the South Carolina upcountry, lectured him about a man's duty to fight, even though he presumably paid his son's Citadel tuition. "Everyone should shut Books," his father ordered on December 2, 1861, "and shoulder his Gun." For some reason, John continued to mark time at school while letters from home stoked his discontent. His sister even referred to a family acquaintance as "one of the Canine species" for refusing to enlist. Anderson must have wondered if his family was needling him for staying in school. Everywhere he turned, he was reminded that other men had stepped forward in defense of their new nation. Even a casual stroll down the streets of Charleston must have felt like a walk of shame. On every corner veteran soldiers stood in an exclusive circle, boasting loudly of their heroics and chortling about an enemy convulsed in fear at the mere sight of a Confederate bayonet gleaming in the sun. Their stories exhilarated Anderson, who knew that only shedding Yankee blood could satiate his ambitions. Veterans told stories of fighting at First Manassas within "ten steps of the Yankees line of battle," killing them in savage hand-to-hand fighting before stepping "on their dead boddies" to mark their conquest. This barbarous desecration was mentioned in passing, and Anderson kept his ears tuned to the stories of the veterans, recalling their numerous "gallant deeds." The effect of these tales, he wrote to his sister, was "enough to make anyone's heart fire with rage." Anderson could no longer be restrained. The time had come, he announced, "in fighting with the Bayonett."[51]

Anderson followed the herd of Confederates who believed after the Battle of Manassas that Southern soldiers could not be conquered, since God had clearly marked his generation for immortality just as the Revolutionary heroes had acted on a providential mission against England. His romantic desire for war also originated within the private ambitious designs of a slaveholding family; expectations for achievement were unbearably intense for young men of Anderson's class, who also sought the adulation of women as the crowning moment in becoming mature and respectable. Anderson, like scores of other slaveholding men, ran off to war with the cultural baggage of Romantic literature, classical history, and the Revolutionary heritage, all aroused into action by a fiery sense male honor.[52] On learning about the fall of Nashville in early 1862, he promised his sister that the surrender of the Tennessee capital would lure the Yankees farther south, where "they will get the most complete brushing that a set of Vandals ever received. . . . I hope the next news from those parts will be of one of the most glorious Victories that ever shed honor on the 'Colours' of any nation." Significantly, Anderson upheld the sentimentalist assumption that the bravest would show themselves because of superior blood lines. "Those western pioneers [Confederate soldiers] have been inured to hardships and trials elsewhere than on the field and are made of better blood than those of the older [part of] the country. It takes men of the bravest kind to put to flight such men as these, and that the point of the bayonett, too. I believe in fighting with the Bayonett," he declared, "for our Powder is getting very scarce anyway and the Yankees can't stand the Bayonett."[53] Promising to lead with the bayonet affirmed Anderson's belief in the sentimentalist view of war as a contest of individual heroism in which the individual would determine the war's outcome. His need to puff up Southern manhood, even when the soldiers in question were in another theater of war, underscores how solidarity was in part an act of imagination that could be made real on paper when he identified with other Southern men fighting in distant parts of the Confederacy.

The South Carolinian's sentimentalist dream of warfare was nearly realized in the summer of 1862, when Confederate authorities rushed the Citadel cadets to meet a Federal offensive at James Island. For the next few weeks, continuous thunderstorms pounded the camp, turning everything around the men into a wet morass from which the enemy never emerged. Drenched and deeply disappointed over the lack of action, the young men followed orders and returned to the Citadel. Their forced return sparked a rebellion among some of Anderson's youthful comrades, who felt "wronged and dishonored" by an order that violated "the will of every single Man." A group of cadets swore to remain in the field until there was a showdown with the Yankees. Anderson stayed away from the troublemakers, despite his worries that he might appear cowardly. Even though he acknowledged the mishaps and misunderstanding of the expedition, Anderson converted his quixotic foray into a coming-of-age adventure of boys becoming men. "We have had quite an exciting time for the last week in the Citadel. We were ordered out on the Island to take part in the fight, but after remaining there for a few days during which it rained all the time, we were ordered to return to the Citadel. It was against the will of every single Man but we had to obey the order." [54] Capitalizing "Man" was not an accident by Anderson, who turned to pen and paper to create a dramatic narrative of an event that could just as easily have been recounted as a dreary failure. The young South Carolinian's writing aesthetic, honed through years of formal education, did not determine what he wrote, but formalized rules of writing influenced its meaning. He articulated his thoughts within accepted writing structures that figured into how he wanted to be seen by others. Such a thought process was likely so ingrained in Anderson that he was not aware of his own intentionality when he transformed a mundane assignment into a daring enterprise where boys became men.

Through this carefully crafted account Anderson conveyed the sentimental promise of war. He did so not in a reflexive way, but because he accepted and believed in the language of male honor as an affirmation of an individual's self-worth. The code of honor, as he discovered in the ranks, could not adjust to the unexpected twists and turns of war. In other words, honor did not always bring clarity and purpose to individual choice, because the military subsumed individual will. Anderson admitted to his sister that he had lost his self-assuredness after his company's controversial order to return to the Citadel, where many of the boys organized a rebellion. "I was greatly tempted to join in it [the rebellion] myself but was restrained when I contemplated the pain it would give my Parents and friends to know that I had become so lost to all sense of honor and responsibility to commit such an act. I have there fore concluded not to join any such proceeding." The fallout for the recalcitrant cadets was severe, and many left the institution. Worst of all, Anderson wrote, "the Public generally are very hard down on the Men who have left in the scrape. Everything seems to be working against them now." He heard of one cadet whose parents had "discarded" him over the incident. "Such a thing would strike me a death blow," Anderson wrote, "and bring eternal disgrace upon me, or perhaps it would have the effect to make me rise above the buffetings of this 'dim spot' and trim my pinions for a loftier and nobler flight than I would have otherwise aspired to, but such is nor ever will be my fate if left to my actions." [55] Anderson quickly learned that he could not reconcile the idealized story of himself as a warrior with his own ambitions for fame. His words were knotted around individual will, the demands of the military, the expectations of comrades, and the hopes of the community. Trying to pull loose in any one direction could easily result in the unraveling of a soldier's reputation, his isolation within the ranks, and, in some instances, alienation from his own community.

A little more than one year later, during the winter of 1863, Anderson realized his ambitions in Lee's Army of Northern Virginia when he embarked on what he described as a "little adventure" during the inconclusive Mine Run Campaign. Anderson's language regarding his experience was vintage sentimentalism, blurring the harsh reality of a grueling military maneuver driven by obedience to central authority. Riding on horseback, the South Carolinian surveyed the marching column from a small eminence as the troops snaked up and down a treacherous road. They were slipping and falling in frigid, icy weather, but the mishaps could not penetrate the well-ordered vision of war that Anderson re-created on paper. He claimed that by reading the faces of Lee's veterans, he could see that they were in "fine spirits" — a curious claim, given that the men were sloshing up and down roads in wicked weather. "It was a sight to see the guns glistening in the noonday sun," Anderson wrote to a female acquaintance whose approval and, possibly, affections he sought. This "charming sight" turned grandly sublime when Anderson imagined that he was among a host of warriors "moving on to Liberty or to Death."[56]

The reality was starker. At the end of an exhausting sixteen-mile hike, with temperatures sinking below zero, the Confederates collapsed along the side of the road, sleeping in the open without tents or fires. Sheer exposure took down scores of veterans. But Anderson consciously ignored how this merciless march in horrid conditions had stolen the lives of countless men. He concluded his letter with a sentimental flourish: "I have long been anxious to see an Army in motion, and since my desire has been gratified in that respect I have a still more eager one to be amidst the whistling of balls and the rolling thunder of artillery."[57]

This march was one of the severest in the history of Lee's army, but Anderson's narrative transformed undeniable hardship into a pure triumph of willed behavior on behalf of the Confederate nation. Sitting atop a horse and taking in the panoramic scene from above must have enhanced his aesthetic of grandeur and his love of the spectacle. Anderson wanted his audience to feel the power of an army united in action while also recognizing his interpretive authority as a man who was capable of exerting his will over any situation, regardless of the privations. Anderson also assumed a commanding position as an interpreter of events through a prose and vocabulary that conveyed stability and coherence. War's messiness fell outside the framing of Anderson's plotline, which ultimately resolves itself through the triumph of individual will and the collective discipline of the Southern soldier. Underlying the entire story is the self-perception that Anderson was at the helm. His account is not a patchwork of disparate images from the field. He does not bring into view the diverse range of experiences and feelings of others who were in that same physical space. There is only one perspective in Anderson's mind, and it is his alone. Anderson expresses no confusion about future movements, no sense of chance or contingency, no feeling of trepidation about an impending battle, and no sense of savagery lurking beneath the drama of an army on the hunt.

The following spring, when Grant and Lee's armies opened the 1864 Overland Campaign, Anderson's long-awaited encounter with the enemy occurred in the frenzied fighting of the Wilderness. Anderson was wounded during the melee, but he returned months later to the Petersburg trenches as a pragmatic veteran who elevated professional duty to the army above any lofty ideas about the Confederacy or dreams of individual fame. As a cadet, he had capitalized the word *Public* in a letter to his sister to emphasize the power of the people to make or break a man's reputation. As a veteran, however, Anderson cared more about the opinion of those inside the army than the views of those who were outside it. "Gen. Lee is evidently making preparations to meet a grand attack of Grant," Anderson wrote without emotional theatrics or a call to patriotism. "Able-bodied men in every 'harmproof' department in this Army are being put in the Army of fighting men. We will get a good many men by the operation. Your good friend Mr. Bivings will have to face the balls again and prove his formerly reputed valor in arms. It will be like the rending of the hold of a drowning man to many of them, but Genl. Lee has given the order and obeyed it must and will be."[58] The emphasis on obedience is crucial in this passage, as it demonstrates Anderson's acceptance of the Confederate military as the arbiter of what constituted honorable behavior. Duty would no longer be a choice left to individual conscience—a shift from the position Anderson had taken at the Citadel, where he thought his fellow cadets had the right to follow their own code of honor as they saw fit, even though he condemned their decision to buck adult authority.

The crisis facing his Southern nation and the Confederacy's desperate need for manpower spurred Anderson's move toward pragmatism. His core value of male honor and his political commitment to the Confederacy remained steadfast and secure, but the substance of Anderson's letters and his narration underwent a subtle shift to a harder and less sentimental view of war. He now admitted that the promise of mastery—the highest expression and expectation of willed behavior in the army—was an illusion. The individual was no match for the centralized authority of Confederate military power, which repeatedly demonstrated its might over any man trying to evade service. The South Carolinian did not believe that the spirit of the men or individual heroics would turn the tide against the enemy. Southerners simply needed to get the job done as dependable soldiers. If his fellow countrymen could not find it in themselves to volunteer with enthusiasm, then he fully supported the stern measures of his nation. One month before the surrender at Appomattox, Anderson sent his sister a personal letter that read more like an official military report than the dramatic narratives that he penned at the Citadel and Mine Run. "Four men were shot in the presence of the Brigade today for desertion," he declared. "They were from Horry Dist. And belonged to the first S.C. Vols. It was by no means a pleasant sight, but the merited justice of a deserter. The ceremony is very effecting and enough to deter anyone from following in their footsteps." Anderson also wrote in a very direct way about his approval of arming slaves, and he did so without a hint of embarrassment that the Confederate government had to call on black men to stave off submission to the Yankees. "The Senate has passed the bill to arm the slaves and there is little doubt the House will do the same. It comes in at a late hour, but still may be better late than never. They have been afraid to take hold of it and have doubtless given it mature deliberation."[59]

The silences in Anderson's 1864–65 correspondence are also especially telling. No thrilling accounts of daring maneuvers and individual heroics were served up for the people at home. His missives do not follow the arc of a dramatic story in which Anderson, as the narrator, asserts himself as an omniscient observer who extols warfare as a moment for individuals to show themselves as real men. He becomes almost anonymous in the trenches of Petersburg, just a cog in a machine, but he still finds meaning in the daily acts of soldiering and in his comrades. "The weather is pretty cold in this part of the country—we have been having frost by the whole-sale and you may be assured that 'the Soldier, in his blanket on the ground' does not have the most pleasant of feelings. But I am pretty well to do with my blue blanket and two heavy Yankee blankets. I gave Peter one white blanket and Mr. Darby one and am now left with three."[60]

Emotional proclamations promising bold action for the cause of honor and the South faded away. Anderson's attention turned to the accounting of the clothing, rations, and equipment of soldiering; he wrote an entire letter describing the architecture of his winter hut. To his family he made it clear that the truth of his existence resided in the materiality of his world, in his bond with his comrades, and in circumstances beyond his control. Material culture further reveals his move away from a sentimentalist projection of war to a more pragmatic posture. "The pistol I left at Richmond to be repaired has 'gone up,'" he explained. "The workman was sent to Ala and I guess took the pistol with him. I find them quite a useless weapon here in the Army by the side of shell and minie balls." This perspective was certainly an adjustment for the young man who in 1862 thought the Confederates did not need powder, but only bayonets, to settle things with the Yankees.[61]

Anderson's ideas about courage and masculinity became malleable because of a pragmatic turn that allowed him to embrace a new view of himself as a veteran soldier who prized doing his duty above all else. Yet his final letter from Appomattox shows that he had not divorced himself entirely from sentimentalism:

> I am glad that I have an opportunity to relieve your anxiety. By the blessing of Heaven I am in full vigor of health. True since the 30th of March I have seen many a hardship and made many a narrow escape, but the hand of God has been between me and all harm. We all mourn for our country and every man's face wears a haggard, dejected, and troubled look; but we can only say it must be the will of God and therefore right. We are now surrounded by more than one hundred thousand of our Enemy and are all prisoners of War.[62]

Anderson's fear of shame and the need to save face frustrated deep introspection as Lee's army dispersed. The formality of Anderson's writing style was an extension of how he thought, and it abetted his attempt to keep distasteful truths at a distance from himself and from others. Anderson was a vanquished soldier who confided to his family that he had many "narrow escapes" during the chaotic retreat, but he refused to tease out the drama of his survival stories. Only the mysterious "hand of God," he wrote, explained why he was still standing. No longer did Anderson make predictions about the future: it was uncertain what lay before him on his return to his slaveless plantation in South Carolina.[63]

Even though David Beem, John Anderson, and George Vinson had witnessed similar sights on the battlefield, had been subjected to similar restrictions in the ranks, and had endured similar hardships in the field, if they had ever been in the same room together the conversation would likely have been awkward. Their narratives demonstrate that place, rank, social class, and personality led to different experiences in the ranks and remind us that the act of communicating on paper varied widely among Civil War Americans. Yet they also show how difficult, if not impossible, it was for Civil War soldiers to translate their grievances against the war into an alternative cultural conception that directly challenged the dominance of sentimentalism. Letter writing, moreover, was not just functional; it was also an attempt to render the world into understandable terms. Texts on both sides tended to follow a predictable pattern in which tangled memories of experience often vanished into emotionless chronicles of who did what where. In looking at the act of writing itself, one can move beyond the details of movement and action and gain insight into how Civil War soldiers thought.

For semiliterate soldiers like Vinson the act of writing felt unnatural because he came from a civilian world where face-to-face conversation typified everyday experience. The challenges of corresponding to those back at home were so great—both practically and intellectually—that some soldiers withdrew and became silent, while others broke the communication barrier by writing in a stream-of-consciousness form, as if they were speaking directly to the reader in a familiar colloquial style. Vinson falls into the latter category; his letters were constructed with little structure and can best be described as free flowing, spontaneous, and driven by a sense of urgency that was spelled out in fragmented prose. Vinson's letters, therefore, can be seen and read much like oral recordings.

Vinson unfortunately never spoke of combat at length, but plenty of other soldiers filled in those gaps, including William W. Hewell, a semiliterate soldier from Georgia. Hewell's description of an artillery barrage at Gettysburg shatters formal literary conventions and overwhelms the reader with sensory horrors. "I heard then [shells] coming and I would faul down and lete thene pase over," he wrote. "Thare was two wente some two or three feate abuve my head and hite the ground some five or six feate from me[.] I didnten no whate minit I would bestruck and kild bute I come out safe."[64] This passage mirrors the movements of Hewell's mind and his state of shock, putting the reader in the field, where the disorientation and danger are overwhelming. Hewell's writing conveys the fractured thoughts and numbed feelings of a man who has just passed through the wrenching experience of combat.

Hewell and Vinson cannot speak for all semiliterate soldiers, but their voices affirm the importance of social class in understanding Civil War soldiers as writers. The uneven rhythm of the prose, the ragged cadence, and the phonetic spelling mark their lack of formal education of the sort men like Beem and Anderson received. It is hard to imagine that Hewell and Vinson grew up studying Thucydides's *History of the Peloponnesian War*, that they knew anything about Romantic literature, or that they listened to stories of classical heroics in the family parlor. Unfortunately, the truckloads of soldier letters typically quoted by historians rarely include semiliterate men like Hewell and Vinson. Their exclusion, one might argue, is not a serious issue, given that their use of honor, duty, and courage would still suggest that they were pressed into action by the cultural current of militarized manhood circulating in the United States and Europe in the nineteenth century.[65] Yet this ideal of militarized manliness best described the educated and the privileged, missing how self-understandings of manliness were formed in a range of highly particular social settings, and how culture functioned with more subtlety, allowed for greater contestation, and was never a fixed thing in time and place. The creators of *Private Voices* have reached a similar conclusion in their substantial collection of some ten thousand letters from semiliterate Union and Confederate soldiers. Private soldiers who had never sent a letter in their life until the war's outbreak wrote "by the ear," without regard for how posterity might receive their words. They wrote with an unusual freedom in content and in form. Even if a soldier's skills were rudimentary, the desperate need for news forced him to pick up a pen or pencil, knowing that his survival, as well as his homefolks', depended on his words. Unrestrained by the conventions of punctuation and spelling, the creators of *Private Voices* conclude that semiliterate soldiers on both sides who used "nonstandard grammatical forms" created letters that "are frequently more powerful than ones by educated counterparts."[66]

However, the examples of Beem, Vinson, and Anderson also show the limitations of drawing strict lines among soldiers based on social class and region. Sentimentalism, for instance, ran through the lives of all three men, and it encouraged them to be transparent, given the need for a free expression of emotions to those at home. In admitting that they experienced fear and that they had lost their sense of mastery in the ranks, these men violated antebellum expectations of manliness. Combat experience could cause soldiers to repress their emotions, but much more frequently it resulted in ambivalence and the awareness that killing might harden a man's heart and put him on a path to savagery. Soldiers thought they could save themselves from this fate by preserving feelings of sympathy through their correspondence, but once they became veterans, they grew frustrated with their loved ones for composing letters that read like they came from a different time, when the war felt romantic and soldiering was supposed to lead to moral improvement and individual redemption.

Civil War soldiers expected loved ones to understand the war as they actually experienced it, but when this did not occur, they did not become mute or feel estranged from their families. The desire for eminence and reputation was too powerful for them to stop writing, and the need for emotional support and affection was too essential for them to give up on family members. Until the end of the war, men on both sides wrote home with an eye for how they might be perceived by loved ones. While this could lead to the sort of formulaic writing seen in Pierson's Port Republic letter to his sister-in-law, poor men like Vinson could not rework their experiences into highly stylized portraits of war. Men like Pierson could never have imagined that romantic letters had the unintended effect of distorting civilians' perceptions of soldiering and fostering the bullet-proof naïveté that soldiers came to resent.

Soldiers never stopped reminding the people back home that opinions from the home front were fanciful creations imagined within the isolated comforts of home (except for scores of Confederate women like Christiana Vinson, whose trials garnered her husband's sympathy). The persuasive force of the men's arguments to civilians came not from ideas or abstractions, but from exhausting marches, living off of horrible rations, and burying fallen comrades in anonymous graves. From these experiences, unbreakable emotional communities grew among men who were fiercely devoted to each other even as bitter feuds and contentiousness infiltrated their regiments. Their shared suffering and mutual understanding enabled comrades to turn to each other as the arbitrators of duty, honor, and courage. The flexibility with which they judged each other and themselves as veteran soldiers attests to a sympathy that came from a pragmatic reading of life in the ranks. On the ground, in the midst of mayhem and death, soldiers felt for those who were suffering, and in some cases their feelings of sympathy extended to the enemy. While men in uniform had little choice but to do and witness horrible things, under the "right" circumstances they would act on their own conscience, not the army's.

# 4

# Courage and Cowardice

—

UNDER A FIERCE VIRGINIA SUN, Charles Bowen of the Twelfth United States Infantry imagined his own death as he stared across a barren landscape. "Here we lay until 3 o'clock when a charge was ordered on the rebel works," Bowen wrote. "Now there was not a man of us but knew what the result would be, crossing a mile level in the teeth of dozens of batteries, to say nothing of the musketry . . . but orders must be obeyed."[1] Just before the advance was sounded, Charlie filled his canteen and checked his weapon, then gave a sick comrade his pocketknife, a diary, and a locket containing his wife's picture. As he watched his friend head behind the lines with his most treasured possessions on earth, Bowen took his place in the ranks. Moments later, just as he emerged into the open expanse, enemy shells engulfed the charging line in smoke and fire. The first solid shot whirled past Bowen, knocking a file of soldiers ten feet in the air. Scattered survivors barely came back together before canister blasts ripped ugly gaps into the charging formations. "Men were cut in two & hurled [into] a disfigured mass of flesh & rags to the ground," a stunned but whole Bowen later reported. "Arms, legs, headless trunks, & heads without bodies were strewn in every direction."[2] Night brought an end to the fighting, and the morning sun unveiled a maze of trenches zigzagging in every direction, cut into the ground by men who were shocked to be alive. "How in the name of wonder I have escaped without injury is a mystery to me," he wrote, but his survival seemingly made Charlie uneasier about what the future might bring. "But perhaps," he added, "I am only spared to fall on another field. Hard & bloody work will be done around here for probably more than my term of service." Bowen tried to make light of his ordeal, joking to his wife that he had expected to be discharged from "earth & army at the same time."[3] No attempt at humor, however, could soften the jagged memories of blasted battlefields covered with human carnage and traumatized survivors. Over the course of a six-week period beginning on May 6, 1864, sixty thousand men had been shot down in the Army of the Potomac, and another ten thousand had been lost in the subsequent assaults against Petersburg. Ulysses S. Grant's army was morphing into an endless funeral train, and Bowen did not want to add to the procession, particularly since his enlistment was nearly up. The New Yorker even hinted that he might stand back in the next battle, let his time run out, and allow others to do the fighting for him. The idea, though fleeting, sickened him. Why disgrace himself after earning a reputation for fearlessness under fire? If more suicidal charges awaited Charlie and his comrades, he would do his part. "I intend to fall as a soldier," he promised his wife, "with no dishonor to the name I bear, if I fall at all."[4]

Bowen kept his word; for the remainder of his service he withstood enemy bombardments outside Petersburg, dueled with Confederate sharpshooters, and even volunteered to go to the skirmish line so that he could kill enemy artillerists. Bowen experienced many near misses before mustering out of service in the fall of 1864, and on the eve of his return to New York, Bowen warned his wife that he would not be "coming home as a *clean civilian*": she should expect a "*dirty, uncouth* 'Yank' to come through the door with the dust of old Virginia about an inch thick all over." He recommended that she wash him "for an hour or two" to see if "I am the same Charlie you used to know or some base imitation from the army."[5]

Bowen's life story raises two related questions about the experience and impact of Civil War combat: Why did Civil War soldiers continue to risk their lives in battle, and how did the survivors cope with the trauma of warfare? Both questions have promoted imaginative and diverse responses, but the binary nature of the debate suggests that soldiers were either victors or victims of combat. In one camp, scholars portray soldiers as highly motivated to fight and capable of recovering relatively quickly from battle. The opposing camp downplays ideological commitments and emphasizes the institutional and coercive factors that pushed volunteers to fight with discipline on the battlefield.

In evaluating the impact of combat on the rank and file, the interpretations of both sides have merit, and it is easy to see how a historian acting in good faith could select the sources to argue that men were either willing or coerced to face enemy bullets or that they were rejuvenated or unmade by the experience of combat.[6] It appears that we are stuck in a historiographical cul-de-sac where we circle endlessly around matters of representativeness. The individuality of each volunteer, moreover, makes it nearly impossible to generalize whether soldiers remained essentially the same men after their baptism of fire. There were many faces of battle, and veterans showed many layers of their being, even in a single engagement.

A more profitable line of inquiry shifts attention away from the question of combat morale, which has largely helped to sustain the dichotomy between those who mastered their fear and those who did not. In other words, rather than concerning itself with identifying factors of motivation as it relates to the soldier's state of mind after a battle — disillusioned and traumatized, or triumphant and renewed — this chapter focuses on the ways that men in Civil War armies adapted to the practical and cultural mechanisms of authority that were both visible and imperceptible to those in the ranks. Soldiers were not always aware of the forces that shaped their thoughts and actions because they, like all historical actors, were embedded in a symbolic world that was physical as well as cultural and social.[7] Within this broader context it is possible to understand how soldiers came to articulate their view that killing other human beings was just and necessary, and how they came to live with the turbulent memories of the battlefield as a source of pride and deep meaning in their lives. This line of inquiry is not intended to test the truthfulness of soldier accounts or render judgment on the realism of their combat writings. Rather, this approach focuses on the ways that cultural ideas of sentimentalism, gendered ideas of male honor, established medical knowledge in the nineteenth century, and physical coercion compelled soldiers to think, and act, and write about their world in certain ways that affirmed, accommodated, and challenged existing practices of power in the military.

This chapter begins with a brief overview of what Union and Confederate soldiers expected of themselves and their comrades when under fire. Their dreams were not of ghastly deaths or of cowards stampeding to the rear, but of men always facing the front, disciplined and orderly, who charged the enemy with unflinching bravery. The next section explores how the experience of combat posed serious challenges to the idealistic expectations of the rank and file, whose members were shocked by their own conflicted feelings about what fighting did to them and to their comrades. Battlefield survivors were flummoxed by the ways that combat blurred the boundary between the courageous and the cowards, which in turn made it difficult for Civil War officers to identify and punish men who were seen as shirkers. Military surgeons played a critical role in disciplining battlefield malingerers, and their practices reinforced the sentimental idea that courage came from character and that the body and mind, if properly disciplined, could withstand the hammer blows of war.

Civil War soldiers shared a similar understanding of how the mind and body coped with combat stress, but experience taught them that unforeseen circumstances could control men regardless of any intrinsic qualities. They learned to become flexible in thought and action with every bloody engagement, but this shift toward pragmatism never threatened their commitment to male honor, comradeship, and the cause they fought for. These "loyal" and "brave" veterans generally retained their faith in the individual as an agent of change, and the tactics of the day actually made it possible for men to keep seeing the war as an individual experience. At the same time, members of the rank and file were plagued by doubts, despair, and dejection in the wake of every battle — the inevitable by-products of waging an intimate killing war in the nineteenth century. The final section of this chapter explores the contradictory consciousness of Civil War fighters, who could simultaneously see themselves as victors and victims of the battlefield. The continuous cycle of being made and unmade by combat is illustrated in an extended examination of New Yorker Charles Biddlecom's story. His letters home show the difficulties in squaring the paradox of why men who opposed the inhumanity of war and hated military life decided to stay in the army and, through killing, affirmed their sense of manhood and their belief in the political cause for which so many of their comrades had given their lives.

Rumors of a battle worried New Yorker Ambrose Arnold as he opened up a letter from his wife. With every word he read, Arnold was overcome by the conflicting feelings of shame and pride in learning that his young son had offered to take his place in the ranks. This gesture so moved Arnold that he nearly broke down and cried while writing his response: "Dear Wife I cannot fear the battle when such little ones as Denny Vollluntere to go with me for his little form will keep off the leaden hail from his Father but I must stop for I am getting as babiesh as a child altho a warrior."[8] Arnold's self-description as a gentle warrior conveys the early war expectation that volunteers were to show womanly traits of sympathy and compassion without sacrificing their aggressiveness and fearlessness, qualities that were understood as innate to manhood. Both Northerners and Southerners looked to soldiering as an opportunity for emotional uplift and moral improvement through discipline in the ranks. Each side believed that through physical suffering in the field and fighting for the nation, volunteers would shed the enervating effects of the civilian world yet resist succumbing to the savagery of killing and losing their Christian selves as they became hardened veterans. There was, in the eyes of Americans in 1861, no better arena to demonstrate a man's self-worth than the battlefield, where the individual could rise above the melee and show himself to be a man of courage and character through his bold and daring acts.[9]

Once in the ranks, it did not take long for soldiers on both sides to see how military life could feel like a maze in which every path seemed closed off to moral improvement. Volunteers did not know where to turn in an environment that looked, sounded, and felt so unnatural, especially without the presence of mothers and wives who could have steered men away from sin. The inner struggle to restrain the animalistic impulses of war reveals itself in hundreds of thousands of letters home. Whatever mischief volunteers indulged in at camp, they looked to combat as an unambiguous moment of manly purification. They were shocked to discover, however, that mighty collisions of armies unleashed a surge of conflicting emotions, and for the first time in their lives (for most soldiers), feelings of fear, courage, pride, sorrow, and hatred churned inside men who felt estranged from their own selves.[10] Even when heroic acts under fire followed sentimental scripts to perfection, soldiers did not emerge from the battlefield without wondering what would become of them if they kept killing. Would prolonged exposure to violence deaden the pure emotions of sentimentalism to the point that they would become unfeeling brutes? Historian Earl Hess, in one of the most important studies on the experience of Civil War combat, raises the critical questions that confronted the rank and file: "Was the warrior a patriot, or only an executioner? At what point did his killing cross the line between culturally acceptable violence and outrageous barbarism?"[11] The responses from the ranks were extraordinarily varied, but the very presence of any evidence demonstrates a degree of introspectiveness that is often seen as lacking among Civil War soldiers. As historian James Broomall argues, combat released men to express "levels of emotionality and vulnerability that were previously deemed the domain of women only."[12] Broomall also notes how the strains of war caused men to not only rely on women for emotional support, but also turn to their comrades for assistance, refusing to retreat into themselves and hide behind the mask of martial masculinity.

The correspondence between an Ohio officer and his wife after the Battle of Shiloh reveals a striking degree of emotional openness from a man who plumbed the depths of his interior world without fear that his wife would see him as weak or unmanly. "I still feel the horrid nature of this war," he shared, "and the piles of dead Gentlemen & wounded & maimed makes me more anxious than ever for some hope of an End but I know such a thing cannot be for a long long time. Indeed I never expect it or to survive it."[13] He let his guard down to his wife, and in confessing his fear, he also conveyed his deep ambivalence toward the battlefield. Yet this same soldier derived immense satisfaction from his own acts of bravery, and parts of his letter read like a highlight reel of his individual acts of heroism. He asked his wife to send him newspaper clippings that showcased the courage of his command, and he sent his sons bullets and shells as mementos of their father's valor. Why he collected artifacts is impossible to say, but it is reasonable to suggest that the things of war materialized the dangers that he had felt at Shiloh and that he found so difficult to describe on paper. These Shiloh mementos did not mark a romantic embrace of war. In fact, the officer's mood swing was abrupt and dramatic in writing home, moving from a deep sadness over the destruction of human life to a fiery rage when he thought of the thousands of men who were nothing more than shameful cowards. "How few know the dangers attending this war," this same officer wrote in a subsequent letter about Shiloh. "The very men who were most clamorous for fight were the first to run, and leave a few to Stand the brunt of Sunday."[14]

Few battles offered shirkers a common "rallying ground" like Shiloh, where broken-down and frightened men clung to the landing along the Tennessee River, plainly visible to those who were still fighting. In most engagements, it was extraordinarily difficult to distinguish the warrior from the coward without a degree of visual mastery over the fighting, but this proved elusive. Smoke, trees, boulders, and hills limited sight lines to a soldier's most immediate surroundings. To the surprise of men on both sides, the eye proved inadequate when it came to reading the field, and they had to trust their ears to decipher what was happening on the ground.[15] Hearing the act of cowardice, however, was beyond anyone's auditory powers, and the eye also proved inadequate in catching shirkers, who knew how to "disappear" in the smoky cover of battle. It would have been easier for Civil War soldiers to single out the crime of cowardice if their comrades had vaulted for the rear, running in a panic-stricken state like the fictional character Henry Fleming in Stephen Crane's *Red Badge of Courage*. Dramatic escapes, however, drew unwanted attention. Skilled shirkers were usually more deliberate, less obvious, and always strategic in finding a "secure" exit from the battlefield. Just as the distinctive popping sounds of skirmish fire filled the air, scores of soldiers suddenly fell ill, slinking away to a field hospital, where they sought a medical exemption. Some helped wounded comrades to the rear even though orders specifically prohibited such acts of charity as the self-serving work of a coward. Other anxious soldiers clung to the wagon trains as if they were carrying out some official duty, insisting that even though their bodies had given out, they were still under fire and assisting the army within the boundaries of the combat zone.

Not even military law, with its black-and-white rules, could govern the vagaries of the battlefield, and the rigidness of the regulations actually worked against a consistent prosecution of battlefield deserters. The military justice system boiled the charge of cowardice down to an airtight question: Did the accused run or stand firm before the enemy? Straightforward answers, however, were elusive, given the fragmented reports that came from the battlefield, which rarely translated into coherent and consistent court-martial testimony. Witnesses for both the defense and the prosecution frequently failed to reach broad agreement over who did what, when, or where. Court testimony consistently reveals how the accused frequently tried to shift attention away from his alleged actions by raising doubts about the motives of his accusers. Long-standing disputes among comrades often leaked into the testimony, even though the regulations stipulated that such evidence was not relevant to the primary question of battlefield performance.

The case of Captain Thomas B. Rodgers of the 140th Pennsylvania is a valuable example of how difficult it was for soldiers who had old scores to settle to hear one single voice of truth. Of the 5,000 Union soldiers who surrendered at Gettysburg, only Rodgers was accused of allowing himself to be taken a prisoner.[16] During the fighting in the Wheatfield at Gettysburg on July 2, 1863, the 140th Pennsylvania and the rest of Samuel Zook's brigade retook Stony Hill before the regiment's right flank crumbled under a Confederate counterattack. Many of the Pennsylvanians refused to surrender, taking their chances and trying to cut their way out to safety. One man who did not escape was Thomas Rodgers. The Confederates captured him, and he was charged with misbehavior in the presence of the enemy for allowing himself to be taken prisoner. His captors sent him to Libby Prison, and after nine months his Confederate captors paroled him. While Rodgers was stuck in prison, members of his regiment leveled charges of cowardice against him, accusing him of "misbehavior before the enemy," "allowing himself to be taken prisoner by the enemy," and "neglect of duty." Three witnesses were called against Rodgers at his court-martial. One claimed that the captain was seventy-five yards behind the regiment, hiding behind a large rock near a belt of woods. A second man said that he didn't see Rodgers anywhere on the field until he was captured. A third soldier claimed that Rodgers was resting among other Confederate prisoners behind the shelter of a massive rock. From the prosecution's perspective, the witnesses offered testimony that was deeply inconsistent. The three men could not agree on critical points. One soldier had Rodgers behind a rock, and another saw him behind the regiment. Two men never saw the captain with Confederate prisoners. And one man admitted that he had never seen Rodgers during the entire battle. When Rodgers was given the opportunity to cross-examine the witnesses, one man admitted that the smoke was so dense and the boulders so thick that he could not see very far. Another soldier confessed that he wasn't certain of the distance between the regiment's firing line and the rock that Rodgers supposedly used for shelter.

Rodgers insisted that his fellow officers had orchestrated a plot against him, simply because they wanted him out of the service to clear the way for another officer in the 140th Pennsylvania, who wanted Rodgers's position as lieutenant colonel. He proceeded to bring to the stand a series of witnesses who attested to his bravery. Corporal George Rose placed Rodgers in the front of the regiment. "You had your sword drawn, and said 'Keep cool, boys, and fire low,'" Rose stated. "You had first come along the line, and was standing in the rear of our company. The company was firing at that time." Private William Griggs also saw Rodgers at the front of his regiment: "You had your sword drawn, and was telling the boys to go ahead, and to keep cool and fire low: that we were driving them like hell! The regiment was firing at the time—You went up as far as we men." Private Hugh Shaw offered the most heroic depiction of Rodgers: "You were kneeling down on your knees when a rebel Serg't. came up and ordered you to throw down your saber. You replied, you would not surrender your saber to a private. The Serg't said he would run you through with his bayonet if you did not surrender. You replied, you did not care a damn! but you would not give your sword to any man but an officer." The tense moment came to an end, Private Shaw recounted, when the Confederate took Rodgers to his officer so that he could surrender his sword. Unlike the witnesses for the prosecution, who charged that Rodgers hid behind a rock like a coward, the witnesses for the defense insisted that Rodgers was in the midst of his unit, right on the firing line, cheering his men forward before he manfully surrendered to a horde of attacking Confederates. Reconciling these divergent accounts is impossible, and it is easy to appreciate how maddening it was for Civil War soldiers to determine who was telling the truth when it came to battlefield conduct. Any officer who served on a court-martial entered a briar patch of thorny accusations, imprecise testimony, and shaky memories that frustrated Civil War soldiers, who sought straightforward questions, answers, and verdicts that spoke directly to whether the man ran or not. The absence of clear proof, coupled with the inclusion of circumstantial evidence, kept the court from convicting Rodgers, just as it did with countless other men charged with cowardice. The case against Rodgers was somewhat unusual. He appears to have been targeted for cowardice for purely political reasons.[17]

The porous divide between the front and rear of the battlefield also frustrated soldiers who wanted to segregate the battlefield along firm lines of cowardice and courage. Court-martial defendants frequently insisted that they had fallen out of the ranks for legitimate medical reasons, and that they could not be guilty of misbehavior before the enemy if the battlefield had not been in sight. Such legalism might seem trivial, but courts fixated on what constituted the actual spatial area of fighting. If one could hear the guns and see the billowing smoke, was the individual's unit under fire? What if stray bullets whizzed overhead but the enemy was beyond the field of vision? What if the unit was encountering walking wounded? Did this mean that soldiers were behind the lines and any infraction could not be construed as misbehavior before the enemy? Or did men hobbling to the rear, bloodied by enemy bullets, mark the edge of the battlefield? All of these questions caught Civil War soldiers and officers off guard, and many shirkers were able to slip through the cracks of the justice system as a result. The diffused nature of Civil War fighting is further illustrated by archaeologists, who have found the remnants of killing well beyond the intense killing zones.[18]

The story of Lieutenant George Gillis of the Seventy-Seventh New York Infantry nicely illustrates the difficulty the courts had in determining the sphere of combat. Gillis had been under suspicion for missing the Battle of Chancellorsville, and at Gettysburg he was charged with being absent without leave, but Gillis protested that ulcers on his leg made him unfit for duty. For much of July 2, 1863, he had kept up with his regiment by riding either in an ambulance or on his own horse. Suddenly, and without notice, Gillis disappeared within a few miles of Gettysburg when the men broke ranks to make coffee. During his subsequent court-martial, witnesses testified that they could see the smoke from the battlefield and hear the blasts of the cannon during their break. The court was clearly trying to establish that the approaching storm of battle, with all of its impending fury, caused Gillis to run for cover. Or was it that the storm had already broken and Gillis had simply fled as soon as he sensed danger? The curious timing of his departure — and Gillis's long history of becoming invisible when the shooting started — was the court's accusatory angle. Trying to mark the boundaries of the battlefield became unnecessarily litigious when Gillis procured a surgeon's certificate of disability that offered him a get-out-of-combat-free card. Suspicions about Gillis probably lingered despite his certified medical issue because of his personal history and the peculiar circumstances of his departure, but nothing more could be proven in testimony. While it is impossible to say whether or not this was Gillis's design, it was the scheme of many men who lurked on the margins of the battlefield, lingering among the supply wagons or helping at a field hospital. If challenged, they could claim that they were still exposed to the violent winds of battle despite being partially disabled.[19]

If a Union or Confederate soldier faltered under fire, he likely worried more about his case being tried before the soldiers' court of opinion, where men could render damning verdicts in their letters home.[20] Reports or rumors of cowardice were never private affairs, given the common practice of family members circulating soldier mail among family and friends. Plenty of soldiers refused to name names when they wrote about this issue, not wanting to get entangled in a grapevine of rumors between their home community and the regiment, but that did not dissuade some from identifying those crippled with fear. "It was laughable yet outrageous in these battles," wrote a Pennsylvania soldier, "to see commissioned officers with their backs to the foe[,] their coattails straight out and waiveing their hands at some of their men who had followed their example crying go back boys go back boys and stick up to them[.] I dont know whether it is right to tell on the divils or not but I reckon if I mention no names it wont matter much for it will all come out when the war is over." One North Carolina soldier who considered war a violation of God's laws also shied away from calling out individual soldiers in his letters to his wife. Still, he wanted her to know that it was common for men to lose all bodily control on the firing line. At Chancellorsville, he was shocked to see that one of his fellow soldiers had soiled his pants. "I have noticed him very Closely Since the fight & I perseived that his pants is little stained," the man concluded, "but I think that he has washed them since the Battle[.] dont let no Body see this."[21]

Rather than make public accusations against questionable soldiers, which could easily lead to embarrassing revelations about the entire unit, regiments frequently handled issues of malfeasance internally. How individual companies investigated and prosecuted different cases is difficult to determine. Both Union and Confederate order books reveal only the verdict and the penalties, without the accompanying testimony, but it is clear that on both sides, men were rarely shot for the sole crime of cowardice. Punishments of humiliation, pay deductions, and hard labor were preferred against those convicted of abandoning their posts under fire.[22] In Lee's Army of Northern Virginia, for instance, officers in an Alabama brigade were required to perform roll call just moments before they were called to the front. Charges were subsequently preferred against every man found absent. The brigade commander instituted a "skulkers parade" to dishonor the "missing in action," a common ritual of manly degradation in which the convicted, after having their heads shaved and a placard harnessed to their bodies, were forced to make the humiliating march to headquarters in full view of their comrades.[23] After watching three men promenade in front of his unit wearing barrel shirts emblazoned with the word *coward* and being prodded along by a sentry's bayonet, a Georgia soldier could not imagine living with such an indignity. "Who had not rather be shot a hundred times by Yankees than to suffer such ignominious punishment," he wondered. He reminded his family of the necessity of using coercion and shame to keep men going forward in battle. "Still it is necessary," he decided, "otherwise a great many would bolt in the hour of danger."[24] Civil War officers did not loosen the screws of military discipline on the survivors who returned to camp. Little time was lost before enlisted men were subjected to the strict regime of returning to the parade ground for daily drilling, cleaning weapons, sweeping the company streets, and the posting of guards. Inspections also took place without delay, and any men who had lost their muskets, bayonets, and accoutrements under fire were hit with fines.[25] All of these exercises were intended to engage both the body and the mind, in an attempt to keep the soldier from his own dark thoughts after a battle, when he was most vulnerable to folding under the pressure of the "croakers" (cowards) at home or following the example of shirkers in the army.

No Civil War army ever faced a mutiny after a battle, even in the wake of a defeat of biblical proportions. Within a few weeks after a major campaign, armies generally recovered and soldiers felt restored and ready to return to the battlefield. At the same time, no measure could satisfy the professionals' demand for absolute obedience from their men under fire. While volunteers did transform into formidable veteran units in a relatively short period of time, generals on both sides came to accept that they would never get their men to act in consistently predictable ways, particularly during times of sustained exposure to battlefield violence, when even "good men" could suddenly crack under the cumulative physical demands of active campaigning. Civil War officers inherited a military tradition in which they received little training about how to improve the physical health and emotional welfare of the individual soldiers under their command.[26] They put their trust in the volunteers' rugged individualism, as did the men themselves, who thought they could endure any hardship or conquer any fear through their own exertion.

Until the end of the war, soldiers on both sides generally agreed that culpability for coming undone under fire rested entirely with the individual.[27] This

*Courage and Cowardice*

assumption stemmed from a basic understanding about the very moral, intellectual, and physical foundation of a person's being. A man of character, of pure
spirit, and of patriotic heart could face his fears in combat and suffer the harrowing consequences, whatever they might be, with quiet dignity and fortitude.[28] A coward was seen as a man without shame, a man whose disgraceful
behavior was spawned by a defect in his internal makeup. Upper-class soldiers
were prone to believing that only a certain kind of man would take to the military life and that nature, not nurture, predetermined who would run at the sight
of cold steel. This perspective interlocked with the standard racial assumptions
and medical knowledge of the day to deny soldiers of African, German, and
Irish descent the honor that automatically came to a white man shouldering a
musket.[29]

After 1863, with the dramatic influx of immigrant soldiers and African
Americans entering the Union ranks, Northern doctors turned to scientific
racism to measure battlefield performance. Although black and ethnic soldiers
repeatedly proved their dependability under fire, visual evidence of valorous
behavior could not crack notions of white supremacy and biological theories of
racial inferiority.[30] In an 1863 Union manual for discharging soldiers, Union doctors read that not only were the Germans and Irish more prone to fake an illness
than the Americans, but each nationality also had "favorite diseases" to simu-
late. The manual offered officers a physical description of a malingerer, a form
of racial profiling to be used in conjunction with a "rigid cross-examination."
According to this guide, "The typical malingerer has dark brown or hazel eyes,
dark hair, and dark complexion; his face is stealthy, dogged, lowering; his eyes
suspicious, furtive, restless; and his manner habitually constrained and exhibit-
ing violent attempts at composure."[31] African American soldiers were praised
for possessing "physical qualities" of the "highest type of the soldier," but there
was a consensus in the medical establishment that "the Negro soldier is, unquestionably, less enduring than the white soldier; less active, vigilant, and
enterprising, and more given to malingering."[32] Even when battlefield reports
confirmed that US Colored Troops (USCT) soldiers had been killed, published
accounts virtually ignored the men's bloody condition. "According to the unspoken rhetorical logic of the Civil War era," writes historian James Downs,
"to depict formerly enslaved people as bloody would be to acknowledge their
suffering and in so doing suggest that their suffering connoted patriotism."[33]

At the same time, skin color and ethnicity did not necessarily figure into
the thinking of army surgeons, who never imagined how exposure to extreme
terror might deliver a physiological blow to a man of any background that
would render him helpless and unable to do his duty. Quite simply, the physio-

logical causes behind mania, dementia, depression, melancholia, anxiety, and neuralgia, among other diagnoses, were simply not well understood among surgeons or soldiers.[34] Both sides turned to hopelessly vague terms such as "low spirits," "irritability of the heart," and "fatigue" to describe a wide range of conditions that were often attributed to a defective soul or immoral living. It was as if Americans of that era were suffering from a medical night blindness when it came to battlefield trauma, since no one knew what to do with a soldier sinking under the stresses of war.[35] A veteran who drank, for instance, was seen as morally weak and prone to temptation rather than as having an addiction rooted in the harrowing experiences of battle. Suspicion often turned on soldiers who had "low vital conditions" and spent their days languishing in camp in a "morbid state." If they were suffering from the blues or claiming a weak constitution, one Union doctor argued, then this class of soldiers was only seeking an exemption and did not deserve sympathy. He believed that their behavior was essentially manufactured, having arisen by "all those abuses to which soldiers are addicted—indulgences in alcoholic drinks, masturbation, excessive tobacco chewing, etc."[36]

Why were so many Union and Confederate doctors unable to at least concede that the terror of combat might deliver a physiological blow that left undetectable scars on the body? This is especially puzzling, since they highlighted mysterious cases of soldiers with sterling combat records suddenly fleeing the battlefield in a fit of uncontrollable excitement. While some surgeons simply ignored such contradictory behavior, others acknowledged that they did not understand the full effect of combat on a man's mind and body. There was also a glaring omission in their reports, as Civil War surgeons never took notes regarding memory and never asked a soldier to recall a damaging image of the past or to recount the moment of terror. There was no conversation, no confiding, and no attempt to understand. It appears that the soldier was left in isolation to brood in his thoughts.[37]

The top priority of Civil War surgeons was caring for the soldier's physical body, not his emotional welfare. The demands placed on surgeons were extreme and highly contradictory, and as a result the line between treatment and coercion was a fine one. A Northern surgeon spoke for many of his professional peers when he explained what the army expected of doctors: "To a military man a recruit is a piece of mechanism, to be adapted to the needs of the military service."[38] Balancing the responsibilities of being a caregiver while also acting as a guardian of discipline was tough to reconcile. If a soldier was prostrate, crying out in pain but without a visible injury, then doctors almost always circled back to the core belief that he was deficient in character. If a Union or Confederate soldier suffered a physical wound, then both sides generally pursued the following course: patch the injured man up and send him back to the front, where the final stage of healing would begin as soon as he inhaled the acrid smoke of battle. A Union surgeon in the Army of the Potomac, for instance, after studying a regiment plagued by homesickness, recommended that combat was a restorative agent for depressed soldiers. *"Battle is to be considered the great curative agent of nostalgia in the field,"* he asserted. "The regiment," he added, "was but a regiment in name — its thoughts were all at home, while its members were here. At Chancellorsville they fought nobly — they won a name — they had something to be proud of — they gained an *esprit de-corps* . . . and from that day to this, there has been but little or no sickness, and but two or three deaths." [39] Killing to cure cowardice was not the prescription of a medical outsider, but a bloody remedy accepted by the soldiers themselves. [40]

Although Civil War soldiers and their surgeons agreed that shirkers were flawed and nefarious by nature, they were more often bitter enemies than aligned in thought and action. The rank and file came to resent doctors for advancing the cause of military necessity or showing favoritism to a crony at the expense of the patient's welfare. On entering a surgeon's tent or a general hospital, a Civil War soldier became less of a person and more something to suspect, to doubt, to interrogate, and ultimately to repair (if necessary) before being sent back to the field. Weary soldiers often left sick call grumbling about the incompetency of regimental doctors who denied them leave or prescribed medicines that were akin to taking poison. Popular condemnations of surgeons as drunken butchers mask the impressive scientific achievements of the Civil War medical corps, progress born of doctors' tireless efforts to cure the sick and learn from the dead. [41] Their devotion to science and to caring for the patient was often lost on soldiers, who resented doctors for the power they possessed over a man's body. Whether a man was fit to fight or should retire to a field hospital usually came down to the judgment of a doctor, which was no easy task, for an experienced malingerer could fool the conscientious as well as the compassionate. Scores of legitimately sick men suffered needlessly because of the charades of shirkers, whose trickery could lead surgeons to be cynical and suspicious of anyone reporting to sick call. A frustrated group of Union doctors admitted that "one rogue cast suspicion on a dozen honest men." [42]

Medical textbooks offered little guidance in exposing the ruses of malingerers. The underlying problem, as most Civil War surgeons came to see it, stemmed from the soldier having too much authority over his own body. At sick call the patient controlled the examination through stories of ill health corroborated by feigning symptoms that were of a subjective quality. Those "playing old soldier" favored rheumatism and epilepsy, since the symptoms could be easily manufactured. Constant observation and tough interrogation did not always crack a determined malingerer. Some of these men wanted out of the army so badly that they were willing to mutilate their own bodies in order to create the appearance of poor health. Some shirkers were reported for inserting an onion into their rectums so that an hour later, when standing at sick call, their faces would be flushed and their pulse accelerated. Others were able to imitate a hernia by inflating areolar tissue with a "fine pointed blow-pipe." It was also common for soldiers to chew on a cartridge of gunpowder and then rinse the mouth with vinegar for a few minutes to produce a "brown furred tongue." Upon examination, many surgeons would mistakenly conclude that the soldier was suffering from a dysfunctional thyroid. Some men took to swallowing small pieces of tobacco to induce a predictable fit of vomiting that left their bodies utterly prostrate and unfit for duty. In the Confederate army, there were cases of soldiers lacerating the insides of their mouths so that they would spit blood, and there were also reports of men stealing the stool samples of sick patients to claim that they were suffering from diarrhea.[43]

W. C. of the Sixty-First New York Infantry stands as the quintessential malingerer, one who knew all the tricks of the trade. According to three Northern surgeons, W. C. reported to sick call shortly after participating in the Battle of Fredericksburg, complaining that his entire body ached, his head throbbed, and he was too feeble to go on active duty. Treatments at a field hospital were ineffectual, and W. C. was forwarded to a military hospital in Washington, D.C., where his condition deteriorated. He became deaf shortly after his arrival, his left leg went lame, and he refused to leave his bed, but the doctors were unable to find a physical cause for any of these maladies. They were particularly troubled by the patient's involuntary discharge of semen, known as spermatorrhea, which was attributable to erotic dreams and seen as proof of a "general loss of 'mental powers.'" Their suspicions aroused, the doctors began to investigate, giving W. C. clean sheets, shirts, and undergarments before a surprise bed check that showed no evidence of an involuntary discharge. As W. C.'s case started to unravel, he began masturbating every night, but he was adamant that only erotic dreams had instigated his repeated emissions. His doctors were not convinced that his mind was in disarray or that his imagination had unraveled in perversity, noting that "he exhibited to us, with some triumph, indubitable evidences, such as we had sought, but the ready explanation of a manufactured article was too obvious." Even though the doctors agreed that W. C. was falsifying his spermatorrhea, they could not force him back to the front. W. C. told his doctors to have mercy on him, since his leg throbbed with pain that radi-

Winslow Homer's *Playing Old Soldier* depicts a popular ruse used by veterans to escape the grinding duties of military life. Some soldiers took more drastic means, including self-mutilation.

(Winslow Homer, American, 1836–1910, oil on canvas mounted on Masonite, 40.64 × 30.48 cm [16 × 12], Museum of Fine Arts, Boston, Ellen Kelleran Gardner Fund, 43.129; photograph © 2018 Museum of Fine Arts, Boston)

ated throughout his entire body. He rested his crutch under his knee to induce swelling in his leg while he was sitting in bed, but the doctors were not fooled. To nudge him out of bed, they refused him food or water unless he was willing to get up and walk to the serving line without a crutch or cane. For three days, W. C. remained in bed, his body limp but his spirit defiant, an act of protest that finally resulted in his transfer to a hospital for malingerers, where he deserted within weeks.[44] While the army's case against W. C. would appear irrefutable, it is noteworthy that he also exhibited symptoms of nervous shock, a condition that European physicians connected to the experience of extreme fear shortly after the Civil War.[45]

It is quite possible that W. C. was enduring some form of mental trauma as a survivor of Fredericksburg, but his innocence or guilt is really not of primary consideration. More importantly, he exemplifies how Civil War–era physicians were poorly positioned to judge whether a soldier was a malingerer or a genuine victim. W. C. was like many men who entered the hospital without any visible injuries but in time, long after battle, experienced troubling symptoms of physical and mental decline. Difficulty sleeping, depression, excitability, general irritability, erratic heart rate, a shaky memory, throbbing headaches, a loss of hearing, and a diminishment of arm and leg strength, often to the point of paralysis, were common complaints of combat veterans. It was not until World War I, more than fifty years later, that these symptoms were attributed to the concussion of exploding shells. During the Civil War, such symptoms raised suspicions rather than sympathy. In the Confederate manual for military surgery, Julian Chisolm offered a widely accepted medical perspective on any soldier who walked away from the battlefield without visible mental or bodily injury. "Being stunned by a bomb," he wrote, "is a piece of good fortune to many, who prefer hospital life to the exposures and privations of the field; and as long as the war lasts there will be some who will have partially-paralyzed limbs and painful spines from this cause. To be 'stung by a bung,' and be demoralized, is a condition which hospital surgeons classify among the most intractable of diseases."[46]

In Union and Confederate medical departments, the often-violent techniques of "rebuilding" soldiers through pain were far from effectual. Men on both sides considered such measures a violation of the reciprocal contract between national army and soldier, a point captured by an African American who condemned the medical establishment for its brutal indifference to those in the ranks: "If a man Says he is Sick it is the Doctors Priveledge to Say yes or no if you cannot work then you are Sent to the Guard House Bucked, Gagged and Stay so till they See fit to relieve you. . . . Now do you call this Equality[? I]f so

God help Such Equality."[47] Wearing the Union blue, as many black soldiers discovered, did not give them the right to be masters of their own bodies. White soldiers on both sides also complained of feeling small and vulnerable before a military regime that might inflict unspeakable physical pain. The threat of medical torture unquestionably scared men back to the battlefield or caused others—in exceptional cases—to commit self-mutilation rather than return to the front. Self-mutilation was extreme by Civil War standards, but such desperate acts point to the severity of the psychological struggles for some Civil War veterans.

The same sentimental belief that bravery stemmed from character and a disciplined body and mind was closely associated with nineteenth-century notions of distinction and heroism. The potency of male honor revealed itself in the headlong frontal charge, the highest ideal of Civil War heroism, but such aggressiveness is seen today as a stunning example of ineptitude on the part of officers who failed to adapt tactics to changes in technology.[48] Some scholars believe that Civil War soldiers were prisoners of boyhood fantasies of achieving martial fame, and that once in the army they tried to act out their dreams in bold attacks that proved suicidal. The persistence with which both sides continued to attack, according to some critics, defied the lethal reality unleashed by the rifled musket.[49] Yet such an argument ignores the actual mechanics of Civil War combat. The popular perception that Union and Confederate armies stood in massed formations, refusing to leave open ground as they blasted each other into oblivion, is grossly overstated. When there was a general attack— with soldiers advancing shoulder to shoulder and elbows touching—the men entered a killing space that was much smaller than scholars have imagined. Earl Hess has conclusively demonstrated that guns sighted to 300 yards were lethal only within 75 yards, and after that distance the bullets sailed harmlessly above the height of the average soldier. "The next danger zone," observes Hess, "lay at the far end of the trajectory, the last 110 yards (about 240 to 350 yards from the shooter)."[50] Using those calculations, only 185 yards constituted a true killing zone, giving Civil War soldiers the spatial freedom to act with little fear of getting hit in most cases. Hess's important findings show that under most tactical circumstances, soldiers could live out their dreams of heroic action without committing themselves to certain death.

Even when trench warfare prevailed during the last two years of the conflict, a narrow killing space still gave the attacker a reasonable chance of success, which largely explains why Civil War officers remained devoted to frontal assaults in the face of rifled weapons and massed artillery. Whether an advance succeeded or failed, Civil War regiments struggled to maintain their orderly

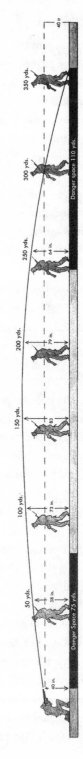

40 in.  50 yds.  58 in.  100 yds.  73 in.  150 yds.  83  200 yds.  79 in.  250 yds.  64 in.  300 yds.  350 yds.  40 in.

Danger Space 75 yds.  Danger space 110 yds.

This drawing shows that the danger spaces for attacking troops was very small against rifled muskets sighted for three hundred yards. Only the first fifty yards and the last fifty yards constituted a killing zone. Bullets would likely pass over the heads of attackers during its midrange flight. This illustration helps explain why extreme displays of male bravery were not suicidal acts of warfare driven by a maniacal code of death before dishonor. The weaponry, though lethal at close quarters, made it possible for Civil War soldiers to fight the war as they had imagined it in 1861. (From *Arms and Equipment of the Civil War* by Jack Coggins and reprinted with permission from Dover Publications) formations prescribed in tactical manuals of instruction, which were of little guidance when the moment came to actually enter the battlefield. Clouds of sulfurous smoke engulfed the field, pierced by demonic noises of hissing shells and the furious shouts and disarrayed screams of men shooting each other down. The pandemonium that ensued rarely conformed to neat patterns of charge, countercharge, and retreat. When survivors tried to reconstruct their experiences on paper, they often threw down their pens in frustration, complaining that words could not capture the touch, smell, and sounds of killing. "Soon into the war," historian Michael De Gruccio observes, "expressing how one lacked words became its own cliché."[51]

Despite the frustration of trying to describe the indescribable nature of war, soldiers kept bringing the grisly sights of the battlefield into their families' homes. Their letters were incredibly varied in form and content, but they almost always centered on the basics of who did what and where, who was killed, and who survived (though to classify the heaps of letters simply as terse reports does injustice to the rich variety of soldier writings). Moreover, even if these missals home did not conform to a common style, they did reveal shared cultural pressures. Men of all backgrounds faced a similar gendered expectation to infuse their letters with a spirit of martial masculinity. As a result, Civil War soldiers self-consciously strove to project the appearance of strength and control in battle narratives that made their own heroism and that of their comrades "true." Exaggerations and falsification abound in the sources, of course, but no more so than in any other body of historical records. Soldiers' battle stories tell of their own truth as they pieced their worlds back together in ways that appeared real to them. If we are to penetrate the consciousness of Civil War soldiers, then it is important to concentrate more on patterns of speech and the categories used by the soldiers to organize and make meaning of their experience than on the factual accuracy of the narrative.[52]

Pennsylvania's Francis Adams Donaldson left an account of the Battle of Fredericksburg that stands apart from the war writings of soldiers obsessed with putting forth the appearance of heroism, because Donaldson was unafraid to show that brave men could be bitter, twisted, and confused in the midst of battle. Questions about his own behavior at Marye's Heights explain Donaldson's sense of detachment and critical irony in this extensive letter written to his aunt on December 18, 1862. "I will try and state concisely the facts of the case and let you and my friends be the judges whether my conduct at that battle reflects upon me as a soldier," he wrote. "I feel much mortification at being compelled to explain my conduct in time of battle." He added, "I wrote plainly, and trust in speaking myself as I do, I may be fully understood as not, in any way, trying to puff myself up or desiring to boast of myself."[53] The voice Donaldson assumes throughout the letter sounds official, but his narrative does not read like a dry report, with stilted language and emotionless prose. Donaldson wants the reader to stand in his shoes and to sense the experience of combat as it happened in the moment.

Donaldson felt edgy as the Army of the Potomac prepared to cross the Rappahannock River on December 13, 1862, to enter the town of Fredericksburg for the inevitable order to assault the Confederate bastion of Marye's Heights. Strikingly handsome with his clean-shaven face and stylish cropped sideburns, he looked and loved playing the part of the soldier even though at 160 pounds and five feet eight inches tall he was not physically imposing. Donaldson had enlisted in 1861, was captured at Balls Bluff on October 21, 1861, and was exchanged and returned to duty only to be shot in the arm on May 31, 1862, at the Battle of Fair Oaks. While recuperating in his Philadelphia home, where he had worked as a clerk before the war, he joined the 118th Pennsylvania as a captain. The change proved disastrous for Donaldson, who came to detest the regiment's commander, Lt. Colonel James Gwyn: the headstrong Donaldson was enraged by Gwyn's demanding ways.[54]

Gwyn's shouts suddenly pierced the air as he rode up to the 118th Pennsylvania while they positioned themselves to advance to the Rappahannock River. Donaldson could see that his commanding officer was "full of liquor," a prebattle ritual for the officer, who became "domineering, abusive, and even brutal" when he sought courage from a bottle. Donaldson could only imagine what was running through the minds of his men when they saw that their superior was intoxicated once again. "I did not care to go into battle with a drunken commander," Donaldson wrote tersely. Hours would pass before the men came under fire. The march to the river was slow; thousands of troops were jammed together as they funneled across the pontoon bridges. During the lull Donaldson "looked upon" what he considered "a wonderful scene." "I could see the enemy's batteries, extending along the heights in the rear of Fredericksburg," Donaldson wrote, "all ready to commence the work of death upon our army then crowning the city. The glitter of the arms of the soldiers flashed and blinded the eye, the city appearing to be literally packed with troops." Firing erupted in the distance, and Donaldson stood with his command, waiting, bored, and feeling anxious at "doing nothing." He broke out a deck of cards with three other officers, but the order to march abruptly concluded the game. None of the players "could be induced to keep them." "Capt. Crocker explained the situation exactly," Donaldson recounted, "when he said he did not care to have the only thing found about his clothes, when dead, to be a Euchre deck. So, we threw them away and laughed at each other for being superstitious." Officers had instructed the men to be silent as the column moved forward, but a Private Ayers was constantly "jabbering and singing." Donaldson was not amused. He had had enough of Ayers's antics: he told him that they would see the enemy soon and that "I would then hear him sing another tune if his legs did not carry him in a contrary direction, which I was determined he should face the enemy for once in his life." Ayers looked "'taken down,'" and Donaldson overheard him say "the Captain was down on him for some reason or other," but the officer did not have time to allay his subordinate's hurt feelings.[55]

As the 118th Pennsylvania marched down the steep banks of Stafford Heights toward the pontoon crossing, a panoramic view of the battle opened before Donaldson in "all its grandeur and horror." "We could see the blue lines of infantry moving quickly up the hill, and then as quickly melt away." The futility of it all, Donaldson noticed, was immediately impressed upon the soldiers, "who felt defeat before encountering." "I heard many comments from the soldiers as they gazed upon the battle and generally to the effect that they wished the troops then engaged would drive the enemy, a wish that was just a trifle selfish, it is true, but which expressed very generally the sentiments of the soldiers." The regiment had no such luck, and thus continued its march into town, where Donaldson's attention shifted to the destruction of Fredericksburg, a scene that he found both alluring and repulsive. "Books and battered pictures lined the streets, bureaus, loungers, feather beds, clocks and every conceivable thing in the way of furniture lay scattered on every side." A horse eating out of a piano that had been gutted by soldiers and turned into a makeshift feedbox caught Donaldson's eye, as did men cooking their coffee over fires made from fragments of fine household furniture. Initially Donaldson thought nothing could justify this wanton destruction, but the Pennsylvania captain's moral outrage fizzled out rather quickly. Shell holes in a nearby building revealed the library of a "person of culture." "I took from the collection a nicely bound volume of Waverly (Ivanhoe) intending to retain it as a souvenir," he explained to his aunt. "Thus you see that even I, a commissioned officer, was guilty of vandalism, but I justified myself in this *theft* by believing the city would, certainly be destroyed by fire before we got through it."[56]

Shortly after Donaldson returned to his place in the ranks, the regiment received its call to the front. George Slow, a servant hired by Donaldson, took the officer's "watch, money and papers" when "my attention was called to another colored fellow standing on the end of a door that lay upon the pavement in front of the regiment." He was "laughing and grinning at the soldiers," and from where Donaldson stood, "his teeth looked like a chalk mark on a black board." "Suddenly a solid shot wizzed over our heads, struck the front of a house back of us, glanced, flew up into the air, and, descending upon the other end of the door, bounced Mr. dark several feet into the air. It was the funniest sight I ever saw. We just shouted with laughter to see the poor fellow fly through air and land upon his back about 10 feet away, with his wooly on end and himself turned almost white through fright." The "merriment" among the men was short-lived, because Lt. Colonel Gwyn suddenly appeared, apparently drawn to the scene by the sounds of laughter. Donaldson noticed the redness of his superior's face, more evidence that the commanding officer "had been actively engaged in getting himself into proper condition to lead the unit." For no apparent reason except to impress the troops to his "indifference to danger," Gwyn rode "to the front and centre of the regiment," and to Donaldson's shock he put the regiment through the manual of arms. At one point, Gwyn demanded that Donaldson repeat the command "Support Arms," but the captain protested, telling his superior that "I had already done so and my men were then at 'support.'" "'I don't care sir, repeat it again,'" Donaldson recounted. "There being nothing for me to do but obey, I stepped out from the Company, and facing down the line, in as loud a voice as possible, gave the command to support arms. The whole occurrence was so ridiculous that the men grinned audibly."[57]

The order to load brought the men back to the deadly task at hand. The Pennsylvanians then followed the rest of the brigade to the front, marching through Fredericksburg, where streets lined with wrecked homes were occupied by Union soldiers to escape the battle. Donaldson did not damn them as cowards or dismiss them as laggards. "They were stragglers," in his opinion, "or men who had been 'in' and were demoralized." He understood why they had slipped away in a battle that had used their allotment of courage in doomed attacks. "Their silent, sullen aspect did not encourage us much," noted Donaldson, who could tell that his men were starting to waver under increased artillery fire. In the midst of the turmoil, Donaldson noticed that the shells that "struck near us performed many curious tricks," bouncing off the street, ricocheting off the buildings, and tearing through window shutters before ending back in the street and "just missing the company." The zigzag trajectory of the shells reminded Donaldson that survival hinged on sheer luck, a point reinforced a moment later when a single shell sailed over his men and exploded in the regiment behind them, killing and wounding sixteen men.

The narrow escapes unnerved Donaldson's soldiers to the point that some started to scatter, but order was restored thanks to the men themselves, who made their own adjustments without instruction from above. Donaldson watched his company avoid "the centre of the street" by "keeping to the pavements on either side of the streets."[58] In this way, it reached the outskirts of the town, where "the tempest of shot was fearful at this point" and formations started to fall apart. The men managed to cross a canal ditch before seeking shelter in a ravine, some four hundred yards away from the Confederate position. Instinctively, the troops "hugged closely the foot of the hill," yet confusion prevailed until suddenly, and seemingly out of nowhere, the order to charge was given. "By whom I do not know," Donaldson reported, "and indeed, I did not hear the order at all, but took up the movement as I saw others doing. The regiment now became very much mixed, each man appearing to be on his own hook."[59]

The Pennsylvanians raced from the ravine for the next line of cover at a brickyard, and Donaldson paid his customary attention to the terrain, its particular features, and how the men used the ground to enhance their chances of survival. In the middle of the yard stood a brick kiln, he recalled, "from which the bricks were flying in all directions as the shot tore into it." No one knew what to do next: "no orders could be heard owing to the roar of the battle." At that moment, one of Donaldson's sergeants "was struck in the crown of the head, the ball passing directly through the brain." Donaldson was standing with two other officers in a protected position when he saw his comrade fall. He rushed to the man's aid, giving him whiskey, but when he went back to the other officers, everyone was gone and there was "not a man of the regiment to be seen." For the rest of the day Donaldson lingered along the outskirts of town, "longing with my whole heart and soul to be with my comrades." He finally spotted one of his fellow officers, a Lieutenant Wilson, who "appeared to be oblivious to the extreme danger he was in and would occasionally stop to look at some of the dead, apparently to ascertain their regiment." Donaldson thought he was a dead man walking. "I stood transfixed, momentarily expecting to see him torn to pieces. At last he reached the brick kiln and appeared not to have known he had done an act of bravery that, I venture to say, not one single man of the thousands comprising both armies would have dared to have done."

Night fell before Donaldson located his unit, and almost immediately he renewed his public feud with Gwyn, although neither man was on secure footing when it came to their behavior in front of Marye's Heights. At the peak of their argument, Donaldson offered his sword. Gwyn told him to keep it. Most of the men were happy to see Donaldson, fearing that he had been mortally wounded or killed. Private Ayers, who had been dressed down by Donaldson earlier in the day for making such a racket, had his opportunity to exact revenge without violating military protocol. When saluting Donaldson, he "bawled out at the top of his voice in unmistakable sarcasm—'Capt., I have been at the front *all the time.'* I have nothing to say. Ayers had the best of me." The next day Donaldson in-

This photograph shows the perspective of Francis Donaldson as he emerged from the edge of Fredericksburg and looked across the plain stretching up to Marye's Heights, which can be seen in the background. Donaldson's valuable narrative of this futile attack reveals a more flexible code of conduct that men on both sides utilized as a way of protecting their reputations by finding the liminal space between courage and cowardice.
(Library of Congress Prints and Photographs Division, Washington, D.C.)

sisted on an inquiry, believing that his reputation was under suspicion because of the colonel's harsh remarks. The officers of his regiment convened informally for a few minutes, and, without ever calling Donaldson to testify, they concluded that "I had [not] done anything at all that could call forth the slightest censure from the Colonel, as my reputation was established in the regiment."[60]

What is the meaning of this whole account? Donaldson's narrative succeeds like few other wartime letters in scrambling the ground-level view of war. Neither rank nor intelligence, virtue nor courage could bring order to Donaldson's perceptions of the battle. Though the advancement to the river and into town was clear, everything became chaotic from the moment Donaldson stepped onto the battlefield, where blinding smoke, exploding shells, and whizzing bullets commingled with the screams of the wounded and the shouts of officers consumed men in a sensory bedlam. With an unusual degree of openness, Donaldson gives the reader access to what was going on in his mind, to see what he saw in the moment and to feel the confusion that enveloped his entire

*Courage and Cowardice*

Francis A. Donaldson, in a lengthy letter to his aunt, did not try to hide from his questionable behavior at Fredericksburg. His frank assessment of his own conduct did not cause him to renounce courage as a core value, but his words challenged the romantic excesses of popular culture, which favored dramatic renderings of soldiers always charging under the flag without the human slaughter.

(Courtesy of the Civil War Museum of Philadelphia and The Abraham Lincoln Foundation of The Union League of Philadelphia) body on December 13. It is striking that Donaldson, even in the midst of such turmoil, was drawn to the freakish trajectories of the enemy shells, some finding their mark and blowing up bodies while others sailed harmlessly overhead, crashing into buildings or plowing into the earth without effect. Donaldson wanted his reader to see that no man could possibly hide from the capricious forces of war, and that randomness permeates his entire account.

Donaldson's narrative offers a striking contrast to the visualization of combat in popular print culture, where the quick mass production of lithographs and engravings, particularly in the North, celebrated courage and patriotism at the expense of terror, blood, and the general disorder produced by combat. The Currier and Ives print of Fredericksburg, for example, featured General Ambrose Burnside sitting on a white charger, overlooking the crossing of the Rappahannock River with his artillery blasting into the town while his soldiers capture a few hundred Confederates along the river. Such romantic imagery completely obscured the slaughter of Union infantry. The initial coverage of Fredericksburg in *Harper's Weekly* also averted the eyes of the reader away from Marye's Heights, where the battle was lost. The front page of the first issue to cover the battle showed an illustration of Union soldiers surging up the banks of the Rappahannock, and subsequent issues continued to orient readers away from the disastrous Union attacks. Illustrations of other military operations published in *Harper's Weekly* around the same time utilized similar heroic conventions to emphasize the power of individual soldiers to bring order and purpose to combat.[61]

The importance of Donaldson's account does not reside in any claim that his Fredericksburg narrative is more realistic than these artistic depictions of combat, or that he wrote about war with a greater truthfulness. Rather, in reading Donaldson's letter, one gets the impression of standing with the author, whose narration is more than a static snapshot of battle. It feels like a picture in motion, capturing the sounds and sights as they entered Donaldson's mind, a swirling kaleidoscope of conflicting and violent images strung together in narrative form and lacking the visual coherence of the battlefield as it was portrayed in popular print culture. There is a transparency to Donaldson's way of writing that enables the reader to see combat for what it was and grasp how it could unmake a soldier both emotionally and physically.

At the same time, Donaldson never suggested that the destructive effects of battle inevitably demoralized the troops. Most did their part, in his estimation. Even among his dutiful men, though, moments of absurdity caught Donaldson's eye and were important enough for him to include in his narrative: looting soldiers sitting in plush chairs around fires built of mahogany wood, transforming war-torn streets into a peculiar domestic space fit only for veterans; fellow comrades laughing at a black man catapulted into the air by a shell just moments after mocking the white men as they marched off to their destruction; a drunken superior forcing his regiment to practice the manual of arms under fire; an officer snapping under the strain of combat, jumping from his cover to yell obscenities at the Confederates while waving the battle flag in an act of pointless defiance that another officer then emulated; and a soldier whose valor "brought himself into prominence" among his peers for the first time, but who then disappeared after the battle on a drinking spree that lasted for nine days.

Donaldson never tried to analyze these peculiar moments, but his inclusion of these episodes does help explain why he did not draw a firm boundary between courage and cowardice on the battlefield. To some degree, this was a tacit admission that men could not trust their own perceptions in a world where they once believed that the facts would simply speak for themselves. Donaldson managed to re-create the ambiguities of battlefield conduct without jettisoning his belief that some men were inherently courageous while others were not. Yet he refused to treat the battlefield as a morality play where a person's virtue or character showed itself in heroic fashion. In the Pennsylvanian's mind, even the courageous look more lucky than brave. Lieutenant Wilson's indifference to danger elicited feelings of admiration in Donaldson, but his comrade looked like a lost child, wandering in front of the reserve line at the brick kiln to the most exposed position on the field. Donaldson saw nothing dramatic or inspiring in Wilson, who "appeared to wear a charmed life" without ever knowing that he "had done an act of bravery."[62]

When Donaldson broadened his gaze on the battlefield, he did not automatically damn every shirker. Some of them had slipped to the rear out of physical and mental exhaustion, not because of moral weakness or a loss of manliness. Donaldson was surprisingly empathic in his analysis, largely because the attacks at Fredericksburg were breathtakingly futile. The power of circumstances stands out in Donaldson's account, explaining why he nodded approvingly at his men for adjusting on the fly when they used the ground in an attempt to gain tactical advantage or to save themselves from annihilation. Neither orders from above nor an internal drive to uphold male honor could discipline the troops to behave with predictability. Such actions could have been construed as a dereliction of duty, but Donaldson did not take issue with soldiers who became free-floating fighters off on their own, moving beyond the command and control of their officers. Perhaps he was simply trying to deflect attention away from his own questionable decision to remain behind the front line. Nonetheless, Donaldson wanted his readers to see the battlefield as an arena without design, where the binary of courage and cowardice dissolved in the fog of war.

In reading Donaldson's depiction of Fredericksburg, one can see that the violent forces of combat failed to completely destroy concepts of courage and cowardice. Yet the jarring gap between the ideal of fighting and its chaotic reality did push soldiers toward a pragmatic philosophy of war, one that valued flexibility in thought and action over a prescribed code of conduct. This shift in thinking acquired its persuasive force by being acted out in battle, where circumstances proved just as important as a soldier's character in determining life or death or victory or defeat. Having seen how the invisible shockwaves of battle debilitated "good men," who suddenly gave out after establishing themselves as dependable comrades, battle-tested veterans like Donaldson were surprisingly quick to modify their expectations of soldiers under fire.

Pennsylvanian Amos Judson provides another good example of this fluidity in thought. Judson, a veteran of some of the most lethal campaigns waged by the Army of the Potomac, returned home in 1865 and promptly set about writing a unit history. In his chapter on courage, Judson admitted that he could not rely on his comrades to stand firm under fire. At one moment, a man acted with resolution, but an instant later, the same soldier was shaky, hesitant, and desperate to disappear from the front. A soldier needed to ration his courage. If it were depleted under fire, Judson argued, then it was permissible for a veteran to seek temporary refuge from the shooting, to restore his body and mind, and then return to battle. A man who stood on the firing line, even if he wavered after a few volleys, compared favorably to the laggards who fell by the wayside because of sore feet, rheumatism, diarrhea, or some other ailment. The degree to which attitudes softened is impossible to measure, but this spirit of accommodation found expression in the language that soldiers used to characterize unmilitary behavior. The epithet *coward* never disappeared from the lexicon — especially when it came to accusations against African Americans and ethnic soldiers — but a softer vocabulary emerged that shamed deviant behavior without unmasking the man. The use of terms such as *shirking, skedaddling,* and *malingering* became a popular way of implying cowardice without blackening a man's reputation. The phrase *broken down* was an important part of soldier speak; it signified a complete loss of spirit, emotions, and physical strength. As important as these shifts in language were, however, they also reveal the great distance that still separated Civil War soldiers from a modern understanding of trauma and why they never relinquished their faith in the individual's capacity to stand up and fight.

Reaching into the world of New Yorker Charles Biddlecom gives voice to the mixed and fluid ways in which Civil War soldiers tried to be obedient in the ranks without being reduced to subservience; how they struggled to survive without shirking or malingering; and how they aspired to heroism without taking unnecessary risks. Charles Biddlecom despised military life almost from the moment he enlisted. He felt a deep sense of solitude in the ranks and was almost always absorbed in bitter thoughts about the war. In time, he came to see himself in a different light. Ironically, Biddlecom's transformation came through the heartbreaking experience of battle. Standing up to enemy fire, seeing the blood of comrades, and killing Confederates gave him a sense of self-worth as a fighter for the causes of Union and emancipation.

The 1861 rush that carried Biddlecom into the Twenty-Eighth New York was a short-lived adventure of soldiering. Rheumatism and chronic diarrhea incapacitated Charles even before he fired his gun in battle. He was granted a medical discharge on August 22, 1861, and returned to his modest farm of 147 acres in Monroe County, New York, where his wife and three children were waiting. Two years later, with conscription hanging over his head and the burning desire to earn his family's respect, Charlie was "induced" into service, receiving a bounty of one hundred dollars when he enlisted in the 147th New York Infantry. He boarded a train for Elmira, New York, feeling the need to prove himself a man, since he thought of himself as the "black sheep" of the family. "They never gave me much credit for being much of a man," he confided to his wife. Why had he bowed to family pressure when he could have paid a commutation fee and stayed at home, away from the other miserable conscripts forced into the army? Patriotic rhetoric barely stirred his emotions. He did not see himself as a "freedom shrieker" or a "Union Saver."[63] Yet once he stood on the battlefield, the flow of cynicism about cause and family nearly evaporated. He would not hide; he would fight, silencing those at home who had cast him off as a perfect failure in life. He promised his wife that no one at home would see him as worthless once he demonstrated that he was considerably brave. With a grim resolve, he was determined to build a soldier's reputation that would always be a source of pride to their children.

When Biddlecom stepped off the train and marched into the Elmira barracks, a guard issued him ragged blankets and served putrid rations. That night he could not fall asleep, shivering throughout the night and believing that he would "freeze to death." As soon as he awoke, Charles knew he had to escape the army. "I have the foundation of a discharge already laid in the shape of a bad cold and rheumatism," he informed his wife on October 6, 1863.[64] Biddlecom predicted a quick exit from the army due to his illness, but the military rejected his requests. His "forced" journey south continued to Virginia, where he reached his new regiment, the 147th New York. He felt a cold chill of isolation standing alongside the veterans of his new regiment. He wanted to hunt down the Rebels, yet also felt that it did not really matter, "for it is all the same whether we fight or run, the war will drag its dreary length."[65] The fog of an unknown future enveloped Biddlecom, who did not believe his officers could offer the guiding light of capable leadership. Every march seemed pointless and self-destructive, providing sufficient evidence for Biddlecom to claim that those in charge did not care that they were slowly killing their men. Charlie only had to look at his body for proof. He started to wear down during a November march: his legs swelled, diarrhea struck, and eventually he collapsed by the roadside. In a twenty-four-hour-period he expelled "over thirty passages of the bowels and passed so much blood and mucus and become so weak that I could hardly stand alone."[66]

Back in camp Biddlecom sought a discharge for rheumatism, but officers and doctors alike saw his condition as the classic ploy of a malingerer. Biddlecom's decision to accept a bounty validated their perception of him as one of those unscrupulous men trying to swindle the bounty system. What choice did he have, Charlie asked his wife, when those in power assumed that he was a sneak, a cheat, and a liar who should waste away in the ranks? The choices seemed obvious: desert or prepare for a torturous death. Charles reluctantly planned to flee, even instructing his wife to destroy his letter, "because if I am found out it will make a devil of a rumpus. So burn this up or put it away where no one will find it."[67] Two weeks later, a local newspaper scuttled Biddlecom's plans by mistakenly listing him as absent without leave. Biddlecom's animus toward the army and the government vanished—at least for the moment—once his precious reputation came under question. Biddlecom choreographed a letter campaign with his family, contacted local papers, and spread the word by mouth that he was indeed in Virginia and faithfully serving in the Army of the Potomac. The rumors were eventually quelled, but the false report raised the specter of living under the shadow of disgrace. Biddlecom knew he could not exist in such darkness, but he continued to imagine alternatives that might allow him to leave the army without loss of prestige. His thoughts were fuzzy as he tried to devise an acceptable plan that would not lead people to see him as a hopeless coward.

No plot of escape back to New York materialized, but Charlie kept thinking about his family, and, rather than feel emotionally uplifted, he disclosed to his wife that thinking of the family had "a bad effect on my mind" and made him "discontented."[68] The sentimental belief that love for family and nation would renew each other did not always flicker in the hearts of all soldiers, particularly during those hollow times when stomachs were empty, clothes were tattered, and tedious days were spent drilling in front of officers barking orders. Understanding the context of daily life in camp helps to explain why Charlie did not frame his disillusionment as a choice between cowardice or bravery. Extreme loneliness and estrangement from family and his own comrades caused scores of men like Charlie to shut down and raise the white flag of demoralization. "Cursed be the day that saw my name drawn as a conscript and d—d be the hour that I made up my mind to come as a draft," he wrote. "I think sometimes that if it was not for you and my children I would blow out my brains. D—n the South. D—n the war and all that had anything to do in getting it up."[69]

On Christmas Day in 1863 Biddlecom sat alone, gazing into the dreaded unknown without "a single soul to talk over old times." Before him arose a vision of a rudderless Army of the Potomac, flailing about in "this desolate land of sin and slavery, . . . [for] 'the balance of our lives.'" Overtaken by morose thoughts, he could not bring himself to write a "cheerful" letter with "a little sunshine in them." Looking to the heavens did not relieve his depression. Above him were hundreds of buzzards, "wheeling in circles . . . over some horse or mule that has worn himself out in the country's service. I think the time has come when it should be written . . . [that] 'Man's made in the likeness of the Devil and but little above the Brute.' For man is acting as a mule or a horse and thought less of than" in the army. It was a "sad lonesome day" for Charlie, who hoped, "God grant that I see no more such, but rather let the grave close over me and with its dark portal shut out all earthly hopes and care."[70]

The darkness gathering over Biddlecom was not an isolated front hovering over the army; the icy winds of neglect were felt all the way from his home state of New York. He told his wife that he was suffering in the ranks for his parents, "to please them and their pride in having it to say that their son and brother did not dodge the draft." He now deeply regretted his attempt to earn their approval, since he never received words of encouragement from his father and his letters always managed to offend his mother and sisters. "Now, I do not wish to be harsh in my feelings towards them," Charlie explained, "but I do sometimes think that while I am suffering almost to the pains of death in the most trying of all places a man can be placed in, that they do not appreciate fully the reasons why I am here, and have not that feeling for me that it is my right to expect."[71] What can one make of this exchange? It reveals how the war penetrated Northern and Southern households, simultaneously pushing families together and pulling them apart. Civil War soldiers grumbled incessantly about civilian naïveté or indifference, but they pressed on, knowing that they had to live up to their own grim resolve to be brave, given the high expectations of family and friends who had sent them off to war.

Biddlecom could not even look to the spring of 1864 as a time of renewal and hope, because the return of sunny skies, warmer temperatures, and leafy trees marked the descent into an inevitable campaign of death and destruction. Charlie once again found himself on the edge of malingering. He hobbled around camp, crippled by rheumatism, his leg badly swollen, knotted, and veiny. The pain was excruciating, and Biddlecom trusted that the board of surgeons would grant him a discharge. "I hope to be one of the condemned soldiers," he wrote on March 19. "Still, I can't tell how it will be as very much depends on who is in command of the company at the time the examination comes. If everything works agreeably, I think I shall be in Macedon one of these fine spring mornings. At all events, I shall try to get out as hard as I can."[72] Two weeks later, Biddlecom realized he could not let mere reality get in the way of his hope. The medical establishment, as an enforcer of discipline, ignored the soldier's voice when it came to his own body. The surgeon first asked Biddlecom, "Are you a conscript or sub?" "If the answer was drafted," Biddlecom added, "the doctor would ask, 'why didn't you pay $300? You ought to be sick.' If the poor devil was a sub, the doctor used to say, 'didn't you get paid for coming? Go and drill. I can't do anything for you.'" For the next week, Biddlecom watched as "men would come in from duty and just lie down and die."[73] Knowing that "the government has used us mean," he imagined that in the coming campaign every soldier "will try to keep his body out of the way of stray bullets and out of the way of fragments of shell."[74]

As the Army of the Potomac formed into columns on the morning of May 4, 1864, initiating the two-month-long Overland Campaign, several different ways of maneuvering out of the army tempted Biddlecom. Charlie's tent mates had cornered him and pressured him to join the euphemistic "Blue Ridge Corps" — a band of deserters whose compass only pointed north. "There is [also] the Coffee Brigade for those that are always five or six miles back from the front cooking coffee," Charlie quipped. "Then there is the Corps of Confirmed Dead Beats that are in the hospital or riding in the ambulance." Biddlecom predicted that the ranks of the "Dead Beats" would be robust, since "there isn't a doctor in the army that can find out who is really sick, or who is making themselves a little sick and feigning a great deal that does not ail them."[75] After considering all of his options, in what must have been an agonizing decision, Biddlecom turned his back on the route to "freedom."[76] Charlie headed into the Wilderness with the rest of the Army of the Potomac, beginning a long cam-

*Courage and Cowardice*

paign of continuous marching and killing. Every battle left a sickly residue of grief and despair that no Civil War soldier could easily shake off.

Yet when dark memories of bodies ripped apart by shells and punctured by bullets shadowed him, Charlie found reprieve in knowing that he had passed the ultimate test of manhood. This was a moment of personal triumph for Biddlecom; no friend or family member could question his worthiness. In asserting himself as a man of courage, Charlie felt as if he had crossed into a world beyond civilian understanding. He had found his warrior voice. "I must not hold back now after going through so much danger," he wrote from the trenches of Petersburg. "I have won a character as a soldier that I think something of. Our folks never gave me credit for being much of a man when I was at home. Now that I have won the confidence and respect of my officers, I must try and keep it while I stay in the army, that my boys may have it to say that Father was not an absolute failure in all things."[77] The opinions at home mattered less to Charlie once he had entered the unique brotherhood of fighting men. The intense emotional bond forged with his fellow comrades was undeniable, unbreakable, and unknowable to those who had never stood on the battlefield, locked together, standing shoulder to shoulder, waiting for the moment when soldiers lost their sense of self and fought for their unit without regard for individual safety.

Biddlecom's experience during the Overland Campaign demonstrates that combat could be exhilarating in one moment and then, in the next instant, that the grand spectacle of battle could suddenly turn into a confused uproar of smoke and noise, a cacophony of voices of the timid, the brave, and the crazed. The emotional drain of these continuous operations nearly brought Biddlecom to the breaking point after Cold Harbor on June 3, when his regiment finally settled into camp. "Men are beginning to get sick now that the excitement of battle is cooled off a little," a jaded and depressed Biddlecom confessed on June 12. "They are thinking over the narrow escapes they have had and counting up those friends that have been killed or wounded. . . . Sad are the faces and full of grief. Dreary foreboding fills our hearts as we think of what has been done and what is yet left to be done."[78] A break in the action did not bring relief; in Biddlecom's mind, danger lurked everywhere. He obsessed about his safety, imagining that a horrible sickness was shadowing him around camp. If he ended up at a field hospital, Charlie told his family, then he might as well be sent to a morgue, given that few soldiers left a surgeon's tent with both feet on the ground.

Biddlecom could not imagine spending another day in the ranks, let alone the two more years remaining in his enlistment. "I hate this life worse than a cat does hot soup," he exclaimed to his wife. "If I ever get out I will stuff my old uniform with straw and stand it up in one corner to look at when I feel out of humor just to remind me that home with its little cares and troubles is not the worst place in the world for a man to enjoy life."[79] Eleven days later, when Biddlecom was issued a new blouse, he had to bid farewell to his old coat. He still wanted to send the jacket home, but not to hang it as a punching bag for life's frustrations as he had earlier imagined. He now wanted to display his coat as a sacred artifact attesting to his services and sacrifices. "I should like to save it as a souvenir of the hard fought battles of the Wilderness, Laurel Hill, Spotsylvania, North Anna, and Petersburg. I should like to keep it with all its dust, samples of different soil from Culpeper to this place. 'Tis not much of a coat now," he affectionately observed, "the skirts torn and ragged, and it is sadly ripped under the arms. Still, as I look at it as it hangs on the butt of my musket, I think more of it than I ever did of any article of dress I ever owned in my life before."[80] Charlie drew attention to the stained uniform, with its blood, holes, and dirt, as indisputable physical proof of his courage, and giving up his old uniform felt like a disgraceful act. That soiled coat embodied the profound changes in how he saw himself. The man who said that he was not a "freedom shrieker" or a "Union saver" now felt a sudden emotional passion for the cause and a deep affection for his comrades.

Surprisingly, the battlefield had filled a void in Biddlecom's life. Yet his confusion about combat was revealed in his equivocation over how to treat his dirtied sack coat. Should he preserve it as a treasured artifact of emotional and patriotic value, or burn it with the rest of the ragged and filthy uniforms? Biddlecom's indecision over keeping the coat underscores how he was both drawn to and repulsed by the killing fields of the war. He was stunned by what he had seen and done. So many comrades had fallen by his side, but their deaths, though heart-wrenching in the extreme, reinforced his devotion to the Union and sealed his sense of obligation to those still living in the ranks.

The openness with which Biddlecom mourned his fallen comrades was far from unusual in Civil War armies, but the expression of devotion could not mask the enduring horror of seeing men killed. Union soldier Ambrose Henry Hayward, for instance, led his family to believe that the fighting at Ringgold, Georgia, had rejuvenated him. He reported on December 2, 1863, "It is glorious to be a Soldier after the Battle is over when we have returned to our comfortable quarters to rest on our Laurells bravely won, to think and talk of dareing deeds we each and all have done, and to show the narrow escape from the enemys bullets. One has had his haversack shot away, another his Clothes riddled, another his bayonet scabbard cut off."[81] Hayward's sense of jubilation and pride gave way to bitterness and depression some two weeks later, when he wrote home

*Courage and Cowardice*

This *Harper's Weekly* illustration depicts the Union attacks at Ringgold, Georgia—a debacle, according to Ambrose Henry Hayward, yet he could not contain the emotional rush of killing. He wrote to his family, "It is glorious to be a Soldier after the Battle is over when we have returned to our comfortable quarters to rest on our Laurells bravely won, to think and talk of dareing deeds we each and all have done."
(Library of Congress Prints and Photographs Division, Washington, D.C.)

that "I experienced more fear & dread at Rinngold than at either Chancellorsville, Antietam, or Gettysburgh." He had kept these torturous feelings out of his first letter, but the awful images of dying friends could not be repressed. They played in his head continuously, leading him to describe the horrific situation in future correspondence:

> We did advance but only to meet death more certain. many a good
> fellow in the first Brigade had fallen not to lay where they fell, but
> wounded and dead rolled together down the steep rocky soil of the
> mountain. I saw poor Fithian when he was struck. he had just spoke
> to me about his gun. it would not go off. The ball struck him in his side.
> He dropped his Rifle. I saw that I could not reach him. I turned away
> dreading to see him roll down the mountain. I could tell you more

Pennsylvania's Ambrose Henry Hayward, like many other soldiers, looked to the battlefield as the ultimate test of manliness, but he also did not hesitate to disclose his disgust for the butchery of battle and the irrepressible dread of having to face the enemy's bullets again. (MASS-MOLLUS Collection at the U.S. Army Heritage and Education Center)

Corporal Henry Fithian was one of Ambrose Henry Hayward's closest friends, and as with so many other soldiers, there was an intense emotional bond between the two men. At Ringgold Hayward watched his comrade tumble down a steep rocky ridge to his death, a scene that he could not easily forget. He wrote to his father, "I saw poor Fithian when he was struck. he had just spoke to me about his gun. it would not go off. The ball struck him in his side. He dropped his Rifle. I saw that I could not reach him. I turned away dreading to see him roll down the mountain."
(MASS-MOLLUS Collection at the U.S. Army Heritage and Education Center)

of such tales but it is as unpleasant for me to bring them back to my memories as it is for you to read them.[82]

The dark and frightening incidents at Ringgold lodged in Hayward's consciousness, but, like Biddlecom and many other soldiers, he found grandeur in war and derived political and personal meaning from the deaths of his comrades. These sentiments sustained men in trying times, giving them just cause to keep killing even as they expressed their disgust at the ghastly sights and fiendish sounds of the battlefield. In looking back at the Overland Campaign,

Biddlecom still felt exhilarated by the lurid spectacle of thousands of lean, dirty men working together in the grinding machine of war. In some instances, the lust of war could blind Civil War volunteers to their own transformation and how far removed they were from realizing the sentimental dream of soldiering, but Biddlecom only had to use his eyes, nose, and hands to see, smell, and feel how he had become someone he no longer recognized. His sack coat was crusted in dirt and blood, hanging loosely off his smelly and emaciated body; his face was blackened with smoke; and his skin was leathery brown from the constant exposure to the blazing Virginia sun. By the time Grant's army had settled around Richmond in early June 1864, Biddlecom was no different than a battle-tested Confederate defending Atlanta, a soldier marching across Georgia under Sherman, or one of Lee's veterans trying to kill him from behind a Virginia trench.[83] He had survived the Overland Campaign and stood at the end of a long road strewn with corpses and shattered bodies, barely hanging on to a thread of idealism for the cause of Union.

Without question, killing made the man during the Civil War. The strength of nineteenth-century Americans' ideal of male honor melded personal aspirations with high political ideas in both Union and Confederate armies. For a man who hated the army from the moment he enlisted, who despised his officers, and who was contemptuous of the Lincoln administration, Biddlecom's indignation against the war never materialized in a bodily renunciation of the cause. Although he left the battlefield dazed, something switched in his thinking at a deeply personal and political level. This was common for Civil War veterans, who often discovered purpose in their cause after the shedding of blood. Charlie no longer brooded about the cause after the 1864 fall of Atlanta and Union victories in the Shenandoah Valley. He reversed his earlier political positions and became a champion of emancipation and a supporter of Lincoln. Biddlecom's example is especially revealing—not because he proves or even suggests that all Civil War soldiers were either dutiful or driven by blood lust, or because his story reveals that the war was often seen from the ranks as an empty exercise in organized murder. Rather, Biddlecom illustrates how the act of fighting gave rise to a pragmatic outlook in the Union armies and possibly—though not to the same extent—in Southern armies as well. Pragmatism does not suggest a loss of idealism or the prevalence of disillusionment. On the contrary, Biddlecom exemplifies how men could change their thinking, and even embrace ideas that they once opposed, without rejecting the intrinsic importance of beliefs. Through the ordeal of combat, Biddlecom discovered the necessity of revising his political and ideological stance on the war, given that supporting the Lincoln administration and the political aim of emancipation offered Biddlecom the best chance of achieving final military victory and getting him home as soon as possible.

Biddlecom's writings point to the difficulties in determining whether soldiers were permanently compromised by combat or impervious to trauma. In the case of the temperamental New Yorker, battle strengthened his devotion to the cause, like many other men on both sides whose sense of honor and courage became more intertwined with the cause itself as the war progressed. Yet ideology was not a bombproof emotional shelter from war's psychological destruction. Letters from Virginian Charles Trueheart also show how a man could write about his devotion to the cause with incredible feeling and bold statements of loyalty that hid his fear and anxiety about being a human target. Trueheart informed his family from the Petersburg trenches that the "piquet fire [is heard] all the time with occasional shelling continues along the line as usual." "Hardly a minute in the twenty four hours elapses," he added, "without my hearing the crack of a musket frequently the whiz of a Minnie." The auditory onslaught wore Trueheart down, and he could not quiet the noises resounding in his head. "Of course I am heartily tired of this state of things," he concluded, "but this and much more, and worse, is, as nothing to the grand all important object for which we are fighting and enduring these grievous things."[84]

It is undeniable that ideology helped Trueheart cope with the accumulated stress of siege warfare, but the interpretive power of this moment is not fully realized unless his words are seen as more than registers of morale or declarations of motivation. The investigation needs to go beyond the meaning of his words and delve into the heart of the circumstances that permitted and produced such thoughts and actions.[85] Trueheart's words were born of chaos, and the act of bringing coherency to his life on paper when he wrote this letter prompts additional questions. How did Trueheart want to be heard by those at home? When we try to answer this, other questions arise. Why did he bring his readers into the dangerous trenches of Petersburg, to surround them with the unearthly noises of war? Why did Trueheart confess his fears and then all of a sudden leave that fiendish place without describing his life in full? None of these questions can be answered unless one understands how he came to articulate this within the realities of his cultural, material, political, and military world.

Hundreds of thousands of soldiers shared Trueheart's ability to pick through the painful memories of battle, finding emotional strength and patriotic resolve to face the bullets again. Too often historians have interpreted the "willingness" of soldiers to fight as proof of motivation or agency, but this creates the false impression that Civil War soldiers gave themselves to cause and comrades in a straightforward manner. Instead we must situate the men's words within their perilous world. Historians Lesley J. Gordon and Diane Miller Sommerville have found examples of men on both sides who were incapable of recasting their terrifying battlefield experiences into a heroic and patriotic narrative. Their conclusions show the limits of ideology and sentimentalism: some veterans felt strongly about why they were fighting, but found that those same motivational beliefs could not free their minds of such disturbing memories.[86]

Avoiding any stereotypical view of soldiers as either victims of or as victors over combat calls for an evaluation of soldier letters within the flow of events over an extended period of time. Extracting reactions from a single letter leads to the perception that soldiers gave clear expression about surviving, when in actuality their perceptions of battle rarely led to a single revelation or truth about the battlefield. Biddlecom is again useful in illustrating this point. He was a man of ideas and adamant about why he was fighting, but he was also aware of his physical entrapment in the army. "I have tried my gun on the Rebs to my satisfaction," he confided after his first encounter with the Confederates, "and now I should like to come home. But I suppose Uncle Abe will keep me at this war as long as I can shoot a gun."[87] In just a few sentences Biddlecom captured the complexity of his service. He accepted his powerlessness in the ranks as a "natural" condition, while the very symbol of his loss of freedom—his musket—gave force to and made true his sense of male honor. The driving need to prove one's manliness, so strong in the letters of all Civil War soldiers, compelled men, often unknowingly, to affirm the power structure of the very military regime that they denounced for exploiting the soldier.

In becoming veterans, Northern and Southern volunteers came to accept that subordination to the army was necessary and even desirable, but they continued to see themselves as citizen-soldiers serving their nation as independent men. Their inability or refusal to expose the tensions of their existence leads us to ask how soldiers came to hold contradictory positions and still adhere to the army's demand for disciplined fighters. Pragmatism offers an explanation because it gave individuals a degree of flexibility to navigate within conditions that were not of their own making. The malleability of courage and cowardice as concepts illustrates how soldiers could rework codes of conduct from a situational angle without running afoul of the military justice system or overthrowing the dominant medical, cultural, and military beliefs that sanctified courage as a character trait or a moral quality. The contradictory consciousness of Civil War soldiers comes into full view when one tries to understand why men kept returning to the battlefield. It is understandable that members of the rank and file could not fully comprehend how impersonal forces of violence, high ideals, cultural values, male honor, and physical conditions were pressing down on them from all directions, compelling them to think and act in ways that they could not always explain to themselves. Within the constrained but fluid world of soldiering, Civil War veterans could live out heroic war stories as they had imagined them in 1861 while simultaneously managing their conflicted feelings of the horrid things they saw and did in the fury of battle for a cause they were willing to kill and die for.

# 5

# Desertion and
# Military Justice

———

AT THE OPEN END OF A THREE-SIDED SQUARE, fifteen North Carolinians stood next to freshly dug graves prepared for their dead bodies. These men— all soldiers in the Army of Tennessee—came from two Tar Heel regiments. They had been arrested for desertion in early April 1864 and sentenced to die on May 4 near Dalton, Georgia. The solemn cadence of the death march had announced the arrival of the prisoners on their day of execution. General Alexander Welch Reynolds, the officer in charge, granted the condemned a few minutes to pray before a chaplain stepped forward to read the Twenty-Third Psalm, promising them in their last moments that restful waters and green pastures awaited them, even in "the presence of mine enemies." General Reynolds asked the men if they had any final words. A number of the men begged for mercy, insisting that they had left the army to save starving families, without any intention of fighting against the Confederacy. Intermingled with the pleas of innocence were the comforting words of comrades and company officers, who were huddled around their doomed friends, bidding them a final farewell. Suddenly, and without notice, General Reynolds turned toward the prisoners and commanded: "May God have mercy on your souls." As he walked away, the guards rushed forward, and according to one witness, they took "each one to a stake, tied them first, and then bound a cloth over their eyes." Some of the condemned started to pray out loud, while others were shouting and clapping their hands. They would not leave this world gently.

Squads of ten men faced each deserter, and when General Reynolds raised his handkerchief, the distinctive metallic clicking sound of hammers being pulled back by 150 riflemen caused "the unfortunate men at the stakes," in the words of one observer, "to shudder and tremble as though a galvanic battery had been applied to each."[1] The signal to fire came with the delicate dropping of a handkerchief. The execution squads unleashed a ragged volley that sprayed bullets in all directions. Most missed the chests of their human targets, and as the smoke dissipated, only two lifeless bodies could be seen dangling from their posts. The other thirteen men could be heard "screaming in their agony and imploring and beseeching the men to finish the work so badly done." One poor soldier was heard yelling at the executioners to kill him "for God's sake" and "not to shoot his flesh to pieces." A Virginia officer watched in horror as the provost guards rushed forward and without hesitation put their guns "close to their hearts or heads & fired."[2] Once the provost guard had silenced the cries of the condemned, the entire division marched past the mangled corpses in silence, a solemn reminder that deserters, even in death, could never outrun their disgraceful act.

Historians have ignored the killing of these fifteen North Carolinians, one of the largest mass executions of deserters during the Civil War. The magnitude of this violent encounter was exceptional, but the incident embodies three distinct yet intertwined questions that explore the act of deserting, the ways that national armies used coercion to instill discipline and punish runaway soldiers, and how the press and print culture shaped the public's perception of deserters, particularly those killed by a firing squad. All three inquiries follow overlapping paths that lead into the imagination of the deserter, so that we may see his world as he perceived it, with all of the confusion, ambiguities, and uncertainties of openly contesting the army's power structure. A thick description approach is utilized to create deeply contextualized stories of deserters so that we catch them on the run, maneuvering inside camp, sorting out their options, communicating with wives and families, and plotting out strategies of resistance. The wealth of material in personal letters home, official reports, court-martial testimony, soldier diaries, and newspaper accounts provides an incredible range of perspectives on the pursuit and prosecution of deserters, but at the same time, the historical record is far from complete. Ritual executions by their very nature distorted that record through the physical annihilation of the condemned, whose voices, of course, were silenced.[3] Much of the source material comes instead from the pens of military officers, government officials, and the press. The result, as historian Lorien Foote notes, is that there is no "modern work" that "provides the perspective of the deserters themselves."[4]

To that end, the stories below do not make up a master narrative about the motivation of deserters or chart the ebb and flow of desertion as it related to the overall military situation. They are intended to show a range of perspectives and experiences of men who wrestled with the decision to flee the army, and what they did once they were on the run. Quite simply, the act of desertion possessed its own situational logic, rooted in time and place and shaped in decisive ways by the politics and the personality of the soldier. Despite the profound differences among the deserters in this chapter, they all conceived of loyalty in fluid ways that unsettle the assumption that the link between cause and morale is the baseline for understanding why some men deserted and others did not. Given the emphasis on motivation, morale, and cause in this approach, it is not surprising that scholars have tended to cast deserters as men who were not sufficiently ideological or political and thus were more susceptible to despondency and disillusionment. James McPherson, for example, has put forth such an argument, writing in his invaluable *For Cause and Comrades* that deserters were mostly "conscripts, substitutes, and bounty men" and that they "were motivated marginally if at all by duty, honor, or ideology."[5]

The general tendency among Civil War scholars has been to acknowledge McPherson's conclusion about deserters as deadbeats, in contrast to the vast majority of soldiers, the ones who held up under fire thanks to their patriotism and political commitment. While the substance of McPherson's argument has value, the methodology behind the conclusions is problematic. Any attempt to measure loyalty privileges the written sources of the elite over those of the poorly educated. Furthermore, any sampling of letters is incomplete and can only offer a static glimpse into the opaque world of morale. Trying to calculate the depth of a soldier's war weariness by counting the sentiments in his letters reveals little about the shifting contexts in which soldiers wrote letters over a period of time. Given that the archives never describe the lives of historical actors in full, the fragmented voices that come from the documents affirm that deserters, though not idealistic, still could be deeply political, ideological, and governed by a flexible sense of duty and honor that was the hallmark of pragmatism.

Every state in the Union and in the Confederacy contained deserters who found refuge among sympathetic civilians, many of whom were still support-

*Desertion and Military Justice*

ers of their respective armies but were hostile toward the centralized authority coming from either Richmond or Washington, D.C. The available statistics, though hotly debated, suggest that 100,000 to 120,000 Confederates deserted, while somewhat fewer than 300,000 men permanently left the Union army. Out of approximately 1 million soldiers in the Confederacy, this comes to a desertion rate of roughly 10–12 percent, while the Union number bumps up to 14.3 percent based on 2.1 million Union enlistees.[6] The numbers on both sides likely underrepresent the actual number of men who took unauthorized leave. The absence of these men officially constituted desertion in the eyes of the Union and Confederate military, but even though such men were gone for substantial periods of time, they were not prosecuted by Union and Confederate officials who failed to account for the difference between deserters and absence-without-leave. Many of these soldiers also left the ranks more than one time. The most serious issue when it comes to studying desertion during the Civil War is the uneven documentation, especially on the Confederate side during the final two years of the war.[7]

The reasons why a soldier would take such risks and desert can rarely be boiled down to a matter of loyalty or war weariness. No single factor can explain desertion as a social protest. Poverty, disaffection for the cause, privations, resentment of tyrannical officers or the national government, and cries for relief from their home could spur desertion. In other words, without recognizing desertion as a collaborative act between soldiers and their communities, it is impossible to understand why some men fled. All in all, the issues were interconnected and interdependent. Only when enlisted men organized among themselves, plotted against their own army, and then left en masse with weapons in tow did desertion signify an outright rejection of the cause.

Deserters on both sides were drawn to cities to get "lost" among the multitudes, but communities of runaways largely existed in the mountainous regions in the North and the South—mostly along the spine of the Appalachian Mountains, which run from north Georgia through central Pennsylvania. These rugged areas with impenetrable forests and few roads were noted for harboring thousands of disaffected soldiers who left the army for communities characterized by a fierce localism, independence based on powerful ties of kinship, and relatively insulated economies. The physical isolation intensified a deep suspicion of outsiders that was exacerbated by conscription when national governments came calling for bodies to fill the ranks. Both regions witnessed tremendous violence against the draft, but no social protest in the South compares to the 1863 draft riots in New York and Boston. The Richmond Bread Riots, which were actually part of a chain of protests throughout the South in the spring of

1863, erupted over the failure of state and national government to assist the wives of soldiers, not the draft.[8]

On the whole, deserter resistance took on a different look in the Southern mountains, in part because it was a war zone, whereas the North was relatively free of enemy occupation. Desertion in the Confederacy also differed because the Southern nation drafted a higher proportion of men and extracted more agricultural goods from its citizens than the North did. It is reasonable to claim that the pressures were greater on Southern civilians and that violence was more intense below the Mason-Dixon line. Because most Civil War action took place in the South, there the line between soldier and civilian blurred, especially during the final year of the war, when the Confederacy hemorrhaged deserters. Their desperate resistance against home guard troops and militia units fractured communities in cycles of violence for generations to come.[9]

In the North, civilian violence was almost always aimed at representatives of the Federal government. Of the many deserter strongholds in the North where people turned to violence to oppose the war, the lumber area of Appalachian Pennsylvania attracted a cagey band of draft evaders who resisted Federal authorities.[10] Copperheads and Democrats—though they opposed the war for different reasons—were mixed up in the struggles in the lower Midwest among deserters, civilians, and Federal military authorities. In the South, upcountry areas were not the only rallying points for Confederate runaways. The Piedmont of North Carolina, the Mississippi Valley, and the piney woods of southeast Georgia also attracted significant numbers of deserters. By 1863, when Confederate resources were dwindling and young boys and decrepit old men filled the ranks of the home guard, the militia could not stand in the way of an experienced combat soldier.[11]

At the beginning of the war neither Union nor Confederate forces ever issued a formal policy regarding deserters, and officers pursued a wide range of impromptu policies, largely because both sides had expected the prosecution of deserters to be a straightforward matter. If a soldier left the army with the intention not to return, military law defined the offense as a crime punishable by death. What was clear-cut in the regulations, however, became confusing and contentious when volunteers started drifting away from camp for a few days to a few months at a time. The fine line between desertion and straggling lacked precision and was frequently violated by citizen-soldiers who insisted that they had the right to take leave when it suited their needs. Time and time again soldiers who were accused of desertion argued that they had left the ranks with every intention of returning once they took care of pressing personal affairs at home. Such departures, they insisted, should be treated as absence without leave rather than desertion. Unauthorized visits home for Confederate soldiers, as historian William Blair discovered, could actually strengthen discipline, since men could return to the ranks knowing that their families were faring well. Was a soldier absent at roll call but at home, refusing to either collaborate with the enemy or renounce the cause, still a deserter deserving of full prosecution as allowed by military law? The question of intention was unavoidable, and it bedeviled officers because it created a legal opening for chronic absenteeism to flourish in both armies. Sorting out which soldiers were deserting and which were just visiting home frustrated professional military men throughout the war, especially since company officers tended to look the other way, knowing that quick trips home actually bolstered morale and improved a man's physical health.

Sterner measures came in 1862, when military and political officials on both sides tried to sharpen the legal distinctions between desertion and being absent without leave (AWOL). Historian Aaron Sheehan-Dean discovered this complication in Virginia, where state planners tried to use the language of desertion to enforce a clear standard of loyalty but members of the rank and file continued to recognize the varieties of absences and "understood their enlistment as a contract between the state and themselves, one that created mutual rights and responsibilities."[12] Because Southern armies frequently operated within or near a soldier's community, the problem of taking French leave in Confederate commands was acute. If the family farm was nearby, it was virtually impossible for officers to stop their men from slipping out of the ranks for a quick visit home.[13] During Sherman's advance on Atlanta in the summer of 1864, for instance, Georgia soldiers were in close proximity to their communities. Some men were tempted to desert to relieve suffering families, while others took advantage of Sherman's lenient policy of amnesty.[14]

Civil War officers struggled to find a consistent classification system for straggling and deserting. The imprecision in the language of desertion actually concealed the military and political costs of runaway soldiers, given that stragglers were usually repeat offenders, costly to apprehend, and constantly draining the army's strength on the battlefield. Confederate John Bell Hood lumped all stragglers together as deserters driven by the desire for plunder. Fatigue or any other extenuating circumstances apparently did not figure into his calculations.[15] In that same vein, an outraged Union officer in Louisiana could not see the difference among deserters, pillagers, and battlefield cowards. "'Straggler' and 'pillager' are identical terms," he argued in a dispatch on June 3, 1864. "They are the cowards that diminish our ranks when confronting the enemy, and swell the list of prisoners captured by the enemy. . . . Death would not atone for their disloyalty and crimes."[16] In the end, Civil War officers at all levels weakened their own authority by conflating straggling with desertion as a military and legal term. As a result, thousands of absentees were coddled when military law dictated that they should have been tried for desertion. As long as a Civil War soldier did not give himself up to the enemy or leave camp with an armed band of deserters, he knew he had more than a fighting chance to prove that his intention was never to abandon the army.[17]

Without a stable category for classifying deserters, the military justice system in both armies proved erratic in procedure and inconsistent in sentencing. Regulations actually exacerbated the situation by granting commissioned officers at the regimental level immense discretion as judges and jurors over their men. August Kautz's widely read *Customs of Service* permitted regimental officers from lieutenant to colonel to punish men on the spot and to inflict summary punishments rather than prefer formal charges that would lead to a general court-martial. Regimental officers could return a deserter to duty without a trial as long as the soldier's pay was docked for the time missed.[18] The number of infractions was so large in both armies that the high commands followed Kautz's suggestion. After Chancellorsville, for instance, the officers of the Twentieth Indiana Infantry received the following circular from army headquarters: "All cases of straggling by enlisted men during the recent movements of this command will be disposed without appeal to a General Court Martial. All property lost will [be] charged to them on the muster rolls opposite their names, and such punishments as can be imposed by other tribunals will be adjudged and carried. It is utterly impossible to try all these cases by a General Court Martial, and the interests of the service require that some prompt punishment should be inflicted."[19]

By 1863, cases involving straggling, desertion, and battlefield conduct were largely tried at the brigade and regimental levels as long as the penalties did not call for execution before a firing squad, excessive hard labor, the suspension of more than one month's pay, or extended incarceration of the accused. If the prisoner's case could not be resolved at the regimental level, the soldier would have to stand before a general court-martial of thirteen officers who represented the various regiments of his brigade. It was not unusual for a court to have fewer than thirteen officers, but regulations stipulated that the court could assemble as long as five members of the court were present. General courts-martial could rule over any violation of the Articles of War, including the Ninety-Ninth Article, which cast a wide net over any soldier whose conduct was prejudicial to good order and military discipline.[20]

Were the scales of justice balanced in brigade and regimental tribunals? It is difficult to say, even with the reams of surviving testimony of Union general courts-martial. Similar legal paperwork is virtually nonexistent from Confederate armies. Plenty of regimental books survive on the Union side, but they only record verdicts, fines, and punishments for a range of infractions, without the accompanying testimony.[21] When the testimony was recorded at the general court-martial level, trial transcripts were not copied verbatim. Even the most carefully transcribed testimony failed to capture the personalities and the politics that infiltrated the proceedings. The judge advocate, the person in charge of the court, often lacked experience in issues of military justice — which was no small matter, given that he was responsible for advising the court about procedures, serving as chief prosecutor, and acting as the prisoner's chief adviser. The obligations were in obvious contradiction, and the accused was almost always at a disadvantage: the judge advocate could not possibly serve all parties with impartiality. Nonetheless, it remained the responsibility of the judge advocate to object to any leading questions that might cause the accused to unintentionally incriminate himself. In court-martial records reviewed for this study, not a single example of a judge advocate objecting to leading questions could be found. In fact, it was unusual for defendants to have any representation at all. It would not be too much to say that the hundreds of thousands of Civil War soldiers who were shuttled through the military justice system did not receive sufficient legal counsel or protection from their accusers.[22]

The court testimony offers invaluable insight into the thinking of a deserter after his arrest, but his words were not entirely his own — they were shaped by the very military system that compelled the testimony to be given.[23] Deserters responded to their interrogators in thousands of different ways, but their answers, though given at a moment in which they were forced to talk in order to avoid conviction, offer glimpses into a soldier's relationships with his comrades, his officers, and even his family. The official transcripts of courts-martial are limited, recording only fragments of testimony that tell more about the maneuverings of a soldier caught in a legal system than his life prior to the act of deserting. State-sanctioned killing sparked open debates in the ranks as well as at home over the use of physical violence against delinquent soldiers. The terror of comrades killing comrades in cold blood had a shattering effect on language, leaving stunned bystanders speechless and rendering them unable to fully describe what they had witnessed. The silences and missing voices point to the underlying challenge of trying to see the world from the perspective of the deserter, who is often heard through the words of his condemners. The four case studies below are deeply contextualized narratives, filled with prosaic details that are essential to uncovering how soldiers sized up their choices in the moment with all of their spontaneity, amid the ambiguity and uncertainty of the turbulent war.

## WILLIAM P. ALLEN
### *Virginia Nonslaveholder*
### Thirteenth Virginia Infantry

On the surface, William Allen's military service record in the Thirteenth Virginia Infantry would suggest that he was a classic Civil War soldier: dutiful to the cause, dependable in the ranks, and stalwart to the very end. After enlisting on April 22, 1862, likely as a conscript, Allen was marked as "absent without leave" in May and June of that year; he missed the Seven Days Campaign, but rejoined his regiment for Second Manassas, Antietam, Fredericksburg, and Chancellorsville. There is reference to him deserting in March 1863 but no details, and he may have deserted again or gone AWOL during the 1863 Pennsylvania Campaign. The records are impossible to reconcile when it comes to his unauthorized leaves, but overall the evidence casts Allen as a typical Virginia soldier who found his way home for short visits but returned apparently without punishment or penalty. The muster rolls list him as present for the months of September and October 1863. The six muster rolls for his company in 1864 are missing. Allen's wartime letters, however, show him in the ranks in April before he took a bullet on May 6, 1864, at the Wilderness. It is likely that he received an extended medical furlough. However, he did not hide out at home during the final months of the war — something that scores of convalescing Confederates did to avoid service. Instead, Allen returned to the army in early 1865, only to be killed at the Battle of Fort Stedman on March 25.[24]

The outline of Allen's military career comes from the muster rolls or Compiled Service Record (CSR), which tell a seemingly straightforward story of duty and devotion. The CSR is the foundational source of a soldier's service in either the Confederate or Union army. Each record contains a paymaster card that covers two months of the war, stating when the individual enlisted and if he was present, sick, detached, absent with or without leave, wounded, killed in action, discharged, or deserted. This notation of status was marked on the last day of the second month. During the preceding sixty days, a soldier could have been absent without leave for any length of time, but his muster card would still list him as present as long as he stood in the ranks on the final day of the second month. The recording method is far from comprehensive, and the CSR, by its very format of registering information, excises crucial context from an enlisted man's wartime experience, including the soldier's own voice. Fortunately, Allen's entire body of correspondence — rather than sporadic and scattered letters — survives, bringing to the surface a world of constant violence, physical coercion, and economic deprivation that encircled Allen and limited his options. This happened with soldiers on both sides, forcing them to act in the moment in ways that seem oddly contradictory and inconsistent with their own political interest. Allen's story, above all else, reveals how *loyalty* is a slippery term that can mean voluntary allegiance, on the one hand, or coerced obedience, on the other. Civil War soldiers moved back and forth between both poles as they responded to events on the ground. Loyalty, in other words, was not a straightforward choice based on a hierarchy of attachments, or prioritized and ordered in ways that led to predictable courses of behavior. Allen, for instance, was a dependable soldier on the battlefield but, in camp, a reluctant Confederate who became more accepting of desertion at the same time that his obligation to stay in the ranks grew stronger out of a desire for survival and to remain close to his brothers in the ranks.

William P. Allen witnessed the meteoric rise of the Army of Northern Virginia, which started with Lee's successful Seven Days Campaign in the summer of 1862 and culminated with the stunning victory at Chancellorsville the following May. These victories, although extraordinarily bloody, galvanized the rank and file around Lee, who enjoyed the unrivaled confidence of his men. For soldiers like Allen, the ascendancy of Lee's army was so violent and costly that faith in future victories did not eclipse the fear of being maimed or killed in one of Lee's bloody offensives. Even when standing on the victorious field at Chancellorsville, Allen felt desolate and empty, gripped by a constant feeling of "dread," as there would be no reprieve from the killing or release from his harrowing memories of the "awful slaughter." The image of his captain's skull, smashed by a grapeshot, his brains splattering all over the ground, could not be repressed, and he knew that such horrors awaited him in the inevitable battles to come.[25]

Back in camp all Allen wanted to do was disappear from the army. His sense of urgency did not arise from a crisis at home, although life on the farm was undoubtedly harder with the absence of Allen and his four brothers. The Union army, however, approached his family farm of some 180 acres, which was nestled in the foothills of the Blue Ridge Mountains less than twenty miles north of Lynchburg. The house was a substantial wooden structure of eight rooms with a separate summer kitchen that fed a family of seven, apparently without the labor of a single slave.[26] William and his four brothers in the Thirteenth Virginia, as well as his brother in the Fifty-Eighth Virginia, benefited from a community network of friends and family who personally shuttled information and goods between the army and home. The flow of goods not only met the immediate needs of the Allen boys in the Thirteenth Virginia, but through 1863 there was enough surplus farm produce for William to become an entrepreneur. He relied on his mother to send apples and whiskey, then sold them to his comrades for a handsome profit. Few households in the South or North were as fortunate as the Allens', given that most soldiers were tethered to their home by fragile communication lines. In Greensboro, Alabama, for instance, G. Ward Hubbs found that while the war "cemented the commitment between hometown and front line," the destruction and dislocation isolated the Alabamians in Lee's army from their loved ones and deprived them of needed resources.[27] The breakdown certainly spurred desertion, a situation that historian Judith Giesberg also found in her study of poor women in the North. They "had few resources at their disposal" at the onset of the war, and enlistments followed by the draft drained soldier wives of basic necessities, making it virtually impossible for them to send extra clothing and food to their husbands in the army.[28] Not everything ran smoothly at the Allens' Amherst County home, and Allen and his brothers grew frustrated when the mail service was irregular or civilians were slow to arrive with needed packages. Yet these disruptions were generally temporary, and they never threatened the customary bonds with neighbors and kin that kept William afloat in the army.

No news from home, no matter how comforting or encouraging, could calm Allen when he thought of having to return to the battlefield. His anxiety reached the point where he considered joining a band of deserters heading for his native Amherst, but "tha is no chance to get to come home at this Time unless a man would run the Blockade and that I do not expect to do if I was to Run the Blockade I Sertanly never would come back here." On nights when there was no full moon, squads of soldiers were sneaking away from camp. "Night before last tha was 6 of the amherst boys left last night," Allen alerted his mother without a hint of alarm or disapproval. "Tha is some ten or fifteen talking of leaving again to night all of the . . . Pinky Davis and his set has gone."[29] The planning and organizing to desert among battle-tested veterans in the wake of a smashing Confederate victory is shocking, especially in a unit known for its reliability in the Army of Northern Virginia. There is no evidence of dissatisfaction with the regiment's officers. One possible clue explaining the unrest comes from Allen's pen: he feared an immediate resumption of the killing, given the rumor that the Yankees had been reinforced by fifty thousand men since Chancellorsville. He could not hide the dread he felt for a future of "so much hard fighting [that it] is enough to dishearten any person on either [side]."[30]

As Allen had predicted, the provost guard apprehended the deserters before they crossed the county line into Amherst. His fugitive comrades returning to camp shackled in irons and surrounded by guards looked no different than captured runaway slaves. In that instant, Allen must have felt some relief that he had stayed put, but the desire to go home was irrepressible. "What would I give if this war was over," he declared, but it was a longing that could get him killed if he acted on it. "It is not worth a man's while to talk of leaving here now," he wrote his sister on June 1, 1863. "Tha would be sinton [sentenced] to [the] penitentiary for five years or to shoot him if he was to leave without good papers." Just hours after finishing this letter to his sister, Allen stood at attention, shoulder to shoulder with his comrades, to witness the execution of an Amherst deserter.

The orchestrated killing did not subdue all of Allen's fellow soldiers. "Tha is some more has ran away from tha regiment," he noted, "and tha will be shot if tha ketch them."[31] Even if a runaway soldier avoided execution, other punishments could serve as a deterrent. Allen discovered this firsthand when the provost guard caught his two brothers and they were subsequently tried and convicted for being absent without leave. "Tom & Henry has bin court martial[ed]," he informed his sister on June 1. "Tha took the pay from them while tha was not here and one more month extra which was 4 months pay taken from them and 9 extra dutys."[32] Although William knew that his brothers were fortunate to escape with their lives, he still condemned the sentence — not just for what it did to his siblings but as evidence of a world that had lost its moral way. "I call this a pore unjust war," he declared in an outburst of indignation. He was disgusted with the heavy-handed policies of military life, and the revulsion he felt for the battlefield fueled his sense of injustice. At no time, however, did it coalesce into a clearly articulated position against the Confederacy. Allen says nothing about secession, slavery, Confederate politics, or a Union army fighting for emancipation. To interpret Allen's silences as an absence of ideology, however, overlooks the political essence of those seven words as a bold renunciation of war as an act of inhumanity. Without question, he harbored radical thoughts against the Confederacy in his private world, but his failure to find clear political alternatives underscores how difficult it was for Civil War soldiers to separate themselves from the dominant culture. Allen's sense of persecution was an admission of helplessness that arose within the everyday struggles of soldiering, where confusion, not clarity, was the "true" state of consciousness of the rank and file.

Although Allen went back and forth about desertion, he never looked at the battlefield as a test of manhood, only as an arena for needless slaughter. On the cusp of the Battle of Gettysburg, he drew no comfort in the public perception of Lee's army as an invincible force, confessing to his sister on June 1 that "it seems like the fighting does no good[.] what would I give if this was over."[33] His wish was partially answered when the Thirteenth Virginia was detached for provost duty in Winchester, Virginia, keeping him away from the killing fields of Gettysburg. Allen was likely with his unit, but a gap in his CSR records raises unanswerable questions. One historian believes that Allen deserted from July through August 1863 and came back under President Davis's proclamation of amnesty. This is possible, but a brief letter from William pins him as in the ranks of the army on August 31. The gaps in the official transcript and the discrepancy with his private letters frustrate any attempt to categorize him conclusively as a deserter.

The roadblock, however, is also an opportunity, because it forces attention away from static categories and toward the more fluid ways that soldiers like Allen processed their world within the conditions they inhabited. In the spring of 1864, when the newspapers preached optimism for the upcoming campaign and officers boasted of their men's determination to keep fighting, Allen broke with the dominant message from the Confederate press and defied the powers that ruled over the Army of Northern Virginia. To those at home he stressed his fear of having to face enemy bullets again, and of all the rumors swirling around the camp, he related the one that offered little hope of final success. "It is Said that they Yankees will have four hundred thousand to attack us," he estimated on April 20, 1864. He did not select stories of men who felt confidence in the future or devotion to the cause. Rather, Allen called attention to the overwhelming size of the Union army and to Confederates who had bolted for home, an act that he refused to condemn. In fact, he was an active partner in their crime. While standing guard along the Rapidan River, Allen defied strict orders to shoot runaways on the spot, refusing to aim his musket against his Amherst comrades who waded across the river and deserted "to the Yankees." "We wase down on picket when they left," Allen informed his sister; "we saw James when he swam the river."[34]

Allen's refusal to shoot deserters along the Rapidan River apparently went unpunished — an understandable act of leniency, given that the Army of Northern Virginia needed every available man for the great battle in the Wilderness. During the second day of fighting, when the Confederate wing collapsed and Lee tried to rally his broken troops, a bullet hit Allen's thigh and sent him sprawling to the ground. Neither bone nor artery was shattered, and he was fortunate to make it off the field, beginning a journey that eventually landed him in the Confederate hospital system, where he spent the next eight months convalescing. Allen could have easily become a "hospital rat," a derisive term given to soldiers who prolonged their medical absence by faking an injury. Allen refused to wait out the war in a hospital ward or at home, and it is very likely that he was unable to secure a medical discharge when he returned to duty in February 1865. Maybe in good conscience he could not leave his brother alone in the regiment. It is impossible to say, as Allen's letters home give no explanation for why he remained in the ranks. He made no mention of fidelity to the cause or of faith in final victory at a time when men of all ranks deserted in droves to a Union army on the verge of cutting off the lifeline of supplies for Lee's army.

Returning to his regiment in early 1865 must have seemed strange to Allen, who entered a landscape gashed by trenches, devoid of trees, and seemingly absent of people. No one dared show his head at the front out of fear of sharpshooting, and behind the lines he found his comrades living some ten or fifteen feet underground in shelters he called "shebangs." "This is one of the most confinding places that I ever I was," he explained, but even with the added protection of logs and earthen trenches, Allen did not feel safe, as he explained in a letter on March 24, 1865. Even in the Petersburg trenches there was nowhere to hide from the Yankee shells that exploded in every direction, killing a few of Allen's comrades who were resting near their quarters. The constant fear and physical hardships wore Allen down, narrowing his thoughts and actions to the bare-bones struggle of survival in the ranks. There was little time or energy to contemplate what a Union victory or Confederate defeat might mean, and the options directly in front of Allen fed his desperation. Running to the enemy or away from his own army could get him killed or seriously wounded. If he defied the odds and found safe haven in a community of deserters, Allen was risking a lifetime of social ostracism from his own community.[35]

In the end, Allen decided that his best chance to live remained inside the army rather than outside it. He came to this momentous decision with the resumption of ritual executions, as the highly choreographed destruction of human life persuaded Allen that he had no choice but to see the war to its unknown end. "Evary man who are caught now and braught back here," Allen bluntly stated to his brother near the end of March, "I would not give two cents for his life."[36] Allen's reading of the situation was accurate and attributable to General Lee's General Orders No. 8, which called for the execution of any man who merely suggested deserting to a comrade. "The evil habit prevails with some in this army of proposing to their comrades in jest to desert and go home," the general wrote. To stop this "evil" practice, Lee warned his men that the "penalty for advising or persuading a soldier to desert is death."[37]

As he had done throughout his Confederate service, Allen kept the pain and misery of his life from causing him to commit a rash act that could get him

William Allen returned to the Army of Northern Virginia just weeks before Lee launched his last offensive against Fort Stedman, which is pictured here. Allen was likely killed on the other side of Stedman's wall when he received a fatal wound. His brother, Tinsley, carried his lifeless body from the field, and when he informed his family of William's death, Tinsley did not turn him into a Confederate martyr. He simply wrote: "All I hope hes better off then he was here." (Library of Congress Prints and Photographs Division, Washington, D.C.)

punished or killed by the army. His strategy, carefully calculated and cautiously executed, kept him alive until a Yankee bullet pierced his chest during an attack against Fort Stedman on March 25. His brother Tinsley was on the field, and he carried William's lifeless body off behind the lines. Once arrangements were made for burial, Tinsley wrote to his sister. He poured out his feelings of sorrow and loss, but he refrained from memorializing his brother as a martyr for the Confederate cause, a fitting decision that certainly would have met with William's approval. Tinsley reminded his family that their brother was leaving this world for heaven, where he would never feel the dread of fighting that came as soon as the morning sun rose above the trenches. "All I hope hes better off then he was here dear," Tinsley wrote with a mixture of relief and sadness. "I tell you thir is no pleasure to be seen here such times as there are now."[38]

*Desertion and Military Justice*

Without question, Allen was a dependable Army of Northern Virginia soldier who never failed his comrades in battle, but his combat record, coming exclusively from his CSR, only tells a partial story. The monthly pay musters appear to be an unimpeachable testament to Allen's firm sense of duty, but this conclusion presupposes that a man's mere presence in the ranks, whether he was Union or Confederate, stands as an unambiguous statement of loyalty. Historians often reinforce the loyalty/disloyalty binary by relying on the CSR's categories of present, absent without leave, or deserted to demonstrate whether or not men did their duty faithfully. These categorizations tend to fix loyalty as a stable quality acted up and expressed as soldiers' independent choice. This approach misses essential context, including the voice of the soldier, whose sense of loyalty was not a single entity, but multifaceted, fluid, and shaped in ways that the soldier himself could not control. In all military theaters, Civil War soldiers discovered how the forces of war reworked the understanding of allegiance on a continuous basis. As historian Edward Ayers brilliantly explains, "Loyalty was often the product of events rather than its cause, emerging after the fact to serve as an explanation for actions that grew from necessity, impulse, or acquiescence. Loyalty often sustained and reconciled decisions already made, often by someone else."[39]

Allen's entire military career illustrates Ayers's important point that loyalty cannot be understood as a simple question of individual consent and choice. Allen's letters, when combined with the CSR, capture the instability of Allen's place in the ranks and make it clear that to characterize him or any other man as having served faithfully is to resort to an empty value judgment that does not account for how he feared the violence his own army could inflict on his body. Allen had seen too many comrades executed, fined, imprisoned, and punished to carry out the logical outcome of his political beliefs and desert for good as he so desperately wanted to do throughout the war. His letters home create the false impression that he suffered from low morale, the hopelessly vague and analytically barren category of description that obscures more than it reveals about soldiers' political action. Allen's letters do more than register a mood; they get beneath a clerk's jottings on each muster card of the CSR to reveal that he had his own conception of honor and his own critique of the war as a violation of humanity. Survival called for pragmatism in thought and action, but it also staved off tough political questions about the possibility of Confederate defeat and the revolutionary consequences of emancipation in the slave society for which he reluctantly gave his life.

## CHARLES WALTER, EMIL LAE, GEORGE KUHNE, JOHN FOLANEY, AND JOHN RAINESE
### *Bounty Men*
### 118th Pennsylvania

The 105 conscripts and substitutes who joined the 118th Pennsylvania were not welcomed as the saviors of an army desperate for manpower. They had entered service under the threat of conscription, conveyed by the Enrollment Act of 1863, a measure that passed on March 3 and was wildly unpopular in the North. Cries of injustice reverberated between the home front and the armies, but in reality the draft was really not a draft after all. Every community wanted to fill its quota with volunteers without having to resort to forced enrollment. States, towns, and the national government devised a range of cash inducements known as bounties to induce volunteerism without having to actually conscript men to satisfy the Federal demand for 1 million bodies.[40] Though it was intended to make the draft more palatable, this system ended up feeding the corrupt and greedy. A total investment of some $7 million — dispensed at the local, state, and national levels — was largely squandered on marginally competent Union soldiers during the final two years of the war. Some of the men carried out their duties conscientiously, but significant numbers were poor and more preoccupied with survival, even if that meant using the uniform for profit. Too much emphasis has been focused on the criminality of the bounty jumper, as historian Brian Luskey has argued, obscuring how the economic crisis of the war years transformed labor relations: coercion supplanted consent, and the citizen-soldier became a wage slave sold on the cheap.[41]

To be fair, plenty of so-called bounty men entered the army leaving a wife and young children at home. Poverty, not enrichment, pressed them into service. Others fell victim to the fraudulent methods of bounty brokers, who had a nose for people in desperation. The brokers' recruiting practices were generally ruthless, preying on the ignorant and poor, especially non-English-speaking immigrants and African Americans. Brokers, who were almost always white, would threaten to arrest African Americans for some fabricated crime if they did not enlist in the army. Rather than risk time behind bars, black men usually followed them to the recruiting station.[42] Drugs, drink, and force were also wielded against unsuspecting men, whose last memory was entering a saloon before they awakened confused, dazed, and penniless, wondering how they ended up in the Union army. Scores of Irish immigrants came to this country under the false pretense that they would work as laborers, whereas they actually had been recruited to serve as substitutes and the agent had pocketed their bounty. Joining the army was not a clear matter of individual choice.[43]

Bounties and substitution soared in cost and in numbers during the last year and a half of the war. Despite horrible corruption and breathtaking inefficiency, the Enrollment Act served its purpose in reinforcing Union armies for the final push against the Confederacy. However, the surge in enlistments came at a steep price for the Union veterans already in the field, who understandably felt betrayed by a government that doubtless took for granted their selflessness and suffering for the cause. While the veteran faced a dangerous enemy at the front without regular pay or rations, his property back home was likely being taxed by his state and local government to pay for the "hired" volunteer, who was viewed with circumspection. Bounty men and substitutes were seen as foreign mercenaries who would likely disappear at the first volley, but before the levy of substitutes and bounty men even reached their assigned regiments, they began deserting in droves. By late summer 1863, army officials knew that leniency would promote a general disregard for military discipline. Examples would have to be made if this evil was to be eradicated.[44]

In August 1863, the veterans of the 118th Pennsylvania found themselves in a miserable camp along the lowlands of the Rappahannock River, not far from Beverly's Ford, where the sweltering heat and swarming mosquitos slowly sucked the vitality out of the regiment. One officer found a graceful way of writing about the degrading filth and misery of their wretched situation: "I and all my comrades fairly stink, so foul are we all." The arrival of a whiskey ration on July 31 showed that the officers did not share well. At dress parade, a number of captains and lieutenants were staggering drunk, tottering about as "unsteady as sailors," slurring their words, forgetting commands, and generally setting the worst possible example for the men.[45] The Pennsylvanians, despite their admirable combat records, were a troubled command, prone to bicker and politic among themselves. Substitutes of mostly German and Irish extraction and 120 conscripts landed within this fractious command on August 6.

The veterans saw their new comrades as nothing more than foreign mercenaries masquerading as Union soldiers who would run off with their bounty money at the first chance. One soldier in the 118th Pennsylvania, falling back on the common Victorian assumption that a man's moral nature was in his look, damned the recruits as soon as he saw them because of their "sinister physical appearance."[46] Captain Francis Donaldson was not as harsh as the others; he only considered the recruits a curious lot, given that they all insisted that they were officers and "styled each other as Col., Capt. and Lt." Before going to bed,

Donaldson informed them, "that there was but one Captain in the Co., and that—myself." He concluded in his diary, "They are a pretty stout lot of fellows, and appear to make light of their surroundings and act very impudently. I'll take that mob [out] of them before 48 hours pass."[47]

Despite the precautions of extra sentinels around camp and a mandatory escort to the sinks, not all of the recruits were so easily subdued during those next forty-eight hours. Privates John Folaney (also known as Faline or Geacinto Lerchize), a twenty-four-year-old Italian, and John Rainese (also known as Gion or George Rionese), a twenty-three-year-old Italian, managed to get by the guards at the Rappahannock River's Beverly Ford on August 8. Five days later, the provost arrested both men near Bristoe Station without any authorized passes or paperwork. Very little is known about their backgrounds or the circumstances under which they enlisted. The men were carrying a package containing $220, an unusually large sum of money for an enlisted man. The most damning evidence against them was Rainese's written plan (translated from the original Italian for Rainese's subsequent court-martial) asking for assistance to escape and revealing his intention to alter his physical appearance. In his concluding statement at his trial, Rainese offered the implausible story that he got lost while looking for water even though a river nearly encircled the regimental camp. The court was not persuaded; they convicted him of desertion and sentenced him "to be shot to death by musketry in presence of the Division."[48] Rainese's partner in crime, John Folaney, told a similar story of getting lost while searching for water. He grew hungry and tired and decided to sleep in the woods, but the next day, while he was searching for his regiment, the provost guard arrested him. Folaney protested in a written appeal before the court, "If I had wanted to desert I had plenty of chances in Philadelphia. I did not want to desert." The members of the court were not swayed. Folaney too would be executed by a firing squad.[49]

Charles Walter, Emil Lae, and George Kuhne—the three other men who would be executed next to Folaney and Rainese—never even made it to the camp of the 118th Pennsylvania. They slipped away from the troop escort on August 6, and six days later they were captured near Bristoe Station. Little is known about their background or the circumstances of their enlistments. They all gave false names to the provost officer; they all had discarded their military uniforms for civilian clothing; and they all represented themselves as peddlers. Kuhne and Lae claimed to be heading to Alexandria to procure a sutler wagon, and Walter explained that he was on his way to obtain salt for local civilians. None of the men carried passes or papers granting them permission to operate as sutlers within the lines of the Army of the Potomac.[50]

The three men were tried separately on August 21. They stood before the court with an interpreter at their side who translated their wish to waive their right to a defense lawyer. This was neither an unusual move nor a sound one in Civil War military courts, but the judge advocate appears to have done nothing to assist the defendants. They failed to call any witnesses on their behalf, possibly because there were none. They were strangers in the 118th Pennsylvania, alone and isolated, without a friend in the ranks or an ally in the officer corps who might defend their character. The prosecution effectively established that the men deserted the troop conveyance, discarded their uniforms for civilian clothing, and used aliases when captured by the provost guard. As with Folaney and Rainese, the prosecution did not call attention to their status as substitutes or play on the stereotypes of foreign soldiers as inherently cowardly and untrustworthy. The testimony made no mention of bounty jumping, and none of the prosecution's witnesses suggested that these men intended to re-enlist and collect another enlistment bonus. There was not a single question about the circumstances surrounding their enlistments. The court kept the focus on the issue of unauthorized absence, leading to convictions for Walter, Kuhne, and Lae and a sentence to be shot to death by musketry for the act of desertion.[51]

With General George Gordon Meade at the helm of the Army of the Potomac, overturning the verdicts of the five men in the 118th Pennsylvania was out of the question. His command was suddenly awash with substitutes who were widely seen — fairly or not — as a grave menace to military order. Just two days after the trial of Walter, Kuhne, and Lae, Meade issued General Orders No. 84, in which he referred to the five deserters in the 118th Pennsylvania as "that class who are trading upon the necessities of the country and have embraced enlistment with a view to desertion for the purpose of gain." "It is hoped," he added, that "the prompt punishment awarded to their crimes will have the effect to deter others from attempting a like criminal and dishonorable course of conduct." To ensure that every man knew Meade would "unhesitatingly punish such cases with the severest penalties of the law," he instructed that General Orders No. 84 "be published to every company in this army at the first retreat parade after its receipt."[52] Meade received a petition that asked the general to have "mercy in behalf of our wives and children, and we also desire you to change our sentence to hard labor instead of death, as we think we have been wrongfully sentenced; as we, being foreigners, were led astray by other soldiers, who promised us there would be no harm done." Meade was not moved, nor did he budge when Lincoln telegraphed him on August 27 to inform him that the deserters from the 118th had asked the White House to intervene and grant clemency; instead, believing that examples needed to be made, the president supported Meade's decision to carry out the execution.[53]

The days leading up to the execution were extremely tense in the regiment. Extra guards encircled the camp, no one was allowed to leave, and no visitors were permitted to enter. The prisoners were essentially under suicide watch, their possessions searched and potentially dangerous objects removed. A lancet was found in Lae's Hebrew prayer book, which everyone surmised he would have used on himself. August 29, the appointed day of the execution, began early for the 118th Pennsylvania. Men were detailed to carry the coffins, to serve as guards, and to fill the graves. By late afternoon, the three divisions of the Fifth Corps were moving into position across an extensive plain, where they formed three sides of a hollow square. From the open front to the rear, the ground gradually rose, forming a natural amphitheater and enabling the soldiers to look down on the execution site as if it were a stage. At least fifteen thousand men waited in silence as the five condemned soldiers marched onto the field wearing white wool shirts, blue trousers, and manacles, proceeding slowly to the somber sounds of the death march. They stopped at their freshly dug graves and were forced to sit on the edges of their coffins. In what might have been the first interfaith gathering in the Americas, a priest, a rabbi, and two Protestant clergymen approached the condemned. The mixing of prayers of different faiths struck many of the spectators as a religious ritual not of this world. Captain Donaldson, who had little compassion for deserters, could barely contain his sorrow for the condemned during their final moments. "My God!" he wrote: "Think of the terrible thought of these helpless men as they marched to their graves, think of their awful condition as seated on their coffins they gazed at the twelve men standing before them sternly waiting [the] order to take their lives. Oh it was a dreadful sight to see them there, swaying backward and forwards so utterly helpless and forlorn."[54]

Orders from headquarters specified that the execution had to take place between 12 P.M. and 4 P.M. At 3:45 P.M. General Charles Griffin broke the silence, yelling in his "shrill and penetrating voice": "Shoot these men, or after 10 minutes it will be murder, shoot them at once." The sergeant of the guard quickly bandaged the men's eyes with white cloth, while the fifty men in the firing squad hurried to within six paces of the condemned, where they were ordered to halt. Then the long-awaited order came from the captain's mouth: "'Ready,' 'Aim,' and 'Fire.'" Four of the men fell back heavily, "their heads striking the coffin lid making a dull sounding thud while the bullets passing through the bodies, were seen skipping and bounding over the open fields." One of the lifeless men remained in an "upright position." The band then struck up the song "The Girl I Left Behind" as the men of the Fifth Corps marched off with the brutal image of a mass killing seared into their memory through a deeply melancholy and sentimental song.[55]

Just as General Meade had hoped, the execution of August 29 garnered immediate attention from newspapers across the North. In front-page stories that ran the next day, the *New York Times*, the *Chicago Tribune*, and the *New York Herald* endorsed Meade's use of the death penalty without sensationalizing the event. The spectacle of twenty thousand soldiers witnessing the killing of five condemned deserters was a story packed with drama. There was, to be sure, an inevitable degree of voyeurism to the journalistic accounts, but the stories were not for the reading public's pleasure or perverse gratification. The articles offered similar political and practical lessons: the nation possessed the power to kill citizens who were deemed disloyal, and the recent scene should be re-enacted in order to defeat the menace of the professional deserters. In a typical pronouncement, a *New York Times* correspondent wrote from Beverly Ford: "This is almost the first execution of the kind in this army, and its effect upon the thousands present was plainly visible and will undoubtedly produce good results. The eyes of all the conscripts in the corps were upon these unfortunates." A similar argument was put forth by a contributor to the *Albany (N.Y.) Evening Journal*, who had long believed that the death penalty was "a relic of barbarous time, but [that] the exigencies of the times," when the very discipline of the army was at stake, warranted such extreme violence. "I witnessed the fearful scene without feeling much sorrow for the unfortunate victims." He wrote on August 30, "They were not soldiers. They were worse than the armed traitors whom we meet in battle, and their doom was a stern vindication of military justice."[56]

The power of the press's message resided in the detailed descriptions of the last hours of the condemned. A sample of thirteen articles from twelve different newspapers stressed the orderliness and efficiency of the event in fairly detached accounts of emotionless reporting.[57] Although the writers showed little sympathy for the deserters, they did not turn them into moral monsters. Not a single narrative seized on the ethnicity or the physical appearance of the convicted. No one theorized that their desertion stemmed from a lack of character in the immigrant makeup. Except for Philadelphia's *Illustrated New Age*, Northern newspapermen did not try to imagine the tormented state of mind of the condemned, nor did they dwell on the terror of those final moments. The largely uninformed narratives depicted August 29 as a solemn affair, carried out with great reverence and performed with exceptional professionalism. Even when the army killed its own, Northern journalists pointed out, military men were not without compassion. The respect shown for the different faiths of the deserters, particularly Meade's decision to postpone the execution so that a priest and a rabbi could be in attendance, helped assuage any fears that the army had descended into a state of savagery.

By the first week of September more personal details emerged in the press about Charles Walter, Emil Lae, George Kuhne, John Folaney, and John Rainese. Nothing could remove the stain of being a deserter, but the reporters also humanized the men by reminding the public that the five men were sons, husbands, and fathers whose grieving families would have to live with their dishonorable legacies. Their humanity was on display during their final moments of life, as the newspapers described the men as calm, resigned, and seemingly at peace with an army that was about to kill them — the same manly traits that they supposedly lacked when they came into the army with their "villainous" looks. While the deserters were distraught over an act that they considered unjust, no one recorded any final pleas of innocence or any gestures of defiance. One newspaperman described an affectionate farewell between Folaney and Rainese, who were apparently childhood friends in Italy, and there was a tender embrace between the Rabbi Szold and Lae before the latter sat down on the edge of his own casket.[58] The newspapers also scrutinized the moment when the firing squad unleashed a pointblank volley into the chests of the convicted. Readers were assured that the men died instantly as they fell back into their caskets, except for one who remained slumped over as if he were still clinging to life. Anyone seeking titillation in reading about dying men in agony and screaming in pain while blood gushed from their bodies would not find it in the Northern newspapers.

Civil War executions invariably left even the toughest veteran feeling deeply conflicted over the killing, but sympathy for the condemned had its limit. Most veterans believed that justice was done on August 29, given that bounty jumpers were criminals disguised as soldiers. Historian Steven J. Ramold, in his sweeping and important study on discipline in the Union army, sums up the attitude of veteran soldiers toward deserting bounty men. "A soldier who deserted after a period in the army at least sacrificed something, be it time or blood, before they decided to leave, but bounty-jumpers had no intention of serving any time at all. Consequently, soldiers despised the bounty jumper as someone who diminished the role of a soldier, mocked its value, and was therefore not worthy of mercy or consideration."[59] Henry Kline, a Pennsylvania soldier writing just five hundred yards from the execution site, expressed a popular view among the witnesses: "For my part I do not want to see many more such sights, but I think they deserved what they got any one that sells himself for money and then deserts should suffer the penalty of the crime for he knows what the penalty is before he does it. I hear that there are some more to be shot in the 3rd corps this week, and I say shoot every one of them."[60] Another soldier considered the penalty just, but he hoped to be spared any more such awful sights. "We had hoped after witnessing the execution of the five deserters near Beverly Ford that it would never be necessary to witness another. It is a sight that no one need be desirous of seeing."[61] This was a common response of men who had watched comrades face a firing squad. After the war, the survivors of the 118th Pennsylvania put together a regimental history, and one of the unnamed contributors explained why the battlefield was easier to endure than the horror of witnessing a military execution:

> It may seem strange to some that men who could shoot at others in
> battle without compunction should feel so serious about the fate of
> five deserters. It is one thing when soldiers with heated blood and
> inflamed passions, face-to-face and hand to hand in fierce conflict,
> inflict horrid wounds or death upon others. It is a very different thing
> to look forward to a scene in which men are to be done quietly to death
> without any of the circumstances, which rob war of half its terrors and
> hide its real character.[62]

There was no place in Northern print culture for soldier ambivalence about the execution of deserters, even bounty jumpers. The public would see an orderly rank and file, not built on force but forged through consensus. In late September, Alfred Waud and Edwin Forbes published two very similar engravings of the execution in *Harper's Weekly* and *Frank Leslie's Illustrated*, respectively. Their illustrations reinforced the public's perception of the August 29 execution as a scene of order and justice. Although Waud and Forbes stood within a few yards of the firing squad and their human targets, their sketches have an air of detachment. They do not elicit feelings of pity or terror, largely because the execution squad is made up of anonymous men, their faces and gun barrels covered by a mighty blast of smoke. The viewer is kept at a safe distance from the violence of the scene because only the backs and sides of the condemned are in sight. Waud's drawing is more effective, offering a ground-level view of the shooting, positioning the reader just to the side of the open graves and not far from the dead men, who are splayed across their caskets without a drop of blood on their bright white shirts, which would seem better suited for a baptism than an execution. The reader's attention cannot remain fixed on the

On September 26, 1863, *Harper's Weekly* ran Alfred Waud's "Execution at Beverly Ford." This drawing, like his other depictions, captured the precise and dramatic moment when the firing squads unleashed the volley of death. In Waud's sketch, the killing must compete for the viewer's eye: though it occupies the foreground, the thousands of Union soldiers arrayed on the hillside fill out much of the engraving. Their perfect formations and orderly presence assured audiences that justice had been served through a display of disciplined power.

dead men for long, as they are nearly displaced by the hills in the background, where the Fifth Corps is arrayed. Thousands of Union soldiers stand at attention, towering over the grisly killing.

Both Waud and Forbes's engravings are similar in this regard; they successfully convey the visual power of a *disciplined* rank and file through perfectly dressed formations. There is no unbridled rage, no sign of restlessness, only a controlled violence that Waud and Forbes brilliantly convey in the most static element of their work. Neither artist wanted his readers to think that the Army of the Potomac was veering toward mass executions reminiscent of the French Revolution, nor were any questions raised about the economic chaos behind such corrupt recruiting practices in the North. Waud left nothing to chance with his readers. He added a brief commentary to complement his careful artistry: "It may be therefore fairly asserted that desertion is the greatest crime of the soldier, and no punishment too severe for the offense. But the dislike to

*Desertion and Military Justice*

kill in cold blood—a Northern characteristic—the undue exercise of executive clemency, and in fact the very magnitude and vast spread of the offense, has prevented the proper punishment being applied That is past; now the very necessity of saving life will cause the severest penalties to be rigorously exacted."[63]

| John A. H. Foster | | John Starbird |
| :---: | :---: | :---: |
| *Lawyer* | *and* | *Clerk* |
| 155th Pennsylvania | | Nineteenth Massachusetts |

The nooses were tightened, their eyes were bandaged, and their feet were bound together; with a tap of a drum, the trap door opened and Ransom Gordon and Daniel Geary of the Seventy-Second New York Infantry fell to their deaths, their necks snapping instantly "without barely a convulsion." For five full minutes, the bodies hung untouched in silence, hardly swaying, until the provost general of the Army of the Potomac, Marsena Patrick, finally climbed the gallows. He looked into the mass of soldiers standing before him and proclaimed that Gordon and Geary deserved to die for raping Mary Stiles on June 18, 1864. Stiles had cooperated with officials and took the stand at the court-martial of Gordon and Geary, where she had offered unsparing details of the violent attack. Gordon and Geary raised no objections to her powerful and damning testimony. They confessed their guilt just moments before they were launched into eternity. "In the presence of such a Mass of life as stood before & around me, with the dead hanging beneath my feet," Patrick recorded in his diary on July 15, "my words will not soon be forgotten by those who stood before me."[64]

Unfortunately, Patrick did not record the words or phrasing in his journal, though his entries leading up to the execution of Gordon and Geary do give us some clues as to what was on his mind. From the beginning of the Overland Campaign on May 5, 1864, Patrick was aghast at the epidemic of straggling that had swept through Meade's command, creating an atmosphere that emboldened the Army of the Potomac's basest characters to terrorize civilians and, in the rarest of instances, even violate the sanctity of womanhood. The disintegration of discipline had concerned many of Patrick's fellow officers, who lobbied at headquarters for a sweeping use of violence against deserters, battlefield shirkers, cowards, and stragglers. A few officers even advocated for drumhead courts-martial in the midst of active operations.

At the Battle of the Wilderness, John Foster of the 155th Pennsylvania turned his back on his comrades and disappeared into a throng of stragglers. Without notice he reappeared in camp nearly three weeks later. How Foster managed to run away without getting arrested by the provost guard opens his narrative. The privilege of rank and being a combat veteran made all the difference for Foster, who eluded the provost guard and avoided a court-martial without any formal inquisition. How Foster reconciled himself to his act of desertion, when he had built an outstanding combat record and considered himself a dutiful soldier, is inseparable from his pragmatic outlook. Foster was not suffering a crisis of will when the fighting opened, and he still believed in the political cause for which he was risking his life. His concept of duty became malleable under battlefield conditions in which Foster decided that he had the prerogative to judge how he should carry out his duties as a man who was battle-tested. The fierce fighting at the Wilderness undoubtedly spurred his revision in values, but in giving himself to the cause of self-preservation, Foster did not believe he was acting in bad faith toward his nation or comrades. His past physical suffering justified his need to adapt on the fly; without it he feared that his body and mind would collapse from the wear and tear of war.

Foster looked to the spring campaign with trepidation. His physical health remained shaky, but his captain showed little empathy, insisting that Foster carry a musket and forty rounds as if he were still a private. "All agree that it is a positive shame in giving me a gun to carry," an indignant Foster wrote on April 27, 1864, "but if we go on a hard march and I cannot carry it and keep up I will throw it away. It won't cost me over twenty dollars, and I will not be troubled with one for that amount." His surly mood led to a defiant prediction to his wife: "I will not go into an engagement if I can possibly avoid it."[65] Just one day before the fighting erupted in the Wilderness, Foster reaffirmed his promise that he would vanish once the fighting erupted. "In all probability [there will] be a battle here or near here some of these days, but I am going to try and keep out of it, if there is any possible chance."[66] The next day Foster found himself along the picket line, advancing toward an entrenched enemy stretched along a wooded ridgeline. Whether Foster continued with the 155th Pennsylvania and took part in the actual assault is difficult to say. Before the Wilderness became a protected national park, a relic hunter discovered Foster's silver identification badge at the staging area for the Union attack. Foster's letters, however, fail to shed much light on his movements. He mentioned the advance of the skirmish line, but his letters do not provide the details that one would expect from a participant in the fighting. Whether he came under fire or not, it is clear that the marching had aggravated Foster's bad leg. He left his command without an authorized pass and slipped by the provost guards, which was no easy feat: they had orders to shoot any man who could not show evidence of a wound when trying to pass to the rear.[67]

It is impossible to know how Foster managed to extricate himself from the front. He was able to secure passage on a wagon, but the journey behind the lines was far from secure. Confederate cavalry often appeared out of nowhere, capturing the "walking wounded" and in some cases executing black soldiers and then hanging their bodies along the roadside as trophies of war.[68] Foster made no mention of Confederate atrocities, but he knew that some two hundred Union soldiers had fallen into enemy hands. With all the risks, staying in the column remained Foster's best option for exiting the battlefield. The wagon train, though a defenseless target for enemy cavalry, offered Union stragglers and deserters the best protection from their own provost guard. A Union staff officer referred to this group of deserters and stragglers as "train rabble."[69]

After reporting to the Fifth Corps hospital in Fredericksburg, Foster boarded a train for Washington, D.C., with another captain from his regiment. They entered the city on May 12, while the enemy shot down the comrades they had left behind in the trenches and woods surrounding Spotsylvania Court House. By any definition, Foster had deserted his command by "disguising" himself in the train rabble, and in Fredericksburg he was briefly put under arrest — probably because he lacked the necessary pass. The specifications of the charges are not known, and two days later he was allowed to go to Washington, D.C., with a fellow officer. For all intents and purposes, Foster should have been arrested as a deserter or sent back to his command.

On arriving in Washington, D.C., Foster rented a room in a boardinghouse with two other officers who had also left the fighting at the Wilderness (likely without authorization). He and his comrades stayed clear of the hospital for fear of coming under arrest. For some reason, the provost marshal would not accept their passes and thwarted their plans to continue heading north toward home. Only their status as officers kept them out of the guardhouse. For the foreseeable future, Foster could draw from a cash reserve — the thirty dollars in his pocket. Most deserters were poor and lacked the disposable income to survive on the run, but Foster had enough money to pay for his room and board without having to steal or return to the military. If the provost marshal raided the boardinghouse, he could continue to pretend to be an officer, which he did not see as much of a stretch, since his lieutenant's commission was stuck in bureaucratic channels. From Washington, Foster wrote his wife, "I reported myself as Lieu't and am treated as such," admitting to her with shocking frankness that he was going to use his fake rank to come home for good.[70] "I am going to play Lieu't for awhile in fact as long as I can," he wrote on May 13. "I don't care what the consequences are, they can't more than shoot me, they can't call me a skedaddler." "I do not know what I will do yet, or rather what I will be made [to] do," a frustrated Foster wrote, "for a person here has to do just as they are let, one dare scarcely go out of the hotel without a pass, that the Provost Mar-shall does not pick them up, so I am very careful not to let them see me when I am out."[71]

Foster encapsulates the difficulties encountered by both Northern and Southern provost marshals when trying to determine whether a man was a battlefield shirker, coward, or deserter. A Union officer in St. Louis could not keep track of the various classes of wayward soldiers. He lumped deserters, ma-lingers, and men on "French furlough" together, complaining to a superior that the city swarmed with "thousands of stragglers (and) semi-deserters." It is im-possible to say what he meant by *semi-deserters*, but his murky language re-veals how quickly the military definitions of *deserter* and *straggler* broke down in real-life situations, and why it was such a challenge to prosecute thousands of soldiers, especially commissioned officers, for anything but absence without permission.[72]

Confined to his room and scouring the newspapers, Foster searched for information about his regiment to see if his closest comrades had survived. By knitting together various reports, he calculated that 125 men had been either killed or wounded — or that nearly one-fifth of the unit's strength had been lost between May 5 and May 12. The staggering losses seemed to ease Foster's mind, since he knew that his act of desertion had likely preserved his life. If critics at home tried to malign his reputation by calling him a coward, Foster could point to his name on the army's honor roll for distinguished service. In fact, he planned to send the documentation to his wife to counter any unfair charges. Such accolades of past heroics, however, meant little to the provost guard, who would sweep him off the street to a jail cell in an instant. Somehow Foster had to escape; his nerves were fraying, and he knew that another day in the ranks would surely break him. He was sending his sword back to his wife, hoping that a transfer to the Invalid Corps would extricate him from the provost marshal while keeping him away from the front. "I am going to get out of the service if possible," he wrote on May 13, 1864. "I cannot stand it out in the front any longer." The next day, with the prodding of the provost marshal, Foster did an about-face and began the journey back to the regiment. Fear of punishment, not honor or patriotism, had forced a reevaluation. "If I am found out," he ex-plained to his wife, "[I will] get myself into some trouble, so I will go back and get myself started right."[73]

On May 20, Foster arrived at a "Camp Distribution" and made his case for a discharge, but he later complained to his wife that his pleas felt pointless, since he did not know a single officer in his new quarters. He was sent back to his regi-ment three days later. His captain turned the other way, barely looking at him

*Desertion and Military Justice*

when he walked into camp. "I never saw him look so mad," Foster wrote to his wife, claiming that he could not imagine why his superior gave him the silent treatment. Foster was deceiving himself. He knew that deserting his comrades in the midst of a campaign constituted an unforgivable act among veterans, especially men who had just passed through one of the most harrowing experiences of the regiment's entire existence.

Both armies were accustomed to fighting for two or three days and then separating for a few months before resuming active operations. The fighting in the Wilderness had unleashed a different kind of warfare in which Union and Confederate forces were almost always in constant contact, seemingly trapped in a perpetual collision of violence that cost Lee and Grant some eighty-six thousand combined casualties. Historian Carol Reardon, in comparing the May operations to previous campaigns, concludes, "The cumulative physical demands of the Overland Campaign far outran anything Northern soldiers had experienced before."[74] For the survivors, there was rarely a moment to rest the body or the mind. When the men were not slogging through muddy roads or digging trenches, they were subjected to an incessant picket fire that randomly picked off soldiers. Even nighttime offered no security, as New Yorker Charles Bowen discovered during the midnight darkness of May 10, when his comrades — after having endured a day of murderous attacks at Spotsylvania — hunkered down on the ground while Confederate bullets whizzed overhead, slamming into trees and cutting through branches that fell to the ground. Occasionally one would find its target in a sleeping man. "Every hour or two some fellow would get hit & cry out," Bowen scribbled in his diary, "but the remainder would merely look up to see who it was & say poor fellow or something like it & then go to sleep again."[75] The inescapable danger and the ceaseless laboring in the field caused men to collapse from sheer exhaustion. It is no wonder that Foster — after coming off an unauthorized leave — was so gruffly received by his thoroughly fatigued and demoralized comrades.

If Foster had any thoughts about leaving the ranks of the Army of the Potomac again, he kept them to himself and said nothing to his wife. Maybe the Army of the Potomac's use of ritual executions neutralized his drive to desert. Senior officers were growing weary of the lenient policy toward stragglers, who were morphing into deserters that moved along the fringes of the army, where they stole and plundered from civilians whether or not they were loyal to the Union. In the opinion of Meade and many of his subordinates, the situation was turning into a serious crisis of discipline. While meeting at Meade's headquarters on May 17, two Second Corps officers sought approval to shoot pillagers on the spot. If this form of rough justice was not a deterrent, then it was suggested that the army should "hang the perpetrators by the road where the troops pass, and to put a placard on their breasts." Meade's staff officer, Theodore Lyman, left the meeting frustrated, knowing that his fellow officers were handcuffed by Lincoln's "merciful policy" of pardoning deserters. Forbearance promoted a general disregard for military law among the vast majority of men, as Lyman believed that "no one could be executed but poor friendless wretches, who had none to intercede for them."[76]

The next day, May 18, Private John Starbird—a man without friends in high places—discovered the hard truth of Lyman's assessment. Of all the deserters and skulkers tried and convicted by a field court-martial convened in General Francis Barlow's division on May 19, Starbird was the only man who faced a firing squad. John Starbird came before the court with a checkered record of defying military authority. After volunteering in early June 1861 and completing his three-month term, the nineteen-year-old former clerk returned to his mother's home in Boston. She was poor, a widow, and had three children to support. All of the kids were younger than John, who was responsible for supporting the family: John's eldest brother had seemingly disappeared after enlisting in an Iowa regiment. To make matters worse, Massachusetts refused public assistance to Mrs. Starbird, since her oldest son was serving in an Iowa outfit. This promise of state aid to soldiers' wives must have pulled John back into the ranks, and on September 3, 1861, he joined the Nineteenth Massachusetts against his mother's wishes. Starbird accompanied his regiment to Yorktown, Virginia, only to desert under very confusing circumstances seven months later in April 1862. He somehow managed to get back to Boston, and it appears that he was able to avoid military authorities for a time by bribing a Boston police officer. In November Starbird decided that he could no longer avoid arrest at home, so he headed to Providence, Rhode Island, and pocketed a two-hundred-dollar bounty for enlisting in the Second Rhode Island Cavalry under the alias John D. Sanborn. He remained in the unit for nearly ten months before deserting in August 1863. One month later, Starbird enlisted in the Thirty-Fifth New York Infantry under a new alias, John D. Ford. Only three days passed this time before he skipped camp with a bounty of two hundred dollars. The following November, Starbird was apprehended by Provost Marshall L. H. Adams and deposited at Boston's Fort Warren, where he was tried and convicted of desertion. A petition on Starbird's behalf to Secretary of War Edwin Stanton tells a hardship story that likely had little effect on that rigid cabinet member. It took the exertions of Massachusetts Senator Henry Wilson to persuade Stanton to free "the deserter" on the condition that he return to the Nineteenth Massachusetts.[77]

As a convicted bounty jumper and deserter, Starbird was hardly in an enviable position among veterans who knew only of his extended absence and criminal record.[78] There were the inevitable sneers and ugly predictions that Starbird would flee as soon as the first shots were heard. Starbird did not disappoint the cynics. At the Wilderness, the Bostonian disappeared just as the fighting opened; he was captured and returned to his unit. Three days later, when his regiment launched a charge against the Confederate position at Spotsylvania, Starbird ran in the opposite direction. Again, he did not get by the provost guard. When a general court-martial was convened on May 18, its members must have known about Starbird's past indiscretions. Few veterans would have even raised an eyebrow over killing a man who was unknown in his own regiment, a bounty jumper, a deserter, a convicted coward, and now had two additional charges of "cowardice before the enemy" against him.[79] A number of other prisoners were also tried over that three-day period for straggling and desertion. Nothing is known about their cases, except that Private Albert Bohler of the Thirty-Ninth New York received a death sentence that the army inexplicably never carried out.[80]

Starbird's trial proceedings moved swiftly, even though he pleaded not guilty. From the transcript of the trial it is clear that Starbird did not have counsel, nor is there any record of the prisoner offering a final plea of innocence. No witnesses were called, either for the defense or the prosecution, since such formalities were unnecessary when the defendant was clearly presumed guilty. News of Starbird's execution and the questionable legality of the proceedings eventually reached the Washington desk of Judge Advocate General Joseph Holt, whose subsequent questioning of Meade elicited a firm response from the general on July 5, 1864. "The trial of this case occurred when we were in the immediate presence of the enemy and in active [operations] and constant engagement with him. So my [judgment of] an immediate example was necessary," Meade concluded, "to check a growing disposition to desertion. I consider I would have been perfectly justified to order the instant execution of the prisoner without trial but it was thought better to conform to the ordinary modes of proceeding so far as circumstances would permit."[81]

Meade's sense of urgency to prosecute and kill stragglers and deserters in May 1864 — still palpable in his July letter to Holt — gave his subordinates the necessary latitude to convict and punish men suspected of being deserters without regard to legal niceties. In fact, the Starbird court-martial was not required to record any of the testimony. Evidence apparently did not matter in the rush to judgment. The sense of expediency hanging over the court on May 18 was heightened by the periodic explosions of Confederate shells. The judge advocate admitted that the court was held too close to the enemy's lines, scribbling in his diary that night. "We commenced the trial of prisoners amidst exploding shells and the roar of artillery. It was a strange thing," he added, "[to see] a Court trying men for their lives, while even the lives of the members of the Court were not worth a moment's purchase."[82]

On May 19, with the ominous rumbling of artillery in the background, Judge Advocate Robert Robertson read the guilty verdict and sentence to Starbird. It was short and direct: "To be shot to death with musketry . . . in presence of as much of the division to which the prisoner belongs."[83] A courier immediately rushed the paperwork to Meade, whose prompt and unequivocal approval ensured that there would be no reprieve or delay. At the crack of dawn on May 20, weary soldiers of the Second Corps slopped across a muddy field and formed a hollow square to receive Starbird, who walked to his grave without any of the usual ritualistic trappings. There was no band playing the death march, no ministers to provide spiritual comfort, and no guard to escort Starbird to his open grave. He walked on his own and sat on his coffin, fixing his gray eyes on his executioners. Eight gun barrels from the Nineteenth Massachusetts were aimed at his chest. Just before the command to fire was given, Starbird yelled out, "'Oh, my poor mother.'" The rifles cracked a volley. Seven bullets struck Starbird's heart and one ball entered his leg. He died instantly.[84]

Only a few eyewitness accounts of the event survive, and the reactions they recount were neither sympathetic nor callous. The men appear to have been numb to their surroundings, as they were virtually sleepwalking to the execution, having had little rest during nearly two weeks of remorseless fighting. "Since writing we have had another hard days fight," courier Jacob L. Bechtel wrote on May 20. "I am nearly wore out for want of Sleep and rest to day. I was out [to] witness the Shooting of a coward of our Division. I will close and get something to eat."[85] Another man recorded in his diary that "the man was shot at precisely seven o'clock and died in a moment."[86] The emotional emptiness of their reactions cannot be explained as the hardening of tender feelings. The soldiers were thoroughly exhausted, to be sure, but they had plenty of sympathy for the comrades who had fallen by their side — and that could include the enemy. However, they would not waste their compassion on a soldier who had disgraced the uniform. The terse words of division commander John Gibbon probably captured most veterans' matter-of-fact attitude toward Starbird's killing. The general noted in his journal: "May 20th, 7:08 A.M. He is just shot."[87]

Word of the execution spread quickly through the soldier grapevine, thanks to the wide dissemination of a general order that announced Starbird's killing with a final warning to all those who tended to wander away from the battlefield. "No man not wounded will be allowed to go to the rear under penalty of being shot on the spot by the Provost Guards. In going to the rear for slight wounds and scratches will be considered as deserting and tried accordingly."[88] Other orders followed, including a Ninth Corps circular which promised that any "person caught pillaging will be summarily dealt with" and that regiment rearguards were authorized to "use their bayonet freely, and if necessary shoot any straggler."[89] The impact of these orders and the prompt execution of Starbird is impossible to measure. It certainly caused some soldiers to think twice before sneaking away from their unit, but the relentless tempo of the campaign allowed for little reflection. Forced marches following the Battle of Spotsylvania — often at night and across treacherous, muddy roads — exceeded what any officer had a right to expect of their men. Sleep deprivation took its toll, leaving men forlorn and despondent or edgy and full of anxiety. Drowsy soldiers also lacked the mental energy to block the haunting memories of wounded comrades writhing in agony and screaming out for mercy.[90] Without sufficient rest, men on both sides struggled to keep up, regardless of how many Starbirds were gunned down as examples.[91]

The weariness weighed heavily on both Union and Confederate soldiers, weakening unit cohesiveness as fatigued stragglers peeled off from the marching column in alarming numbers. Many of these men had no intention of catching up to their commands after a fitful rest. They took to the fields, stealing whatever they pleased from neighboring farms and destroying whatever remained. These men were not exuberant foragers; they were marauders, whose act of desertion marked a trend toward criminality. If their army could not control its men against civilians, military men on both sides feared the consequences on the battlefield, where discipline might unravel. Reports of soldiers committing horrible outrages against civilians kept pouring into army headquarters after Starbird's death, even as the Army of the Potomac had crossed the James River in early June and headed south toward Petersburg. Provost Marshal Marsena Patrick made examples of individuals, but nothing seemed to stop the rampage. A fuming Patrick "found the 6' Corps ravaging the whole Country & killing Cattle Sheep etc. with perfect abandon, while the houses were burning with the 5' Corps Head Quarters in hailing distance."[92] The fury of these men erupted at the end of a savage campaign. They were starving, covered in filth, shoeless, and wearing threadbare clothes, but for the first time in weeks they did not have to fear for their lives. They were now outside the range of enemy guns and could enjoy the fruits of survival.

Civil War officers were not blind to the blows that logistical breakdowns delivered against the bodies and minds of the rank and file. During the sieges of

Richmond and Petersburg that followed, both Union and Confederate armies rotated soldiers from the front to the rear so that their mental and physical health would be properly restored. After an interminable day at the front, an Alabama soldier finally received the order to retire from the exposed rifle pit where he was lying flat in the dirt under an unforgiving June sun. Bullets flew overhead, keeping him pinned to the ground, and all he could do was stare at the "ghastly face" of a slain comrade who had made the fatal mistake of exposing his head just above the lip of the trench: in an instant, the crack of a sharpshooter's rifle had marked the immediate end of that man's life. Once behind the lines, the Alabamian was filled with the euphoria of a veteran who had survived unremitting danger and killing, recording that he and his comrades "were permitted to take off our shoes and accouterments." "We are once more free!" he added joyfully. "We can walk about with out any danger of being *knocked over*. All enjoyed a refreshing wash this morning."[93]

In general, however, Civil War officers framed a breakdown in discipline as reducible to character rather than truly appreciating the role of circumstances and conditions in weakening the resolve of the rank and file. Marsena Patrick was not unusual in merging the straggler and deserter into a vile criminal figure whose mere presence corrupted "good" soldiers. The immediate pressure to maintain order forced generals to act in haste, especially during a time of crisis, when highly visible ritual executions could scare men straight. The risk, however, was of alienating the rank and file by killing a sympathetic figure. There was no chance of that occurring in the Army of the Potomac when John Starbird was gunned down.

### John Futch
### *Nonslaveholding North Carolina Laborer*
### Third North Carolina Infantry

On August 20, 1863, thirteen veteran soldiers from the Third North Carolina fled their camp.[94] That night they picked up their rifles, slung on their cartridge belts, and escaped into the woods. From that point on, there was no turning back on a trek of some three hundred perilous miles that would eventually take them to their North Carolina homes. Earlier that day, Lee had ordered his corps commanders to organize armed parties to hunt down runaways while calling for the president to back the immediate enforcement of the death penalty against deserters. While the Tar Heels could not have known that Lee was cracking down on the army as if it were a wild beast, the impact of the general's orders would be felt with surprising swiftness.

In five days, John Futch and his comrades covered a little more than thirty miles by staying in the bush, walking at night, and avoiding the main roads, yet they remained within the Army of Northern Virginia's expansive perimeter of control. If the band could just get across the James River—patrolled regularly by the local militia and Lee's troops—they would likely be home within a few weeks.[95] Not far from the hamlet of Scottsville, the Carolinians reached the towpath of the Kanawha Canal. From that slight elevation they could take in the wide expanse of the James River. All appeared clear for crossing, but as they neared the banks of the river, a squad from the Forty-Sixth North Carolina Infantry suddenly sprang out of the woods with their rifles leveled, hammers cocked, and their commanding officer, Richardson Mallet, screaming at the fugitives to surrender. At first the men of the Third North Carolina tried to put down their guns, but it appears that one of the deserters fired a bullet into Mallet's chest, setting off a heated gun battle of some thirty shots. Who pulled the first trigger is up for debate, and during the ensuing chaos at least one deserter was killed, another was wounded, and one man likely escaped. The remaining ten soldiers surrendered to their captors while Mallet lay on the ground, his coat saturated with the blood gushing from his fatal chest wound. Some of his men rushed him to the nearby Scottsville hospital, and there, just moments before he passed, Mallet carefully chose his last words so that he would forever be remembered as a soldier who gave his life for God and country: "Tell the colonel I was doing my duty, God's will be done. Amen."[96]

It is miraculous that Mallet's men did not line up Futch and his comrades and shoot them on the spot for killing their commander. Cooler heads managed to prevail, and the deserters were hustled to trains bound for Richmond, where they were incarcerated in the notorious prison Castle Thunder. They awaited trial in dank cells, surrounded by spies, Unionists, slaves, and outright criminals. The severity of the crime ensured that no possible deviation from military law would prevent the army from carrying out the death penalty. When the court was eventually called to order, guilt was presumed and the verdict decided.

The Confederacy's court-martial records were either destroyed or lost during the 1865 evacuation of Richmond, but military service records show that the band of deserters from the Third North Carolina were not repeat offenders when it came to unauthorized leave. A few of the men were prone to sickness and hospitalization, but it is impossible to determine whether they were "playing off" the doctors for a medical discharge or were truly ill. Four were wounded in battle; one was noted for acting bravely in several engagements; two had been captured and exchanged; and three were conscripts.[97] Only one soldier had a record of previously being absent without leave. As a group, these men had built average records. They were seasoned veterans who understood the forces arrayed against deserters and the practical difficulties that they would likely incur. Rising up and risking it all in a spontaneous moment would be reckless. They needed to plan, deliberate, and organize, all of which occurred prior to August 20.

It is no coincidence that the thirteen men came from four North Carolina counties in the eastern part of the state, which ensured that by heading in the same direction they would have strength in numbers for any unfortunate encounters with the home guard or other marauders. Some of the Carolinians stuffed extra cartridges of ammunition in their pockets, and one man stole a pistol to use if he were caught in a tight spot and needed to make an escape.

Deserter John Futch, who was functionally illiterate, offers the strongest evidence of preparation to desert. He spelled out his plans in letters dictated to other comrades, many of whom were barely literate themselves. His attempts to write letters home earlier in the war were met with ridicule, according to his older brother, Charley, who, after circulating John's missives around two North Carolina regiments, could not find a single person capable of deciphering his writing. So John turned to his comrades, who captured his thoughts as they rolled off his tongue in letters that read as if John were speaking directly to the recipient. The result is a supremely important body of papers that gives voice to a class of soldiers whose impoverishment and lack of education made the preservation of such documents less common.

Through the pens of comrades, Futch gave subtle indications to his wife, Martha, that he was returning to North Carolina with or without a furlough. On August 16, he told his wife, "I want to come home the worst I Ever Did in my Life," but he had heard so irregularly from his family since Gettysburg that he was hesitant to do anything. Once he broke away from the army, Futch knew that he would also be cutting his wife off from state support. It appears that he did not want to "take leave" until she collected the state rations allotted to soldier wives.[98] Futch could not say much more to Martha. The officers were closely watching the men, even opening soldier letters to foil any possible plots in the ranks. Futch understandably revealed as little as possible in his dictations, keeping his cards close to his vest, as "it is Said our Letters is Broke open and red." Four days later, on August 20, Futch nearly stated his true intentions, hinting that his days in the army were numbered. As he dictated this final letter, he must have known that he would be vanishing from the army that night. "I expect to bea home before long," he promised.[99]

*Desertion and Military Justice*

Futch's last letter, with its illusionary assurance that he would soon return home, reached his loved ones as he waited to be executed—a bitter endnote to an uneven military career. In October 1861, when the air was thick with romance and fiery patriotism, Futch had voluntarily enlisted in the Forty-First North Carolina Infantry. His particular reasons for joining are beyond the reach of available source material, but Futch remained with the unit through November, when he suddenly and without explanation disappeared from the army's rolls. He presumably returned to New Hanover County, where he had worked as a laborer and owned no property but lived within a network of extended family members.[100] A few months later, in early 1862, he resurfaced in the ranks of the Third North Carolina Infantry, where his brother Charley and a cousin had been serving since the summer of 1861. Within a few weeks of his arrival, Futch fell ill with an undisclosed ailment that kept him in military hospitals until early 1863, when a physician cleared him to return to the ranks. With a heavy heart, Futch boarded a train that took him past the Goldsboro hospital, once a sanctuary from war where Martha was often at his bedside, nursing him back to health. The scene was emotionally wrenching for the North Carolinian, and he poured out his feelings to a comrade who put those most intimate thoughts onto paper. "Oh I thought of old times when [I] passed Goldsboro [and] when I looked at that old hospital I all most Cryed."[101]

Futch's return to camp did not improve his disposition, nor did a reunion with his comrades replenish his morale. Snow, howling winds, and meager rations enervated his already weakened body, and his spirits spiraled downward. He came to regard camp as a place of despair. A single sentence captured his perfect disgust with the life of the soldier: "Bad Guys know Satisfaction to Be Seen in Camp."[102] Futch spent most of his time in his tent, secluding himself from his fellow soldiers unless he was dictating letters to a comrade about his poor health and the army's indifference to his sinking condition. He continued to lobby his captain for a discharge. "My health is so bad and it is so cold here that I am perfectly miserable," he explained shortly after his arrival, "and I am doing my Country no good and myself a great harm."[103] Such complaints might sound like typical soldier grumbling, but the political potency of these sentiments comes to light when recovering the private dialogue between soldiers and their loved ones. After meeting with his captain, who was on leave, Futch's wife urged her husband to leverage his feeble health to secure a military discharge. "Dear husband," Martha wrote on March 29, 1863, "i learn that you have not goin before the [Medical] bord and i want you to go. . . . if you wanted to come home as bad as i do want you to come you would go before it every day and i want you to do it and tri to git home."[104] Futch followed her pointed advice, pressuring his lieutenant and captain to give him an interview with the board of surgeons.

In the spring of 1863, when it became apparent that a highly coveted medical discharge was out of reach, Futch faced the reality of service in the Army of Northern Virginia until the war's conclusion. He did not want to be anywhere except by the side of his wife, whose letters to him were by turns distressing, affectionate, demanding, and instructive. "I wish that I could see you," Martha wrote in a typical letter to John. "My study is about you[.] you do not [k]Now how bad I hate that you air so far from me but I am in joyin my self the best I can and you must do the same but my injoyemen ant much for my study is about you in the day and drems of you at nite."[105] When she awoke, Martha saw the shadow of impoverishment creeping toward the farm, threatening to eclipse the family. She did not spare John bad news, telling him of thieving bandits, of women dressing up as men to humiliate hospitalized soldiers, of the difficulties in receiving financial assistance from the county, of husbands abusing their wives, and of Union soldiers raiding the area.[106] Like all soldiers, Futch was always sifting through much disparate information about home, which was coming at him in letters or through an army grapevine that stretched all the way to his household in New Hanover County, which surrounded the port of Wilmington. The picture emerging was bleak, and Futch likely went to bed at night with a troubled mind, imagining his wife and children living in a land rife with lawlessness. At one point, an exasperated and angry Futch told Martha: "Sary to hear that Some Body had Broke open sisters crib and Stolen her corn the man Dun that had Aught to have to Go in Servis & Stay their as Long as the war Last A Damn old Raskel you aught to take your Gun and go their & Shoot him for he has All ways bin Doing them tricks."[107] Martha would have likely preferred to take aim at the local county administrator, who was holding up the assistance that would keep her child from going hungry. Some three hundred miles to the north, John was not faring much better on army rations, which were so meager that he exclaimed, "It looks like Starvashion here."[108]

Futch's wife was on the verge of visiting the army with provisions and clothes for her needy husband. On April 14 she wrote, "i never in dured so much trubles in my life be fore it semes lik it will kill me if i dont see you one more time dear husban i want to no how you air feren and if you have worm close and slep worm."[109] The reunion would never take place due to the opening of the Chancellorsville Campaign. John headed into battle worried that he would be killed, leaving his wife a widow to face the world alone with their infant child. The epic fight, though acknowledged by the North Carolinian as an indisputable Confederate victory, scared him badly. It was the first time that Futch had entered the hellish cauldron of battle, where exploding shells and whizzing minie balls ripped into human flesh, sending men tumbling to the ground bleeding and crying out for help. Futch later told his wife that as the bullets started flying, he felt certain that "I had seen you for the last time." At one point when the fighting reached a fiery crescendo, "I thought that every man would be killed and there would not be enough to tell the tale of the rest."[110]

As Futch staggered behind the lines, bewildered and physically spent, he sought refuge in a hospital to calm his fatigued mind. A few days later, with his spirits restored, he told his survival tale with an air of desperation, writing, "I never saw the like of the dead never in my life." The irrepressible images of the corpses kept his mind on a question that bedeviled all Civil War soldiers: Why had he lived and others perished? A definite answer eluded him, but in his soul Futch knew that "God brought me though saft." Futch regarded bloated corpses, tangled together in a bloody mess with their equipment strewn all over the field, as the worst thing he had ever seen. He wanted to grab some of the abandoned gear, but he only managed a few "good drinks of the real old coffee." The officers refused to let the men leave the ranks and plunder — an unfortunate decision for Futch, who on returning to camp discovered that all of his belongings had been stolen. A note written after he signed off on his May 9 letter home read, "When I got back to camp all was gone."[111]

By the end of May, Futch had dictated five letters of varying lengths to his wife. His language — as recorded by his comrades — lacks the popular figurative expressions such as "sublime bravery," "fearlessness," or "everyone faced to the front" used by so many Civil War soldiers to convey an exaggerated picture of unity forged through a dramatic rendering of killing, courage, and comradeship. Futch, on the other hand, did admit to his wife that many in his regiment ran away from the firing line, including one terribly frightened man who defecated in his pants while under enemy fire.[112] To ask his wife to keep this news to herself seems a little odd, since Futch, in dictating his letters, spoke candidly with his comrade about the physical and emotional breakdown of their fellow soldiers. The openness between the two veterans would suggest that not all Civil War soldiers retreated into themselves after a battle, seemingly lost in traumatic thoughts and unable to admit feeling terrorized by fear under fire. "Oh I have seen a grate deal of trouble Since you left me," John relayed to Martha on May 20. "I want to see you worse then I Ever did Before Dear Wife."[113]

Futch hoped that the summer campaign would bring the war to a conclusion, but any optimism he felt was washed away when he forded the Potomac River. "I Crosed over the river yesterday," he reported on June 19. "I didant Want to Com by any means Nor I Dont like this state."[114] As he moved with Lee's army into the heart of Pennsylvania, surrounded by lush fields and orchards untrammeled by war, Futch became more discouraged, fearing that letters home would likely never reach him at such a great distance. Worn down with worry and unable to rid himself of the haunting memories of Chancellorsville, Futch could not resist the darkest of thoughts. He sensed that the next battle would be his last, but in trying to comfort Martha he could not hide his sense of utter helplessness to do anything from the ranks. "You must take the best Cear of your self you Can mah [Martha]," he wrote, as he was losing hope that "I will get home some time before I Dy [die].[115]

John and Charley had been able to turn to each other for counsel and comfort while in the ranks, but not for much longer. On July 2, the two brothers moved side by side, advancing up the steep and wooded, rocky slope of Culp's Hill. Charley was on the ground, loading his weapon and firing toward an enemy breastwork, when a Yankee bullet sliced into the top of his head. The moment John looked at his brother he knew the wound was fatal. Blood flowed through Charley's hair and streamed down his face; his mouth was moving the entire time, but the words would not come. Futch picked his brother up and carried him to a safe place near the waters of Rock Creek. For the remainder of the night Futch stayed at his brother's side. At two o'clock in the morning Charley passed, bringing a merciful end to his awful suffering, but for John, the ordeal continued.

Just before the morning sun initiated the final round of killing at Gettysburg, John took Charley's pistol and covered his brother's grave with the soil of Pennsylvania. At that moment, he never felt so alone in the world. "Charley never spoke after he get wonded and he wanted to go home Mity bad before he died," John recounted to a comrade. "He was kild at gettiesburg PV pore felar he got kild a long wase from home I was very sary that I codent get a cofen to bearey him but I breared him the best I cod it was something that I never expected to haft to do but we dont know what we will do til he gets in the ware it."[116] For John, there was no consolation in giving a brother to the Confederate cause, no sense that a higher purpose had been served. Charley's departure from this world of trials and tribulations was the only solace for Futch. "I beleav he is hapy," he told his family, "and no doubt far better off than any of us."[117] As best he could, John tried burying his brother with all of the conventions of the good death in the Civil War, assuring his family that Charley had not died alone and that the kingdom of Heaven awaited him. Though these details were excruciatingly painful for their family to read, John related them to give those at home a place at the dying Charley's side.[118]

When Lee's army retreated to Virginia, rations were short, clothing was difficult to come by, and pay was nonexistent. Constant marching until the beginning of August further punished John, as it did many of Lee's other veterans, who described themselves as broken down from heat exhaustion, hunger, and mental fatigue in what historian Joseph Glatthaar describes as a logistical and discipline crisis that endangered the very existence of Lee's army.[119] Keeping up was especially difficult for Futch, whose shoes were in tatters, forcing him to march in bare feet that eventually callused over with painful sores. "Yet i hast to go bearfooted the botom of My foot is as thick My thome and sores that i ever had."[120] As Futch physically became weaker with every march after Gettysburg, his ability to manage the awful memories of his brother's death decreased proportionately.

The procession of mournful letters written during the retreat from Pennsylvania to Virginia reveals a man convulsed in utter despair. Futch made no attempt to hide his desolation from the comrades who wrote down his words as he spoke them. "Since the Death of Charley I am so lonesome I do not know what to do," he dictated.[121] To fill his letters with such raw emotions, Futch had to unburden himself on the most intimate terms with fellow soldiers who were willing to scribble down his jagged thoughts. Throughout his correspondence, Futch's dictations existed outside a code of Southern honor noted for pushing men to project an appearance of mastery and emotional control. White Southern men were not supposed to acknowledge their frailty, as it would make them look small, helpless, and full of impotent rage. No self-respecting man could hope to earn community acceptance without projecting his mental and emotional toughness. Futch apparently did not care about appearances. He told those in the ranks and at home that he was drowning in the depths of depression, a shocking admission by a Southerner who came from an oral and written tradition where men were supposed to tell stories that reaffirmed their belief in themselves and in their institutions.[122] If John felt any shame over his demoralized state, it did not prevent him from admitting that his mind was not right. "I don't want nothing to eat hardly for I am all most sick all the time and half crazy," he confessed to a comrade on July 19. "I never wanted to come home so bad in my life."[123] These conversations between Futch and his fellow veterans counter the accepted notion that the unutterable experiences of the battlefield united Civil War soldiers in a silent understanding. Futch's exceptional letters suggest that military life did not necessarily wrap them in an emotional cocoon. In fact, they could and did open up about the dangers of battle, a longing for home, their love of their wives and children, and their desire for the killing to stop.

One of the remarkable letters that captures John Futch's words as he spoke them to a comrade who wrote them down as he heard them. In this July 19, 1863, missive, Futch poured out his emotions over the death of his brother, Charley, a loss so devastating that John felt as if he were losing his mind after Gettysburg. "I dont want nothing to eat hardly for I am all most sick all the time and half crazy I never wanted to come home so bad in my life but it is so that I cant come at this time but if we come down south I will try to come any how." Futch's emotional openness was not unusual among Civil War soldiers, who discovered that they could better cope with the war if they turned to each other as confidants. (Courtesy of the State Archives of North Carolina)

and they was left with the
yankes but I hope that we will
live to come home without a wound
for I have seen so many wounded
and died I staid with charly antell he
died he never spoke after he was wounded
antell he died I never was hurt so
in my life I had rather that it
would of bin my self of my experienc
nothing more only I will close so
your kinde and afectionet husband
John Feutch

Dear mother I want to let you
no that I have not for got you
yet nor never will as long as I live
I have wrote to you too or thre
times and never have got eny answer
I want to see you the wanst in
the world and talk with you I will
write to you before long and write you
a long letter dont fanget to write
to me for it is all the satisfaction
I see is to hear from you all so I
will close for the want of something to
write so nothing more only I remain your
kinde son John futch

Futch could not stop talking about his brother's agonizing death, sparing no details in five letters to his family dictated from July 19 to August 6. He
needed to escape for his own sanity and for his family's survival, in contrast to
scores of other Confederates who, as historian Aaron Sheehan-Dean has argued, "increasingly explained their participation in the war in terms of protection of their loved ones. The result was a new masculinity, one that required
both affection and hostility, the former directed toward one's family and the
latter directed toward its enemies."[124] Futch could very well have despised the
Yankees as much as he loved his family, but his feelings, whatever they may

have been, did not translate into a firm commitment to the cause. By the end of the Gettysburg Campaign, he had reached the conclusion that the army did not offer the best protection for his home. This was not an issue of weak morale or a question of nationalism for Futch, but of interests that were at odds with Confederate authority.

In refusing to accept his situation, he struggled to imagine alternatives, and finally reached the momentous decision to desert, which can only be interpreted as a powerful assertion of political motivation. This was a decision born of desperation, to be sure: Futch was well aware of the consequences of getting caught. The previous February he had seen a comrade get his head shaved and get drummed out of camp for cowardice. "I dont want this to Be my case," he insisted at the time.[125] But much had changed since then. His closest comrade in the army had died at Gettysburg; he was broke, starving, and in need of clothes, largely because the Army of Northern Virginia was in shambles. In the month that followed Gettysburg, Lee's soldiers knew that their chances of making it home without getting captured or shot were as good as they had ever been. At the end of July, Futch could stand it no longer, and he told a comrade to let his family know that he was bound for North Carolina even if the army said no: "I am going to come before long if I have to Runaway to do it. . . . Let me know how the times is in old Hanover for I want to be there so Bad I can taste it."[126]

Almost a month would pass before Futch fulfilled his promise to desert, but in the meantime, he and the rest of Lee's foot soldiers were subjected to an unrelenting loyalty campaign. A focused examination of the Army of Northern Virginia during this time is instructive, for it offers insight into the ways the press, the government, and the Confederate army collaborated in the endless pursuit of disciplining the rank and file. To scare, cajole, inspire, and force Lee's men to do their duty, a rhetorical campaign appealed to Confederate veterans as Christian soldiers who stood as the last line of defense between their families and maniacal Yankee hordes and vengeful African Americans bent on subjugating white Southerners. Jefferson Davis's proclamation to all Confederate troops on August 1 lays out the interlocking and long-circulating ideas about race, manliness, and soldierly duties that elites generally employed when trying to direct the political behavior of Southern enlisted men. "Fellow-citizens," the president announced, "no alternative is left you but victory or subjugation, slavery, and the utter ruin of yourselves, your families, and your country."[127] Davis insisted that Union armies were intent on inciting servile insurrection as a way to elevate blacks over white men.

Robert E. Lee praised the executive declaration, telling the president he hoped that "the earnest and beautiful appeal made to the country in your proc-

Along this stretch of the James River, a Confederate patrol intercepted John Futch and his fellow deserters on August 25, 1863. A gun battle erupted, and the arresting officer, Richard Mallet, was killed before Futch and his comrades surrendered. The captured men were sent to Richmond and incarcerated in Castle Thunder, where they were presumably tried and sentenced to death before returning to their camps at Montpelier. (Photo by author)

lamation may stir up the virtue of the whole people, and that they may see their duty and perform it." Lee's response rested on cultural and class assumptions that prevented him from fully appreciating how inequities in power and resources were contributing to his army's near-implosion. As a slaveholding Victorian he saw hierarchy as an inevitable condition, and the structure of the military reaffirmed his existing beliefs during a war that turned him into an uncompromising Confederate nationalist.[128] Lee thus tended to look for "natural" solutions that he thought resided within the individual. Morality, character, and courage, the general stressed, were the critical issues when reforming deserters. "Our people have only to be true and united, to bear manfully the misfortunes incident to war, and all will come right in the end," Lee concluded in that same letter to Jefferson Davis.[129] His private sentiments shaped his public policies. Less than two weeks before the president's proclamation, Lee issued the following plea to the troops: "To remain at home in the hour of our country's need, is unworthy of the manhood of a Southern soldier."[130]

The Confederate press essentially allied itself with Davis and Lee in turning desertion into a problem of individual character and manliness and, in effect, burying any questions of how political and military decisions were responsible for so many Confederates running away. Southern papers frequently ran stories that were purportedly from soldiers, but these accounts must have read like utter fiction to the men starving and sweltering in the ranks. Take, for instance, the popular article "A Deserter's Confession," which numerous Southern papers published after the Battle of Gettysburg. This piece is narrated in the first person, supposedly by an unidentified Georgia soldier who deserted after being denied a furlough, giving in to his desire to see his wife and children. On arriving home, the soldier enjoyed a brief reunion before his wife asked, "'How long is your furlough?'" When the soldier failed to respond, she prodded him with another question: "'What's the matter, James?' said my wife, 'have you a wound?'" James broke down and confessed that he had run away from the army. "'Oh! James! what shall we do?'" she exclaimed. "'What will the neighbors say? What will General Lee think?'"[131] James did not have an answer for his wife until he read Jefferson Davis's August proclamation. He was so touched by the president's exhortations of a potential race war that he "sat down and cried like a child." "'God bless the President,' swelled up from my heart with my sobs. 'May God bless him—he is right,'" the soldier declared. He then showed the proclamation to his wife, who had a similar epiphany. They sat together and cried.[132] After this cathartic experience, the Georgia soldier boarded the train for Virginia, promising never to desert again until independence was achieved.

The naked political purpose of "A Deserter's Confession" is ridiculously transparent, but it captures the approach of the Confederate press. The Georgian's emotional histrionics over the president's words must have brought an incredulous chuckle from many a veteran, but we know little about how less-privileged Confederate soldiers critically read and responded to the dominant message from the press, the pulpit, and the government. Civil War soldiers' perceptions of military reporting, in particular, were a confused mixture of doubt, trust, pessimism, and hopefulness, all of which created a deep feeling of uncertainty and unease about the future. We cannot assume that soldiers accepted elitist messages uncritically, nor should we assert that the men rejected the words of elites as outright propaganda. We do have evidence of a healthy skepticism on the front lines that would sometimes descend into cynicism. Soldiers knew that their officers and politicians, in collaboration with the press, were intent on controlling their behavior and shaping their beliefs. After Gettysburg, for example, there were rumors that desertion was surging in Meade's command and that the entire Army of the Potomac was on the brink of rebellion. A

North Carolinian dismissed the newspaper report as invented by the press and propagated by their generals "to keep our soldiers in good heart."[133]

In the chaotic two months that followed Gettysburg, in which the Army of Northern Virginia was unraveling and men were running off as armed desperados, the press called for punitive measures against deserters, Lee backed military executions, and Davis warned of subjugation to an abolitionist enemy. All of these actions helped form the backdrop behind the trial of Futch and the nine other deserters who were charged with and convicted of the high crimes of murder and desertion. Official documents suggest that the men were not informed of their fate until they returned to camp in Orange County. In a horrible miscarriage of justice, the North Carolinians were denied any legal recourse. There would be no chance for an appeal, no chance to ask for clemency, and no opportunity to alert loved ones of their fates. Division headquarters informed brigade commander George H. Steuart on September 4, 1863, that the execution would take place the following afternoon at four o'clock. "The proceedings of the Court & Gen Order No. 62 from these Hd. Qrs. will not be read to the prisoners until day light to-morrow morning," the orders stated. "You will take all possible means to secure them, handcuffing or tying them & keep the matter secret until the proceedings are read to the prisoners."[134]

At the critical moment when Futch confronted the army's justice system—when he likely tried to defend his decision to go home without permission and might have explained why a gun battle erupted with fellow Confederate soldiers—we have no record of what he said, thought, or felt. Neither his letters nor the court-martial transcripts survive. Yet even if the court documents still existed, his voice would never have been truly heard in a highly public campaign that demonized deserters as the fifth column of the enemy. As we follow Futch from his Richmond prison cell to the dusty drill field in Orange County where he was tied to a stake, blindfolded, and shot, we must remember that we are not seeing the final day of his life through his eyes. We are looking at the world through the mental orientation of those who condemned him. Although it is regrettable that we lose touch with Futch, we gain access to the Confederate elites who possessed the power to use state violence against their own citizens in order to shape the public understanding of the killing.

Just as the morning sky was breaking and the streets of Richmond were virtually empty, the ten condemned Confederates were manacled two-by-two and escorted by a heavy armed guard. They boarded the 6:30 A.M. train for Gordonsville, probably not knowing they were returning to the army so that their comrades could carry out the court-martial's death sentence—even though news of the verdict and the prisoner transfer had apparently become public knowledge. The train ride from Richmond to Gordonsville took most of the day. As dusk settled across the Army of Northern Virginia's camp, the party reached the provost guard tent of Johnson's division. The heavy guard remained, and anyone trying to communicate with the prisoners was pushed away. Early the next morning, the Reverend George Patterson, an Episcopal priest and the chaplain of the Third North Carolina, conferred with Futch and his comrades. The pastor likely informed the men that they would face a firing squad before sunset. Their reaction is unknown, but Patterson spoke to them about the need to prepare for the afterlife, and the newspaper accounts agree that Futch and his comrades opened themselves up to God and found Jesus for this first time. Whether this spiritual awakening actually took place is hard to say, though it is clear from his correspondence that Futch was certainly a religious man who had long ago accepted Christ as his savior. In fact, he even drew a pair of hands, forefingers pointing up to the heavens, at the end of one of his letters. It also seems unlikely that the military would have given correspondents access to the prisoners. But the truthfulness of the story is secondary to the intent of the authors, who portrayed the North Carolinians as men who had cut themselves off from decent society, were without conscience, and were capable of committing a crime because they did not feel they answered to God. In a sense, the press was actually suggesting that the Confederate army, in taking the lives of these men, was actually saving their souls.

The veterans of Johnson's division were ordered to the drill ground on September 5 with the explicit instruction to leave their muskets in camp. They knew that a bloody ritual would play out before them. Once the men were in place, General Edward Johnson and his staff rode into the center of the square carrying a small national flag. The spatial relationships of this formation conveyed the commanding presence of the military as the ultimate arbiter of life and death. The Confederate flag was also intended to visually reinforce the primacy of the national government and the dire consequences of dishonoring that banner. Twenty minutes passed until the afternoon stillness was broken by the methodically slow beat of the death march. No one could see the drummers or the condemned men as the solemn music drifted across the field. Suddenly the ranks parted and the doomed soldiers appeared, marching in step to the grim cadence. They were halted at the spot where they would lose their lives. The executioners appeared next, 120 men with fixed bayonets reflecting the declining September sun.

The discipline and order of the procession, absent of any melodrama, masked the serious concerns of the officers in charge, who worried that the firing squad might botch the execution by purposely missing their human targets. General Johnson would take no chances. He instructed, "For your firing parties the Genl. thinks you had better select men from other Regiments than the one to which the Prisoners belong." Above all else, Johnson wanted his subordinates to "select good men" to do the killing.[135] Selecting "good men" meant finding soldiers who would pull their triggers without flinching and would have no qualms about shooting straight. The fact that Johnson had to take such a precaution speaks to the general unease among members of the military establishment, who had insisted that the verdict be kept secret from the army until the day of the execution because they realized that the rank and file had their own code of justice and might act on it.

When the column halted in front of the stakes, the prisoners were forced to stand and face their executioners while the officer of the day read the sentence. Reverend Patterson stepped forward next to deliver what one observer described as a prayer of "great feeling."[136] Unfortunately, Patterson's words are lost, but his prominent place in the procession sanctified the killings as a divinely ordained moment of justice, not just a raw exercise of man's power. After Patterson finished his prayer, two guards escorted each prisoner to a stake and made them kneel as their arms were tied behind them to a plank attached to the top of the stake. The guards bandaged the eyes of the condemned and made sure that their hats rested over the bandages. A hushed silence momentarily prevailed until the cries of the condemned pierced the air: "'Lord have mercy!' 'Oh, my poor mother!' and 'Oh save me, save me!'" yelled the soldiers in disarrayed tones. Whether Futch was one of those men pleading for his life, we will never know. One can only wonder about what was going through his mind. Was he thinking about the brother he had lost at Gettysburg? Were images of his wife and children pressing forward? Or was he too overcome with terror to even imagine anything that he held dear in his life?

While the condemned begged for mercy, the executioners quickly formed squads of ten men. Five carried loaded muskets; the other five had blanks in their rifles. They stood just fourteen feet away from Futch and his comrades. They waited for the command they had heard countless times on the battlefield before. As soon as the officer of the day yelled *Ready, aim, fire*, a ragged volley ripped into men who just two months earlier had faced enemy shells on the slopes of Culp's Hill. When the smoke cleared, it was discovered that a few of the North Carolinians were gasping for air, their bodies still shaking with life. The twenty members of the reserve squad were quickly ordered forward, and they fired repeatedly into the wounded survivors. By all accounts, this gruesome incident deeply affected Johnson's veterans, who were horrified to see such suffering. To impress upon the witnesses the finality of the punishment and the future risks of deserting, Johnson's entire division, regiment by regiment, marched in silence past the lifeless bodies of the ten men, still affixed to the stakes. The march was deliberately completed in slow time, some seventy steps a minute, so that the soldiers were subjected to the military's absolute control over the bodies of the living as well as the dead.[137]

Most soldiers were not overcome by a renewed sense of patriotism when they saw comrades shoot their own. The ghastly sight sickened patriotic soldiers, but they were also quick to justify military executions as an unfortunate necessity in preserving order in camp and discipline in battle. Less ardent soldiers had a more difficult time reconciling themselves to the death penalty. These men apparently saw Mallet's death not as murder, but as a casualty of war. "It was a terrible sight, and God grant that I may not be called to see anything of this kind again," wrote North Carolinian Thomas Armstrong a day after the execution. "Most of them were good soldiers and brave men," Armstrong added. "This being their first act of disobedience." Another North Carolinian thought the execution was a senseless act that would ultimately turn more men against the Confederacy. "We formed a square so that all could see and after they were shot we then were marched by them," he recounted. "*This* was done to have a good affect on the men *but* I doubt its doing much good for our soldiers are hardened to such scenes. And they all say that they ought to have been imprisoned and there work for the government — I think this would have been better myself."[138] Yet even a soldier like Armstrong, who was appalled by the mass killing and somewhat critical of the army's decision to execute the men of the Third North Carolina, could not ignore the warning of this death ritual: the military establishment would not be a benevolent master toward runaways.

The death penalty did not serve as an effective deterrent against desertion in Futch's old regiment. At least twenty-three additional men deserted the Third North Carolina during the three months that followed the September 5 execution, but the dramatic increase in firing squads undoubtedly scared scores of men into either staying in or returning to Confederate regiments.[139] "Dear Sir the Object of these few lines is in Behalf of a Deserter who we learn is anxious to Return to the Service," a North Carolina civilian wrote to Zebulon Vance on November 25, 1863. "In case he can have a guarantee that he will not be shot or that he can get a pardon from Death he as any other Person would be is horrified at the Idea of being Shot as he says like a dog and he has deserted three times But Says he never will again if his life can be spared this time."[140] Evidence in this study suggests that the fear of being killed stayed with Civil War soldiers and kept them anchored to the ground, for they never forgot the sickening sight of helpless men sent to their graves by the muskets of their own armies. By the middle of October 1863, desertion was on the decline, men on extended sick leave were returning to the ranks, and wayward soldiers were also finding their way back to the army.

The Confederate military and government needed a cooperative press to justify its use of lethal force on the people. There were lessons to be conveyed from the killing of the North Carolinians, and Southern editors took it upon themselves to show how Southern women in particular were complicit in the crime of desertion by imploring their husbands to come home. "Our blood runs cold to think of the deep heart-anguish which their conduct has carried to the hearts and homes of their loved ones," wrote the editor of the *Fayetteville (N.C.) Observer*. "Their names are disgraced forever, and around their memories will forever linger a dark stain that can never be blotted out."[141] Dishonor could be avoided, the *Observer* warned, if civilians would stop inducing their loved ones to leave the army. In describing the execution, the *Observer* singled out the Third North Carolinian who cried out for his "poor mother" before getting shot. The *Observer* wondered—with appalling heartlessness—if "she was like the misguided wife whose original letter we lately saw, telling her husband to come home at once, as they were about to have a peace meeting in the neighborhood to end the war. And he did come home—a deserter—and the avenger is now after him. He too will probably be caught, or killed if he should resist, and then what will be the feelings of the poor wife!"[142] The politicians in Richmond got the message. In December 1863, Confederate authorities passed an act that made it illegal for civilians to assist deserters and for family members to encourage soldiers to return home.[143]

The examples of this chapter illustrate the pragmatic ways in which deserters thought about and navigated their world. The diversity of their experiences does not sustain the idea of a deserter mind-set. Moreover, any suggestion that this "class" of soldiers was not as motivated, dutiful, or ideological as loyal veterans is an impoverished view of political action. Any man who broke ranks with his army, even for a brief period, was challenging how those in power pressed citizens and soldiers to see their interests as synonymous with those of the nation. The readiness with which the men in this chapter pursued their own understanding of the world put them at odds with the dominant political culture, which demonized deserters as shameless cowards and dangerous criminals. Through everyday action, deserters came to understand themselves in ways that clashed with the elites' messages of national unity based on a code of Christian manliness and honor. Their "rebellious" acts were not inherently more noble or admirable than those of soldiers who carried out their duties with greater consistency and dependability. Such value judgments, in fact, can distract historians from focusing on how soldiers' thoughts and actions were fluctuating, unstable, and, above all else, situational.[144]

Although the deserters in this chapter pursued their own interests, they still thought critically about the war without giving in to an honor-driven world that required soldiers to act bravely to the point of self-destruction. One might charge that these men were simply trying to save their skin, and this was undoubtedly true, but the quest to survive was not just an instinctive response to the perils of army living. John Futch's personal theology, for example, formed the basis of his oppositional stance against the war from the moment he had enlisted in 1862. He found no glory on the battlefield, just heartache and suffering in what he believed was a sickening violation of God's laws rather than a sacred test of character as Confederate elites had proclaimed. The near collapse of his household back in North Carolina, his inability to help support his poor wife and child, and his own ill treatment in the ranks did not spur the North Carolinian to rise up and renounce the Confederacy until a collision of forces made it practical for him to try to turn the fantasy of escape into reality. The death of his brother, the catastrophe at Gettysburg, antiwar activities on the North Carolina home front, and conspiring comrades pushed Futch as close as he had ever been to deserting.

It ultimately took the unraveling of the Army of Northern Virginia on its return to Virginia to create the physical circumstances in which Futch could act on long-held ideas. To see this moment as a case of low morale over a military reverse is a failure to see the world as Futch imagined it. He did not organize his thinking around a succession of battles and political events, nor did he give much thought to how his own actions might affect the Confederate army or the course of the war, and questions of nationalism were not fixtures in his mental world. Instead, he woke up every day with worries about the health of his family, the trials on his farm, his own illnesses, starvation, his lack of clothes, the reliability of the mail, and government support for his family—all of which wore down his resolve to remain in the ranks. His vision of the future largely existed outside the high politics of the war. When he disappeared from camp on August 20, Futch was able to uphold his own conception of what an honorable and dutiful Christian soldier should do, a version of manliness that the society in which he was born found contemptible.

Pennsylvania's John Foster is a valuable example of a deserter who possessed strong political convictions for the side that he abandoned. Like Futch, he acted on his beliefs when the ground-level forces of war necessitated a move toward pragmatism. Foster did not use the word *pragmatic*, but his thinking and behavior were inconsistent with his personal past and yet he never saw himself as being unprincipled or self-serving. Circumstances had changed, and out of necessity Foster rejiggered his sense of duty without regard to any abstraction, only to reality as he perceived it in the moment. He spelled out his intentions and acted on his design to desert in the Wilderness, but this act, which was far from impulsive, shows how carefully he reframed his sense of loyalty. This was a somewhat surprising move considering that Foster had built a stellar combat record and wrote of the Union cause with fervency and devotion. In 1863 he condemned the Copperheads on the Northern home front, and he predicted that a volley from a veteran Union regiment would dispense of such traitorous acts. "I am sorry, very sorry, to hear of those peace meetings in old Armstrong," he wrote on April 12, 1863. "I know they expect a response from the army, but they will find it come the wrong way, or rather the right way, but entirely in opposition to the way they think. They who hold these meeting are nothing but mean, cowardly, and dastardly. My God, if there was only a few soldiers about there, I rather imagine their meetings would terminate in a manner not altogether acceptable to them."[145] A little more than one year later, he still re-solved to put down the rebellion, but his desire for survival competed with his idealism for the cause. Within the circumstances of the Wilderness, when his old wound was flaring up and his superior was being abusive, Foster excused himself from any claims that the army had of him, feeling free to answer only to himself when the fighting erupted. Under a veil of bureaucratic authority, he disguised his act of desertion just as thousands of other commissioned officers did — remaining behind the lines until the situation required that he return to the front. Throughout the ordeal he never saw himself as dishonest or cow-ardly, given his lack of a fixed principle of loyalty. The veteran survivors of his regiment felt otherwise and thought he had abandoned them and his political principles, but they too showed flexibility in returning Foster to duty without charging him for his unauthorized absence.

Finally, the examples in this chapter affirm the importance of social differ-ences and class in exploring desertion. In no way does this recommend eco-nomic determinism, insinuate class warfare, or suggest that soldier protest was a direct outcome of class inequities. Yet soldier letters on both sides demon-strate significant differences that class made regarding access to resources, the relationship to the household, treatment by officers, and how a soldier was re-ceived by the military justice system. Historians have been divided over the importance of class in understanding dissent, and those who minimize its role claim that soldier letters lack the language of class alienation. Its absence, how-ever, speaks to the success of the politicians and the press to create the appear-ance of consensus in print culture, giving citizens a sense of collective solidarity and hope without imposing its views on lower classes or ruling with an iron fist. The silences in public discourse offer clues to historians as to what language was available to Civil War soldiers and the boundaries of acceptable speech. Expecting soldiers to have articulated their grievances through the language of a "rich man's war and a poor man's fight," or to have organized themselves as part of a class-based protest, is unrealistic; such actions fell beyond the range of possibilities for the vast majority of Civil War soldiers. The tactical choices available to any Civil War soldier did not originate from a position of strength. Desertion was almost always defensive in nature and was not intended to directly challenge the army's power structure or to undermine the war effort as a whole. A sense of helplessness or emotional despair rarely led a soldier to renounce his cause, let alone desert, largely because soldiers knew they were trapped in a world that they were unable to alter. "The most of our soldiers are in favor of going to N.C. but the most of the officers are opposed to going so I cannot tell how it will be yet but I think it is all a humbug to keep the soldiers from going home," an angry Confederate wrote after Gettysburg. "I will have to stay," he continued, "until I am released by the same authority that bound me here unless I take a notion to run away and come home."[146] He pondered deserting, telling his wife, "Hide my gun so no one can get it and keep the stables secure," but when Lee sent regular Confederates to his North Carolina community, prudence dictated that he remain in the ranks. "I would come if I thought I could get to stay," he concluded, but he knew that he did not stand a chance with Lee's veterans in the area.[147]

It goes too far to argue that an underclass of deserters and other malcontents nearly turned their armies into an unruly mob. The ties of comradeship, even for deserters, proved exceedingly strong, and the shedding of blood in battle usually strengthened bonds of devotion in ways that transcended social divisions in the ranks. It is also crucial to note that the public deaths of the executed soldiers in this chapter brought into relief the contrast between the good death in battle and the shameful demise of those who shirked duty.[148] It is true that Civil War soldiers came to accept executions as a necessity, but their acceptance of these ritual killings overlooks the obvious: men in the ranks did not have a choice in the matter. Northern and Southern veterans justified the ritual killing of deserters and skulkers on the grounds that it could improve their own chances of surviving a battle by weeding out those men most likely to run and leave them exposed in the midst of a fight. Ritual executions likely hardened soldiers to the brutal realities of military life, but it did not overthrow their understanding of what it meant to be an honorable soldier, nor did they lose their sympathy for those were executed, a remarkable outcome when men on both sides came from a civilian culture that privileged male honor as an expression of Christian character.

Confederate papers, like their Northern counterparts, destroyed as well as created a history in which desertion was boiled down to a problem of character. The men's voices cannot be heard in these published accounts, except for the last words uttered before death, when they admitted guilt, prayed for God's forgiveness, or cried out for their mothers. The empty news accounts stripped the deserter of his individuality and served the authors' intention to create a grand narrative out of a single incident. The vivid published accounts of executions in the North and South dwelt on the physical appearance of the condemned. In this way editors conflated class with character, a profound distortion of the historical record that subsumed the deserter in an absurd stereotype of a shameless and lone figure without regard for his family or nation. When one of Stonewall Jackson's staff officers described a captured leader of the Rockingham Rebellion as "a tigrous looking fellow," he felt no need to consider the legitimacy of the man's grievance. In the officer's eyes, the men were clearly uncivilized mountaineers, and that explained everything.[149] By equating appearance with character, Northern and Southern elites could dismiss lower-class grievances as acts of perfidy while still maintaining their sentimental view of war as an ennobling experience for that special class of men who possessed moral and physical discipline. Elites on both sides confirmed their circular argument that only men who possessed character as civilians could show themselves as having character in war. Deserters, on the other hand, were seen as men without scruples whose cunning looks and shiftless mannerisms, rather than the circumstances and the materiality of their world, explained away their political protests as the deceitful work of men who were inherently treacherous.

# 6

# Facing the Enemy and
# Confronting Defeat

———

IN THE WAKE OF THE COLOSSAL UNION DEFEAT AT FREDERICKSBURG, the Army of the Potomac's Amos Judson felt no shame in joining the outcry against the war. He did not offer a partisan rant against the Lincoln administration, however, nor did he denounce General Ambrose Burnside for the needless butchery of some 12,600 men. His criticisms went much deeper, striking at the very core of the North's sentimental culture with its enshrinement of extreme courage and its sanitization of the war's most grotesque elements. Such romance, Judson believed, was partially responsible for the needless slaughter before Marye's Heights. He was particularly incensed at the newspapers for seducing readers with thrilling accounts of heroism at the expense of a realistic depiction of the battle. This mystification of war, Judson felt, violated the memory of the fallen, whose last moments were not of home and country, but of fear and horror. In a letter to his hometown newspaper, the *Erie (Pa.) Dispatch*, Judson refused to hold back, excoriating everyone for believing that soldiering was all valor and fame. "What wicked business this is — this shedding of human blood!" Judson proclaimed. "How much more (if it be not an evil thought) would I rather give life than take it. This is what men call glory. Oh, fools, fools, fools! . . . There now what a fool I was: I promised to resign before another battle, and here I am again. If I ever live to get out of this they'll never fool me into it again."[1]

A few months after the Battle of Fredericksburg, the Army of the Potomac would get its revenge at Gettysburg in a crushing victory that took some twenty-five thousand men from Lee's Army of Northern Virginia. One of the survivors, Captain Thomas Taylor of Alabama, did not wait long to proclaim a semivictory for the South; he would not let the reality of a harrowing defeat stand in the way. Writing on July 17, from the southern bank of the Potomac River, Taylor assured his loved ones that the army's prestige had been preserved through the superior bravery of his comrades. Yet all the courage in the world, he reasoned, could not overcome the impregnable position that the enemy happened to stumble upon. The Yankees, in other words, did not conquer Confederate courage or defeat the generalship of Robert E. Lee through superior fighting. Evidence of Confederate dominance revealed itself during the retreat when the Army of the Potomac turned timid, a cautious advance that told Taylor all he needed to know. The Army of Northern Virginia, at least in his mind, still instilled fear in its adversary. "At night we withdrew for the purpose of drawing the enemy out," he wrote on July 17 in a state of exhaustion, "but they did not seem disposed to follow. On the following day we marched across the mountains toward Hagerstown. Here we halted a few days for the enemy but he did not attack us. The river being up provisions hard to procure, Gen. Lee brought his Army into Virginia again." Nowhere in his analysis did Taylor acknowledge that the Federal army had secured victory, compelling the Confederate army to retreat. In dodging the inconvenient truth of defeat, Taylor also overlooked the fact that his generals had abandoned thousands of Confederate wounded to the Yankees at Gettysburg. Things "look gloomy," he admitted, but no setback could shake his faith in the Almighty's ultimate desire to preserve the Confederacy against such a vile adversary. "I pray [to] God that he will show his power to save by delivering us from the hands of our enemies," he wrote.[2]

Why did Taylor seemingly fall into a state of denial over the loss at Gettysburg and essentially paper over the near physical destruction of Lee's army, while Judson felt free to condemn himself and his fellow Northerners for glorifying war after a humiliating defeat, knowing that he would be vulnerable to the judgment of the crowd? Typically, historians have framed such a question as a matter of morale to be studied by tracking the ebb and flow of military events as a baseline from which to tabulate and evaluate soldiers' opinions. Once the sample is deemed representative, general claims are put forth about ideological beliefs and political commitments as a gauge of an army's will to fight. This approach is valuable in yielding various groupings of soldiers or cross sections of the rank and file.[3] Interpretively rich and densely researched studies have grown out of this methodology, but this approach—with its focus on the substance of what soldiers wrote—cannot entirely explain how and why Taylor and Judson processed defeat so differently.

Both men understood themselves as veteran soldiers, both were deeply committed to their respective causes, and both were disposed toward a pragmatic reading of the war, yet they made meaning of battlefield defeat in very different ways. Judson's ability to achieve ironic or critical detachment after Fredericksburg is striking; it suggests a way of thinking that enabled some Union soldiers to stand outside the North's wartime culture without repudiating the cause or his comrades. Taylor, on the other hand, found it difficult, if not impossible, to read life through the lines of ironic detachment. He did not dig below the appearance of things when he put pen to paper after the failed Pennsylvania Campaign. Rather than confront the complex problems of an army wrecked by the very generals and aggressive tactics that had brought so much success, Taylor rid himself of the intellectual clutter and emotional ambiguity of the moment when the discrepancy between aspiration and reality should have at least temporarily consumed him in doubt. His deep trust in God, his confidence in Robert E. Lee, and his political commitment to the Confederate cause gave him hope for the future, but that does not entirely explain how he came to articulate his thoughts, emotions, and experiences in that moment.[4] Absolutism figured prominently in his way of perceiving, understanding, and ordering the world. For Taylor and other defenders of the Confederate's slaveholding regime, absolutism had the effect of stripping away the confusing and the controversial—the very elements that would have instilled contextual depth and texture in his post-Gettysburg letters. In fact, secondary scholarship suggests that Confederates were generally inclined to represent staggering defeats as victories, refusing, even when the results were unmistakably clear, to admit any weakness or failure with regard to the Yankees.[5]

The words of Taylor and Judson speak not of cultural uniformity in Union or Confederate armies, but to the forms of consciousness or ways of thinking that were available to the rank and file. Ideas were rich and plentiful among men on both sides, and their letters are a potpourri of conflicting opinions and beliefs. On both sides, volunteers discovered how ideas arose in a spontaneous moment, continuously reshaped and revised, or even discarded, according to the circumstances. Pragmatism best describes the wartime shift among soldiers who came to value ideas for their adaptability in helping them cope with a turbulent world.[6] Pragmatism served the Union and Confederate soldiers in similar ways, but it also functioned differently on each side. Pragmatism freed Amos Judson from the shackles of dogma, enabling him to step outside himself and assume a position of ironic detachment against the dominant culture of sentimentalism. In this position, he exposed the absurdities of war with brutal honesty. Like any historical actor, Judson was unable to free himself entirely from his cultural and material world, but he was able to get distance from an oppressive element of his sentimental culture without rejecting the cause itself or emptying the blood sacrifices of his comrades of their political meaning.

Whereas ironic detachment had a presence in Northern culture, Confederates appear to have been stuck in their own interiors by the need for a life structured by absolutism. How does one find evidence for this absence of irony? Reading against the grain of the author's intentions can capture an unstated value or belief or reveal imputed goals and intentions underlying behavior. Absolutism—though not a term that was explicitly used in any wartime letters—had a strong presence in shaping how Confederates brought meaning and order to their world. The power of absolutism derived from a driving need for honor, which was at the core of the South's male power structure buttressed by the enslavement of African Americans. The need for honor during a time of war channeled Confederate perceptions and depictions of their world through the lens of absolutism, a way of seeing that rendered the world in black-and-white terms, and thus did not give them much flexibility to justify or defend their actions in the field. This partially explains why some Confederates struggled to see their own complicity in the war's follies. Their overwhelming need for mastery, or at least the appearance of it, encouraged delusional thinking among Confederates when Southern military and material worlds were collapsing. It is hardly surprising, then, that Thomas Taylor gazed back at his Gettysburg experience though the lens of absolutism and honor, given that manly reputations were on the line and the future of slavery in jeopardy. Although honor did not dictate a fixed code of conduct or create a consensus among white Southerners, it did turn into a coat of armor once Union armies invaded the South. Taylor's depiction of Gettysburg reveals how a code of honor could blunt reality-based thinking, keeping him from recognizing the limits of his own thinking or assuming a range of perspectives when confronting life's deep incongruities.

Taylor, like many other slaveholding Southerners, was inclined to marginalize or even ignore information that challenged self-understanding or might weaken one's appearance at either the individual or collective level. The private and the public sides of an individual, in other words, were inseparable and almost always in equilibrium in the Southern mind, largely because slavery granted whites an immediate and constant affirmation of the self. This is not to suggest that an intellectually coherent Southern mind existed. Debates over political, religious, and social matters were as bitterly contested in the South as they were in the North, but Southerners were more bounded in their thinking, less capable of delineating between group and individual thought, and more inclined to remain behind the walls of community standards. The conflation of the private and the public among Southerners, as Michael O'Brien points out, is revealed in scores of Southern memoirs and reminiscences, whose authors almost never reveal their inner self.[7]

The cultural lens of absolutism tended to filter out contextual information that would have encouraged empathy, self-criticalness, and public candor. This is how Robert E. Lee, when witnessing the collapse of his army after Gettysburg, could reduce the problem of desertion to a straightforward link between character and individual choice, averring that his actions were not behind the collapse of the army and that others were acting against the will of God. This is how a young Virginia officer, on seeing his army disintegrate during the retreat to Appomattox, could still believe in Confederate invincibility, insisting that all would end well if his comrades remained true to their inner selves. And this is how a poor and dejected North Carolina soldier could become fatalistic, blaming individuals rather than condemn the society for which he fought, when he wrote, "Sometimes when I get about half enough to eat and get to studying how thing is going . . . it makes me feel like some body was to blam[e] and not me[.] I am inocent of having anything to do to bring on this ware and dont feel rite suffering here . . . on account of some bodys misdoings."[8] In each instance, by closely aligning God to the Confederate cause, these three men were well situated for an ironic explanation of their situation. Yet when providential designs failed to conform to earthly expectations, their perspective on the world turned darkly fatalistic. Their sense of disgrace became so overwhelming that they threw up their hands and refused to take off their personal armor, as they did not want to be exposed to public scrutiny or tempted to self-introspection. This is not to suggest that Confederates were incapable of disaffection. Thousands of men deserted and scores of women protested against the war, acts of dissent inspired by bread-and-butter issues, military defeat, and a Confederate government that seemed unable and unwilling to meet the needs of its citizenry. Yet their protests were shackled by honor and absolutism, making it difficult for them to recognize the paradoxical effects of their own behavior on the world around them and to assume accountability in those moments when individual action did not lead to clear-cut results. White reaction to Southern defeat further exposes a perspective of absolutism, as ex-Confederates were quick to portray themselves as victims, a perspective that helps explain why the Lost Cause took the form of a mournful eulogy in which white Southerners were the tragic sufferers of fate.[9]

Northerners were no different than Southerners in setting themselves up for an ironic reading of life, since they, too, were relatively self-assured in their ability to read the providential tea leaves. While they shared a firm belief in Providence as the war's final arbitrator, this common conviction did not create a uniform way of thinking. The use of irony allowed Northerners to assume a degree of responsibility for human misery, as it could take the form of a critical sympathy in which human limits and human agency were both recognized and respected. Irony did not always lead to recognition of the other, which was critical to achieving psychological liberation from the misery of war, nor did it encourage nihilism among Federal troops. Irony did leave the men vulnerable to a troubling relativism, as Northern soldiers were more likely to recognize how both sides could mold their wartime experiences into a legitimate defense of war — regardless of their cause. Irony forced them to confront the notion that truth was elusive, fragmented, and constructed, but most Union soldiers, even when facing a metaphysical crisis, felt largely paralyzed to do anything about the contradictions and falsehoods of their existence.[10]

It is possible to detect in soldiers' letters general tendencies of their home region without reducing people to caricatures or stereotypes. To fully appreciate why absolutism took hold in a slave South and why ironic detachment was more readily available in the North, the investigation needs to go down deep into the society and culture that each man inhabited.[11] Detecting regional differences between Northerners and Southerners is particularly difficult, however, since both Union and Confederate soldiers spent their formative years before the war in parallel classrooms, where they read similar books and heard comparable lectures while gazing out the same windows of republicanism, Christianity, liberal capitalism, and Victorianism. Their wartime correspondence, as a result, has a similar ideological cast. Our understanding of nineteenth-century America is often framed around the Civil War and whether the revolutionary consequences of that conflict derived from deep antagonisms between the North and South. The scholarly debate over this issue has produced some of the following generalizations: the South was more religious, the North more capitalistic; the South was more traditional, the North more modern; and the South was more hierarchical, the North more egalitarian.[12] Recent scholarship has downplayed regional differences by emphasizing how Northerners and Southerners were simultaneously modern, traditionalist, religious, capitalistic, hierarchical, and individualistic.

Antebellum regional commonalities drew from a similar national experience that flowed out of broader international trends and influences. The intellectual and cultural exchanges across the Atlantic were of undeniable importance, but these intersections of thought have unfortunately convinced some historians that the regions were merging together in the decade before the Civil War. Northerners and Southerners are seen as both products of and contributors to an aggressive middle-class Victorian culture produced by the emerging democratic-capitalist order of the Age of Progress. Consequently, scholars have been hesitant to claim antebellum exceptionalism for either the North or the South, as both regions participated in a global community of transatlantic capitalistic expansion. To be sure, there were commonalities between the North and South that gave the social life of the antebellum United States a degree of uniformity, as all Americans expressed themselves through the cultural language of sentimentalism while upholding the principles of economic liberalism, Christianity, and republicanism.

Similarities in belief and experience are important and certainly merit further attention, but focusing on shared ideas and behavior can lead us to conflate Southern slave society and Northern wage-labor society into a united land of bourgeois values and middle-class aspirations.[13] The challenge is to uncover something more elemental than ideological and political differences, to expose the exchange between ways of perceiving and the structure of ideology without papering over fundamentally shared ways of living. It is true that some historians, using the soft analytical category of identity, have been too blunt in their depictions of Northerners and Southerners as being fundamentally this or that and thus disposed to act a certain way. Yet suggesting that there are common threads running throughout a regional culture does not mean that everyone in that region wrapped themselves in the same uniform historical cloth. Allowing for claims that broadly describe a cultural center is necessary and desirable, or we will be left with a historiography that rarely has distance on social units above the local and state level. If the current trend continues, we can expect more books that purport to be grand studies of the North and South but that, beyond their titles, are actually microstudies of discrete parts of the United States. As long as scholars are unable to gain altitude on local variations, the micro approach will block lines of sight, obscuring important foundational differences that existed between one society devoted to slave labor and another to wage labor.

As scholars Bertram Wyatt-Brown, Elizabeth Fox-Genovese, Kenneth Greenberg, Lewis P. Simpson, and Stephen Stowe have argued, slavery played the critical role in affirming and stabilizing white Southerners' self-understanding while discouraging a deep exploration of the subjective self. This was not because racism had entrapped the Southern mind, but because the need for absolute mastery in a slave system made it unnecessary, even risky, for a white Southerner to probe the deep recesses of his own consciousness, where life could become ambiguous, where truth could be elusive, and where self-doubt could not be avoided. Assuming the perspective of another had the potential to force white Southerners to place themselves in the position of people whom they deemed physiologically, spiritually, and intellectually inferior. It is difficult to imagine anything more threatening to the South's united and spirited defense of inequality than the notion of a common humanity forged through the universal emotions of love and pity. The idea that bloodlines were of no consequence, that ancestry was insignificant, and that individual feeling should prevail over community traditions was a radical affront to white Southerners, who, while possessing a strong sense of individualism, never allowed this impulse to foment an insurgency against the authority of the family and community.[14] Northerners were not men without honor, as Bertram Wyatt-Brown, Kenneth Greenberg, Lorien Foote, Amy Greenberg, and Kanisorn Wongsrichanalai have observed, but they cared less about appearance than Southerners and focused more on disciplining the inner self as a means of achieving character. The Confederates' sense of self-worth, by contrast, boiled down to the perception of having mastery over others, even if gaining public reputation necessitated a loss of restraint and the use of violence.[15]

Northerners and Southerners headed off to enlist in 1861 expecting a bloodless victory, but they quickly discovered that war creates one of those rare and revealing historical moments when prior habits of mind are exposed because there is no escaping the constant stress on the perception and thinking of the participants.[16] Battlefield reverses were particularly traumatic for soldiers: they staggered from the killing fields physically exhausted and emotionally drained, trying to make sense of the event at both a private and a public level. Although soldiers considered the mayhem of combat incomprehensible and difficult to translate onto paper, they wrote about the military and political impact of battles with incredible insight and understanding. In general, Civil War soldiers looked at military reverses as if they were violent summer storms — fierce, but brief and inevitably followed by clear skies under which their army would have another opportunity to achieve battlefield redemption. For the most part, Civil War soldiers wrote straightforward battle accounts, outlining troop movements, tallying casualties, and assuring loved ones that they were well and that they had done their duty. Both sides were quick to blame others for their defeat, damning incompetent generals, condemning meddling politicians, and chastising civilians for their bulletproof naïveté.

Union soldiers were no different from their Confederate adversaries in reimagining futile defeats as redemptive moments of individual bravery and honor. But we will see in the next section that when the unpredictable and bewildering circumstances of war crushed expectations of what military service was supposed to be like, Union soldiers were critically positioned to question and even challenge the dominant opinions of their society with greater self-awareness than was generally found in the Confederacy. Historian Drew Gilpin Faust supports this generalization about the North, arguing that "one product of the horror of the Civil War was the proliferation of irony, of a posture of distance and doubt in relation to experience."[17] In no way does this suggest that white Southerners silenced themselves when military affairs started coming off the rails. Newspaper editors, officers, politicians, and civilians could be savage in their condemnations of failed generals and government officials. Generals Braxton Bragg and Joseph Johnston and President Jefferson Davis, in particular, came under merciless personal attacks throughout the war.[18] Lincoln and his generals were also not spared the wrath of the press and the public.

At the same time, there were differences in the ways that Union and Confederate soldiers critiqued their respective war efforts, and these differences come into focus when we look at rank-and-file humor. Plenty of Union soldiers were willing and inclined to use irony, ridicule, satire, and self-mockery in fierce commentaries against the war that spared no one, not even the author himself. Confederates, on the other hand, showed great reluctance to tell a joke at the expense of themselves and their cause, especially during the aftermath of a battlefield failure. Southern humor could only reveal the foolhardiness of the enemy or bring into focus the devious designs of the Yankees and their treacherous ways of waging war. They also delivered full broadsides against speculators who profited from the Confederate war effort.

For instance, Georgia's Charles Henry Smith, alias Bill Arp, stood out among Confederate humorists for his folksy attacks against Lincoln and his abolitionist minions in letters articulated in the spoken dialect of a semiliterate poor white. Arp's satirical style assured readers that even the Confederacy's poorest and least educated were as wise as "Mr. Linkhorn," and as devoted to the Southern cause as any slaveholding Confederate. Arp warned "his friend," Linkhorn, of the Confederate soldiers who had fire in their belly to kill Yankees: "Most of em are so hot that they fairly siz when you pour water on em, and that's the way they make up their military companies here now — when a man

*Facing the Enemy and Confronting Defeat*

applies to jine the volunteers, they sprinkle him, and if he sizzes they take him, and if he don't they don't."[19] Arp's wicked sense of humor was extremely popular, and his articles were widely syndicated by 1863, but how his satire was actually taken by Confederate soldiers is difficult to say. The rank and file must have enjoyed reading the words of a man speaking in plain talk against the "shirkers," the "skulkers," and the "dodgers" of conscription, but his satire, which was aimed at firming up the Confederate war effort, generated laughter that might have kept the Confederates from gaining the critical distance necessary to address the political and military problems that spurred Smith's creation of Arp in the first place. Confederate humor got soldiers laughing, but probably not thinking, as their nation went down the tubes.[20]

For the vast majority of Union soldiers in the Army of the Potomac, the Battle of Fredericksburg was no laughing matter. Yet there were humorists in the ranks who were not averse to making everyone part of the punch line. The lopsided defeat did not keep Pennsylvania's George Breck from using satire to indict the entire army in his hometown paper, the Lebanon (Pa.) Courier. He grabbed his readers' attention with a self-mocking headline, "The Masterly Retreat." Although Breck acknowledged that most men charged to their death with spectacular courage, he thought that Fredericksburg should be remembered as "another grand 'skedaddle,' or ought we to use a more polite or rhetorical expression and call it another 'masterly retreat.'" Breck pointed out that his comrades knew "what it means to 'skedaddle' for they have learned it by experience." At the same time, Breck used humor to unmask the cowardly behavior of his comrades, using laughter to soften the blow. As soon as the shells started flying, Breck noticed how many men suddenly "thought themselves unable to walk." Then the order came for the regiment to recross the Rappahannock River. Suddenly, they possessed "all the sprightliness of youth." "Such is the effect of escaping from a place of safety and protection," he concluded with a snide jab at his shirking comrades. "Going to meet the enemy and coming away from the enemy are two different things."[21]

By turning himself and his army into a target through humor, Breck incriminated himself in the Fredericksburg debacle, a stunning and largely unthinkable admission for Confederates, who were in no laughing mood in the midst of traumatic defeats such as Gettysburg, the collapse at Missionary Ridge in Tennessee, and the fall of Atlanta.[22] It was unthinkable to print any jest about wasted valor in Confederate papers. The thought of renaming Pickett's Charge "Pickett's Futility," or of poking fun at Lee's retreat to Virginia by calling it the "great skedaddle," would have been a humiliating admission of inferiority — a jibe that came at the expense of the writer's own reputation. Southern humor might have become dark as the war progressed, but it never evolved into self-implication or mockery after a defeat as it did in the North.[23] These interpretations are in keeping with historian John Mayfield's important findings about how the war changed Southern humor. Mayfield argues that "once an enemy was clearly identified and demonized, the battlefield superiority of masquerade culture — with its indifference to death and its many postures — became the ideal, and Southern men lost their sense of ambiguity and irony."[24]

A comparison of the letters of James Bailey of the Seventeenth Connecticut Infantry and Melvin Dwinell of the Eighth Georgia Infantry — both published in their hometown newspapers — further illustrates the ways that humor created a more expansive political culture in the North than it did in the South. Since his 1862 enlistment in the Seventeenth Connecticut, James Bailey had contributed a regular column to the *Danbury (Conn.) Times* under the pen name "Manton," never missing an opportunity to ridicule army life even if it came at the expense of comrades and the cause. At the same time, Bailey cherished the Union, and no amount of incompetence by his government or his army could shake his patriotic convictions or diminish his love for his comrades. In the aftermath of Gettysburg, however, Bailey could not find the "Manton" persona within himself. For the first time Bailey felt trapped, unable to achieve critical detachment from a dreary, depressing, and destructive war. He could not clear his mind of gory memories of "blood and brains," "bits of flesh," and "splinters of bone." His reading audience wanted a "thrilling description" of the battle, but Bailey knew he could not deliver it. Every time he put pen to paper, the ghostly "white faces" of the dead rose up before him. Unable to separate himself from such horrid images, Bailey gave up trying to become his alter ego. "I have written to you just as I felt," he explained, "something I seldom do, and past and present circumstances have conspired to make a difference. Next week, I trust, to present Manton as he is, which will be sufficient time for *repairing* him."[25] By assuming an alter ego, Bailey gained critical distance from his own experiences and the very society that sent him off to war.

Of course, Southerners also took pen names when publishing their works, but they had more difficulty stepping outside themselves, even when writing in obscurity. Confederate correspondent and Georgia soldier Melvin Dwinell never achieved the same level of critical detachment as Bailey and other Northern writers because he refused to make himself the subject of inquiry in the two hundred letters he published in the *Rome (Ga.) Courier*. In these accounts, Dwinell wrote straightforward narratives about his regiment, the Eighth Georgia Infantry. They are to be read as daily indexes of life, a journalistic approach typical of the day between Northern and Southern correspondents, though each paper had its own distinct personality and political perspective.[26] It is noteworthy, however, that Dwinell was either unwilling or unable to dig deeper beneath the surface of life when writing about the failed 1862 Maryland Campaign. While he employed humor with a political purpose, it was never turned inward, was never reflective, and was always employed to denigrate the enemy. When writing about Antietam, Dwinell recounted a story of a Unionist farmer who condemned Lee's soldiers for their disgraceful physical appearance. A Confederate retorted, "When we go to kill hogs we always put on our old clothes," a clever response that Dwinell considered a most perfect and appropriate expression of wit.[27] Southerners like Dwinell could use humor to cut down the enemy, lampoon poor whites, and debase slaves, but they struggled to laugh at themselves. Confederates typically emphasized their differences in order to gain distance from those worthy of scorn and contempt, rather than using laughter to draw everyone—including the ones telling the joke—into the ridiculousness of life. The almost complete absence of irony in their reading of the world also inhibited their self-awareness, obscuring the very ways they contributed to life's awful absurdities.

Southern humor almost always took the form of ridicule among Confederates, discouraging expressions of empathy for those at the bottom of the army who did not conform to the high standards of courage. After the Battle of Antietam, for instance, when Lee's battered army sought the restorative powers of Virginia's Shenandoah Valley, Dwinell reflected on the campaign while avoiding any hint of controversy that might have brought into question the South's military and political authority. He overlooked the failings of Confederate generalship despite a Union victory at Antietam. He made no attempt to explain the Army of Northern Virginia's near self-destruction in Maryland, despite seeing thousands of men slip away from the ranks because of a nightmarish logistical breakdown. And he showed no interest in exploring the conflicted emotions of soldiers who survived a horrible battle, where they witnessed a bloodletting of some twenty-five thousand men in a single day. While Dwinell was not concerned with probing the more controversial and traumatic aspects of the Maryland Campaign, he was also not oblivious to the war's human destruction or blind to its military consequences. He was justifiably concerned about his unit's appalling decline since its 1861 formation, especially now that it was a pale shadow of its former self. "There is such a thing as killing the life and fire of a regiment long before the last man is killed," Dwinell complained. "It would seem that our officers have been trying the experiment on the Eighth, to see just how much a body of troops could endure and 'stand up to it.'"[28] Yet even in making this criticism, Dwinell put a lid on the potentially dangerous implications of his commentary, refusing to take it a step further and examine the complicated reasons for his unit's demise.

Bailey's writings, on the other hand, have a distinctive Northern accent—expressing mixed emotions, acknowledging the unknowability of life, and exploring the contradictory nature of experience in ways that were not easily accessible to most Confederates. The terms in which Bailey experienced the world did not require him to sacrifice his own judgment for a purified version of life, or to subordinate his own self-understanding to a soldier identity promoted by military and political authorities. Because he could think from more than one primary perspective, Bailey could imagine how his own narrow view of himself both conformed to and contradicted how society might perceive him. Under the cover of "Manton," Bailey scornfully wrote: "I am sick of the 'list of killed and wounded,' tired of the din, and weary of the hard tack. I pale for a change in the order of affairs." But, he added sarcastically, "I am exceedingly grateful for the knowledge that the Rebellion is on its last legs . . . and proud am I to know that our All wise Government is about to employ vigorous measures for the putting down of this accursed rebellion."[29] In this passage, Bailey, who never once questioned the rightness of the Union cause, exposed the gap between the measures and messages of the Federal government and what was "really happening" on the ground level of the war. His use of mockery was not intended to persecute any one group; to do so would have further isolated him and other private soldiers from comrades and civilians alike.

After the fiasco at Fredericksburg, Bailey felt free to mock an army and a government that had, through breathtaking incompetence, sacrificed more than twelve thousand men in a single day of fighting. Bailey used Manton to invent a story about a unit that he sarcastically called the "codfish regiment." It appears that he had no intention of disparaging any particular group of men; rather, Bailey wanted his audiences to laugh at the codfish regiment as a way to empathize with all soldiers at Fredericksburg, even those who were not given a chance to prove their mettle. "During the charges across the plain the boys from time to time cheered on our men, to the danger of attracting the fire of the Gray Backs," he wrote, "but heedless of the danger we continued to hurrah, thus exhilarating our troops, and enabling them to stand the fury as long as they did." "Such is the effects of bravery and strategy," Bailey added, "for we brought ourselves away without the loss of a man, thus saving the expense of coffins and medical haggling."

In this passage, Bailey exposes the jarring gap between the expectations of war and its ugly reality. He reserved much of his ridicule for the highly idealized code of bravery by positioning himself as both a witness to and a partici-

BELLYCOSE APPEARANCE OF OUR BRAVE BOYS AFTER THANKSGIVING.

"Bellycose Appearance of Our Brave Boys after Thanksgiving," which ran in *Harper's Weekly* on December 3, 1864, exemplifies how Northern popular culture allowed for self-mockery and ridicule, even at the expense of the soldiers in the field. Confederate print culture could be highly critical as well, but the South had too much at stake to violate male honor by questioning the manliness of the nation's soldiers.
(Courtesy of Special Collections, Musselman Library, Gettysburg College, Gettysburg, Pa.)

pant in the army's destruction. His use of mockery reveals the degree to which he felt confined by prevailing sentimental ideas of manliness and courage. Yet Bailey was able to break away from this code of bravery by purposely turning himself into a target; that gave him the freedom to deride the foibles and follies of officers, politicians, and the public without appearing heartless, politically seditious, or culturally traitorous. Enlisting himself into the codfish unit was crucial in making Bailey and all of his comrades culpable for so many deaths inspired by the bravado of war. His use of ridicule did not lead to irretrievable cynicism, since ironic detachment gave him the distance to stand back, feel empathy, and express self-deprecation while condemning and congratulating the army he fought for. Without ironic detachment, Bailey would have been incapable of such political sarcasm.

The extent to which George Breck's and James Bailey's words can be found elsewhere is difficult to say, but the wider significance of their humor registered and was reinforced by Northern print culture. As historian Matthew Gallman has shown in his excellent work *Defining Duty in the Civil War*, Northern people were not averse to self-ridicule, especially through political cartoons that mocked pompous officers, pampered women, and poor Irish immigrants as some of the more ludicrous aspects of the Union war effort. In *Frank Leslie's Budget of Fun*, an illustration shows a woman listening to a grizzled veteran who is home on leave and explaining that life in the field has destroyed his health. She barely acknowledges his tale as an interesting story. Gallman points out how this illustration used dark humor to mock Northern women for their indifference to the true nature of the war.[30] Such derision originated within an ironic disposition that positioned many Northerners to read life with a degree of critical detachment. In his impressively researched history of Fredericksburg, historian George C. Rable found countless examples of Northern soldiers using the words "'knaves,' or 'fools' or 'ignoramuses' or 'asses'" to deride those managing the war.[31] Such language is virtually invisible in Confederate self-condemnations after any battlefield defeat, especially in newspaper accounts.[32] What was visible to Bailey and many other Northerners, as a result, were the fundamental antagonisms between the self and society, which gave them a greater capacity to make light of the horrors of combat, criticize bombastic authority, and mock the political hypocrisy of the Union military effort.

A comparison of Abraham Lincoln and Jefferson Davis further illustrates this point, though the two men certainly had idiosyncratic differences as well. Although Davis and Lincoln came from similar rural areas where the tall tale was admired, the divergence in sensibilities between a slaveholding and a free-labor society surfaces in their use of humor. Lincoln showed little restraint in using comedy that poked fun at himself, even as a way to confess his role in the blunderings of the Union war effort. Before a large war rally at the Capitol following the failed Seven Days Campaign of 1862, Lincoln admitted his culpability in defeat. One journalist recorded the president as saying, "If the military commander in the field cannot be successful, not only the Secretary of War, but myself, for the time being the master of them both, cannot be but failures. [Laughter and applause]."[33] Lincoln also loved humorists whose devotion to the Union cause was conveyed through a biting irony, even though the witty stories often came at his expense.

Jefferson Davis, on the other hand, never used humor in a reflective way that could expose himself to criticism or culpability, particularly after a military defeat. In fact, one historian found an unshakeable certitude running through Davis's words and actions, while Lincoln was "not certain of anything."[34] Jefferson Davis was apparently no different from many of his citizens, especially those of the ruling elite, who tended to interpret the war in unambiguous ways. They imagined the conflict as a source of strength, and their absolutism often blinded them to sources of class and racial turmoil in the war. Maybe because the stakes of the war were so high, Southern illustrators were unwilling or unable to implicate the Southern people in the preposterousness of life, since that might unmask individual weakness and could even compromise the war effort.

In Southern print culture, a distinctive Confederate sense of humor lampooned Northern generals to shield Southern soldiers from being unmade by a punch line. Lithographs and engravings, including cartoons and caricatures, highlighted the pages of the *Southern Illustrated News* and *Southern Punch*, but their publication life was brief and their circulation was severely limited. The authors of *The Confederate Image: Prints of the Lost Cause* recovered a rare cartoon series of the 1862 Peninsula Campaign that "poked fun" at Union general George B. McClellan by having him wear "an oversized Napoleonic chapeau." All the Confederate generals were idealized as dashing cavaliers, standing firm and without fear, just as the Southern people wanted to imagine their defenders of Richmond. The failings of Joseph E. Johnston and Stonewall Jackson, the lack of discipline of Confederate troops in the field, and the controversy over white soldiers having to dig earthworks were simply ignored. Extortionists and hoarders in Richmond, despised by soldiers and civilians alike, were drawn in caricature without any sense of their background, except for the speculator who looks Jewish. The problems depicted by these illustrations resided with the individual, not with society as a whole. None of the cartoons ask the readers to adjust their thinking or to assume the perspective of the other.[35]

In the North, the political satire was tougher and more aggressive in pointing to the contradictions of the Union war effort. To be sure, Northern readers could escape through sentimentalized depictions of home life and family. At the same time, political cartoons assumed a harder edge in the North, where artists exposed the absurdities of a Union war effort that met reverse time and time again. The use of satire enabled the illustrator to disclose the intractability of the nation's problems without the audience losing themselves in laughter. "In cartoons," writes Fiona Deans Halloran, "faces, bodies, and gestures are distorted or exaggerated in order to emphasize foibles or hypocrisy and to ridicule."[36] Most of the cartoons made fun of the Rebels, but plenty of satirists looked inward at their own society, sparing no one, in a humorous style that lent itself to ironic detachment.

It could be argued that critical or ironic detachment was a posture toward the world that one could only assume in camp, where soldiers had the time to be reflective and write home. Yet even in active operations, when minds and bodies were preoccupied with the job of being a soldier, Union veterans could step outside their own narrow view of themselves and empathize with the enemy. Fraternization along the picket lines showed men on both sides to be pragmatic in their willingness to disobey orders and converse with the enemy when the circumstances permitted. Self-preservation and a desire to exchange newspapers, coffee, and tobacco explains why men called these illegal gatherings, but the cease-fires were dangerous undertakings along a firing line that was inherently unpredictable and potentially lethal.

Soldiers were fascinated by unauthorized truces, and in letters home as well as in newspapers they gave their readers a close-up view of the enemy. For the most part, men on both sides wrote of fraternization as an act of individual adventure, even though the meetings were fairly mundane affairs. Based on a sample of more than one hundred primary sources relating to fraternization between 1862 and 1864, only a few soldiers unleashed a wrathful denunciation of the other side. The trading of goods and the swapping of stories was essentially a courting ritual, and when picket posts were fixed and the men occupied the ground for a sustained period of time, trust developed and soldiers opened up about the war, their families, and even their disgust with the politicians, generals, and people back home.

Familiarity with the enemy sometimes led to brazen violations of military discipline in which soldiers refused to fire along the picket lines. During the battles outside Richmond in June 1864, a Maine soldier watched his comrades walk upright in the trenches, seemingly oblivious to sharpshooters, when a Confederate yelled across the lines: "'Lie low, Yanks! We have orders to fire!'" A company of Southern skirmishers did not pull their triggers, according to this man, until "both parties made themselves invisible."[37] As the war progressed, Confederate and Federal soldiers were more inclined to stop what they referred to as the "barbarous practice" of picket firing, especially during campaigns when battle lines were stagnant and officers looked the other way, but there were also exceptions involving outright savagery. Cease-fires abruptly ended as soon as USCTs filed into the trenches, as some Confederates relished the opportunity to put a bullet through a black soldier. Other soldiers could not have cared less about the enemy's race when it came to killing along the picket line. In the Army of Tennessee, a Confederate soldier showed no remorse when

*Facing the Enemy and Confronting Defeat*

he wrote in March 1864, "I am fond of that [skirmish] duty. I fired several ronds at the sons of bitches if I should say such a word. I cant tell whether I hit one or not but I tride like the devil."[38]

After Appomattox, both sides represented these unofficial truces as gatherings of American brothers whose sense of honor and spirit of manliness overcame the hateful politics of the day. The gunning down of black pickets turned into a veritable Confederate carnival game during the war, but these savage incidents vanished entirely from postwar accounts. Scholars have since burned away this romantic haze to capture the "real war" where vengeance trumped restraint, motivating Northern and Southern soldiers to kill without mercy and to destroy without conscience.[39] Yankees and Confederates were enemies, to be sure, and as the war progressed, both sides succumbed to awful acts of vengeance that were empty of high ideals. But in overturning the romantic notion of a brother's war, there has been a tendency to dismiss fraternization as a postwar exaggeration by Northerners and Southerners who were drunk on the champagne of reconciliation. In actuality, moments of solidarity showed how soldiers changed the rules of engagement based on circumstances, a flexibility of thought that showed how private soldiers in becoming seasoned in the ranks did not always follow a prescribed code of conduct. The flexibility in thought showed a unique expression of professionalism among Union and Confederate veterans, who could defy their superiors out of a combination of soldiery respect and the desire to survive. Men could look across the lines and see fellow enlisted men who understood the experience of being a soldier, and in that moment, as they felt a sense of solidarity with the enemy, they could not resist the troubling conclusion that the enemy in some ways understood them better than those at home. Yet some Union soldiers drew very different lessons from these encounters. They were more inclined not only to feel compassion for the enemy but also a degree of accountability for their adversaries' plight — an admission of responsibility that was inconceivable to Confederates. After seeing Southern soldiers along the Rappahannock River in Virginia after the December 13, 1862, Battle of Fredericksburg, a Union soldier observed of the enemy: "They are good looking men. They said If we would stop firing they would and so we stoped. It is to bad to make men slaughter each other when they would be friends."[40] Another Federal wrote at the same time about Confederate pickets: "We often see them & talk with them & trade coffee with them for tobacco. They are the same kind of people as we are."[41] A New York soldier during the Peninsula Campaign of 1862 reported home after meeting some Southern soldiers, "It is awful to think that we must look on them as our enemies, and murder each other by the thousand. Ah it is then that I wish this war to an end."[42]

Edwin Forbes shows how fraternization typically centered on soldiers trading goods and swapping stories, but these truces also relieved tension along the picket line, where life could be extinguished with the crack of a single rifle.
(Library of Congress Prints and Photographs Division, Washington, D.C.)

Near the end of the war, as the fighting seemed interminable along the Petersburg front, a Connecticut soldier published in his hometown paper that "the very Johnnies at our front showed familiar faces, and were almost as comrades instead of foes."[43] A Pennsylvania infantryman in Tennessee, after weeks of watching Union and Confederate soldiers meet between the lines, imagined whenever the armies clashed in battle that instead of engaging in a "bloody charge both parties will drop muskets and run and shake hands."[44]

In all of these accounts Union soldiers were able to identify with the enemy because of a critical sensibility that drew from a Northern wartime culture that insisted on the importance of sympathy in the face of human suffering.[45] Seeing shoeless men with filthy and ragged uniforms was visually captivating. When writing about these Confederate ragamuffins, Northerners emphasized the enemy's physical appearance and expressed compassion without any fear of appearing unmanly or unpatriotic to their readers. After the defeat at Chancellorsville, when plenty of Union soldiers nearly gave in to despair, New York's

*Facing the Enemy and Confronting Defeat*

Charles Bowen acknowledged the common humanity he shared with Confederates during a truce along the Rapidan River. Putting himself at incredible risk, he swam to the enemy side of the river to converse with some pickets from Alabama. Fortunately, he did not fall into the hands of a Southern officer, and he swam back without incident. In his letter home, Bowen consciously selected to include elements of his conversation that emphasized the malaise of war and the Confederacy's imminent collapse. Yet even in a report that was calculated to bolster civilian spirits, he could not help but admire Lee's veterans for undergoing hardships that only another fellow soldier could appreciate. In lauding the enemy, he showed no hint of shame and no fear that in praising his adversary he might be putting the reputation of himself and his comrades at risk.[46] "It is wonderful how man can be made to keep the field under such circumstances," Bowen opined. "I almost begin to think of them as the English officer did of Marion & his men, that they cant be *conquered*." The enemy's endurance showed a spirit of discipline and a display of character that Bowen felt any veteran could admire. He grieved over the war's cruelty to Confederates as well as Federals, never losing his sense of connectedness to all of God's creatures, including the enemy, since they were all subject to the bewildering forces of war. "Isn't it terrible to think that after being so friendly with each other," Bowen sadly concluded a month after defeat at Chancellorsville, "the very next day or week, we may be engaged in a deadly struggle. Oh how I wish this unnatural war would close."[47]

Such an expression of sympathy was a troubling development for the Union high command, and officers went to great lengths to limit contact between the lines, fearing that compassion would ultimately destroy discipline. Admiration for Southerners also clashed with a sentimental print culture in the North that, through sensationalized stories of battlefield courage, depicted Union soldiers as more manly than the enemy. Any acknowledgment of Confederate fortitude and suffering contradicted the public image of heroic Northern soldiers as masters of the enemy. In breaking ranks with the dominant voices of their society, Northern soldiers were mourning the death and destruction of war while also acknowledging their complicity in unleashing its horrors.[48]

Empathy for their adversaries promoted a spirit of flexibility in the Union ranks that made the hard-war policy against the South both situational and relatively moderate in its application, depending on whether the household held slaves.[49] There were plenty of fanatics who wanted to torch every field, barn, and outbuilding in the slaveholding South, but for the most part, members of the rank and file showed a mixture of severity and restraint when it came to the treatment of civilian property — except in South Carolina, where Sherman's men could not find enough matches in their rampage of destruction. In making Southern civilians feel the terror, grief, and physical suffering of war, Federal troops were hardly saints, but they certainly were not merciless thugs committed to a concept of total, all-annihilating war.[50]

Moreover, many of these men never lost their capacity to feel the suffering of the enemy, and this helped them to understand the perspective of Southerners who inflicted outrages against Northern armies. It was common for both sides to accuse the other of committing atrocities against their fallen comrades. As historian John Neff observes, "The animosity directed toward the living enemy was easily extended to the enemy death."[51] After the Battle of Fredericksburg, Union dead were laid out for burial and stripped naked of their clothing by Confederates, a ghastly and disturbing sight to behold and an equally difficult one to report home. Yet some Union soldiers would not allow themselves to become embittered over the desecration of their dead. On hearing that the Rebels had stripped "our dead and wounded and left them to suffer," a Union veteran wrote after Fredericksburg, "It is hard to credit this, for I believe the Rebels *are* human, but such acts are diabolical." "One cannot blame them," he quickly added, "to bury a good suit of Union clothes when they are nearly naked in winter would seem foolish."[52]

The sight of dead comrades without clothing also shocked Massachusetts soldier Roland Bowen. He thought the Confederates were justified in leaving the bodies naked, since "we stole or distroyed everything in the City." He even admitted to seeing a hog devour the body of a dead Confederate and commented that "no one would take pains to drive them away." "I was too busy stealing [in] the City," Bowen added, "besides I knew the hogs wanted something to eat. (Such is War)." His statement testifies to the hardening process that occurred widely among veterans, of course, but this conclusion also misses how Bowen came to accept the vilest aspects of war. Through a sensibility of critical or ironic detachment, Roland Bowen saw no reason why a hog should not live off a dead Confederate when the Rebels stole from Union corpses and his own army had gutted Fredericksburg. To conclude that this man had become callous to war's barbarisms tells only part of the story. The sensibility of critical detachment enriches the analysis by showing how Bowen perceived and depicted his experiences. The Massachusetts veteran did not lose himself to the chauvinism of Yankee superiority, nor did his heart become stone. He extended understanding to the Confederates, even defending their desecration of Union corpses out of necessity, because Roland Bowen understood that everyone was foundering in the cauldron of war—even a pig scrambling and scraping to survive.[53]

*Facing the Enemy and Confronting Defeat*

Army debating societies, where Union soldiers staged intellectual exercises that required members of the Federal rank and file to defend states' rights and secession, further demonstrated that Northerners like Ronald Bowen showed more mental dexterity in assuming the perspective of the enemy.[54] Northerners were no more enamored of the moral and philosophical underpinnings of slavery and secession than Southerners were of abolition. Yet even though the men assigned to argue such a position most likely detested and disagreed with such arguments in principle, they were able to put aside their moral and intellectual reservations for the moment and see the world from an unfamiliar and even contrary orientation. A Maine soldier detested Southerners for bringing on the war, sought retribution for the seditious act of secession, and was appalled by enemy atrocities committed against his comrades, but even in his rage, he could find nothing innate in Confederates that would lead them to commit such savage acts. "The system of African slavery," he wrote, "that has prevailed here so long has, no doubt, destroyed much of the finer sensibilities of the Southern people, even of the better class." "But that institution is fast approaching its end," and its demise, he promised, would revamp the Southern character.[55] The cause of the South's deficiencies and backwardness, its very exoticism as a distinct region, was based in place, not on a theory of racial absolutism. Evidence of Confederate soldiers performing similar mental gymnastics in their debating societies simply does not exist. Assuming the stance of the opposition was not part of the Southern repertoire, especially when it came to acting out an argument that was sympathetic to the causes of Union and emancipation.

While Confederates frequently acknowledged the enemy's bravery in battle or their sufferings in camp, they almost never expressed empathy, an emotion interpreted as a sign of giving in, of admitting doubt, and of arguing for the other cause. With their new nation at stake, Confederates avoided such an admission. Southern encounters with the enemy attest to the different ways in which Northerners and Southerners perceptually and emotionally ordered the world. Informal gatherings between the picket lines rarely prompted Southern soldiers to question the Confederate war effort in their letters home. Along isolated picket posts, where officers were scarce and the enemy could be observed without fear of being shot, Southerners felt a predictable connection with an adversary who was enduring similar hardships. Yet they never placed themselves on the same level as Union soldiers. To do so would have been a degrading admission of equality with an enemy that could only be perceived and treated as an inferior. This made it difficult for Confederates to gain perspective on the contradictions of the Southern war effort and even harder for them to assume an oppositional position against their own society. Life generally reflected back on Southerners without any distortion, a near-perfect projection of unity between the self and society.

Most Confederates, including those whose loyalty to the cause wavered, subsequently assumed an angle on the world that protected hierarchy and preserved reputation. After encountering a group of Northern pickets, for instance, a veteran of Lee's army wanted his readers to know that the Yankees praised him and his comrades for their fierceness in battle. He wrote, "They [Union soldiers] acknowledged that we had gained our independence, said that they were very tired of the war, and were very anxious for peace. They finally left us hoping that they would never have to meet us again in battle."[56] A South Carolina soldier further illustrates how fraternizing did not lead to a deeper understanding of the enemy's perspective. Instead, he regarded the picket post as a stage where the enemy became submissive and subordinate, eager to acknowledge Southern superiority. He reported in a Charleston paper that a Union soldier admitted that "he asked for our regiment, and said it was the first fight he had ever been in; that he didn't want to fight our regiment."[57] A Georgia soldier also related how the Union pickets whose military service was expiring would yell across the river: "'Good bye, boys, I am going home. I never expect to fight you again.'"[58]

The Confederate accounts above, like all primary sources, raise the unavoidable challenge of delineating between how people perceived and actually experienced the historical moment and their written depiction of the event. Similarities in content are especially challenging when trying to separate ways of knowing from the ideas themselves. Ridiculing the manliness of the enemy, for instance, was veritable sport in both armies. In writing home, soldiers filled their letters with insults, name calling, and other childish denigrations of the enemy. The frequency of such written remarks would seem to suggest a similar way of thinking in the two armies, and to some degree that was the case, but Southern accounts of fraternization had a distinct quality, for the sources surprisingly lack self-reflection and any spirit of communion with the enemy. The overwhelming desire for political and cultural survival certainly discouraged Confederates from disassembling the incongruities of a society at war in a penetratingly self-critical way. The practical demands of armed resistance, and even its ideological undergirding, do not reach down to the fundamental level of perception. Traces of absolutism — one that relentlessly ordered life in black-and-white terms — hindered Confederates from seeing themselves as somehow responsible for a world that had turned uncontrollably violent and horrifically destructive. Their writings, moreover, are striking in their refusal to acknowledge complicity in organized warfare and the unintended consequences of a limited war transforming itself into a revolution. In the end, Confederate soldiers could not find the common middle ground to collectively mourn the war with the enemy—even when they were standing face-to-face between the picket lines.[59] Historian Jason Phillips's findings support the overarching idea that Confederates could not achieve the same level of empathy that Northern soldiers exhibited along the picket line. His survey of interactions along picket posts shows how Confederates, even during truces, imagined the enemy as a brutal foe, incapable of being human because of an uncontrollable savagery that inspired demonic acts of war against civilians.[60]

Confederates universally condemned the North's hard-war tactics as the work of merciless marauders as soon as the first Northern soldier set foot on Confederate soil in 1861. In comparing the enemy to Vandals and Goths, Southerners racialized the opposition with extraordinary imagination and vehemence. As the war progressed, the distinctions between Yankees and Confederates grew more insistent; by 1863, the Yankees had become a subhuman species in the eyes of many white Southerners. The sensibility of absolutism contributed to this radical and unrealistic visualization of the enemy and the society that sent it off to war.[61] During the Gettysburg Campaign, for instance, the physical differences between war-torn Virginia and the tranquil Pennsylvania countryside prompted one of Lee's veterans to reflect on how Northern and Southern people had evolved into two distinct races. That some able-bodied Northern men stood on the sidelines of war and refused to enlist during an enemy invasion revealed more than an embarrassing lack of patriotism according to some Confederates. It stood as proof that "Yankee" character was innately disfigured and so intensely selfish that they refused to defend their own homes even when threatened by an invading army. This same Confederate decided after his excursion into Pennsylvania that the people constituted "real specimens of the Dutch Boor," with their "heavy brutish lips, [and] thick drooping eyelids." Their appearance revealed "plainly the stupidity of the people."[62]

What about the legions of Confederate dissenters who refused to go away quietly after Gettysburg and Vicksburg, who thought the war effort was doomed, who condemned the Southern government for its many failures, and who wanted peace on virtually any terms? Class complicates the picture, as illustrated in the example of nonslaveholder William Wagner, a semiliterate North Carolina private in Lee's army. No one knows Wagner's position on secession, but he lived in the Piedmont area of the state, where Unionist sympathies ran high. Most yeomen farmers like Wagner did not rush to enlist after Fort Sumter, preferring to remain at home to manage their family farms while single men unencumbered by family responsibilities answered the patriotic call to duty. Wagner's decision to stay on the sidelines until 1862 does not suggest a lack of support for the Confederacy.[63] Whatever his motivations might have been, the passage of the Conscription Act in April 1862 reeled Wagner into the Confederate ranks, and on the Fourth of July he joined the Fifty-Seventh North Carolina, leaving his old nation on its most cherished holiday—though the breaking of ties did not spark open enthusiasm for the Confederacy. Wagner seemed ambivalent about the war; his mind was preoccupied with affairs at his farm, where his wife, Nancy, found herself caught in a perpetual labor crisis.

In Wagner's case, absolutism did not impede his view from the ground, where he possessed an extraordinary eye for the conditions and circumstances surrounding him and how they constrained choices and constricted soldier actions. He felt free to place his readers in the midst of the army without creating the appearance that he towered above war's wreckage. As a result, he wrote about the Gettysburg Campaign with a searing realism that spelled out the demise of the Confederacy. In his first letter written after Gettysburg, penned on July 16 from Virginia, Wagner assumed a blunt and direct approach: "Dear I can say to you that I seede more then I Ever had Expected to see on this trip. We had a Ruf time of it."[64] He wasted no ink in memorializing the dead as Confederate heroes. Tabulating the number of losses from various North Carolina units conveyed the "truth" of his existence. Some units, Wagner reported, "is nearly all cut up."[65] In all of the images from Pennsylvania in his own mental archive, Wagner could not rid his mind of the memory of helpless men flailing about in the flooded waters of the Potomac as they sank to their deaths. "Thare was lots of our wounded men Drounded in the River comeing croos," he wrote in an attempt to explain the dreadful incident, "and the Waggons washed dow the River and they was drownded O it is dreadfool to think how men does doo I wouldent minde if we Ever had gained anything or Ever could Expect to gain any thing but Jes keepe on fiteing til they have all the men killed up and then the Big fellows hav all."[66]

Wagner's story reminds us that absolutism did not keep all Confederates from revealing the war as it was, not how they wanted it to be. He wrote about life in the ranks without the slightest regard for public acclamation or even his own reputation as a Confederate soldier. Undoubtedly, he saw himself as a man of honor and of God who was sacrificing for his family and defending his household, but the fear of humiliation was not so overwhelming that it filtered out the doubt that comes with introspection. Wagner never hesitated to tell the people back home that he felt helpless, that his mind was a mess, and that the war was an unstoppable tragedy. Wagner's confessional style discloses the reality behind the crisis in Lee's army. His eye and pen showed a greater awareness of the contextual factors of war that commanded soldiers' lives. Wagner's sojourn through the bountiful Pennsylvania countryside convinced him that further resistance against an enemy with such abundant resources would be futile.

Confederate failure in Pennsylvania deepened Wagner's sense of fatalism, but resignation never silenced his critical voice. Defeat never prevented him from wondering about the source of God's wrath either, even as he remained ever hopeful that peace would end a war that he consistently described as a "time of truble and sorrow."[67] That phrase was not a hollow refrain, but an admission of deep confusion and of being subjected to mysterious forces—both manmade and supernatural—in which it was impossible to discern the Lord's purpose. In the middle of August, at the peak of his frustration, Wagner confessed, "I don't hardly know what to doo any more but I have to Bare it all patintley."[68] He remained in the ranks only to fall into the hands of the enemy on November 7 at the Battle of Rappahannock Station. Two months later, at the age of thirty-two, Wagner died of chronic diarrhea in Point Lookout Prison in Maryland, where his body was interred in a mass grave.

It is also important to note that not all slaveholding Confederates succumbed to an absolutist view of the world that dulled their critical faculties. South Carolina's Alexander McNeill prayed fervently for God to rescue the Confederacy after Gettysburg, never imagining that the Almighty would abandon his people, but recognizing that "we have grown too self reliant and vain glorious, trusting too much in our strength and forgetfull of the divine agency in this struggle as in all thins else." While his faith comforted him, McNeill stressed to his family that the Confederacy needed to improve logistics and take better care of the animals that carried needed supplies to the troops. The time had come to end all exemptions for military service, he argued, or "our liberties are gone and we are doomed to become vassals to a braggart and insolent foe." McNeill did not lose himself in a diatribe against the Yankees to puff up his reputation. Rather, he spoke plainly about the Confederacy's dwindling resources, a fact that he refused to hide or ignore. "In our march through Maryland and Pennsylvania, the agricultural pursuits no where were interrupted and we could see no lack of men to fill up the ranks," he wrote on July 17, 1863. "You must not imagine that I have despaired," he quickly added, "but I state these simple facts and they are truths apparent to a casual observer."[69]

McNeill's sense of duty did not wane during the final two years of the conflict, though it was punctuated by moments of rage against a foe he believed was waging a villainous war. "My blood had been made to boil today while reading an account of the hellish deeds of Shermans soldiers in our sister state Georgia. Numbers of their fair daughters of that fair state have been *despoiled* and *dishonored.*" "The deep uncontrollable feelings of my heart," he confided to his wife, poured out in a cry for "Gods vengeance upon these perpetrators."[70] The South Carolinian channeled his fury into a reasoned argument that the best defense of his home depended on the future success of Confederate armies in the field. To that end, in the letters he wrote after Gettysburg McNeill stressed the need to submit to the duties of a soldier, an obligation that drew its emotional fire from a racialized Confederate discourse. Newspapers throughout the Confederacy projected a united message of solidarity based on the invention of a separate Yankee race. The differences, insisted Southern writers, were not imagined, but real, tangible, and rooted in the visible realities of physiology. The acts of Union soldiers convinced McNeill and other diehard Confederates that Northern traits were "natural" and "fixed." Federal pillaging was portrayed as an extension of the "villainous" nature of the "fanatical" Northern people rather than an act of war. Such projections help explain how absolutism hindered Confederates from empathizing with an enemy whose essence was seen as unalterable and unredeemable. In a study of Confederate demonization of Union soldiers, George Rable found that Southerners became intransigent and absolute in their view of Yankees as a subhuman people as the war progressed. "Confederate newspapers poured out reams of anti-Yankee polemics," Rable affirmed, "and such diatribes not only shaped public opinion but influenced the war's course. Given the dark assessments of enemy character, the fight simply had to go on because the Yankees embodied nearly every contemptible characteristic in the human imagination."[71]

The move toward biological racism encountered scant resistance among Northern soldiers, suggesting that Northerners and Southerners thought along parallel lines when it came to the need to subordinate African Americans. Stopping the analysis at the content of racial ideologies is problematic, however, for it obscures how Northerners and Southerners puzzled through the contradictions of black military participation in strikingly different ways. Although the substance of their ideas came from the same witch's brew of racism, vast numbers of Union soldiers showed a mental dexterity about racial perceptions that was understandably beyond the reach of Confederates of all social classes. Historians agree that significant numbers of Union soldiers came to accept blacks in the military, even if they retained their deep racist beliefs and considered emancipation a threat to reunion.[72] There were, of course, firm limits to how far racial perceptions and political perspectives would change. Few Northern soldiers considered African Americans to be brothers-in-arms or equals in the ranks, but such hardened opinions should not obscure the transformations in racial thinking that took place within Federal armies—a process mirrored in hospitals by scores of Northern female nurses. The realization that slaves were crucial to the Confederate war effort forced Northerners, regardless of gender, to at least reconsider emancipation and their attitudes toward African Americans. Vast numbers of Federals ultimately reached the practical conclusion that the institution of slavery had to be dismantled in order to subdue the Southern rebellion. The flight of runaway slaves was indisputable evidence of a revolution at work, and it placed pressure on Northerners to reconfigure their thinking about African Americans.[73]

The power of circumstances dictated by military necessity caused a rapid change in Northern soldiers' opinion about emancipation and the use of freedmen as soldiers. Many of their reservations were practical in nature, not racial, and based on the concern that throngs of freed people would cling to army columns and impede their ability to maneuver. Whether a soldier was an abolitionist, a war Democrat, or an antislavery Republican was less important than the experience of what he saw and did in the field. Trying to chart the evolution of soldier thinking sustains a needless binary debate over whether Union was more important than emancipation or vice versa. Instead the focus should be on how Union soldiers reached the point that they were able to step outside themselves and see the perspective of their black comrades.[74]

Pragmatism did not rob men of long-held beliefs, especially when it came to race, but it did enable them to value flexibility of thought when circumstances demanded quick and agile thinking. The Army of the Potomac's Charles Bowen, for instance, despised abolitionists for what he called their celebration of "Niggerhead equality." Yet the New Yorker possessed the mental agility to modify his racial attitudes and show empathy with black men as comrades. After seeing a gallant charge by black soldiers at Petersburg, he acknowledged that the African Americans were risking their lives for a higher cause. To his mother, who blamed the United States Colored Troops for a recent string of military setbacks in Virginia, he vehemently countered: "These blacks have something tangible to fight for. They are fighting for their own personal freedom, they are fighting for the freedom of their wives, their children & their race, & more they are fighting a foe who shows them no quarter in battle."[75] Bowen resembles countless numbers of Union soldiers who made a similar intellectual journey, including Charles Wills of Illinois. When it came to thinking about the arming of slaves, Wills thought that "an honest confession is good for the soul": he wondered if he was "becoming so blind that I can't see why they will not make soldiers." "The only objection I have to it," he concluded, "is a matter of pride." The words of Wills and Bowen affirm historian Christian Samito's recent argument that the service of African American soldiers—as well as that of the Irish—"trumped race" in the minds of many Northern soldiers, who reached the conclusion that wartime contributions justified claims to citizenship above all else.[76]

Furthermore, the examples of Bowen and Wills interlock with the dominant narratives in Northern literature about slaves becoming soldiers. These popular stories revolved around the ways that freed people could transform themselves through war and become soldiers entitled to the rights of citizenship. The lack of a fixed and unalterable image of blackness during the war is very telling. *Harper's Weekly* and *Leslie's Illustrated* featured inversion stories of former slaves taking over abandoned plantations, wearing their ex-masters' clothes, and lounging about chairs and sofas in the parlor of the "Big House." Despite the use of racial stereotypes, popular literature challenged established notions of black men as weak, childlike, and effete. Once in uniform, former slaves emerged from the pages as heroic, as fierce in battle as whites. This does not discount or even diminish the white supremacist Unionism preached and practiced by Democratic and Republican soldiers, but at the same time, these men saw firsthand that blacks were not submissive or inherently docile. As a result, there was a fluidity and dynamism to how Union soldiers imagined their black comrades. This was reflected in a print culture that simultaneously celebrated black heroism in battles—especially after the celebrated assault of the Fifty-Fourth Massachusetts against Fort Wagner on July 18, 1863—and used stereotypes to deny African Americans full status as citizens.[77]

Not far from the assault on black soldiers that Bowen witnessed stood Confederate Edward Porter Alexander, a colonel of artillery who moved in the highest military circles of Robert E. Lee's Army Northern of Virginia. On a number of occasions, Alexander had watched his fellow Confederates lose all sense of restraint when meeting African Americans in combat. At the Battle of the Crater on July 30, 1864, Confederates massacred black soldiers in droves, shooting them in the head and slitting their throats long after they had thrown down their muskets and surrendered. In defense of his comrades' murderous behavior, Alexander explained: "The sympathy of the North for John Brown's memory was taken for proof of a desire that our slaves should rise in a servile insurrection & massacre throughout the South, & the enlistment of Negro troops was regarded as advertisement of that desire & encouragement of the idea to the Negro."[78] Virginian Thomas Smith also spoke for many Confederates at the Crater when he described white officers as "vandals" for bringing "our own slaves against us—surely there will be a day of retribution/justice for such vandalism." The slaughtering of black soldiers, Smith admitted, arose from a "wicked and nefarious" spirit that had poisoned Confederate minds, yet he still believed that the day would come when the Yankees would "acknowledge the justice of their punishment." It is an equally astonishing and revealing admission by Smith that his need for public approval extended to the act of murder.[79]

Thomas Smith and Porter Alexander's refusal to credit black military action as a political act that was conceived of, thought out, and executed by African Americans themselves typifies the thinking of most Confederates. In their minds, United States Colored Troops could only be "incited" to fight Southern whites, and the battlefield, once opened to black troops, became a site of a slave insurrection rather than an area where combat reflected a legitimate political action.[80] Alexander's failure to even dimly perceive former slaves as fighting for their own liberation exposes how racial ideas and honor, melded together through absolutism, walled him off to the legitimacy of black political action. As historian Stephanie McCurry has observed, "It is immensely difficult to understand just how completely white Southerners wrote off slaves in their political calculations."[81] Was the white South's refusal to face reality simply a staggering display of mental obtuseness, or an abandonment of common sense? Closed-mindedness does not begin to explain the blind spots that exist in any worldview, and Porter Alexander is no exception. He was remarkably intelligent, deeply analytical, and always quick to see life as it actually was and not as he wanted it to be. Alexander's mental obstinacy in this particular instance is baffling, but hardly unusual among Confederates who condemned black troops as abolitionist pawns. Such assertions supported the common but ridiculously simplistic judgment against the white South that the fury of racism unhinged the Southern mind.[82]

Alexander's lack of mental flexibility can be attributed in part to the bond of white male power that unified the Confederate rank and file.[83] Such generalizations can be excessive: they disregard how nonslaveholders did not obediently fall into line when Jefferson Davis and a host of politicians and newspaper editors played upon racial fears of a slave insurrection. The thousands of Confederates who deserted did so in the face of a rhetorical campaign that warned of a defeated South collapsing into racial anarchy on a scale of rape and murder that would have exceeded the horrors of the Haitian Revolution. To abandon the Confederate army in the face of such a doomsday rhetorical campaign calls into question the use of identity—whether it be Southern, white, soldier, or Confederate—given that collective political action is never a single or uniform stance. To be sure, white Confederates of all backgrounds hated and feared the notion of an unshackled black population, but that anxiety did not master them, nor did it stop them from defying the military. The example of John Futch from chapter 5 reminds us that not all Confederates were culturally hardwired according to a racial identity. In fact, writings by lower-class and poorly educated Confederate soldiers did not include warnings of "escaped" slaves who would surely go on a rampage of rape and destruction. There was plenty of unrest and disobedience among slaves at home when white men scattered into Southern armies, but it is rare to find a poor Confederate parroting Davis's fearmongering about the inevitability of the slaves unleashing their own version of Saint-Domingue in the Confederacy.

Any suggestion that racial ideas did not infuse Confederate thinking is utterly hollow, but racial ideas, as a discursive expression of power, were neither unified nor impenetrable.[84] The circumstances of war intruded into daily life, pricking pinholes through the consciousness of absolutism and honor through which racial ideas became more malleable in the minds of some Southerners. Why some Confederates were more adaptable than others when it came to race is difficult to say, but strict groupings by class, rank, or geography are not consistent predictors of behavior, as was evident in the debate over arming slaves. This debate took center stage during the final months of the war, and the question split Southern forces into irreconcilable factions. "Opponents had long and credibly warned that white soldiers would vehemently reject the idea of placing slaves in Confederate Gray," historian Bruce Levine has observed in the finest book on the question of Confederate emancipation. Levine found that as the military situation deteriorated during the first months of 1865, "while soldier sentiment remained considerably more ambivalent than many wanted to acknowledge," the "shift in its center of gravity was unmistakable. Most soldiers who expressed a firm opinion now did support arming slaves, and that support continued to grow from day to day."[85]

Dwindling options, Robert E. Lee's strong endorsement of efforts to enroll slaves, and the hope among some Confederates that black men shouldering muskets would enable whites to go home offered the nation its best chance to succeed under the trying circumstances of 1865. Such a dramatic shift in thinking over the place of slaves in the military did not alter white Southerners' understandings of themselves as God's chosen people or soften their hatred of the enemy. Yet the circumstances had changed, and the spike in desertion stripped rhetorical gestures of their power to motivate and unite. Southern private Samuel McAbe, who loathed the idea of fighting next to former slaves, thought it was crazy to spare the lives of black folks while risking his own. "If we don't get the help," he wrote, "we are gone up for sure, they [Yankees] are coming in on every side and half of [our] men won't fight."[86] This was a textbook example of pragmatism from the South Carolinian, whose situational

*Facing the Enemy and Confronting Defeat*

thinking explains why he modified his core ideas about race without rejecting his belief in white superiority or the Confederate war effort.

Why did Samuel McAbe, Thomas Smith, Porter Alexander, and thousands of other Confederates avoid the deep incongruities of life when established truths clashed with the reality of their existence, when the fundamental antagonisms between the self and society should have produced — at least from a modern perspective — those jarring moments in history when people feel compelled to question the core assumptions of their belief system? Smith and Alexander were like many other Confederates whose sensibility of absolutism allowed them to navigate the gusts of war's turbulence without having to change course. Of course, the complex cultural system of signs and language in which McAbe, Smith, and Alexander wrote existed prior to the war, but in the military, with manly reputations on the line and the future of slavery at stake, they veered toward an absolutist rendering of the world, joining other diehard Rebels who were, as historian Jason Phillips writes, unwilling to accept the implication of battlefield defeats. They discarded any shard of information that might challenge their understanding of themselves as invincible fighters whose mastery of the enemy could never come into question.[87]

During the final eight months of the war, when Union armies scored devastating victories in Mobile, Atlanta, and the Shenandoah Valley, many Confederates started to believe that the military decline of their nation was irreversible. Plenty of others continued to look to the future with hope, even when every rumor and report pointed to the South's demise. The vast majority of Confederates preferred death over defeat and dishonor for cultural reasons. Rather than compromise they followed the road to extremism, for absolutism kept large numbers of Confederates from actually seeing their world dissolve before their eyes.[88] After tabulating the staggering number of deserters who had fled his North Carolina unit from January to March 1865; after conceding that Lee's army was helplessly trapped; and even after admitting that "we are forsaken by all the world," North Carolinian Samuel Walkup could not conceive of any other option than to die by the flag. The desperate hope that surrender could somehow be avoided by a supernatural intervention smothered his pragmatism, even when it had become obvious to thousands of other Confederates that God was sitting this war out so that men could follow their own will to survive. "I can only look Heavenward for comfort," Walkup wrote, and "whatever God permits & wills must be submitted to with patient resignation. The terrible ordeal — if brother Wm & I escape ruin & death — it will be miraculous — or if our armies escape it must be by providential interference."[89] Walkup's fatalism under such deteriorating circumstances is clear, but the narrowing of his thinking and the tunneling of his vision reveals how his one way of knowing inhibited and discouraged him from obtaining critical detachment from himself and from the underlying causes of the sagging Confederate war effort.

As a result, Walkup could not easily assume an oppositional angle against society, especially since the dominant narrative of his nation continued to endow reality with a message of redemption through willed behavior and pure faith. Walkup and many other zealous Confederates continued to fight for a world where there was no sense of paradox and no feel for contradictions, just a way of knowing that sought fixed meaning in experiences that minimized context. This is why, during the darkest days of the war, so many Southerners became quixotic by embracing a cult of personality, even when it was obvious that no single individual could rescue the Southern nation from ruin. The faith soldiers put in Lee, which bordered on idolatry, and the general's phenomenal battlefield record convinced Confederates that their salvation as a nation rested with the Army of Northern Virginia.[90] The letters of slaveholder William Biggs, who was stationed outside Wilmington, North Carolina, show how some soldiers continued to swim against the tide of war, even when there was no land in sight. At the end of the 1864 fall campaigns, when military news felt oppressive, Biggs wrote to his sister, "Oct has passed into the eternal Past never to be recalled, but the deeds that were done in that month will be chronicled on the pages of history. Some to show the unconquerable spirit of the Southerners. Others to show the futile attempt of *man* to control every thing as he wishes." Oddly, but most likely intentionally, he left the enemy out of his equation. Rather than confront the possibility that the Yankees had something to do with it, or that, God forbid, the Lord had shown providential favoritism to the Union, Biggs blotted out vital context as he looked into the future by reading into the past.[91]

A little more than one month later, even as the situations in Wilmington and Petersburg bordered on collapse, knowing that General Lee was at the helm of his army and striking at the enemy with his signature audacity settled Biggs's nerves and bolstered his optimism. Lee's generalship satisfied Biggs's need for an absolute truth that validated his own reputation as a Confederate soldier. Yet even as he promised his sister that the enemy could not subdue the fighting spirit of Confederate soldiers, Biggs also sought reassurance from her that the cause was not lost. His words never strayed from the surface of the situation, offering a version of the truth based on appearance rather than rooted in contextual depth. Just a few weeks before the surrender of Wilmington, and writing during one of the many artillery barrages unleashed by the enemy, Biggs still noticed that "a better spirit can now be observed among the men, and everything in my opinion, looks brighter than it did a few weeks since."[92]

Confederates were not alone in making great claims about the spirit and morale of the troops, and such observations tell us very little about how a range of emotional options coexisted and were contingent on each other in the ranks. One can't possibly speak of a single spirit animating any army at any single point during the war. The language of spirit and morale functioned as a way for ruling elites to turn political loyalty into a matter of willed behavior. At this late stage in the war, Biggs could not finesse this issue with an empty statement about *all* the men being in good cheer. In the very next paragraph, Biggs abandoned his glowing optimism with a disturbing report about his comrades:

> The five men who deserted from my Co. have been arrested and brought back. The chances of their escape from being shot are but slim, and I am afraid all of them will share the same fate. I feel particularly for Mrs. Sally [?] Williams, as her son was among the number who left. I have seen him since he was brought back [and] he says he cannot understand what influenced him to desert. I shall use all my exertions to save them from the extreme punishment of death, but fear it will have but little effect. A few days after they left, four more also deserted, who are still at large.[93]

Dismissing Biggs and Walkup as extremists overlooks how soldiers' accumulated experiences—trying to survive in the field, suffering in so many long marches on empty stomachs, seeing comrades who had become like brothers killed in battle—made them part of something bigger that was also part of them, and to step away for individual reasons would have been an admission of doubt and disloyalty. This would have been a difficult admission for any soldier on either side, but it was particularly hard for white Southerners, as Gary Gallagher argued in his influential study *Confederate War*. The Confederate soldiers' understanding of who they were as fighting men was too embedded in their identification with society, not in their struggles or rebellion against it. Continuing the struggle past the fall of 1864 was no fool's errand, Gallagher maintains, given that Robert E. Lee stood supreme in the Confederacy as the hope of a nation, the second coming of George Washington, whose stature rose from a string of battlefield victories that promised a brighter future.[94] Significantly, the hero cult surrounding Lee was a move toward pragmatism among Confederate people who concerned themselves less with the ideas that spawned their nation and instead looked to Lee as their best hope for military victory.

A growing faith in generals like U.S. Grant, William T. Sherman, Phil Sheridan, and George Thomas also signified a pragmatic shift in Union armies by the latter stage of the war. By 1863, veteran soldiers still cared about politics, but to bring the war to a successful conclusion meant getting the job done in the field as professionals. This partially explains why Northern troops stayed away from radical or reactionary options and gravitated toward a politics of moderation from the ranks.[95] Even when they became cynical, Union soldiers almost never doubted that secession and slavery were political and ideological issues worth fighting against, and they were able to support the cause while condemning both the political extremes — the abolitionists for fomenting the war and the Copperheads for supposedly sabotaging Union armies. Even when Northerners were at their angriest, and even when they felt betrayed by their government and the army, they existed in a more flexible political culture, its boundaries expanded by soldiers who were able to stand outside themselves and judge the Union cause critically. The partisanship among Union soldiers could be fierce, and the Democratic and Republican clashes behind the lines drained the Union war effort of energy and efficiency.[96] Irony ultimately liberated Union veterans so that they could confront the war's most jarring inconsistencies, giving them a unique opportunity to expose the reality that lay beneath a sentimentalized fantasy world of soldiering that colored civilian understandings of war. Union soldiers who were disposed toward irony were in a position to recognize the paradoxical effects of their own behavior on the world around them and even perhaps to see how they were at least partially responsible for the unintended and inescapable consequences of their individual actions. Irony did not, however, liberate Northern soldiers of contradictory thoughts or inspire radical visions of black liberation and citizenship.

Northerners could also recognize their responsibility for the awful spilling of blood, which violated every precept of humanity even though it was necessary for the higher purpose of preserving the nation. During a march from Appomattox, Wisconsin's Guy Taylor saw "8 men laid side by side redy to be covard up, and I cood see the others laying all around me that wood soon be laid in another pit." He thought it "hard to see our fellow man laying in such shape but it is not so hard a site to look at as it is to see the men that is wounded." To watch soldiers draw their last breath knowing that "they must die, and they was in such agony," sickened Taylor, but he reminded himself, "War is war." He held no grudge against the Confederates, as "the boys on both side[s] try to make their balls count." Taylor's ability to gain critical detachment and to feel for the other side deepened his love for the Union. He cooked for captured Confederates, and he wrote that when he handed them a plate of hot food, these "stout men set down and cryed before they could eat." The suffering sickened Taylor, but he knew that, just as Lincoln had so eloquently stated in his Second Inaugural, this was a conflagration caused by Northerners and Southerners. "I am in hope that this war has made the American people more wise then what they was 4 years ago."[97]

# 7

# The Trophies of Victory
# and the Relics of Defeat

———

THE REMAINS OF A LONE APPLE TREE, cut down and carved into small pieces by Confederate soldiers, lay along a rutted dirt road that led to the village of Appomattox Court House. Earlier on April 9, 1865, Robert E. Lee had waited under the shade of the apple tree, anxious to hear from Ulysses S. Grant about surrendering his army. Messages between the generals eventually led to a brief meeting between Lee and two Union staff officers, who then secured the parlor in Wilmer McLean's house for the famous meeting between Lee and Grant. Before the Southern general left the village, thousands of Union and Confederate soldiers had seen him near the apple tree. This spot took on immediate historical significance as Lee's last command post before he surrendered the Army of Northern Virginia. Inside the McLean house, Grant dictated the surrender terms to Lee. As soon as the agreement was signed and Lee walked out the door, Union officers "decluttered" the parlor with Yankee efficiency, cutting strips of upholstery from plush sofas, breaking chair legs into small keepsakes, and "appropriating" candleholders and chairs until the room was left barren.[1]

In the meantime, Lee was making his way to his headquarters, slowly riding Traveller down the Lynchburg Stage Road as his adoring troops swarmed

around him in an unforgettable farewell. The general said a few words of gratitude, evidently moved by the outpouring of affection from his devoted soldiers,
before disappearing over the hillside. Within minutes Confederate relic hunters
descended on the apple tree, cutting and hacking away at the limbs and bark so
that the slices of wood could become precious commodities of historical and
monetary value. The cutting frenzy sprang from a mixture of veneration and
entrepreneurialism, and the famous *Harper's Weekly* illustrator Alfred Waud
sketched Union and Confederate soldiers swinging axes and bargaining over
the trophies. The historical magnitude of April 9, 1865, was not lost on the veterans who wanted a piece of history, even if it came at a price.

Items such as the apple tree, whether made or found, were more than souvenirs or trinkets of nostalgic symbolism. Soldiers understood that what they
saved would help shape historical memories and influence public meanings for
years to come. Civil War soldiers were always intrigued by the relics, but their
craving for the things of war became an obsession during the last weeks of the
Confederacy's existence, when both sides were grasping for things to help them
remember the past as they transitioned to a future without war. The demise of
Rebel armies, beginning with Lee's army on April 9, Joseph Johnston's Army
of Tennessee on April 26, Nathan Bedford Forrest's command on May 9, and
Kirby Smith's on June 2, produced a windfall of battle flags, rifles, backpacks,
and other articles of war treasured by both sides but interpreted in very different ways. The material elicited a range of conflicting emotions and feelings —
despair, futility, optimism, pride, and jubilation.

Members of the Army of the Potomac could imagine a thoroughly vanquished enemy at Appomattox because of the Rebels' ragged physical appearance as prisoners of war. Lee's men seemed despondent, standing in silence,
wearing threadbare uniforms covered in filth, and looking emaciated and
feeble. They hardly resembled the warriors who once ruled Virginia, and in this
instance, the surrendering of Southern forces illustrates the impossibility of
simultaneously seeing and knowing.[2] Union soldiers interpreted the broken-
down appearance of Confederates as incontestable evidence of a conquered
South, but beneath the Confederates' exterior of defeat resided a desire for
retribution that could be found in things like Lee's Farewell Address, pieces
of Confederate flags, captured Union boots, and shards of an apple tree that
helped ex-Rebels preserve their sense of manliness while keeping alive the
dream that the cause was not actually lost.

The aim of this chapter is to explore how Civil War soldiers understood
Union victory and the downfall of the Confederacy by combining material
culture and primary documents. This chapter does not concern itself with the

conditions on the Northern or Southern home front that awaited soldiers as they returned home, nor does it explore the long-term problems of veterans readjusting to civilian life. Those important topics go beyond the scope of this volume, and there are many fine works that address the numerous layers of the veteran experience.[3] Instead, the chapter begins by reviewing the last week of the war, and the events that led to the surrender at Appomattox. An examination of Southern reactions to the collapse of their armies follows, then the chapter moves into the ways that material culture figured into the act of surrendering and that relics shaped Rebel perceptions of themselves as conquered soldiers. The Confederate section concludes by following the soldiers home as they navigated a new world where slavery had been abolished and where their loss of mastery was acutely felt, since they had no possessions, virtually no guns, and not a cent to their names.

The Army of the Potomac at Appomattox is the focal point of the next section, and material culture also figures into the ways that Union veterans imagined victory and defeat. The extensive fraternization with Confederates at Appomattox receives considerable attention as a way to locate the fraternal and entrepreneurial spirit that prevailed between the two sides at the end of the war. This section gives special care to the return of Union soldiers to the battlefields in the Fredericksburg area—a pilgrimage that was not a sacred ritual of nationalism, but a poignant reminder of their own harrowing experiences as survivors. The chapter concludes by focusing on how one soldier experienced the Grand Review in Washington and his exit from the army through the mementos that he collected and sent home for safekeeping.

Rather than detailing the surrender proceedings of the various Southern armies or chart the vast multitude of soldier experiences and reactions during the final months of the war, which has been done admirably by other scholars, this chapter highlights the surrender experience of three men—the Union's John Smith of the 118th Pennsylvania, Virginian John H. Chamberlayne of Davidson's battery, and Carlton McCarthy of the Richmond (Va.) Howitzers. They each take center stage at various points in the chapter because their writings shine light on ways that material culture helped soldiers make sense of the end of the war. Confederate cannoneer John H. Chamberlayne, who "skipped" the surrender ceremony parade at Appomattox, accompanied a band of die-hard Confederates to Mississippi during the summer of 1865.[4] He provides the perspective of a radical Confederate who wrote with astonishing introspection while he sought refuge from defeat through self-exile. The letters of Pennsylvania's John Smith that detail his journey from Appomattox to the Grand Review on May 23 and 24, 1865, are an exceptional source for investigating the ways that patriotism and profit inspired soldiers on both sides to collect the things of war.

Unfortunately, there is a dearth of soldier commentators from April to June 1865 in comparison to the outpouring of letters for the rest of the war. Soldiers on the verge of being mustered out of service did not feel the same compulsion to write, because they knew that home was within reach. Unlike Union soldiers, former Confederates were nearly sealed off from their loved ones: their mail system was in shambles, and they were strapped for paper and pens. Those men who had the opportunity to write usually left terse and hasty remarks, jotted down in diary form and bereft of any real analysis. To flesh out the Confederate experience it was necessary to rely on postwar sources like Carlton McCarthy's 1882 memoir, *Detailed Minutiae of Soldier Life in the Army of Northern Virginia 1861–1865*, which is one of the richest Southern sources on the journey home from Appomattox. McCarthy occasionally succumbed to the excessive sentimentality and racial vehemence found among other Lost Cause devotees, but his stories do not hide the embarrassment of being cast out into a world where he had no standing or means of support. McCarthy's piece is a reliable and soul-searching look into the hearts and minds of former Confederates as they shifted their focus from being soldiers to becoming civilians again.

Smith, Chamberlayne, and McCarthy are surrounded by a diverse cast of characters that illustrate how Civil War soldiers who occupied the same historical space at the same historical moment took very different meanings from the last act of the Civil War. Any attempt to characterize the thoughts and actions of hundreds of thousands of veterans is difficult to sustain. Some general observations, however, are both valuable and defensible. Northern soldiers gloried in the triumph of the Union over a slave oligarchy seen as the culprit for unleashing a bloody war by breaking up the Union. With few exceptions, they returned home as conquering heroes, knowing that their sacrifices in the ranks would earn them immortality as the saviors of a free democratic government that had no equal in the world. Former Confederates, on the other hand, could not walk or look in any direction without seeing evidence of their ruination. The war had swallowed Southern society. Cities were destroyed, plantations razed, family members scattered, maimed, or dead, and slaves were liberated and "roaming" free. Approximately 450,000 white Southerners were casualties, out of a total white population of 5.5 million, bringing the death rate to 8.2 percent, compared with 1.8 percent in the North.[5]

In the week that followed the Confederate evacuation of Richmond and Petersburg on April 2, the conflict between the Army of Northern Virginia and the Army of the Potomac rapidly came to an end. Grant's forces hunted down the Army of Northern Virginia with the dogged determination of a veteran army. At every turn they blocked Lee's attempts to move south, while piercing the soft underbelly of the Confederate column with slashing cavalry attacks. By the evening of April 8, Robert E. Lee had nowhere to go. From what turned out to be his final bivouac, he could not look to the east, south, or west without seeing the enemy's flickering campfires. Lee was surrounded, but he would not give up, and he ordered one last attack for the morning of April 9, which was likely the smallest but also the most significant in the history of the Army of Northern Virginia. Initially the Confederates gained some success, temporarily clearing a path to the west, but hard-marching Union reinforcements sealed the escape route and drove the Southerners back into the village of Appomattox Court House. When word of the failed assault reached Lee, he immediately called for an armistice, knowing that Grant would not settle for a negotiated peace but would demand unconditional surrender, just as he had done at Fort Donelson and Vicksburg.[6]

Lee had little choice but to accept Grant's demands, because the Union army was poised for a bloody showdown that would likely have resulted in Confederate annihilation. When news of the surrender swept across the Army of the Potomac, members of the rank and file erupted in joy, tossing their hats in the air, rolling on the ground, and beating drums in an unbridled celebration of victory and life as part of the inevitable chain of human progress. After years of frustration and public ridicule, the rank and file of the Army of the Potomac accomplished what many observers thought was unattainable—the capture of Richmond and the destruction of Lee's forces. Everything changed during the first nine days of April, when Grant had achieved both in what amounted to the knockout blow to the rebellion. The soldiers at the time knew that Appomattox guaranteed the reunion of the nation and the end of slavery. They claimed their part in this magnificent victory, which affirmed their belief in Lincoln's words that America was the world's last best hope. When Grant warned against excessive celebrating, few disobeyed his order out of a soldierly admiration for an enemy who had experienced similar trials of army life.

The show of restraint must be placed alongside expressions of sympathy for a defeated foe rarely found among the victorious party. Northern soldiers showed a remarkable ability to think outside themselves and imagine the perspective of their fallen enemy. Victory certainly made it easier to assume such a position, but Northern soldiers' strong convictions in the notion of Union as both a philosophical position and political goal would have been betrayed if they had not extended a respectful hand toward their enemies in the name of

*The Trophies of Victory and the Relics of Defeat*

peace and reunion. Pennsylvania's John Smith, for instance, hoped that former Confederates would see that the Army of the Potomac had showed mercy toward Lee's depleted command by stopping the needless slaughter at Appomattox when the Army of Northern Virginia could have been obliterated in a single attack. The preservation of Confederate life, he hoped, might spread goodwill and understanding to a conquered Southern people. "The whole Rebel army was in a hollow and we were all around them and the blood would have flowed like water had we ever opened a volley on them," Smith wrote in a spirit of unity and without a hint of vengeance. "But I am glad they surrendered in time," Smith told his mother, "as many a wife and sister and mother and friends have been made happy instead of miserable, by their friends and relatives returning home alive again to renew life, to go to work and live under the dear old flag, and not be fools again. These men had not a thing to do, in any way in bringing on the war; Just think of it a moment."[7]

Sympathy for the enemy did not dampen the Union soldiers' faith in the moral superiority of their cause: they believed they were the agents of God fighting for the survival of the republic so nobly conceived and bestowed by the Founders. Some today might see this as an expression of a militaristic nationalistic culture, but the soldiers saw it as idealism. Grant's men never doubted that Appomattox was a critical moment in the nation's history that resulted in the country's survival against the internal threat of disunion. The capture of Lee's Army of Northern Virginia, moreover, pushed out to sea the fog of criticism that had enveloped the Army of the Potomac from its inception. Men on both sides, including Pennsylvania's John Smith, breathed in the intoxicating air of peace and victory, knowing that they would never have to feel the fears of battle again, with its awful sounds, terrible confusion, and hideous deaths. "You will soon see your Johnnie come marching home," he wrote to his anxious mother in Philadelphia, "with bright laurels on his brow of 45 battles where the bullets yelled sizz, sizz, sizz (I've got you) and the shell screeched like an owl, and ripped and tore big trees down and did not stop for anything. No more of that fighting."[8] The Army of the Potomac's William Berrier succinctly put into words the emotional release of being able to live without fear when he wrote: "My dear I can Say now that the war is over and I am Still living."[9]

News of Lee's surrender threw Confederate soldiers into a vortex of confusing and conflicting emotions. On the one hand, ex-Rebels had been chastened and felt disgraced because they had been "whipped" by an enemy that they had long condemned as inferior, but shame did not cause them to sink into an inescapable state of lethargy. The humiliation was bearable for most Confederate veterans, who found solace and joy in surviving. The immediate prospect of returning home also had a liberating effect, for veterans' desire to reunite with their families was finally within reach. The thought of waking up in the arms of a loved one, knowing that the army would no longer own the day and that the sickening dread that came before every battle were all things of the past and never to be experienced again, instilled men with hope.

Moral optimism and cheerfulness, which had guided men through the hell of soldiering, continued to serve former Confederates as they looked into the abyss of defeat. Plenty of men were nearly incapacitated with rage over the prospect of subjugation to the North, but the characterization of the Southern soldier as descending into a prolonged state of depression is extreme. The day after a Georgia soldier in the Army of Tennessee stacked his musket and received his parole, he looked around camp and could not believe the emotional transformation in his comrades. Men who had been sullen and morose came to life as soon as they exercised their freedom and started home. "Lovely morning," he jotted down in his diary on May 1, 1865. "All nature both animal and vegetable present a cheerful face, the old veteran soldiers wear a smile. The thought of seeing home and loved ones soon is pictured on every countenance." A member of Forrest's cavalry also could not contain his sense of relief when the armies were disbanded. "Had a jolly good time wasn't scared at all," he remembered. "Did not have to do picket duty or shoot at Yankees."[10]

Cheerfulness and faith were seen as interconnected, and for many Confederates, defeat could not break or even weaken their belief in providential protection for those whose outward appearance conveyed faith in the Lord. To renounce God for forsaking the Southern cause would have been a monstrous act of apostasy, particularly for those soldiers whose lives had been spared through so many battles. Plenty of Confederates continued to draw comfort from the mysterious ways of Providence without feeling that Union victory signified God's betrayal of the South. Not far from Appomattox Court House, South Carolinian John Crawford Anderson wrote a final letter to his family, describing the gloom of defeat that hung over camp, yet he could not help but rejoice over his own survival. Such a miracle, he reminded his loved ones, could only have come from God's protective and benevolent hand. "I have seen many a hardship and made many a narrow escape, but the hand of God has been between me and all harm." "We all mourn for our country," he continued, "and every man's face wears a haggard, dejected, and troubled look; but we can only say it must be the will of God and is therefore right."[11]

A scattering of letters and diaries that survived Lee's surrender parallel Anderson's belief that God was biding his time, that the Yankees would eventually feel his wrath, and that when that day arrived, white Southerners would emerge as his chosen people. Virginia officer George Griggs noted on April 10, "I feel very sad but trust in my blessed Heavenly Father for comfort & power to do my duty." A Georgian in the Army of Tennessee uttered a similar opinion, writing, "After four years of bloody conflict, we lay down our arms, horn blowing and drum beating cease. . . . God rules in this earth mysteriously to perform his wonders." Virginian Edward Valentine Jones felt no spiritual paralysis when he saw Lee return from the McLean house. Not for a moment did he doubt in God's mysterious ways when he wrote in his journal, "But the time has come for the Army of Northern Virginia to lay down its arms — Providence wills it so but that same Providence has given to it in history a name and remembrance that time cannot efface."[12] Even on the last day of the Army of Northern Virginia's existence, some of Lee's men claimed Appomattox as a badge of honor that proved their exceptional physical and moral courage, since they were the few who remained with Lee until the end.

The twenty-eight thousand veterans of the Army of Northern Virginia at Appomattox only had to gaze in any direction to see that their ranks were decimated and that the Army of the Potomac was poised for the kill. Grant's men occupied the high ground along the perimeter of what resembled a natural amphitheater around the village and the scattered fragments of the Army of Northern Virginia. Lee's men were virtually helpless at the base of the bowl, with the Army of the Potomac towering above. From their prominent position, some Federals likely caught sight of Lee and his staff officers near the apple tree. When news of the surrender passed through the ranks, many Union soldiers, including John Smith, exercised their new freedoms and headed straight for the Rebel camps to acquire a memento of this historically momentous day. Smith rushed to the scene, but as he walked across a wooden rail spanning a stream swollen by recent rains, he lost his balance and plunged into the waters. "I cried! Cussed!!," he wrote to his mother on April 11. "But made up my mind I would get a piece of that great apple tree if I fell in forty creeks." When Smith reached the tree, he saw one of Grant's orderlies carry off a limb, while other Union soldiers were paying between five and ten dollars for chips. A Confederate standing nearby asked: "'What would you do with it, Yank?' 'Why, take it home as a great relic,' say I to him, so he cut in and cut out big chips." Smith tried to give him ten dollars for the pieces, but the Confederate would not accept the money. "'Here, Yank, with my compliments.'" When Smith returned to his regiment, his comrades hustled off to get their own piece, but they were too late. The tree — including the roots — was gone. They pleaded with Smith to sell some of his pieces, offering as much as five dollars for a sliver, but "I said to them, 'No, go fall in the creek as I did.'"[13]

"Cutting up the Apple Tree under Which Grant and Lee Met, for Trophies," by Alfred Waud, depicts the relic lust among Confederate and Union veterans who sought a piece of history to commemorate their role in bringing an end to the Army of Northern Virginia. Others chopped the tree up for purely pecuniary gain.
(Library of Congress Prints and Photographs Division, Washington, D.C.)

That Robert E. Lee spent so much time near the apple tree, resting under its branches and occasionally conferring with his staff, invested the space with a sacred aura. Those Union and Confederate soldiers who were fortunate enough to get a hunk of the prized wood invested their souvenirs with very different meanings, which in turn validated their respective services during the Appomattox Campaign and the war as a whole. Grant's veterans held up a slice of the apple tree as a tribute to a complete and smashing victory earned by the Army of the Potomac's relentless drive, superior bravery, and exceptional leadership. The shards of the tree marked the destruction of a Rebel foe that heretofore had been considered invincible while also symbolizing the conciliatory tone toward Lee's survivors. It is telling that Union soldiers showed no impulse to desecrate the tree site or to do anything that might denigrate their fallen enemy.

Confederate veterans craved shards of the apple tree out of a deep admiration for their commanding general, but the wooden relic could not be disassociated from the painful memories of surrender. How could any soldier forget the defeat of the white South if he owned a slice of the tree? Wouldn't feelings of shame assail a Southern veteran every time he came in contact with the wooden trinket? Diaries and letters would suggest that Lee's veterans wanted to dis-

*The Trophies of Victory and the Relics of Defeat*

tance themselves from the surrender altogether and that relic hunting would have been unthinkable to any self-respecting Confederate. Yet the search for souvenirs provides a different interpretive layer to the popular generalization that all Confederates forever buried their faces in shame. These wooden shards symbolized a once-mighty military regime, and any soldier who owned the heirloom possessed a sacred link to the incomparable Robert E. Lee. Moreover, he had proof that he had followed the general to the bitter end.

Lee's men were the first to make a rush on the apple tree, catching the eye of Smith and other Federals, who joined the gathering in what turned into a veritable bazaar of trading and selling slices of the apple tree and currency. The Confederates could not get rid of their worthless and burdensome currency quickly enough, and they found in Smith an eager buyer who handed out greenbacks for Confederate bills. His desire for Southern money was a little peculiar, but in the future Smith could display Southern currency as a relic of an extinct nation that had threatened the Union from within.

The trading of currency and the hawking of the apple tree spawned a convivial spirit among the former combatants, and their conversations elicited a range of conflicting Confederate reactions to Lee's surrender. Smith and fellow Pennsylvanian Jacob Zorn described a similar spectrum of Confederate opinions after the surrender. "Some of them feel very indignant in regard to the Surrender," Zorn wrote in his diary, "and express themselves hoping to See the day yet when they will have a chance at us again. Others appear to hail the day when peace will again sound throughout the whole land. They Say they are tired of this war and cant See any use of carrying it on any longer the expressions of the latter are those who done the fighting. and that of the former those who had some easy position and not of the rank and file of the army."[14] N. H. Pardington, also of the Fifth Corps, heard from many fiery Confederates "that they would meet us again if they got a chance." Their comrades told Pardington that these outspoken soldiers "held bomb proof positions in the army, such as musicians & quartermasters clerks & who were all ways out of reach of bullets in time of a fight."[15] Smith also found that some of the Rebels were "very bitter and said it was not over yet," but this class of puffed-up Confederates, in Smith's estimation, were paper-collar officers who rarely if ever smelled the smoke of battle. Like Zorn, Smith put his trust in those men who "were in the ranks, and carried the guns." These Confederates were "satisfied," according to Smith, that the rebellion could never be resurrected.[16]

The broken-down and feeble condition of Confederate horses also spoke to the precipitous decline of the Army of Northern Virginia and the collapse of the Confederate war machine as a whole. Smith, after getting his slice of the apple tree, was taken aback by the Rebels' wretched and listless animals, which were barely breathing. Lee's men explained that their horses had gnawed on fence rails for a week out of desperation for fodder. "Wherever you look you can see the result: horses and mules are lying everywhere: starved to death, and many were shot to end their misery."[17]

While Union soldiers found overwhelming material proof of the Confederacy's fall, plenty of Southern soldiers were oblivious to the physical disintegration of their own army. It is astonishing that so many soldiers in Lee's army, as well as in Johnston's Army of Tennessee, were shocked by the news of Lee's surrender. Self-delusion was an art form for some of these former Confederates, and that might partially explain why they were so stunned by the news of Appomattox. The sensibility of absolutism was also at work, filtering out any evidence that threatened the appearance of mastery among Southern white men. Cultural explanations alone, however, do not entirely clarify why so many Southerners turned a blind eye to defeat. The towering reputation of Lee could deflect a hard look at reality. By early 1864, the Confederate populace saw Lee as no mere mortal. He was a messiah to some, and to others he was the second coming of George Washington. Even ordinary members of the rank and file, who were far removed from the slaveholding elite, refused to bet against the South as long as Lee was on the field. Lee's greatness as a general seemed to have a mystical hold on the people, and it reached all corners of the Confederacy, even in areas far removed from the Virginia theater of war. In April 1865, a soldier in Louisiana who was busy organizing what he described as "patriotic parties" to "bind up the wounds of the mangled Confederacy" still held out hope for Southern independence when it was rumored that Lee had escaped Grant.[18] By early May, when the finality of Lee's and Johnston's surrenders had been confirmed, he confessed to his brother that "my last hope died within me when Genl Lee surrendered, but up to this time I have tried to keep quiet. Now the last prop of the Government is broken and there is no longer any room for hope."[19] Others thought it was a "moral impossibility" for Lee to give up the fight, including one Mississippian who did not encounter a single person as late as April 20 who was willing to accept the news of Appomattox as anything more than a Yankee-propagated story.[20]

For the men of the Army of Tennessee, who were stranded and scattered for some fifty miles between Durham Station and Greensboro, North Carolina, it was not easy to find shelter in self-denial. News of Appomattox triggered an armistice on April 17, and as soon as Johnston and Sherman started negotiating, the Army of Tennessee came undone. One Georgian recalled that "all order and discipline was lost . . . [and] the camps are nothing more than a mob."[21] In contrast to Lee's soldiers, who were almost entirely captured and surrendered in a single day, Johnston's men had time to mill about in camp and ponder their future. All kinds of scenarios and rumors swirled through camp, including speculation as to whether the armistice would turn into a permanent peace or collapse into a final round of desperate fighting. If a soldier showed some awareness of the physical condition of his army, he was likely to put down his musket and head home. Others refused to face the facts of defeat when they contemplated a world where Yankee bayonets would force Southern whites to submit to black equality. Texas Captain Samuel Foster espoused this extreme perspective, brushing off any news that suggested Confederate subjugation and writing defiant entries in his diary. On April 22, he reported that the "rumor says (this morning) that we will start for home in course of the next 10 days, and the rumor comes or purports to come from those that ought to know. Later in the day the report is that we go to fighting again." Although Foster did not know what to believe, he refused to accept the obvious—that a true calamity had befallen the Army of Tennessee and the Confederacy. "Genl Johns[t]on can't make any terms but submission reunion free negroes &c, and we have been fighting too long for that. I have not seen a man today but says fight on rather than submit." Foster's observation is especially curious given that thousands of his comrades were deserting each day during the final weeks of April. But Foster came from a Southern male culture that pressured men to push aside self-doubt and insecurities, freeing them to exaggerate their public persona as part of the high-stakes game of earning their respect and reputation from the public.[22] He could not help but deceive himself about the condition of the Army of Tennessee. Foster's ideological commitment to slavery and devotion to white supremacy, though immensely important to understanding why he preferred death to dishonor, was subordinate to the sensibility of absolutism. The latter filtered out the turmoil and self-doubt so he could confer reputation and honor upon himself without regard to context and circumstances.[23]

The call of honor awoke some diehard Confederates from the stupor of humiliation that hung over the army. These men fancied themselves as the hotspurs of the rebellion, and in the final months of the war they lived up to their reputations as unconquerable warriors who never grew weary of hearing the music of the shell. The battlefield was their grand stage where high ambitions were realized, promotions were awarded, and women were impressed by cool bravery and fierce loyalty to the cause. They saw only fear in the eyes of the enemy, whom they despised as a godless foe deserving of eternal damnation for waging a ruthless war against Southern civilians. Virginian William Roane Aylett, who fell into enemy hands just two days before Appomattox, made a vow that many diehard Rebels took to heart. "For myself," he wrote to his wife, "I'll fight them as long I have a leg to stand on or an arm to strike. Conquer them we must and will for God cannot *allow* that such wickedness should *stand*."[24] Aylett, like other zealous fighters of his ilk, did not draw a line between obligation to God and duty to nation, a position widely articulated by a Southern religious community that helped forge a civic religion that, in tone and in substance, bordered on a crusade. Plenty of white Southerners believed that the fate of Christendom depended on the defeat of the North and its demonic abolitionist hordes, but even the most pious did not conflate patriotism with salvation. Wearing the uniform and taking a Yankee bullet could earn a soldier a lovely tribute in the local paper, but there was no guarantee of an afterlife unless the man had accepted Christ as his savior.[25]

Confederate zealots would not allow Lee's surrender to tarnish the bloody sacrifice of the fallen, whose ultimate act of devotion would surely be forgotten or disgraced in the history books if the cause were abandoned. They felt they had no choice but to carry on the fight. No floodgate could hold back the rage and humiliation of these fanatics, who promised to follow the Confederate flag wherever it might fly. John H. Chamberlayne was one of the few who refused to quit fighting. "McIntosh and myself with several others refused to attend the funeral at Appomattox C.H.," he wrote on April 12, "& as soon as the surrender was certain we cut or crept our way out, thro' adventures many & perilous wh. I cannot tell of now." Chamberlayne and his party intended to rally with Johnston's forces, but if the Army of Tennessee had disbanded by the time they arrived, Chamberlayne would continue on to Texas, where the war against the Yankees, he believed, could be waged indefinitely. It is telling that even at this late stage of the conflict, Chamberlayne did not see himself as a cog in the machinery of the army whose individuality was subsumed within the organizational structures of the military. He still clung to a sentimentalist view of war as a test of individual will, resorting to the somber hues of romanticism in letter after letter. "I am not conquered by any means & shall write to you when I can—Farewell farewell—Love to all my friends. . . . I am not conquered by any means & shall not be while alive. My life is of no further value—Farewell my beloved Virginia—What exile should I fly from himself—The cause was thrown away and such blood."[26]

Chamberlayne's final act of soldiering was full of grand illusions and inspired more by vanity than by ideology or politics. He would not allow defeat to crush his dream of eternal fame as a Confederate hero. From the moment he enlisted in 1861, ambition stalked Chamberlayne, pressing him to fight recklessly on the battlefield, but the promise of glory was never fully realized. He

*The Trophies of Victory and the Relics of Defeat*

fumbled away the opportunity to be part of the epic Battle of Gettysburg by getting himself captured during a horse-stealing expedition in Pennsylvania. As a result he spent much of the war incarcerated in a Northern prison camp while his friends from the University of Virginia racked up battlefield accolades. In 1864 he returned to Lee's army to command an artillery battery in a relatively quiet sector of the Petersburg siege lines, where there were few chances to earn distinction under fire.[27]

Chamberlayne's romantic temperament fueled his impatience for battlefield laurels while also creating a fiery devotion to the Confederacy that became inseparable from his understanding of himself as a man. Like other diehard Confederates, he was infatuated with rebellious figures who hurled themselves toward self-destruction for honor and women, even if the gestures were doomed to futility.[28] Chamberlayne in particular was drawn to the drama of exile, and after Appomattox he would follow a plotline that came straight from Lord Byron, whose personal life and writings were fixated with banishment.[29] But unlike Byron, whose itinerant life brought fame and notoriety, Chamberlayne discovered what it meant to be a man alone and on the run. By the end of May 1865, he had reached Mississippi, feeling fatigued in body and disheartened in spirit, but he remained undeterred, still in search of an organized Confederate force to continue the fight. To his dismay, wherever he looked he found an impoverished and demoralized people who wanted no more of the Confederate war.

With every passing day at his relative's home in Mississippi, Chamberlayne could feel himself losing contact with the world around him. Writing to his close friend in Virginia, George W. Bagby, Chamberlayne described his slow downward spiral. "I know scarcely anything of what has happened anywhere," he wrote on June 20, "more especially of Virginian matters I am ignorant to a painful degree—an ignorance of which I grow vastly impatient; but, you know, here is my only home, the only place where I can claim bed & board, without being a burden." His sense of unworthiness as a man is striking, and perhaps more acute than what most of his peers felt. Yet in the initial months after defeat, ex-Confederates certainly wondered if they could be anything but soldiers. "To shoot a few squirrels; to talk with my friends and kinsfolk; & studiously to avoid thought on the past or the present or the future," Chamberlayne added, "I do not see what I can do as yet, and by remaining here I avoid being so great a burden as I would be there [Virginia] to any." He had no energy for the world, and he could not imagine that the world had much use for him, as he was—at least in his estimation—nothing more than a "brokendown soldier." In the end, Chamberlayne thought he could never return home, since "Virginia is dead, my very heart weeps for her, she that was—with her that is what have we to do?"[30]

Every morning on his relative's farm in Mississippi, Chamberlayne awoke feeling numb to the past. All the sacrifices, suffering, and bloodshed weighed on the present, an invisible but pervasive force dragging him down and disorienting him to a point where he could "hardly say . . . [if] I exist." "The war and its objects, its causes, & the cause of its failure," Chamberlayne confided to his longtime female correspondent Sally Grattan, "are not subjects of thought with me as are other things, but are become thought itself, parts of my mind, burned into my heart as with a branding iron.—The failure is such, that not one of the huge losses in its prosecution ever appeals to me; they are but parts of the whole—And that whole, I hope and trust, will be too hard for us to bear & will not be borne."[31]

Even in his abject state of depression, Chamberlayne remained defiant, expressing rage against the North in an apocalyptic fantasy in which the South would rise again. He was no different from defeated people in other nations who believed, as historian Wolfgang Schivelbusch points out, that "the idea of war, death, and rebirth are cyclically linked . . . [and] do not allow for absolute eradication."[32] Chamberlayne and countless other ex-Confederates lived with the illusion that the Southern people were not finished with the Yankees and that revenge would be a righteous act. "Every drop of blood of ours that was spilled is, I believe, as a seed in the ground, whence will spring wrath and armed men. So I live in hopes of the fullness of that time. . . . To move the make the march toward it one hour shorter, is a noble object for life."[33] Chamberlayne's own worlds pulled him up from his depression, transporting him to some future battlefield where he could regain his honor and manliness by slaughtering the hated foe once again.

It was not unusual for former Confederates to indulge in revenge fantasies as a way to assure themselves that their honor would ultimately be redeemed. Their apocalyptic visions really constituted a form of consolation during a time of collapse, rather than a concrete strategy to recapture power through political or military purposes. Some violence erupted, to be sure, and returned Confederate soldiers directed terror against freed people and occupying Union forces, particularly when the troops were black soldiers. These gangs of Confederate veterans or night riders attacked freed people with a shocking cruelty, often inflicting sexual violence against black women as a way to protect the sanctity of white male privilege and womanhood. The attacks were intended to crush black political power and prevent freed people from organizing as a labor force. Did Chamberlayne desire terrorist attacks against black people when he wrote that

*The Trophies of Victory and the Relics of Defeat*

from the blood of the fallen would "spring wrath and armed men"? It is impossible to say, but this desire for revenge—echoed by so many of his fellow Confederates—took flight in a reign of terror unleashed by night riders whose white hoods created the frightening illusion that the ghosts of dead Confederate soldiers had arisen to kill again.[34]

Like so many former Southern soldiers, Chamberlayne looked for something in the past to rescue his reputation in the present, and a captured pair of Yankee boots helped to restore his self-esteem. "Tho' the country is for a time enslaved," he wrote to his friend Sally, "tho friends are dead & exiled, and no man has a home, & tho I have not a dollar in the world, nor any property but one pair of top boots (with spurs attached), still I can laugh."[35] The boots were the property of a Maine colonel whose person and possessions were captured during the 1862 Maryland Campaign when the armies grappled along the South Mountain chain. When Chamberlayne looked at his boots, his mind conjured up memories of a daring adventure. The Yankee shoes became the muse for his epic tale. "We strove with them until night," Chamberlayne wrote, "and we girded our loins in the night season; and we wrestled mightily with them about the rising of the sun, and the voice thereof was the noise of a mighty nation; and we smote them for about the space of two hours, and prevailed against them exceedingly, and took them captive; and took their food, & their raiment, and their horses, and cattle, yea and their creeping things, for a spoil, & for a prey." He admitted to Sally that the story might sound like "nonsense," but the Yankee boots stood as incontestable evidence of the fighting prowess of Confederates, who even in defeat used trophies of war to enshrine their individual and collective valor as Southern soldiers.[36]

Military artifacts like Chamberlayne's Yankee boots were not harmless tributes to a chivalric warfare or simple props for nostalgic tales. Relics possessed tremendous emotional power because they had the capacity to assign meaning to life's experiences. In Chamberlayne's case, the boots materialized gender relations by bonding women to a romantic view of the Confederate soldier as a knightly warrior. Even when muskets were consigned to a fireplace mantel or swords were unsheathed from rusty scabbards for a town parade, they still wielded tremendous influence by triggering emotions such as male pride and aggressiveness. When news spread of a truce and that Johnston was negotiating the surrender of the Army of Tennessee, General William Bates told a Georgia regiment that he "might have to present his sword . . . to our enemies." If this were to occur, he promised, he would tell them that "I, like a man, wrested [this sword] from you at Manassas in 1861."[37] Objects could also induce avoidance, as illustrated by Chamberlayne's peculiar attachment to his Yankee boots. The shoes were a source of pride that helped him cope with the shame and humiliation over Appomattox. He feigned surprise to Sally when he said he could not understand how the Yankee boots "should walk into . . . our confab," yet he deliberately wrote about them at length to prop up his need for mastery, noting that this pair of captured boots was one of his few possessions in the world. Their mere existence, moreover, proved his superiority over a foe who now ruled over him by sheer force, not by daring. All in all, the relics of war allowed Confederate imaginations to roam free, often to dangerous and dark places, infusing the polemical Lost Cause ideology with a romantic glow. In actuality, war relics fused volatile emotions to reactionary politics that came together in the violent enforcement of white rule and black subordination during Reconstruction.

Such relics would soothe the wounded pride of Southern men for generations to come, but in the moment of surrender, Confederates returning home were not laden down with war memorabilia or mementos. As Carlton McCarthy recalled: "To roll up the old blanket and oil-cloth, gather up the haversack, canteen, axe, perhaps, and a few trifles in time of peace of no value" was all they could do when leaving Appomattox. Yet McCarthy and his fellow survivors could hold their heads high as they walked home, knowing that they had "faithfully performed their duty." He did not feel the overwhelming sense of disgrace and worthlessness that cut Chamberlayne to his core. Personality and circumstances largely explain why McCarthy embraced the future without bitterness or rancor. Unlike Chamberlayne, McCarthy had read Lee's farewell address, General Orders No. 9, and the general's words offered his soldiers emotional sustenance by affirming their place in history as men of unsurpassed devotion to cause and comrade. Lee's staff officer Charles Marshall wrote the proclamation, but Lee edited and ultimately approved the language of an intellectually charged message that framed the Lost Cause explanation of Southern defeat—one that twisted the pages of history for generations to come. By emphasizing Yankee numbers as the cause of the Army of Northern Virginia's demise, Lee essentially exonerated himself and his men for surrendering while removing Grant and the Union armies as architects of their own victory. General Orders No. 9, as historian Elizabeth Varon writes, "had layers of meaning and deep, tangled roots" that anchored the "overwhelming numbers and resources" argument, explaining Union victory as a matter of might over right.[38] The general's words were not combative toward the North, but they were certainly passive-aggressive: they suggested that the Army of Northern Virginia had not been outgeneraled or outfought by the Army of the Potomac, but simply worn down by the enemy's ruthless execution of a hard-war strategy that preyed on the weak and terrorized the helpless.

*The Trophies of Victory and the Relics of Defeat*

Lee and Marshall were extremely self-conscious writers who understood the power of words in shaping historical understanding. Both men needed to construct a reality of defeat that lifted the reputations of Southern soldiers. Some of his men were sinking in the tar pit of humiliation, like North Carolinian Henry Chambers, who wrote the following diatribe in his Appomattox diary: "Oh! But it is a bitter, bitter humiliation. All our hopes of independence blasted! All that a generous people value, gone at one fell blow! Worse than all, more keenly humiliated than all is the fact that these worthless fellows whom we have so often whipped, whose cowardly backs we have so often seen, have at last by sheer force of number . . . now lord over us."[39] General Orders No. 9 expunged the humiliation in the ranks with its yearning for dignity, strength, and honor through a narrative of romantic sentimentality that came straight from the Southern chivalric tradition. Lee's farewell words called attention to the "unsurpassed courage and fortitude" of his men, who remained "steadfast to the last." With these words of adulation and respect, Lee assured his men that he had not lost faith in them and that they had been outmanned, but not outfought. Lee and Marshall also crafted General Orders No. 9 with the awareness that a larger public audience would judge their army's actions. Southern civilians would find little to criticize or even question, however, thanks to the carefully constructed script, which defended surrender as the only honorable course for an army whose ranks were decimated and whose supplies had been exhausted. The broken-down condition of the Army of Northern Virginia during the final weeks of its existence cannot be dismissed as an invention of the imagination. Conditions were simply deplorable and soldiers were starving.

Nonetheless, General Orders No. 9 only accounts for the experience of the roughly twenty thousand men who reached Appomattox. It overlooks the epidemic of desertion that ripped through the Army of Northern Virginia during the retreat from Richmond and Petersburg. This massive loss of manpower made Union victory all but inevitable. Lee's last words amount to a cover-up by omission of the startling loss of discipline, which became a lightning rod of debate in his own army at the time. Many of his veterans charged that cowardice had secured Union victory at Appomattox. "If the men will only remain at their posts & trust in God everything would go right," a Confederate soldier wrote during the retreat. "If we lose our country, it is our own fault." A veteran of the Army of Tennessee rendered a similarly harsh judgment: "If true we are a whipped people," he wrote on April 17, "caused by our own actions, as we can safely say one half of the army are deserters from the Cause and like a set of cowards have taken to the woods."[40]

The Farewell Address implicitly and explicitly argued that continued resistance would have been a murderous waste of noble lives.[41] At the same time, General Orders No. 9 enshrined Lee's veterans as a band of loyal brothers whose courage reigned supreme even in defeat. It is no surprise that the address became a coveted artifact that forever linked a soldier to Lee — the idol of white Southerners — while exalting the rank and file as exemplary men of duty. Copyists at Lee's headquarters sent the original copies to corps and division commanders, and from there it is likely that clerks made copies for brigades and that the process was then repeated at the regimental level. Plenty of copies were nailed to trees or tacked to tent posts for the rank and file to read.[42] Some of these copies even reached the Army of Tennessee by the middle of April, carried by Lee's men as they headed south from Appomattox.[43]

The speedy and wide circulation of the address both inside and outside the Army of Northern Virginia is a shocking fact when one considers the rush of practical demands bearing down on soldiers in the midst of disbanding an army. The document was compact and portable: a soldier could keep it handy in a pocket, and if his military record was called into question, the document offered on-the-spot vindication. The desire to have a copy of the Farewell Address, the words of R. E. Lee enshrining his small band of troops with words of dignity and honor, spurred some soldiers to make handwritten copies as a treasured keepsake, but it was also an artifact that possessed the power of touch — something to hold, to read, and to reflect on. As soon as a copy of the Farewell Address reached the hands of Colonel H. Perry, he collected some Confederate stationary and pulled out a bass drum to use as a makeshift desk. With great care, he copied General Orders No. 9 for his own use. When he finished his transcription, Perry visited Lee's headquarters and managed to see the general long enough for an autograph as incontestable authentication of the document's "truthfulness." Virginian John E. Roller also wanted to take a piece of Appomattox history home, and he instructed an orderly sergeant to make a number of copies before passing the papers among the veterans who were still in the unit. "I thought it due to the men who had served to the close of the war," he noted, "that they should have the fact preserved."[44]

The effect of Lee's General Orders No. 9 was felt immediately, as its message of defeat with honor rolled across the countryside. It brought a sense of relief to some civilians, while others were stunned, believing that Lee's capitulation to the enemy was an impossibility. Confederate soldiers outside the Army of Northern Virginia, on the other hand, had witnessed the gradual erosion of their armies for some time, and they tended to accept the hard fact of Union victory with less skepticism. The words of General Lee, moreover, resonated with all men, for they were drawn to the idea that there was a certain nobility in being subdued by the enemy's multitudes who could not conquer Confederates in a fair fight. In a sense, scores of former Rebels saw surrendering—their last act of soldiering—as a redemptive moment for Southern manhood. Just outside Greensboro, North Carolina, for instance, Louisiana soldier William Ellis poured out his conflicted feelings over the surrender of Lee's army and the inevitable end of the Confederacy. Although embittered by the prospect of having to submit to the Yankees, he looked to the future with hope, believing that the blood sacrifice of his comrades would be memorialized for future generations who would judge Confederate soldiers as a valiant and decent people. Even before all the Confederate armies had surrendered, Rebel soldiers extolled their heroic defense, believing that it would go down as one of the classic defeats in world history, one that would stand alongside momentous battles like Thermopylae.[45] "That noble army that has stood like a rock, against which the waves of invasion have beaten fruitlessly for four long years," Ellis wrote on April 12, with the self-adulation that would become standard Lost Cause fare. "That army," he continued, "which has illustrated upon a hundred fields all that we could boast chivalry and indomitable courage. This has furnished the Army of North. Virginia the pride and [illegible] of the nation. Millions yet unborn will recount its deeds of prowess and prattling infants will be taught to lisp the name of Lee."[46]

Generals Joseph Johnston and Nathan Bedford Forrest also issued farewell proclamations that were similar to General Orders No. 9. They cleared the reputations of their men and commended them as the last defenders of a noble cause. "You will return to your homes with the admiration of your people, won by the courage and noble devotion you have displayed in this long war," Johnston declared on May 2 in General Orders No. 22, his farewell address to the Army of Tennessee. "I shall always remember with pride the loyal support and generous confidence you have given me."[47] Forrest offered his troops a more sobering farewell seven days later, bluntly telling his troops, "I do not think it proper or necessary at this time to refer to causes which have reduced us to this extremity; nor is it now a matter of material consequences to us how such results were brought about. That we are BEATEN is a self-evident fact, and any further resistance on our part would justly be regarded as the very height of folly and rashness." The glories of past sacrifice would be tarnished, Forrest warned, if the soldiers did not stack their weapons and go home. He acknowledged that "the Cause for which you have so long and so manfully struggled, and for which you have braved dangers, endured privations, and sufferings, and made so many sacrifices, is today hopeless. The government, which we sought to establish and perpetuate, is at an end. Reason dictates and humanity demands that no more blood be shed."[48]

Lee, Johnston, and Forrest used their farewell addresses to caution against further violence. Johnston pleaded with his men to be "good and peaceful citizens at your home as well as you have performed the duties of thorough soldiers in the field. By such a course you will best secure the comfort of your families and kindred and restore tranquility to your country."[49] Of all the Confederate generals, Forrest surprisingly raised the loudest voice for moderation. He spared no one's feelings by telling his men that the right thing to do was admit defeat, put down their guns, and repress any desire for revenge so that they might reconcile with the enemy and reintegrate into the nation as smoothly as possible. "Civil War, such as you have just passed through naturally engenders feelings of animosity, hatred, and revenge. It is our duty to divest ourselves of all such feelings; and as far as it is in our power to do so, to cultivate friendly feelings towards those with whom we have so long contended, and heretofore so widely, but honestly, differed." In the conclusion of his farewell, Forrest pressed his case further, reminding his men that they had served in the ranks with dignity, gaining an enviable reputation throughout the South, but that their good names would be tarnished if they did not put aside "neighborhood feuds, personal animosities, and private difference." To Forrest it was equally important that his men earn the respect of their former enemies. He then concluded: "You have been good soldiers, you can be good citizens. Obey the laws, preserve your honor, and the Government to which you have surrendered."[50]

Lee also refrained from using any inflammatory language against his former enemy, but he refused to promote a spirit of reunion or reconciliation among his men, whom he called his "brave survivors." Lee's General Orders No. 9 used the words *terms of agreement* to create a distinct meaning at odds with the North's belief that there had been no negotiation and no compromise in the parlor of the McLean house. The Farewell Address suggested equality between former adversaries, a calculated message that could be constructed only by denying what actually had occurred behind those parlor doors. Yet Grant laid down an unconditional demand to surrender, and Lee had no choice but to abide by it.

The idea of a gentlemen's agreement ending the Civil War, however, cannot be rejected as a purely historical falsification inspired by flag-waving nationalism and a militaristic spirit. It is impossible to deny that the actual surrendering of all Confederate forces stretching from Virginia to North Carolina and beyond the Mississippi into Texas was carried out in an orderly and respectful fashion with little to no violence between the opposing forces. The reasons for conciliation are fairly obvious and straightforward. Union and Confederate officers came from a similar military culture of professionalism structured by the Articles of War, which helped contain excessive and uncontrollable violence by organized armies. Above all else, the political objective of the war to suppress the rebellion and restore the Union explains why Confederate armies dissolved without a major incident. In the nineteenth century, civil wars elsewhere typically ended with a murderous final assault on the defeated, but national restoration in the American Civil War required an unusual degree of mercy on the part of the victor. The surrender terms put forth, as a result, were models of moderation and magnanimity. Everywhere but Appomattox, Rebel soldiers were permitted to simply put down their guns, discard their accoutrements, roll up their flags, and head home.[51]

In late May at Meridian, Mississippi, Federal authorities extended extraordinary courtesy to the surrendering Confederates. "No excitement, no disorder," artillery private Philip Stephenson reported with a sense of relief. "The Federal troops were kept well in hand[,] were not allowed to insult us, and they showed no disposition to do so. There was no marching out, lining us up opposite the Federal forces, and our general surrendering his sword to the victor, no pomp and parade of triumph."[52] In North Carolina, Sherman's bummers, who were noted for a vengeful spirit against slaveholding Confederates and who were ratcheted up by the news of Lincoln's assassination on April 15, still refused to do anything that might hurt or humiliate their former adversaries in the Army of Tennessee. They felt compassion for the average Confederate soldier, believing that he had fallen victim to the slaveholders who deceived the poor man into fighting.[53] Johnston's troops were instructed to stack their rifles and accoutrements and disperse, but each regiment could carry six muskets home. One Georgia soldier was shocked by the lack of Federal supervision when his company turned its guns and cartridge boxes over to a Confederate ordnance officer, who then transported the material to Greensboro. For the next three days, the soldiers waited in camp for their blank paroles. Once they arrived and were filled out, the entire regiment left for home as a functioning organization with the intention of disbanding at Washington, Georgia. Countless other units in the Army of Tennessee returned home in the same way—still maintaining their unit organizations with their weapons and flags.

The spirit of conciliation is often seen as a uniquely Appomattox phenomenon, but in actuality there was less goodwill shown to Lee's men in Virginia than to Confederates at the other surrender sites. Only the Army of Northern Virginia had to participate in a surrendering parade. Union officers who were part of a surrender commission apparently insisted on a formal parade of Confederate infantry marching between opposing ranks of Federal troops. In the eyes of Lee's lieutenants this was a march of shame, a degradation to be avoided, but they had little choice in the matter, since the Federals controlled the distribution of the paroles. This slip of paper almost always protected the surrendering Confederates from future molestation by Federal authorities. They could not, in other words, be arrested on the way home and sent to a Northern prison camp as a prisoner of war.

A cold and drizzly morning gave way to sun as Lee's men assembled for the last time. There was little speculation as to their destination. Everyone knew they were embarking on a march that would end with the extinction of their army. The thin procession of Confederate troops passed by the site of the uprooted apple tree and splashed across the North Branch of the Appomattox River before ascending an extremely steep hill that crested at a wide plateau opening up to the village of Appomattox, where five thousand Federals of the Third Brigade, First Division, of the Fifth Corps lined both sides of the road and waited in silence. At the helm of the column rode Confederate general John B. Gordon. His appearance cued Maine's Joshua Chamberlain, who thought Lee's veterans deserved "the honors due to troops" and accordingly gave the command "at a shoulder," which the Federals executed with soldierly precision.

In recognition of the soldier salute, the Confederates came to shoulder arms as they passed the Maltese Cross, the designated flag of the Fifth Corps. Lee's men continued to march until they reached the left end of the Union line, anchored near the McLean house.[54] They then turned to face their former adversaries, stacked their rifles, hung their accoutrements on their bayonets, and rolled up their flags. This process was repeated throughout the day, and by late afternoon the Federals had confiscated some fifteen thousand rifles and seventy-two battle flags. Scores of Confederates refused to participate in the march; they simply left their muskets in their empty camps before starting for home. Some companies tore their battle flags into small mementos rather than surrender their beloved banners to the enemy.[55] A number of flags were made of silk, often from the wedding dresses of the wives of prominent officers. One Union soldier noted the feel of the banners, remarking that "some few of them were silk, but the most of them were of very course goods."[56] The material carried tremendous emotional and ideological power, reminding Confederates that the struggle was not just a war to retain slavery, but a defense of Southern womanhood.[57] Giving up the flags likely touched on Southern male fears that the Yankees would violate the virtue of their daughters and wives. The symbolic power of the battle flag resided in its connection to the blood sacrifices on the battlefield, where so many comrades had given their lives under it. To hand over

*The Trophies of Victory and the Relics of Defeat*

these cherished flags — connected to so many powerful memories — felt like the ultimate act of betrayal of the dead.

By all accounts, Union forces carried out the surrender parade with great solemnity and respect. In victory, of course, it was easier for Northern soldiers to feel sympathy for an enemy, and they had also forged a kinship with an adversary who knew the life of a Civil War soldier, unlike the people behind the lines. "Poor Fellows," Union officer Joshua Lawrence Chamberlain of Maine wrote a day after the surrender. "I pitied them from the bottom of my heart. Those arms had been well handled & the flags bravely borne." These dejected Confederates coming from the corps of John B. Gordon and James Longstreet were veterans whom Chamberlain "had faced a score of times & almost recognized by face."[58] The complete absence of bravado and bombast on the part of the Federals preserved a tone of reverence that would normally have been reserved for the funeral of a dignitary. The exceptional silence and solemnity impressed the Confederates deeply, convincing them that they had received the honor due to them as soldiers and as men. Some were so forlorn, however, that they could hardly speak, while others were more expressive, even making witty remarks as they stacked their weapons. Pennsylvanian John Smith overheard one of Lee's men say good-bye to his rifle: "'My dear wife; I hope that I will never see you again. If you kill as many Rebels as you have killed Yanks you will do very well.' Kissing the gun, with the remark 'Good-bye.'" Another Confederate could not part with his musket soon enough. "'Good-bye gun. I am darned glad to get rid of you. I have been trying to for two years.'" To these soldiers, their weapons became the personification of a comrade who bore witness to battle with a sturdy dependability. Over the course of the war a soldier developed a practical relationship with the tools and materials of war, but that relationship was more than functional. Such relics were soaked in memories of violence and blood, forged during incredible physical and emotional duress. A rifle, flag, tent, uniform, canteen, and haversack could fill a man with a range of emotions and meanings, but these things were not just containers of memories. They could shape behavior, filter perceptions, and serve as conductors of action.[59]

There was little humor when the color bearers gave up their beloved flags. "Many had tears streaming down their faces," Smith observed. "It effected them more than others; the thought of having carried the flag through so many battles and then were compelled to surrender at this time. I tell you, it was an affecting sight, looking at those brave men."[60] The Confederates' filthy uniforms, their bare haversacks, and their banners shredded by Northern bullets offered incontestable evidence of an endurance, devotion, and manly spirit that would forever reside in the things of war. At the same time Union soldiers visualized

Confederate defeat as an irreversible fact. The worn cartridge boxes empty of rounds, the broken scabbards, the tattered shoes, and the frayed battle flags were the remnants of a defeated army and a dead nation.

Union soldiers stationed along the surrender route tore off pieces of the captured Confederate flags and sent them home. Smith packaged a number of Appomattox artifacts collected from Confederates, including two printed Confederate songs and a ring traded by "a fine looking Reb." Of all his souvenirs, Smith treasured his piece of "a Rebel flag," with its stenciled letters, r and g. "The two letters that are on it," he explained to his mother, "would be . . . of the word Fredericksburg," where his regiment suffered horrible losses. "Take . . . the pieces and when I get home I will tell you all the particulars about them."[61] The fragments of cloth ripped from rebellious banners materialized victory for civilians who knew that the Rebel flag, above all else, represented the soul of every Southern community's war effort.

A few minor but ugly incidents rippled through the surrender parade, when former combatants started reminiscing about battles in an attempt to settle old scores through banter. "'What regiment is that?,'" Smith recalled one Confederate asking. "'Corn Exchange Regiment,'" was the reply. "'Oh, we gave it to you at Shepherdstown and Fredericksburg.'" The men of the Corn Exchange fired back a quick rebuttal: "'Then you have to surrender to us now.'"[62] Even this petty bickering could not stop Smith from feeling for Lee's broken-down men as they stacked their arms before they started "for home, without a cent." "Pretty rough for these brave fellows," he added.[63]

Not all of Lee's men could suppress their hostility and humiliation when it was their turn to disarm in front of their enemies. Orderly Sergeant J. E. Whitehorne of the Twelfth Virginia, who had wept openly on April 9 when learning of Lee's surrender, could barely contain his rage during the surrender parade. He glared at the Union soldiers arrayed to his front, looking to see if any would show a sign of disrespect. "They did not look at us, did not look defiant, did not make disrespectful remarks," he noted in his diary, leading him to the mystifying conclusion that "the Yanks, are afraid of us now."[64] As ludicrous as Whitehorne might appear today, his reactions show the dynamic of honor at work, with its inexorable pressure on white men to present the right appearance, even if it meant putting their heads in the sand and ignoring indisputable signs of an army in chaos. Whitehorne's dislocation from reality might be idiosyncratic, but his zealotry for the Confederacy—intensified through a sensibility of absolutism—illustrates how loyalty to the cause was not fueled entirely by nationalism and ideology. Honor and absolutism worked side by side to erase life's inconvenient truths.

*The Trophies of Victory and the Relics of Defeat*

Even Confederates who were not as belligerent as Whitehorne looked to the Yankees for validation of their courage. If the respectful demeanor of the enemy was not enough, these men turned to possession to confirm their standing as dutiful men. Keepsakes such as shreds of battle flags, sidearms, swords, parole passes, and even their muskets were made sacred for having passed through the fire of battle. One Northern soldier captured this perspective in a letter he wrote just days after Lee's surrender. "We lay at Appomattox Court House and helped to guard Lee's Army until they were all paroled," N. H. Panghorn explained to his parents. "Our boys and Rebels would be in each others camps talking and trading pen knives, finger rings, hats & caps and all kinds of little keeps sakes or as the Rebels say: trick. . . . There was a good many instances where relatives and old friends met who had but a few hours before been trying to kill each other." Panghorn finished his update by concluding that these exchanges between former enemies proved there was little chance of a second Southern insurgency. "The most of the rebels that I talked to said they were fairly whipped and had been surrendered by Gen. Lee. They said they could go home now without fears of being taunted by their neighbors, but they said they did not like to desert for they did not think a deserter could be respected either by friends or enemy." [65] The objects former Rebels carried home were vessels of a "living" legacy that would remind future generations that they too possessed the Confederate blood of valor and honor, a legacy that boosted Southern pride through Reconstruction and well into the twentieth century, as any caretaker of these cherished heirlooms had to uphold the honor of the war generation. [66]

The end of the Civil War brought Union and Confederate veterans to a precipice from which they surveyed the very different landscapes over which they would journey home. Southern veterans became civilians as soon as their armies disbanded and they received their paroles. That first day—when there was no bugle sounding morning roll call or drum announcing afternoon drill— a strange sensation overcame soldiers, who once again tasted the freedom of choice and action. The day after the formal surrender of Lee's artillery, Carlton McCarthy felt tremendous relief knowing that he would never again have to endure the privations of soldiering, of living in a "muddy, smoky camp among gloomy, hungry comrades." [67] He exulted in life, with all of its insecurities and potential troubles, without giving much thought to the immediate consequences of victory or defeat. After stacking his weapons on April 12, a North Carolinian could breathe the air of freedom for the first time in years. "We started for home," he wrote, "all greatly relieved that the war was over and we were alive." [68]

Not all Confederates reconciled themselves so easily to defeat, finding little comfort in being in the land of the living when surrendering was nothing more than subjugation. The loss of the monotonous and highly routinized schedule that had felt so onerous during the war also suddenly left some Confederates feeling as if they were sheep without their shepherd. The day after Lee surrendered to Grant, Joseph Whitehorne woke up in a daze, not knowing what do after years of having officers script and direct his days. "The war has been going on so long I can't realize what a man would do now it's over. All I know is to drill, and march, and fight. How can we get interested in farming or working in a store or warehouse when we have been interested day and night for years in keeping alive, whipping the invaders, and preparing for the next fight."[69] Whitehorne was hardly alone in wondering what a soldier might do on returning home when all he had was lousy and tattered clothing and very little money in his pocket.

Hunger was the paramount concern of former Confederates. Their foraging skills served them well, since it was impossible to rely on the generosity of strangers. Diary entry after diary entry describes a wide range of encounters with a civilian population just barely scraping by, especially lower-class whites and freedpeople who were fighting their own battles against starvation. There were also plenty of civilians who were confirmed Unionists during the war, and they felt free to come out of the closet after Appomattox. Now they could boldly hurl insults at a begging Confederate before slamming the door in his face. Other veterans ran up against outraged farmers who had been victimized by bandits masquerading as former Confederate soldiers. Throughout the Confederacy there was a breakdown in law and order, and the countryside witnessed shocking violence and rampant thievery. Carlton McCarthy referred to himself and his comrade as survivors when they came upon a farmer who had lost some horses to a group of Lee's Appomattox men. After much stalling, the farmer invited the veterans inside, and a plate was put before them with "the heads, tails, fins, and vertebrae of the fish." Seeing that their host was offering them breakfast leftovers, McCarthy and his friend rushed out of the house, feeling insulted and indignant, but also firing off a final salvo: "You are meaner than 'any epithets at our command.'"[70]

For the most part, however, it appears that Southern civilians tried to accommodate the returning soldiers as best they could, giving them food and water and welcoming them as men of duty who should feel no shame about surrendering. After leaving Appomattox an inconsolable Whitehorne and some comrades approached a house looking for water when they spotted a young woman baking bread. A lively conversation ensued, and he later wrote in his diary that at once "she made me feel that the world will not come to an end."[71] Cordial greetings only sustained Confederates for so long, especially for sol-

*The Trophies of Victory and the Relics of Defeat*

diers from the Deep South, who struggled to find adequate provisions from a land wrecked by war. Ex-Rebels who kept journals filled their pages not with anger or bitterness over the lost cause, but with terse descriptions of anxiety and frustration about surviving the trip home. "We all suffer from the scarcity of provisions," read a typical notation from a Confederate; "the country is completely ruined."[72] A wave of crime and destruction also swept through towns and cities in rioting that eclipsed in scale anything that had occurred during the war. Veterans from Johnston's and Lee's armies pillaged Greensboro and Charlotte, North Carolina, and Augusta, Georgia. In all of these places, soldiers targeted and looted warehouses with a wanton desire to destroy and steal, out of both rage and necessity.

Despite the wanton destruction, Confederate armies demobilized in a relatively peaceful manner, especially in comparison to other citizen-soldier armies that disbanded in the nineteenth century. There was no mass reprisal against the defeated, who returned home without weapons to communities where there was some presence of Federal military authority.[73] Resistance to the Federals was futile, but veterans often lost their restraint when they encountered freed blacks on the road home. Their mere appearance pierced the shield of white honor, reminding former Rebels that their failure on the battlefield had resulted in their loss of mastery over African Americans and that they were the generation who had lost slavery. They believed that only retaliation could restore the "natural" racial order. In one example near Selma, Alabama, a group of paroled Confederates confronted hundreds of free blacks who were headed to Montgomery to enlist in the Union army. Since the former soldiers no longer had muskets, they armed themselves with rocks and stoned the blacks until they retreated into the woods. "We scattered many a band of them in this way," an Alabama soldier recalled without a hint of regret, "and often some seeing the fate of those heads would flee to the woods before reaching us. Of course they were free, and could go if they wished, but we hadn't come to the point yet where we could realize it."[74]

The idea that Confederate veterans came home catatonic with despair is a gross exaggeration of the mental state of Southern men. Internally, to be sure, returning veterans were in turmoil, but in public they had little choice but to show a brave face, knowing that power was up for grabs. Survival, at both a political and a practical level, kept the vast majority of white Southerners from spiraling down too far. Fundamental questions over who would control black labor, who would have a political voice, and who was entitled to national citizenship awakened white Southerners from the dejection of defeat. Too much was at stake for Confederate soldiers to mope on the sidelines of civic life. A con-

*trolled despair* best describes the initial reaction of Southern veterans as they stepped through the front doors of their homes, overjoyed by their survival and relieved that they had escaped the army's grinding machinery of death, but also wondering, as Confederate Carlton McCarthy put it, how they would begin the transition from "survivors" stuck on "the neutral ground between war and peace — neither soldier nor citizens."[75]

Northern soldiers did not become civilians overnight, as their Confederate counterparts did at Appomattox. The staggered surrenders of Rebel armies necessitated that a substantial number of Union forces remain in the field until the war's work was finally finished. During the third week of May, Confederate forces still operated in the Trans-Mississippi Theater while a French puppet regime in Mexico edged toward the Texas border. Union troops east of the Mississippi River could not be disbanded and sent home. Their availability kept the Trans-Mississippi secure as the region transitioned from war to peace. As a result, a substantial number of Northern units remained on active duty after Appomattox, including the United States Colored Troops, who were consolidated into a single corps and assigned to duty along the coastal areas in the South. Of the 1 million active Union soldiers in service at the end of the war, approximately 150,000 veterans from General George G. Meade's Army of the Potomac (less its Sixth Corps), Sherman's Armies of Tennessee and Georgia, and General Phillip Sheridan's cavalry were available to participate in the Grand Review in Washington, D.C., on May 23–24, a military procession intended to honor the Union troops and to celebrate the end of the war.

En route to the nation's capital from Richmond during the middle of May, four corps of Sherman's army group traversed portions of the Spotsylvania, Wilderness, Chancellorsville, and Fredericksburg battlefields. The vast majority of the men were encountering the Virginia battlefields for the first time, except for one corps composed primarily of regiments that had fought at Chancellorsville. Those survivors of General Joseph Hooker's debacle served as unofficial guides of the field. They told harrowing stories of survival on the spot where their units had fought two years earlier. Returning to the place of such awful violence actually helped some of the men heal from these painful memories of the war. Standing on the killing ground rekindled a connection to the dead by filling the living with tender sentiments for beloved friends and fellow soldiers.

Most of Sherman's men did not have a guide, however, and they were left to wander across the woods and fields. With every step, regardless of the direction, they saw trees chewed up by gunfire or skeletal remains protruding from the Virginia soil. Ohioan Marion Roberts, who slipped away from the marching column at Spotsylvania, stumbled upon piles of dead Union soldiers. That

*The Trophies of Victory and the Relics of Defeat*

night he devoted his entire diary entry to the utter lack of respect and regard shown for the fallen:

> Arriving near the spot we saw the timber cut the men were not totally covered—and bones would protrude—often a head with gaping jaws, feet hands &c—passing thro' a strip of timber some of the party counted 67 unburied Union soldiers or their skeletons we did not see how many there were of this kind as it was not our object—suffice it to say there are hundreds of skeletons who have never been buried and lie as they fell dead in battle more than one year ago. . . . Skeletons of unburied soldiers were found lying close by entirely uncared for.[76]

Roberts expressed a recurring motif found in the writings of those who toured the battlefields around Fredericksburg. Their impressions, though varied in details, touched on four similar themes: that the indignities inflicted against the Union dead demanded immediate redress by the U.S. military; that the battered condition of the landscape conveyed the fury of combat as a physical truth; that the individual soldier mattered, and his personal story of suffering and sacrifice resided in the remains of the dead; and that the act of touring the fields elicited both the joy that came with surviving and the mournful sorrow for those who had fallen and would never return to their families.

Sherman's men did not try to purify the battlefield as a heroic space where war regenerated men or the nation. The badly scarred terrain, with its exposed graves and trees gnarled and twisted by artillery fire, reminded veterans of the hell they had escaped. Every battlefield vista was one of human carnage, making it impossible to forget or suppress images of suffering soldiers who had died an agonizing death. Some skeletons at Spotsylvania revealed the last moments of a soldier's life to a touring Indiana veteran who saw that "some [men] had collected as they lay wounded such sticks and twigs as were within their reach and had striven to erect a barrier to protect them from further injury." Another skeleton had a knapsack strap across the leg, evidently an attempt to "bind a severed artery." "And now," he concluded, "the leather lying loosely about the bone told pathetically of the vain effort."[77]

New Yorker R. Cruikshank witnessed a similar scene at the Wilderness, noting in his diary that at the edge of the woods there was "a soldier [who] lay under a small tree, his white handkerchief torn in shreds tied to a limb about four feet above him. Evidently he had been wounded and was not able to move from the field and had tied his handkerchief to the tree to attract attention. None came and he had to die alone." The isolated death of this poor soldier, who was one of thousands on the fields around Fredericksburg, deeply moved

Cruikshank and the other soldier-tourists. They were appalled by the dehumanization of the dead. The sight of the skeletal remains awakened the imaginations of veterans like Cruikshank, who wondered about the last moments of the dying soldier as he lay abandoned on the field during the horrible last moments of life before death set him free. "We know not how long he was exposed to the elements suffering from hunger and thirst before death came to relieve him of his suffering," Cruikshank concluded in his diary entry. "This is only one case in thousands who have died in the same way."[78]

From Spotsylvania, Cruikshank continued his tour at Chancellorsville, where he was initiated to war when he had fought in the Army of the Potomac. As he surveyed the fields and woods sprawling before the charred ruins of the Chancellorsville Inn, he could not stop thinking about his fallen comrades and the sad disposal of the bodies, half-buried and rotting in some unidentified pit. Even though he resigned himself to never finding their unmarked graves, Cruikshank could still pay his respects by visiting the ground where his regiment had clashed with the enemy. To his great surprise, Cruikshank managed to locate "the very spot where they fell." As he headed back to Sherman's column, Cruikshank suddenly felt as if he had been transported back to May 2, 1863, running to the rear among terrified men whose broken formations were doused by the enemy's "shower of shot, shell and bullets." Through it all, he and a "handful of men" managed to get up the hill to the Chancellorsville House, where he remembered thanking God at the time, amazed that his life had been spared when so many had fallen. To return to the ground after two more years of hardship and danger could only be attributed to providential grace and "His protecting arm above and around men through all the dangers," Cruikshank wrote in his diary on May 15. "I had passed through in the last two years of army life with the prospect to soon be restored to my family again."[79]

For the most part, returning to the battlefield did not inspire Cruikshank or Sherman's veterans to reclaim the hallowed ground they visited as the place where martyrs fell on the national altar. The dead were remembered, instead, as individual soldiers whose personal life stories mattered more than any symbolic connection to the Union cause or the end of slavery. The sight of so many graves reminded Sherman's veterans of the dear comrades lost over the last four years, of men whose families would never see them again and whose bodies were turning to ash in a distant land without any marker of respect or show of decency. Members of a Pennsylvania unit, while walking over the ground where they had fought at Chancellorsville, could not return to the marching column without first caring for the dead. Once they had located their fallen comrades, according to veteran Michael Schroyer, they "picked up the skele-

*The Trophies of Victory and the Relics of Defeat*

tons and brought them home with them." They even found the partial remains of their colonel's corpse, whose body, as Schroyer explained, "had been interred by what was known as sodding. That is the ground was shoveled up and thrown over his body." "He was lying on his back and was recognized by a tooth brush and several other articles, which were found in his clothing," Schroyer noted. "The bones were placed in a box, put in an ambulance, taken to Washington and then shipped to his home."[80] It was not uncommon for soldiers in Sherman's command, who never fought in the Fredericksburg area, to take out shovels and dig proper graves for the unknown Union dead they found.[81]

The physical destruction of the landscape awakened no romantic views of warfare among Sherman's bummers. The gruesome sights elicited common phrases such as "deplorable losses," "fearful fighting," and "dreadful history" in journals and letters home, where they denounced the inhumanity of killing and refused to mythologize the war. "In our imagination," wrote a Pennsylvania soldier from Chancellorsville, "we could see the awful battle raging; columns moving back and forth, men cheering and cursing and swearing, the cannonading, the volleys of musketry, the moaning and groaning of the wounded, the stampede of the army, the woods afire from exploding shells and filled with the dead and dying, the wounded praying that we would help and save them. All these thoughts returned and are indelibly impressed upon our minds."[82] Yet Sherman's soldiers were drawn to the macabre and ghastly, even willing to pay money to see relics that testified to the ferocity of the fighting. Scores of Sherman's soldiers saw the stump of the famous oak tree, twenty-two inches in diameter, felled by intensive musketry fire at Spotsylvania's "Bloody Angle." The remains of the tree were on display in a Spotsylvania Court House building, and the custodian of the relic charged a modest price for a view. At the same time, a steady stream of Union soldiers headed to the actual site of the famous tree. Curiosity, of course, drew them to the battlefield, but the tree itself materialized the violence and terror of combat. If there was any question about the killing power of Civil War weapons, the massive oak stump verified the lethality of the battle while implicitly affirming the bravery of the men who withstood missiles that carried such a destructive force.[83]

By May 17, the last of Sherman's forces had moved north of the Fredericksburg area, leaving behind a war-ravaged landscape for a victory celebration in Washington. Waiting for his comrades to reach the nation's capital was Pennsylvania's John Smith, whose mania for relics brought in a bonanza of choice items from Appomattox. The campaign had taken a toll on his only pair of shoes, forcing him to march in bare feet, and by the time his unit had reached Richmond, Smith could barely walk. A surgeon sent him to a Washington hospital

The twenty-two-inch oak tree felled by bullets at the "Bloody Angle" became an immediate tourist attraction for Sherman's men as they passed through Spotsylvania Court House on their way to participate in the Grand Review in Washington at the end of the war. Such relics appealed to soldiers, who hunted for battle wreckage as hard evidence of their ordeal under fire.
(Photo by Hugh Talman, National Museum of American History)

to recuperate while the rest of the Army of the Potomac completed their over-land march across Virginia. Even though he had comrades in adjoining hospital beds, Smith felt unsettled, telling his mother on May 8, "I feel lonesome being away from the Regt." Yet when he looked around the ward and saw so many wounded and maimed soldiers, he stopped feeling sorry for himself. "I look at them," he added in the same letter, and "I feel grateful that I came through it unharmed with my legs and arms all right."[84]

Smith was not one of the 150,000 white veterans who took part in the Grand Review on May 23–24. The lacerations and cuts on his feet had not healed, and marching with his unit was out of the question, but the doctors gave him a pass for two days so that he could stand on the sidewalk and celebrate the Army of the Potomac on the first day and Sherman's veterans on the second. Smith stood among one hundred thousand visitors who poured into the city to cele-brate the end of the rebellion and pay tribute to their veterans. The soldiers formed on Pennsylvania Avenue, not far from the Capitol, which was adorned by a magnificent banner that proclaimed: "The Only National Debt We Never Can Pay, Is the Debt We Owe to the Victorious Soldiers." Smith stood near the reviewing stand, where President Andrew Johnson, his cabinet, and General Grant took in the spectacle. "I tell you it was a grand sight; one of the great-est things and the greatest mass of people I ever saw in my life. All the distin-guished Generals and all the prominent men of the country it seems to me were on the stand."

Smith's eye, as usual, did not just track the people but also focused on the things of war. The torn bunting from Lincoln's presidential box at Ford's The-atre, which had been ripped by John Wilkes Booth's spur when he jumped to the stage after shooting Lincoln, caught his attention as a sad reminder of Lin-coln's absence. The passing of brigade after brigade marching in lockstep with veteran precision thrilled Smith, who could barely contain himself when his own regiment, the 118th Pennsylvania, passed by and the crowd erupted in ap-plause. The tattered regimental flag, with a knot of campaign ribbons hang-ing from the staff, drew everyone's attention, according to Smith, who saw the banners as proof of his regiment's bravery. As a material relic that had passed through the gauntlet of war, it had fluttered in the smoke of battle; was riddled by enemy bullets; and had been carried by men who gave their lives for the honor of being its bearer. The flags kept alive a heroic image of the rank and file as saviors of the Union, but at the cost of important context. The campaign rib-bons told their own story of hard fighting, and for the veterans, these stream-ers affirmed how they wanted to see themselves — as dependable soldiers who never shirked in battle.

Smith returned to his regimental camp after the Grand Review, and when he was not occupied with the harmless drudgery of drilling and guard duty, his thoughts drifted to the future. He wondered how family and friends would receive him, even though he knew that he had "earned" his reputation through fighting, having compiled an impressive combat record and a promotion to corporal. Yet Smith worried about preserving his standing as a soldier because he knew that some veterans would come home fabricating tales of heroic adventures and peddling stories for profit, even though they had essentially been "playing" soldier for four years without having to do any of the bloody work. Smith had noticed how established shirkers suddenly worried that they might be exposed as scoundrels when the regiment returned home. They were angling for ways to cover their tracks so that they might be received as combat veterans. "I often told you about the pot robbers men that cook for officers so they wouldn't have to go in a fight," an indignant Smith wrote to his mother. "Would do any thing to keep out of a fight well they are getting brave now and want to come back to their company and take a gun [now] the fighting is over."[85] He likely imagined them showing off their weapons to family and friends or prominently displaying them in their parlors, always present to welcome guests to the "home of a veteran." Smith hoped that the War Department, whether intentionally or not, had put up a barrier to the ploys of these quasi-soldiers when it refused to issue new muskets to the troops. Smith understood the cultural power and status a musket imparted to a veteran returning home, since anyone would assume that a man with a rifle must have killed Rebels. He wanted the world to know that he was a "fighting man," and he would not let his hard-earned reputation stand on his words alone. He knew that this weapon would help validate his service in the immediate future and tell stories about his history long after he was gone. In one of his final letters before going home, Smith decided that he would purchase his weapon; he informed his mother, "As the Government demands $6.00 for the gun I have decided to take my gun home."[86]

Unlike most of his comrades in the Corn Exchange Regiment, who went home on June 2, Smith had to remain in camp because of an administrative issue with the date of his enlistment. Saying farewell to his comrades was emotionally wrenching, and Smith admitted to his mother, "I felt sad at being left behind after toiling and marching with them for nearly three years in their many defeats and few bright scenes." Once again Smith would miss an opportunity to feel the warm embrace of a Northern people who had often been damned during the war for failing to appreciate the sacrifices of the soldiers. Past grievances, however, were cast aside among veterans who felt an overpowering sense of nationalistic unity in the immediate wake of the Confederacy's collapse. Smith

*The Trophies of Victory and the Relics of Defeat*

encouraged his mother to go to the local parade for the 118th Pennsylvania's final march, reminding her to take special note of the flag "that I stood under many a time in all engagements with the except[ion] [of] Shepherdstown."[87]

At the conclusion of military service, Union soldiers gloried in their role as the savior in the Union and the destroyers of slavery, but in the moment of jubilation they did not turn militaristic.[88] Quite simply, Northern veterans wanted to discard their uniforms and go home as soon as possible, knowing that their work was done, that the nation had been preserved, and that there was no necessity to remain in the field. "I shall never be a Soldier again if I can help it," Pennsylvanian William Berrier wrote to his family. "At home with my Sweet little Family is where I want to be Where I can eat drink and Sleep when I please and go where and When I please. It will be the greatest pleasure that ever I enjoyed to be with my family once again I never knew how good I had it before, but so it is and the War is over."[89]

Throughout the summer of 1865, Unions soldiers were mustered out of service at a startling rate, but administrative delays continued to keep Smith in the ranks until the middle of July. While waiting for the necessary paperwork to pass through army channels, he occupied himself with checkers, reading, letter writing, and taking stock of his extensive collection of military souvenirs. On July 2, he compiled an inventory of his relics as part of a letter to his mother: "I sent a Rebel jacket by a man by the name of McCarthy. Fix it up and wash it, Mother. Also three rings made from a Rebel shell fuse; I received them at Appomattox C.H. The gold ring that I had on my finger broke while I was on the skirmish line at Gravelly Run. I was firing at the Rebls. I sent you a Rebel $100 note. Save these relics for me." Except for the broken golden ring, Smith did not explain why he collected these items or what they meant to him. He clearly treasured these mementos, but he never told his mother how she should display or care for them. Maybe Smith intended to keep his mementos in a box so he might release the memories of the military campaigns that resulted in the capture of Lee's army and effectively ended the Civil War. Or maybe he hoped to hawk them at a profit.[90]

In the end, no narrative emerges from Smith's relic collection; we have to put together the pieces of a puzzle that can never be fully reconstructed because the evidence is too fragmentary. But these relics are pregnant with interpretive possibilities that fail to surface in written sources.[91] Smith's fetish for Confederate items, including a shell jacket, was certainly unusual, and Smith must have gone to extraordinary lengths to keep and transport the coat, even asking his mother to clean it so that it might be properly preserved. Maybe these Confederate items were exotic to him, or possibly he treasured them as the fragments of a regime that had fallen to mighty Union armies. Nothing in his Confederate collection hints of vindictiveness toward the enemy, nor do the items capture the trauma of combat. Smith did connect the broken ring to a skirmish at Gravely Run, pointing out that he cracked it while shooting at the Rebels, but he said nothing more about the incident. What is striking is the lack of mementos from his beloved 118th Pennsylvania. Smith did save a piece of canvas from his shelter tent, but that is the only recorded item connected to his daily experiences in the ranks—a shocking fact, since he felt an incredible bond with his comrades.

The most curious item in Smith's collection was a Confederate letter found at Jetersville, a hamlet located along Lee's retreat route to Appomattox. Smith offered a pithy summary of the letter for his mother: "The Reb writes to a friend that he is afraid that this Company will have to go to the front and fight and he don't seem to like that. He don't know what soldiers enlist for."[92] In his own letter, Smith scoffed at this Rebel soldier—not because he fought for the Southern cause, but because he did not live by the soldier's universal calling to fight. The respect that Smith accorded to the enemy grew out of his experience around Petersburg, where he routinely fraternized with Lee's men to trade for Southern stationery, songs, and even buttons. His face-to-face interactions with Southern soldiers might explain why he became such a committed collector of all things Confederate. Smith's Southern mementos speak to his empathy for the enemy as a fellow soldier who happened to fight on the wrong side. Above all else, his collection gets to the pulse of a political moderation rooted in Smith's commitment to Union. Such a position helped encourage sympathy for the very men who had been trying to kill him for four years. This spirit of reconciliation, evident in Smith's relic collection, found written expression in the *Sixth Corps*, a newspaper published by Union veterans who described a shared religious service between Union soldiers and former Confederates just weeks after Appomattox:

> It was a solemn and impressive scene. Over fields red with blood
> strewn with the dead and dying, and enveloped in the smoke of battle
> had all those prayerful men fought their way to the throne of the
> Almighty . . . and [seeking] forgiveness for the past [and] asked by
> earnest men who had often looked the "King of Terrors" in the face on
> many a battlefield. Let us all hope, and all pray that as a merciful God
> has spared us to see the end of the great rebellion, and made us all once
> again citizens of this earthly Union.[93]

*The Trophies of Victory and the Relics of Defeat*

# Epilogue

—

No Civil War soldier consented to military service in a straightforward manner. How men negotiated power relations in the ranks while also navigating the cultural and political currents of their respective societies assumed a highly individualized form; it varied sharply depending on place and the particular time of war. We have to imagine Northern and Southern veterans at the center of a concentric circle of cultural, political, and military authority. These bands insulated thinking and constrained behavior, but these boundaries were permeable, bendable, and fraught with contradictions that allowed for contestation. Moreover, the cultural and structural bands that encircled the world of Civil War soldiers twisted their actions and thoughts in convoluted and contradictory ways. The unique ways in which soldiers coped, compromised, and sometimes conquered the pressures of war can obscure the irresistible power of those same forces in shaping the range of choices available to citizen-soldiers as they fought and died on behalf of their nation.

Within this turbulent and often oppressive environment, soldiers came to see the necessity of being adaptive in thought and action. Quite simply, they became pragmatic. Pragmatism was not a word that soldiers used, let alone defined, but its presence was felt. Pragmatism assumed innumerable forms and permeated all aspects of military life, but it did not lead men on either side to disavow Christianity, reject ideological beliefs, abandon sentimentalism, or scrap their conception of history as a divinely ordained march toward progress. Depending on the circumstances, Union and Confederate soldiers could lean on God or put more trust in themselves, their officers, and their comrades without slavishly adhering to some abstract truth, principle, or allegiance. The fluid ways that Union and Confederate soldiers read and reacted to their situation, finding ways to live with the contradictory elements of their violent and volatile existence in the ranks, did not follow a formulaic pattern. Experience, above all else, grounded soldiers' understanding of the war, and because of their direct encounter with the terror of battle, the loneliness of camp, and the physical exhaustion of forced marches, Civil War soldiers leveled what they considered unchallengeable judgments about the war.

The words and actions of Boston's Oliver Wendell Holmes Jr. tells a compelling story of a former abolitionist and die-hard Unionist becoming a committed pragmatist over the course of his military service, from 1861 to 1865. To some his transformation looks like a free fall into a pit of disillusionment, but nothing could be farther from the truth. Pragmatism actually helped preserve his Union principles, and his decision to essentially put them in storage originated within the distinctive political culture of the Army of the Potomac and the Union's dismal military record in Virginia. Holmes had witnessed his share of battlefield mishaps, and he had seen too many lives squandered in wasteful attacks. As the cycle of defeat and recrimination repeated itself, Holmes grew more frustrated with the political wrangling in Washington and the bickering in the ranks, when officers and enlisted men should have been focused on the business of killing to keep the same mistakes from happening again. If Union armies were to succeed, soldiers would need to adapt to changing circumstances and abandon failed habits and practices, in Holmes's opinion. Building a more efficient military machine mattered more to the Bostonian than anything else, and he put his trust in the rank and file, for they had shown themselves able to follow orders without regard to personal safety or outcome. Could the nation continue to depend on these weary foot soldiers when so much blood had been wasted? Holmes had his doubts, unless the call to duty became less reflexive and prescriptive and more adaptive and fluid to circumstances as they evolved. The need for flexibility in thought as well as action, as Holmes saw it, would enable soldiers to draw on their experiences as they did the job in the field. What contributed to success under certain circumstances might be avoided under different conditions. As the pressures on the ground shifted, pragmatism allowed for adjustments and accommodations that would give the foot soldier in the Army of the Potomac a fighting chance at both surviving and defeating the enemy in battle.[1]

The narrative below follows Holmes through the Overland Campaign to see pragmatism in action — not just in words, but also in deeds. Holmes never sat around the campfire discussing pragmatism with his fellow veterans, nor did he see himself as part of an organized intellectual movement devoted to pragmatism. Quite simply, his philosophy of soldiering was to have no philosophy at all. Adaptability and duty were his watchwords, and when blended together they empowered men to approach war from a situational perspective. Holmes was not unusual in practicing pragmatism, and the narrative below, while staying close to the Bostonian's personal history, will incorporate examples of other veterans who had pragmatic dispositions.

Four days after the disastrous Union attacks at Cold Harbor in June 1864, Oliver Wendell Holmes Jr. wrote his most important letter of the war to his parents, one that addressed the concept of duty:

> I started in this thing a boy I am now a man and I have been coming
> to the conclusion for the last six months that my duty has changed—
> I can do a disagreeable thing or face a great danger coolly enough when
> I *know it is a duty*—but a doubt demoralizes me as it does any nervous
> man—and now I honestly think the duty of fighting has ceased for
> me—ceased because I have laboriously and with much suffering of
> mind and body *earned the right* . . . to decide for myself how I can best
> do my duty to myself to the country and, if you choose to God.[2]

What brought him to this point, where he elevated individual conscience as the supreme arbitrator of duty? The 5′11″ gray-eyed Holmes, who had been wounded three times since his 1861 graduation from Harvard and his enlistment in the Twentieth Massachusetts Infantry that same year, had always understood his life well, but something indefinable had overtaken him once the Army of the Potomac had entered the Wilderness on May 5, 1864.

Over the next few weeks, a ruthless form of warfare descended on the Army of the Potomac, and Holmes, while serving as a staff officer at the Sixth Corps headquarters, could feel his mind and body wearing down from the unremitting labor and incessant danger. He took brief notes in his diary, often scrawling fragmented sentences describing the terrible sights that he had encountered. On May 8, he wrote that he "found woods afire & bodies of Reb . . . our men just killed & scorching." On May 13, he noted that "the dead of both sides lay piled in the trenches 5 or 6 deep—wounded often writhing under superincumbent dead." And in a letter to his parents dated May 16, he reported with barely a trace of emotion that nearly every regimental officer "I knew or cared for is dead or wounded." At the end of the letter Holmes confessed that while he was in the saddle, caught in the swirl of events and fearing for his life at every turn, his dearest attachments vanished from his mind: "The duties & thoughts of the field are of such a nature that one cannot at the same time keep home, parents and such thoughts as they suggest in his mind at the same time as a reality — Can hardly indeed remember their existence — and this too just after the intense yearning which immediately precedes a campaign."[3]

The ambivalence in Holmes's words is a powerful reminder of how difficult it can be to preserve idealized notions of home in the midst of an active campaign. At the same time, as Holmes pointed out, the frustrations actually deepened a man's love for his family. Killing rarely drained men's sentiment for those they held dear, but combat did raise troubling questions. Were codes of conduct, issues of morality, and God's relationship to his people fixed, knowable, and universal? Or were they fluid, open to revision, and situational? Such profound and capacious questions rarely brought simple yes or no answers. Clear-cut binaries of duty or disobedience, morality or immorality, and bravery or cowardice proved unstable in the ranks, and when they became messy, pragmatism guided Holmes and scores of other soldiers through a world without black-and-white choices.

Pragmatism did not deliver intellectual clarity or restore emotional stability for Civil War soldiers who wanted absolute certitude in life. In fact, the turn to pragmatism implicitly acknowledged that confusion and uncertainty were part of the soldiers' condition in the army. The intellectually arrogant Holmes, whose Harvard degree did little to hurt his confidence, admitted to feeling a sense of doubt with a degree of regularity, but most Civil War soldiers did not veer beyond a healthy skepticism of established knowledge and recognized forms of power. These men did, however, share Holmes's willingness to let those at home see and feel the emotional turmoil roiling in their minds by crafting letters unobstructed by romantic sentimentalism. Holmes's June 7 letter to his parents was a bludgeon of reality, not a delicate letter inviting conversation about his future in the army.

One might point to battlefield trauma as leading Holmes to lash out at his parents, but such speculation focuses too heavily on the Overland Campaign as a turning point in Holmes's life without fully considering his long history in the army. His declaration to do his duty as he saw fit marked the logical outcome of his move toward pragmatism — something that he did not identify by name — which had been building steadily in the Bostonian since Burnside's calamity at Fredericksburg back in December 1862. Because of typhoid fever, Holmes "for the first time" did not accompany his "Regt. going to battle." "A feeling worse than the anxiety of danger" overcame him, and while watching his friends disappear across the river and into the smoke-filled town, he broke down. As "weak as I was I couldn't restrain my tears," he explained.[4] As with all sentimentalists, getting in touch with an intensely pure emotion elevated the soul, and the shedding of tears was a source of manly pride for Holmes and other soldiers who wanted their loved ones to know that army life had not stripped them of the capacity to be tender and kind. The mixture of sympathy and sorrow inside Holmes turned to rage when his father became a Pollyanna about Fredericksburg. Without a shred of subtlety or any pretense of diplomacy, Holmes castigated his father, whose Boston home was a sort of cocoon: "I see no farther progress—I don't think either of you realize the unity or the determination of the South. I think you are hopeful because (excuse me) you are ignorant. . . . I am, to be sure, heartily tired and half worn out body and mind by this life, but I believe I am as ready as ever to do my duty—But it is maddening to see men put in over us & motions forced by popular clamor when the army is only willing to trust its life & reputation to one man."[5]

Holmes's breach of parental etiquette alerted everyone at home that he was a troubled man in the wake of Fredericksburg, yet the defeat clarified his thinking as to how the Union might subdue the Confederacy. He never doubted that the Northern cause was superior to the South's reckless gamut for independence, but claiming the moral high ground, as he pointed out to his father, would never overcome the determination of the Southern people or defeat their armies. Holmes found reason for hope in the Fredericksburg disaster, where he witnessed an unforgettable display of bravery from men who showed no hesitation in following orders that committed them to destruction. Such wastefulness of manpower could not continue. Only when efficient leadership harnessed the discipline and courage of the volunteer, Holmes believed, would Northern armies possess the military might to crush Southern forces. Fredericksburg had also convinced Holmes that soldiers and officers needed to learn to kill with greater efficiency, tighter discipline, and unquestioning obedience. Once in battle, military men at all levels needed to adapt their operations and tactics to the situation and look at military manuals as guides, not gospel.

Of all the lessons that he learned from Fredericksburg, Holmes touted experience as the greatest teacher in the army, and no civilian could ever be a pupil in this rough-and-tumble class. Herein lies the essence of pragmatism as a philosophy discovered by *doing*. From this core assumption, veterans on both sides advanced their case to do their duty as they saw fit (even though they realized that no man could act on his own and pursue a course of action without regard to outside influences). On the one hand, pragmatism called for blind obedience in battle, but on the other, duty must be adaptive if soldiers were to

Major Oliver Wendell Holmes Jr. possessed the pragmatism of a hardened veteran, an outlook that accommodated his enduring belief in Union while also giving him the flexibility
to judge his own actions and personal beliefs from a situational perspective. Like many
other veterans, he insisted that his unique experiences in the field gave him the authority
to judge what was right, that no civilian had any right to question him, and that only he
could determine the rules for action while at war. "I have laboriously and with much suffering of mind and body," he wrote to his father in 1864, *earned the right . . . to decide for
myself how I can best do my duty to myself to the country and, if you choose, to God."*
(Library of Congress Prints and Photographs Division, Washington, D.C.)

survive and armies were to succeed. Holmes's conception of duty, as the historian David H. Burton writes with such grace and insight, "had less to do with great causes and was more a matter of doing the necessary tasks in an efficient way. Individual survival and military success were linked to the least wasteful and quickest methods."[6]

To be sure, pragmatism was not just a functional tool of self-interest; it was not anti-ideological and not incompatible with sentimentalism. Not once, for instance, did Holmes shrink from the idea that Union was worth his life, but for soldiers on both sides, high ideas often took a back seat to the immediate demands of military necessity. At the same time, pragmatism's emphasis on professional training and obedience had the potential to constrain critical thought. This did not keep soldiers from assuming the role of armchair general, and in some instances Northern soldiers gained a critical detachment from military operations through irony and humor. The seeds of soldier anger that were sown in camp never sprouted into rebellion on the battlefield. Veteran soldiers on both sides put aside their grievances and faced enemy bullets with an iron resolution to get the job done. Religious soldiers on both sides never doubted God's role in granting either victory or defeat, yet they did not undervalue the need for hard fighting from the rank and file. Pragmatism did not compete with the faith of Louisiana's Reuben Pierson, for example, even as he held up the skill and bravery of officers and men as the great determiner of events. Pierson drew faith from knowing that his army was a well-oiled killing machine under God's direction. "This has been one of the most trying times I have ever witnessed since I have been out," he observed after Chancellorsville. "The fortitude and endurance of the men have been taxed to the utmost extent. Still they bear it all almost without a murmur. With such soldiers and our present leaders our enemies can never accomplish the unholy design which they have formed for our subjugation."[7]

Holmes was neither an atheist nor an evangelical who believed in providential intervention, and his pragmatism did not prevent him from feeling ambivalent about killing. His feelings were similar to those of a Pennsylvania soldier who wrote of a mixture of relief and trepidation after surviving Chancellorsville: "[I still live] but have once more trod the bloody field of battle. have again seen my comrades fall and heard their dying groans, yes I have been spared perhaps to witness the like again."[8] Even zealots on both sides could not fully reconcile themselves to all that they had done and seen on the battlefield. The adaptability of pragmatism softened a culture of militarized manliness by giving soldiers more latitude in defining manly behavior in camp and in battle. Situational awareness, as Francis Donaldson showed in his exhaustive account of Fredericksburg, allowed for a range of acceptable behaviors in the liminal space between courage and cowardice. Given the coercive methods used to instill uniform behavior in every Civil War army, soldiers could rework codes of conduct as they saw fit. Although countless men ran afoul of the military's judicial system or recoiled from the horrible violence once on the field, Civil War soldiers largely fought the war as they had imagined it as volunteers in 1861. Adjustments were made, as Holmes duly noted, but a more flexible and adaptive understanding of courage kept more men alive and increased the chance for military success. Honor and male aggressiveness certainly compelled men to carry out well-choreographed assaults, but the idea that Civil War soldiers were beholden to boyhood illusions of war infantilizes them by ignoring how they adjusted their expectations and tactics on the battlefield without suffering a crisis of manhood. The limited killing range of rifled weaponry made it possible for Civil War soldiers to show the power of individual action in shaping events, a tenet of sentimentalism that Holmes and countless other Civil War soldiers never relinquished.

The relentless pace and constant killing of the Overland Campaign coupled with a new staff position kept Holmes from gaining his footing in the Army of the Potomac. On May 16 and May 30 he wrote similar letters that asserted his right to choose his way without familial interference. In the latter missive, he delivered a stinging rebuke to his family, one that was almost as severe in tone as the admonishment in his June 7 letter. Holmes was furious that his parents thought he planned to resign before the end of the campaign. "I must say I dislike such a misunderstanding, so discreditable to my feeling of soldierly honor, when I don't believe there was a necessity for it," he wrote with pure contempt for parental authority. "I am convinced from my late experience that if I can stand the wear & tear (body & mind) of regimental duty that it is a greater strain on both than I am called on to endure—If I am satisfied I don't really see that anyone else has a call to be otherwise." In case it was not already apparent to his family that Holmes had been transformed by war, he reminded them: "I am not the same man (may not have quite the same ideas) & certainly am not so elastic as I was and *I will not acknowledge the same claims upon me under those circumstances* that existed formerly."[9]

Holmes's emotionally charged letters to his family open up the possibility of battlefield trauma and simultaneously reveal the difficulties in making such a diagnosis. Holmes fits the pattern of so many other veterans who were shocked by how they could normalize the obscene incidents of war. At the same time, his May letters and diary entries reveal a mind filled with anxiety and a body nearly broken down from continuous operations. His fears were neither exaggerated nor unusual, especially coming from a man who had been wounded three times. Survival was not something that Holmes or any other soldier took lightly, yet Holmes wanted to transfer from staff work and go back to the Twentieth Massachusetts Infantry because he considered a line position more honorable than servicing headquarters. He gave up on this idea when he learned that only a few of his old comrades were still in the ranks of his old regiment, and in light of this information, as well as his own frail physical health, Holmes honored his promise to his family: "I mean to leave at the end of the campaign as I said if I'm Not killed before."[10]

Holmes managed to escape the sharpshooters and the mortar rounds around Petersburg during the summer of 1864 and to enter Harvard's law school in time for the fall term. Before he departed from the army, Holmes dashed off a letter to his mother: "This morn'g I spent on the picket line it was being pushed forward—hot & nasty as Orcus—I think there is a kind of heroism in the endurance. . . . I tell you many a man has gone crazy since this campaign begun from the terrible pressure on mind and body."[11] Holmes's pragmatism was on full display in this excerpt, but it did not overshadow his sentimentalism. Both forms of courage accommodated a range of behaviors of men performing their duty. Holmes also watched men in the trenches discarding old habits of fighting and adopting new tactics in order to survive and defeat the enemy. The evolution in how brave men fought did not make Holmes nostalgic for the field fighting in 1862, nor did he seek the fanfare of the home front as he packed up and left the army for good. Though the fall presidential elections were looming as Holmes neared the end of his enlistment, it is not surprising that he made no mention of the politics of the war, the preservation of the Union, or the crusade to end slavery. These causes and ideologies divided the ranks, weakening discipline and keeping the men from killing with the professional efficiency necessary to end the rebellion. Some might see Holmes as disillusioned, but as he left Petersburg he never doubted that the future of civilization rested on the success of the Union armies. His heart overflowed with sympathy for his poor comrades, who hunkered down in the trenches, sweltering in the heat, dodging sharpshooters, while their bodies and minds were slowly surrendering to the harsh and unforgiving circumstances of war.

Few soldiers offer a more revealing and articulate explanation of pragmatism than Oliver Wendell Holmes, but his unusual ability to be introspective should not disqualify the importance of his example. Holmes pinpointed the essence of military service during the Civil War: the overpowering will to survive coupled with a desire for military victory that demanded that soldiers adapt to everyday considerations.[12] Holmes was well aware of the shifts in his thinking,

After the war, the forage cap that Oliver Wendell Holmes wore while serving in his beloved Twentieth Massachusetts became a treasured keepsake for the future Supreme Court justice, who, like so many veterans, identified closely with his regiment. "I really very much doubt whether there is any Regt wh. Can compare with ours in the Army of the Potomac," he wrote. "Everyone says this, perhaps, who belongs to a good Regt but still I fancy I am right from the evidence of many things."

(Oliver Wendell Holmes Jr. Object Collection, Historical & Special Collections, Harvard Law School Library) but for most soldiers, changes in thought occurred deep in the subconscious, and they can only be gleaned by historians through a run of letters that covers an extended period of time. Only then is it possible to see how the absolute demands of duty, loyalty, and ideology were always under negotiation with comrades, officers, and their families at home; in addition, those demands rarely come across in full when scholars extract quotes from soldier letters without showing how those words were articulated within the flow of events. Pragmatism did not empower soldiers to do as they pleased, as was evident in Holmes's feuding with his parents. The fear of blackening one's reputation or tarnishing one's honor also kept a soldier under the watchful eye of the community.

Holmes considered combat a rite of passage that led a volunteer away from his civilian life and into the community of veterans. No soldier looked at the break as a severing of ties, but Holmes was no different than other veterans who were quick to assert their "right" as the ultimate arbitrator of truth, especially when it came to their behavior in the field, because they were the ones who were on the ground, experiencing the horrors of combat and the miseries of camp. After the bloody fights outside Richmond in 1864, New Yorker Charles Bowen reminded his wife that battles were nothing more than indiscriminate and indecipherable affairs that were ungovernable by man or God. "Men must die on the battle plain," he bluntly stated, "& I dont know as I am better than anyone else that falls. So Ive made up my mind that if its my luck to *go under*, why under it is, & if I am lucky enough to come out as the *top of the heap* it will be after having done my *whole duty* as far as I know it."[13]

In the face of organized warfare, where mass armies were all-powerful, Bowen was no different than Holmes in asserting his individuality while accepting the weakness of human agency. Yet like the vast majority of Civil War soldiers, he never renounced sentimentalism's core belief in willed behavior, even though there were times when he felt as if he were a cog in an impersonal army. It did not take long for recruits to become veterans who appreciated the necessity of an efficient military bureaucracy as an enforcer of discipline and as a standard bearer of professionalism in the ranks. Any veteran knew that lives depended on the supremacy of military organizations over the individual. At the same time, Civil War soldiers resisted the authoritarian excesses of the army, never losing sight of their rights as citizen-soldiers who drew value from the war at a very individual level. Although individualism and idealism waned from time to time, they generally prevailed in Civil War armies because pragmatism helped soldiers manage the discord between the idealistic expectations of war as a test of character, an adventure of individual heroism, and the grim reality of a man trying to survive in a vast and destructive war machine.

All in all, the degree of cultural change that resulted from the Civil War was modest. Such a position counters the claims of scholars who have identified the war as a transitional moment in American cultural history.[14] Some have argued that the Civil War put the United States on a trajectory toward organization, bureaucracy, and centralization, thus leaving behind antebellum values of pity and compassion as a response to human suffering. Others have insisted that the cultural politics of war, as seen through popular stories, sensationalized accounts, and commercial literature, revealed the importance of individual experience and the persistence of idealism over the organized war.[15] These dichotomies are artificial constructs because they overlook the ways that organizational efficiency and individual humanitarianism depended on each other before and during the war. Moreover, the traditional interpretations fail to put the everyday actions of the rank and file at the center of the story. Showing how enlisted men shaped military, political, economic, and cultural systems, but never in isolation from their wives and families, and how those same systems impinged on soldier lives — often in ways imperceptible to those in the ranks — is crucial to restoring the pragmatic dispositions of men trying to survive in the ranks while also trying to preserve social networks at home in circumstances that were rarely of their making.[16]

The ambiguous ways in which Northern and Southern soldiers processed their experiences would suggest that the Civil War did not revolutionize American culture. At least from the perspective of the ranks, the war did not alter the trajectory of their thought or create a crisis in values. Experience taught soldiers that discipline, duty, and organization were not incompatible with sentimentalism's faith in sympathy, compassion, and individualism. During the final months of the war, Confederate and Union soldiers continued to write about cheerfulness as a triumph of willpower, even as men were wasting away in the trenches of Petersburg because their armies lacked the organization and efficiency to feed and train them adequately. Providence still reigned supreme after Appomattox, but many of his followers could not shake the gnawing wartime fear that life was not what it seemed to be, that the facts did not speak for themselves, and that maybe God had just decided that it was every man for himself. When veterans wrote of their battlefield heroics, they did so in the emotional tones of sentimentalism, yet when they rewrote their wartime stories in memoirs and regimental histories, they did not try to hide the mental anguish of combat that scores of soldiers had confessed to in their wartime letters. At times military life proved so jarring and strange that men turned introspective and discovered that there were many layers to their being, but at the time they continued to insist that they were not profoundly altered by battle-

Charles Bowen sent the following note on a small sheet of paper regarding this remnant of the Twelfth U.S flag. "Ther is enclosed in this a piece of our regimental colors which was shot away from the flag[staff] at the Battle of Gettysburg & picked up by the Color Sergt. A few moments after he drop'd with a ball through the left breast. After the fight he was picked up insensible but tightly grasping this piece of the colors. This wound was not serious and he is again at his post. One of the boys who carried him off the field took the rag from his hand & gave it to me. I have carried it since in my pocket but now send it home and I want you to give it to Mother to put among her collection of curiosities. If I live to return it will remind me of the many dangers passed through under its folds, & if I fall, you will have a piece of the gallant 'old flag' under which I fought to remember me by." (Courtesy of Gettysburg National Military Park)

field trauma and that there was only one self, whose highest attainable form resided in character.

Northern and Southern soldiers finished the Civil War living partly in the Victorian world and partly in the modern world. Pragmatism's value became imprinted in their minds while they performed their military job. The daily acts in camp as well as battle assumed supreme importance when the fighting ended, and wartime memories took their shape and meaning depending on the circumstance and situation of the creator. It is hardly surprising that veterans on both sides were drawn to commemorating their everyday struggles in the ranks, given that both sides were disgusted by the politics of war and that Union soldiers wanted to preserve their military victory through a conciliatory peace. As part of the first phase of remembrance, artifacts and relics like pistols, swords, bayonets, uniforms, flags, and muskets assumed immense importance in creating a heroic vision of soldiering, for these tools of killing became the sacred links to the blood sacrifice of fallen comrades. The emotional and political power soldiers invested in things exerted incredible influence over their actions and thinking, as Charles Bowen demonstrated in a letter to his family from his winter quarters in December 1863. He enclosed a piece of his regimental flag, riddled at Gettysburg, dropped and nearly lost, its silk stripes shredded into pieces. In that battle the color sergeant had fallen with a serious wound, and Bowen recalled that though the man was "insensible," he was "tightly grasping this piece of the colors." Bowen kept it in his pocket, but sent it home to his wife so that his mother could keep it in her "collection of curosities." "If I live to return it will remind me of the many dangers passed through under its folds, & if I fall, you will have a piece of the gallant 'old flag' under which I fought to remember me by."[17]

As Bowen's words attest, the relics of war exerted tremendous power over members of the rank and file. Through material objects it is possible to pierce the inner world of Civil War soldiers, to come in contact with deeply held thoughts and potent emotions that shaped how soldiers acted in the world.[18] At the same time, the things of war proved malleable in use and meaning, giving veterans a flexible certitude in explaining their service to themselves and to outsiders. In the end the birth of wartime pragmatism laid the groundwork for a militarized version of reconciliation that obscured the terrors, hypocrisies, and absurdities of war in exchange for a triumphant narrative of American manliness that reigned supreme on the battlefield. This new expression of pragmatism lost its razor edge to cut through the mystification of war as it had done for the soldiers, who had always looked for ways to adapt to their violent world so they might have had a better chance of surviving a war that offered little romance.

# acknowledgments

On more occasions than I care to remember, my wife, Beth, kept me from divorcing this book. When I wanted to abandon the project and move on, she served as a mediator, guiding me through the difficult times when I felt that I had nothing more to say. Beth never gave up on me or the manuscript that has been a part of our lives for nearly ten years. Our collaboration on this project is something that I will always remember with fondness, despite the drama. There is not an idea in this book that I did not run by Beth first, or a word that she did not read. Her editorial eye cut through my tangled prose, and she unraveled numerous grammatical dysfunctions. Whenever I look at this book, I will always think of her first—her intelligence, her humor, and her enduring faith in me, particularly during the trying times at Johns Hopkins, when she never left my side.

Falling into the hands of Mark Simpson-Vos at the University of North Carolina Press felt like a gift from above. Mark is an exceptional editor, the best I have ever encountered, and during the process of making this book he has become a trusted friend who deserves much of the credit for getting this manuscript across the finish line. I am grateful that Michael Parrish and Gary Gallagher, the editors of the Littlefield History of the Civil War Era, entrusted me to write about such a rich and important subject. Even though we had very different opinions about what this volume should accomplish, they gave me the freedom to write the book as I envisioned it. Dr. Gallagher once again showed himself to be an ideal mentor—as he was when I worked with him as a graduate student at Penn State. He pays his students the highest compliment by putting friendships aside and asking tough questions regarding content, methodology, and interpretations. He challenged and pushed and challenged me some more, and all the while he remained a steadfast friend who was always there for me on both professional and personal matters. Outside of my parents, there is not a person who has had a greater influence on me than Dr. Gallagher.

Lorien Foote made this a better book with her wise suggestions to remove unnecessary theory and sharpen my arguments. Her enthusiastic support for this project proved critical to the manuscript's publication. Jessica Newman at UNC Press handled my numerous requests with incredible efficiency, intelligence, and good cheer.

I am blessed to be surrounded by so many talented historians who are also wonderful friends. Brian Luskey, a former colleague at West Virginia University (WVU) and now a neighbor in Gettysburg, has been a champion of this project from the beginning, encouraging me to take chances and embrace new methodologies. His own work on soldier economies, moreover, has deeply informed my thinking about the daily life of enlisted men. Aaron Sheehan-Dean of Louisiana State University has a unique talent in getting authors to see possibilities in their work that the author cannot fully articulate. No matter what was going on in Aaron's life, he was always quick to answer my calls, and I always hung up the phone feeling more confident about the direction of my work. Aaron's gifts as a historian — formidable as they are — do not exceed his generosity as a friend; I will always be grateful for the time he flew from Baton Rouge to stay with me on an uncomfortable couch at Johns Hopkins during one of my treatments. Keith Bohannon has been a dear friend since 1986, when we were seasonal historians at Fredericksburg National Military Park. I have such admiration for Keith's skills as a historian, and his eagerness to help me with this project has enriched this book in so many ways. I cannot thank him enough for his steadfast friendship, wonderful sense of humor, and historical wisdom. Robert E. L. Krick of Richmond National Military Park was on speed dial during the writing process, and every call was greeted with his inimitable sense of humor and his encyclopedic knowledge of the Army of Northern Virginia. I only wish that more of these conversations had occurred in person.

I have never been completely persuaded by the popular observation that teachers learn as much from their students as students learn from their teachers. But James Broomall, the director of the Moore Civil War Center at Shepherd University, is certainly an example of the student teaching the professor. I worked with Jim when he was a graduate student at the University of North Carolina at Greensboro (UNCG) and I was an assistant professor. He read widely, refusing to be hemmed in by my strict disciplinary boundaries. He turned me on to the concept of cultural hegemony and got me to see the importance of integrating material culture into this study. Jim's own scholarship on emotional history and Confederate soldiers has influenced so much of *The War for the Common Soldier*. I also owe a great debt to Katy Shively of Virginia Commonwealth University. Her unsparing critique of my introduction kept me from writing a bland synthesis without argument. She helped me to find my own interpretive voice, encouraging me to stake out my claims in opposition to the established historiography. Katy's own work on soldier self-care had a profound impact on my thinking about soldier pragmatism.

Thoughtful conversations with the University of Georgia's Stephen Berry have enriched my thinking on cultural history of Civil War soldiers. Our time touring the Gettysburg battlefield was not only a great deal of fun, but also gave me an opportunity to try out some of my thoughts about the cultural world of common soldiers. Charles Holden of St. Mary's College of Maryland has been a constant source of support and advice over the long life of this project. Late-night conversations at the Southern Historical Association's annual meeting have had a lasting impression on me. Earl Hess of Lincoln Memorial University took time from his demanding writing schedule to read my entire manuscript. His comments helped me better situate my own work within the historiography and reminded me to strike more of a balance between the Eastern and Western Theaters. *The War for the Common Soldier* could not have been written without Earl's pathbreaking scholarship on soldier motivation and battlefield tactics. William Marvel offered major stylistic and content suggestions to the entire manuscript. I did not follow all of his advice, but his extensive comments had a major impact on the book. I'd also like to thank Carrie Janney, Joan Waugh, Ed Ayers, Megan Kate Nelson, Judy Giesberg, Joseph Glatthaar, Jason Phillips, A. Wilson Greene, Sarah Gardner, Brooks Simpson, David Thomson, Bill Link, Robert Bonner, Brian Jordan, Steve Cushman, Kent Gramm, Lesley Gordon, Tim Orr, Christian Keller, Wayne Hsieh, Katherine M. Aldridge, Sandy Abend, and William Miller, who all commented on selected chapters. Numerous students have made important contributions to this project, including Brian Johnson, Kaylyn Sawyer, Emma Murphy, Mary Roll, Cassandra Wells, Dan Willever, and Robert Novak at Gettysburg College, and Joel Christenson, Jake Struhelka, William Feeney, David Goldberg, and Lauren Thompson at West Virginia.

A number of institutions provided essential support for the completion of this manuscript. I started the book while at the University of North Carolina at Greensboro, where I received valuable research leave to get this project off the ground. Laura Lawfer Orr and Tish Wiggs helped research the lives of James

Bailey and John Futch, respectively. At West Virginia University I worked with an impressive group of graduate students, and I also received critical research support while I held the Eberly Professorship of Civil War Studies. At Gettysburg College, President Janet Riggs and Provost Chris Zappe have done all they could to advance my work as the director of the Civil War Institute (CWI) and the Fluhrer Chair of Civil War History. Within the history department, Tim Shannon and Michael Birkner have been ideal colleagues and even better friends. Rebecca Bergren, who heads the Center for Global Education at Gettysburg College, helped to arrange my fellowship at the IAU College in Aix-en-Provence, France, where I found a vibrant intellectual community under the leadership of President Carl Jubran. My time with the students at IAU and its outstanding faculty rejuvenated me after long days of writing. Friday afternoons at Café Happy Days were particularly special, and I so enjoyed conversing about art, literature, and history with Cathleen Keenan, Alan Roberts, Leigh Smith, Claire McAlpine, and John Gasparach. Back in the states, I am surrounded by supportive friends who were always there to listen and encourage while showing great restraint in not asking me why the book was taking so long. Lunches with Chris Kauffman at Gettysburg College were always fun and rejuvenating. Since Michael Freeman and I met in State College in 1988, he has become a trusted confidant and a friend like no other. Talking art or politics or going to an occasional concert offered much-needed respites from the demands of the book. David Smith, the cofounder of the Grateful American Book Prize, has done so much to promote the study of history in the United States. I always look forward to our dinners in Washington, D.C., knowing that the conversation would be lively and engaging.

Over the years I have developed important relationships in the National Park Service, where I started my career as a professional historian in 1985. The expertise of various park interpreters has helped me puzzle through very challenging questions. James Ogden of Chickamauga and Chattanooga National Military Park has been extraordinarily generous with his time and knowledge at all stages of the writing process. So much of this book has been shaped by Jim's deep research on Civil War soldiers. He is the consummate public historian, and I have admired his skill and dedication to reaching general audiences since I worked with him in the 1990s at Fredericksburg and Spotsylvania National Military Park (FSNMP). Other National Park Service historians who have contributed to this book include Ernie Price and Joe Williams at Appomattox National Park; Bert Dunkerly at Richmond National Park; and Greg Mertz, Beth Parnicza, Eric Mink, Noel Harrison, and John Hennessy at FSNMP. Eric was especially helpful in untangling the court-martial case of John Starbird. John

Heiser, Chris Gwinn, Greg Goodell, and Scott Hartwig—all from Gettysburg National Military Park—have helped me with the book at crucial times, and they have also been important collaborators in working with Gettysburg College students on the battlefield.

A number of other institutions played an important role during the research of the manuscript. Cathy Wright of the American Civil War museum— a former student of mine at UNCG—opened my eyes to fantastic collections of flags and other artifacts that were originally part of the Museum of the Confederacy. At the National Archives, every Civil War historian's best friend is Trevor Plante, who knows the military collections like no other. His intelligence and patience have rescued many clueless researchers like myself, and my chapter on desertion is immeasurably better because of his good advice. I also received valuable help at the National Archives from Bryan Cheeseboro, who tracked down John Futch in the census records. Graham Dozier of the Virginia Historical Society helped me navigate the magnificent collections of that venerable institution. Other archivists and institutions that have fielded research and image requests include Amy Lucadamo in Special Collections, Musselman Library, Gettysburg College; Bentley Historical Library at the University of Michigan; Wilson Library at UNC Chapel Hill; the Archives of the Kenosha County Historical Society; the Indiana Historical Society; the Civil War Museum of Philadelphia and The Abraham Lincoln Foundation of The Union League of Philadelphia; the Museum of Fine Arts, Boston; the Smithsonian National Museum of American History; the State Archives of North Carolina; the Harvard Law School Library; Special Collections at Mercyhurst University; and the John Nau Collection, Houston. Dale Coye and Pamela Rhein provided important information on their ancestors David Coye and Charles Bowen, respectively.

At the Civil War Institute, I am greeted every day by an exceptional group of people who fill the office with laughter and intelligence. As the associate director, Jill Titus has been indispensable to the educational mission of CWI, mentoring students, teaching classes, and overseeing the Brian Pohanka Internship program and the public history minor. Despite these heavy demands, she always found time to chat with me about the book or to handle an administrative task that allowed me to focus on my teaching and scholarship. My partnership with her has been one of the most rewarding experiences in my professional career. Ashley Whitehead Luskey is a recent addition to CWI, but our relationship goes back to my days at WVU, where I worked with her when she was a rising doctoral student. In our graduate seminars, she and I engaged much of the theoretical work that underpins this book, and I also profited from her reading of my chapter on regional sensibilities. I take great satisfaction in her professional achievements, and I look forward to our future collaborations at CWI. Heather Miller is at the administrative helm at CWI, and she is a master of logistics and office management while playfully deflecting my practical jokes. She, Ashley, and Jill organize the CWI summer conference, which attracts some three hundred people for a week of discussions, lectures, and battlefield tours every June. It is a massive undertaking, but a joyful one, because the participants bring so much knowledge and exuberance to the event. To single out any one attendee would be invidious, so suffice it to say that I have felt much love and support from our attendees over the years, especially during my extended stay at Johns Hopkins. They always inquired about the progress of my book, and they encouraged me to get the book done. I am so looking forward to sharing *The War for the Common Soldier* with them when we rally together in June. Diane Brennan, while at CWI, handled a wide array of responsibilities and requests while I was researching this book. Her contributions were truly indispensable to the completion of the manuscript, especially during my fellowship in France.

This book has a long history, and for me it originated with a 1972 journey to Gettysburg. My mother, Charlotte Carmichael, was the ringleader of the trip, and from the moment I set foot on the soil of Adams County, I was obsessed with becoming a Civil War historian. Many times friends and family told me that I should keep history as a hobby, that I should find a more practical pursuit, but my mother would not allow me to surrender to the naysayers. She gave me one of the greatest gifts that a parent can give a child — the lasting belief that in life all things are possible. I could never give up on this book because I could still hear her voice today as clearly as I did when I was a boy, telling me that I could accomplish anything. My biological father, Jorge Parreno, came into my life when I was in high school. We have certainly made up for lost time, and I admire my father for risking it all and leaving Ecuador to immigrate to the United States, a move that made it possible for the rest of the Parreno clan to come to this country. I look forward to the day when we can go with my sister, Kim Jennifer Parreno, to visit Quito and the town of Puyo, where my father was born. In marrying Beth, I have found myself in the midst of a warmhearted and festive German/Austrian-American family. I have especially enjoyed getting to know George Ortwein and Uncle Harry Ortwein, who is a voracious reader of history as well as a stalwart companion on the battlefield. My in-laws, Jack and Janet Getz, have been much more than boosters of this book, and they have been unfailing in their support. They have enriched my life with their visits to Gettysburg, our trips to their home in Westfield, New Jersey, and our adventures in Europe and Alaska. It is hard to find the words that adequately express my admiration for them, but in their daughter, Beth, I am reminded every day of what loving parents can do for a child.

I am very fortunate that my girls, Cameron and Isabel, have a passion for learning about the past. I suspect that it comes in part from living in a town where history is inescapable. Even their favorite ice cream shop—Mr. G's—is located in a Civil War building scarred by gunfire, and next to a wartime tree that witnessed Abraham Lincoln pass down Baltimore Street before delivering his address at the national cemetery. Since our move to Gettysburg in 2010, the girls and I have canvassed much of the battlefield, fording creeks, clambering over the rocks of Devils Den, and wading Willoughby Run. During these expeditions, they have come to know many of the soldiers in this book, since their father cannot help himself from assuming a park ranger persona whenever he steps on the battlefield. It was only fitting that when I finished my manuscript in France, we took a celebratory hike. We were not close to any battlefields of note, so we settled for Mont Sainte-Victoire, the famous motif of the French artist Paul Cézanne. It was quite an adventure, and one that we were not prepared for, given that Big Round Top had been our steepest climb to date. We averted tragedy, though barely, and as soon as we came off the treacherous slopes we headed straight to a café. While sitting there drinking our Oranginas, we all felt a sense of relief to be off the mountain. I could not help but to think of those Civil War soldiers who had written such beautiful letters of love for their families, expressing without inhibition their longing to feel again the embrace of their children. Cameron and Isabel probably thought that I gave them an extra hug that afternoon to mark our hiking conquest and the fact that we came off the mountain in one piece, but I held them extra close that day simply because I could.

# notes

ABBREVIATIONS

ANHP    Appomattox Court House National Historical
       Park, Appomattox Court House, Va.

BC    Bowdoin College, Brunswick, Maine

DU    Perkins Library, Special Collections, Duke University, Durham, N.C.

FSNMP    Fredericksburg and Spotsylvania National
       Military Park, Fredericksburg, Va.

GC    Gettysburg College, Gettysburg, Pa.

GDAH    Georgia Department of Archives and History, Morrow, Ga.

GNMP    Gettysburg National Military Park, Gettysburg, Pa.

IHS    Indiana Historical Society, Indianapolis

KMNMP    Kennesaw Mountain National Military Park, Kennesaw, Ga.

LSU    Louisiana State University, Baton Rouge

MOC    Eleanor Brockenbrough Library, Museum of
       the Confederacy, Richmond, Va.

MU    Mercyhurst University, Erie, Pa.

NA    National Archives, Washington, D.C.

NCSA    North Carolina State Archives, Raleigh

NYHS    New-York Historical Society, New York, N.Y.

OR    *War of the Rebellion: The Official Records of
       the Union and Confederate Armies*

UNC    Southern Historical Collection, Wilson Library,
       University of North Carolina at Chapel Hill

UNCW    University of North Carolina at Wilmington

USAHEC    United States Army Heritage and Education Center, Carlisle, Pa.

UVA   Alderman Library, University of Virginia, Charlottesville
VHS   Virginia Historical Society, Richmond
WL    Washington and Lee University, Lexington, Va.


INTRODUCTION

1. John Pardington to Sarah Pardington, October 12, 1862, in Lassen, *Dear Sarah*, 24. All subsequent Pardington correspondence is from this source.

2. John Pardington to Sarah Pardington, October 12, 1862.

3. A brilliant explanation of providential understandings during the Civil War era can be found in Noll, *The Civil War as a Theological Crisis*, esp. chapters 1, 5.

4. John Pardington to Sarah Pardington, March 24, 1863, 88.

5. John Pardington to Sarah Pardington, September 21, 1862, 11.

6. John Pardington to Sarah Pardington, December 16, 1862, 48.

7. John Pardington to Sarah Pardington, January 18, 1863, 62.

8. John Pardington to Sarah Pardington, December 24, 1862, 51–52.

9. John Pardington to Sarah Pardington, February 21, 1863, 77.

10. John Pardington to Sarah Pardington, February 21, 1863.

11. John Pardington to Sarah Pardington, June 5, 1863, 125.

12. John Pardington to Sarah Pardington, June 5, 1863.

13. John Pardington to Sarah Pardington, June 5, 1863.

14. Philip Hamlin to his father, October 29, 1861, Hamlin Family Papers, transcripts at GNMP. The original letters can be found in the Hamlin Family Papers, Minnesota Historical Society, St. Paul.

15. Quoted from Berry, *All That Makes a Man*, 182.

16. Glatthaar, *March to the Sea and Beyond*. D. H. Dilbeck has reached a similar conclusion in *A More Civil War*. On the ways that Americans have remembered Sherman's march, see Rubin's *Through the Heart of Dixie*.

17. My understanding of pragmatism draws entirely from the magnificent work of Louis Menand. See his *The Metaphysical Club*, esp. the preface and chapters 2 and 3.

18. An excellent analysis of the citizen-soldier concept can be found in Bledsoe, *Citizen-Officers*, esp. chapter 1.

19. On the discourse of sentimentalism, see Fahs, *Imagined Civil War*. For a brilliant discussion of Victorian sentimentality and the Northern soldier and civilian experience, see Clarke, *War Stories*.

20. For an innovative and essential book on the survival strategies of Civil War soldiers, see Meier, *Nature's Civil War*.

21. Bell I. Wiley's pathbreaking *The Life of Johnny Reb: The Common Soldier of the Confederacy* and *The Life of Billy Yank: The Common Soldier of the Union*, published in 1943 and 1952, respectively, towered over the field for a generation. Wiley's work was interpretively thin, and at times nothing more than a glowing tribute to the men in blue and gray, but historians did not challenge his work or his findings. This inexplicable lull ended in 1986 with Glatthaar's *March to the Sea and Beyond*. He cleared the scholarly horizons of the romantic haze left by Wiley's two volumes, opening a vista for historians to see Civil War soldiers as thinking men who were deeply ideological, highly motivated, and reflective about their experiences in the field. A surge in soldier studies followed

Glatthaar's work in the 1980s and 1990s. Of the many fine books on Civil War soldiers, Linderman, *Embattled Courage*; Hess, *Liberty, Virtue, and Progress*; Mitchell, *Civil War Soldiers*; and McPherson, *For Cause and Comrades* are also very important for the questions they raised about the inner world of Civil War soldiers. No consensus emerged from their findings, but their inquiries were lasting, and they frame the mainstream approach to the subject to this day. What motivated men in the ranks? How did they endure the war? How did they negotiate their loyalties to home, army, and nation? What meanings did they make from their experiences? These are the questions that have animated the field over the last twenty-five years. The sheer number of secondary sources on Civil War soldiers has an oceanic feel, but the methodological center of this expansive field is located in questions of ideology and motivation. A sampling of this work includes Barton, *Goodmen*; Glatthaar, *March to the Sea and Beyond*; Hess, *Liberty, Virtue, and Progress*; Mitchell, *Civil War Soldiers*; Frank, *With Ballot and Bayonet*; Power, *Lee's Miserables*; Prokopowicz, *All for the Regiment*; Woodworth, *While God Is Marching On*; Sheehan-Dean, *Why Confederates Fought*; Phillips, *Diehard Rebels*; Manning, *What This Cruel War Was Over*; Glatthaar, *General Lee's Army*; Noe, *Reluctant Rebels*; Gallagher, *Union War*; and White, *Emancipation in the Union Army*.

22. The mind of the Civil War soldier has preoccupied scholars since Wiley's publication of *The Life of Johnny Reb* in 1943. Since then historians have been persistent in dissecting and quantifying worldviews of the common soldier, resulting in a rich intellectual history from the ground up, but this obsession with measuring ideology has kept historians hunkered down in well-developed historiographical trenches. At a feverish pace scholars continue to uncover and sift through the many layers of soldier motivation and ideology. For excellent overviews of Civil War soldier historiography, see Mitchell, "'Not the General but the Soldier'"; Foote, "Soldiers"; Sheehan-Dean, *View from the Ground*, 9–30; and Glatthaar, "A Tale of Two Armies," 315–16.

23. The methodological insights employed in this volume draw from a number of superb scholars, including Currarino, "Toward a History of Cultural Economy"; Farge, *Allure of the Archives*; Darnton, *Great Cat Massacre*; Rockman, *Scraping By*; Wickberg, "Intellectual History vs. the Social History of Intellectuals," *Rethinking History*, and "Heterosexual White Male"; Lears, "The Concept of Cultural Hegemony"; and Burke, *What Is Cultural History?*

24. Wickberg, "What Is the History of Sensibilities?"

25. Although *sensibility* is a slippery term (and cultural theory sometimes does more telling than showing), it is an important concept that builds on but does not replace worldviews and ideology. See Wickberg, "What Is the History of Sensibilities?," 669. For a sophisticated use of the concept of sensibilities, see Reddy, *The Navigation of Feeling*. The pioneering work of sensory history, especially on the American South by Mark Smith, is informed by the concept of sensibilities. See Mark M. Smith, *How Race Is Made*.

26. On the interrogation of written sources, see Cushman, *Belligerent Muse*, 3.

27. This insight comes from Farge, *Allure of the Archives*, 28.

28. The case for representativeness is deeply problematic, traceable to a questionable methodological assumption that if the research is sufficiently comprehensive, then it can be dissected, counted, and reconstructed to uncover mainstream views. The obvious problem with almost any claim of representativeness is that the available source material does not reflect all social groups. Historians typically issue the caveat that their research

disproportionately draws from the educated and the privileged, but they continue to argue over what constitutes the representative opinion of the rank and file, even though by their own admission they are working from an imperfect sample that makes any claims of representativeness unsupportable. Ginzburg makes a strong case against the search for representativeness, insisting that it places too much attention on *what* people thought rather than *how* they thought. See his *The Cheese and the Worms*, 32–33.

29. For an overview of guerrilla warfare, see Sutherland, *A Savage Conflict*; and McKnight and Myers, *The Guerrilla Hunters*.

30. On the veteran experience, see Jordan, *Marching Home*; Marten, *Sing Not War*; Gannon, *The Won Cause*; Brian Craig Miller, *Empty Sleeves*; and McClurken, *Take Care of the Living*.

31. William C. Way to William Sanders, August 19, 1863, in Lassen, *Dear Sarah*, 37.

## CHAPTER 1

1. For a perceptive analysis of Homer's wartime artistry, see Wood, *Near Andersonville*.

2. William Henry King Diary, May 6, 1862, in Joiner, Joiner, and Cardin, *No Pardons to Ask*, 2.

3. Amos Judson, "Army Correspondence," June 10, 1861, Judson Papers, Waterford, Pa., 1861–1865, MU.

4. On the role of ambition, see Berry, *All That Makes a Man*.

5. Mitchell, *Vacant Chair*, 25.

6. On differing conceptions of liberty in Union and Confederate armies, see McPherson, *What They Fought For*, esp. chapter 1.

7. On the sentimental message conveyed by Civil War soldier portraits, see Coddington, *Faces of the Civil War*.

8. On the cultural power of sentimentalism in Civil War armies, see Gallman, *Defining Duty in the Civil War*; Fahs, *Imagined Civil War*; and Clarke, *War Stories*.

9. E. B. Mendenhall to "cousin Mary," January 1, 1862, Glenn Papers, UNC.

10. On the organization of Civil War regiments and the psychology of service, see Bledsoe, *Citizen-Officers*, esp. chapter 2; Glatthaar, *General Lee's Army*, esp. chapters 2 and 3; and Mitchell, *Civil War Soldiers*, esp. chapter 3.

11. Geier, Orr, and Reeves, *Huts and History*, esp. chapters 7 and 8.

12. Richard F. Miller, *Harvard's Civil War*, 183.

13. Milton McJunkin to his mother, July 26, 1862, in Palm, Sauers, and Schroeder, *Bloody 85th*, 48.

14. John Pardington to Sarah Pardington, February 21, 1863, in Lassen, *Dear Sarah*, 77.

15. Hardy, *Fifty-Eighth North Carolina Troops*, 56.

16. Orr, "'All Manner of Schemes and Rascalities,'" 82, 100.

17. Charles Biddlecom to Esther Biddlecom, March 21, 1864, in Aldridge, *No Freedom Shrieker*, 124.

18. Hinman, *Corporal Si Klegg and His "Pard*,*"* cover page.

19. Letter from "Leigh" in *Memphis Appeal*, July 11, 1862. On the training of citizen-soldiers, see Bledsoe, *Citizen-Officers*, esp. chapter 3.

20. Sears, *For Country, Cause, and Leader*, 83–84, 90.

21. Haydon Diary, June 14, 1862, in Sears, *For Country, Cause, and Leader*, 251. All subsequent Haydon Diary entries are from this source.

22. Haydon Diary, June 20, 1862, 252–53. For additional examples of green soldiers posing the greatest danger to their comrades on the picket post, see William T. Shepherd's July 5, 1861, letter to his mother, in Hackemer, *To Rescue My Native Land*, 38.

23. For an analysis of the "Picket Guard," see Fahs, *Imagined Civil War*, 118–19.

24. Haydon Diary, November 28, 1861, 136.

25. Haydon Diary, November 26, 1862, 292–93.

26. Haydon Diary, April 18, 1863, 320.

27. Charles Bowen to Kate Bowen, December 18, 1862, in Cassedy, *Dear Friends at Home*, 201. Unless otherwise noted, all subsequent Bowen correspondence is from this source.

28. Charles Bowen to "Dear friends at home, one & all," January 23, 1863, 219.

29. Charles Bowen to Katie Bowen, January 27, 1863, 223.

30. Charles Bowen to Kate Bowen, February 7, 1863, 232.

31. On the persistence of sentimentality and how soldiers could become hardened to war without losing feelings of sympathy, see Clarke, *War Stories*; and Neff, *Honoring the Civil War Dead*, esp. chapter 1.

32. Charles Bowen to "Dear friends at home," December 27, 1862, 204–5.

33. Charles Bowen to Katie Bowen, January 27, 1863, 223.

34. James Coye to Rhoda Coye, March 21, 1863, James Coye Papers, in the private possession of David Coye. Copies also available in the library at FSNMP.

35. James Calvin Zimmerman to Adaline, August 2, 1863, James Calvin Zimmerman Papers, DU.

36. Charles Bowen to "Dear friends at home," February 23, 1863, 242.

37. Charles Bowen to "Dear friends at home," February 23, 1863, 239–40.

38. Charles Bowen to Kate Bowen, April 11, 1864, 429.

39. Charles Bowen to Kate Bowen, April 11, 1864, 428.

40. My interpretation of Callaway's life follows the lead of Berry in *All That Makes a Man*.

41. For an excellent summary of Joshua K. Callaway's prewar life and military career, see Hallock, *Civil War Letters of Joshua K. Callaway*, xi–xvii.

42. Scholarly explorations into the impact of Civil War armies on the environment include Brady, *War upon the Land*; Nelson, *Ruin Nation*, esp. chapter 3; and Meier, *Nature's Civil War*.

43. Charles Biddlecom to Esther Biddlecom, December 14, 1863, in Aldridge, *No Freedom Shrieker*, 64.

44. Geier, Orr, and Reeves, *Huts and History*, esp. pt. 3.

45. *Regulations for the Army of the Confederate States, 1863*, 52–55; *Revised Regulations for the Army of the United States, 1861*, 74–77.

46. William Henry King Diary, May 20, 1862, in Joiner, Joiner, and Cardin, *No Pardons to Ask*, 15.

47. On the public health issues facing the USCT, see Humphreys, *Intensely Human*; and Downs, *Sick from Freedom*.

48. Joshua K. Callaway to Dulcinea Callaway, May 5, 1862, in Hallock, *Civil War Letters of Joshua K. Callaway*, 10. All subsequent Callaway letters are from this source.

49. Joshua K. Callaway to Dulcinea Callaway, May 24, 1862, 18, 19.

50. Joshua K. Callaway to Dulcinea Callaway, August 13, 1862, 49.

51. Weicksel, "The Dress of the Enemy."

52. On the ways that antebellum notions of death prepared Civil War soldiers for the carnage of war, see Schantz, *Awaiting the Heavenly Country*.

53. Romans 5:1–11.

54. Philip Hamlin to "Dear Friends," December 5, 1862, Hamlin Family Papers, Minnesota Historical Society, St. Paul.

55. Both quotes and the summary of Callaway's camp routine can be found in Joshua K. Callaway to Dulcinea Callaway, June 16, 1862, 27–32.

56. The issue of military discipline and punishment receives fuller treatment in chapter 5.

57. "General Orders No. 4, December 6, 1861," "1862, Hd. Qrs. Rodes Brigade," and "General Orders No. 2," January 8, 1863, Rodes Brigade Order Book, NA.

58. Joshua K. Callaway to Dulcinea Callaway, July 20, 1862, 44–45.

59. William Dorsey Pender to his wife, September 28, 1862, in Hassler, *The General to His Lady*, 179–80.

60. William Henry King Diary, Jane 22, 1862, in Joiner, Joiner, and Cardin, *No Pardons to Ask*, 34.

61. John Waldrop Diary, August 29, 1863, Richard Woolfolk Waldrop Papers, UNC.

62. For the best scholarly treatment of Confederate camp slaves, see Woodward, *Marching Masters*.

63. Charles Bowen Diary, May 10, 1864, in Cassedy, *Dear Friends at Home*, 461–62.

64. The isolation of Grant's forces west of Vicksburg reveals the difficulties of sustaining army-community networks. See Ballard, *Vicksburg*, 159–60.

65. Judith Lee Hallock carefully calculated Callaway's mailing patterns. See Hallock, *Civil War Letters of Joshua K. Callaway*, xvi–xvii.

66. Joshua K. Callaway to Dulcinea Callaway, May 24, 1862, 18–19.

67. On the ways that emotion, morality, and ideology linked soldiers and civilians together, see Clarke, *War Stories*.

68. Joshua K. Callaway to Dulcinea Callaway, June 19, 1862, 33.

69. Joshua K. Callaway to Dulcinea Callaway, June 23, 1862, 35.

70. Joshua K. Callaway to Dulcinea Callaway, October 27, 1862, 62.

71. Joshua K. Callaway to Dulcinea Callaway, July 23, 1863, 115.

72. Joshua K. Callaway to Dulcinea Callaway, September 24, 1862, 137, 138.

73. Joshua K. Callaway to Dulcinea Callaway, November 1, 1863, 157.

74. W. F. Aycock to Dulcinea Callaway, December 5, 1863, 167.

75. On the bonds of comradeship, see Gallagher, *Confederate War*; Glatthaar, *General Lee's Army*; and Power, *Lee's Miserables*.

76. Kenneth Noe carefully delineates between the first wave of Confederate volunteers and those who came into the ranks under the pressure of conscription or as draftees. He centers his work on why men enlisted and questions of motivation, but these standard inquiries produce fresh insights into Confederates who were not immersed in war fervor. See his important work *Reluctant Rebels*. For an incisive analysis of the methodological challenges in unpacking soldier motivations to enlist, see Brown, "North Carolinian Ambivalence."

77. Dotson, "'The Grave and Scandalous Evil Infected to Your People.'"

78. On the varied expressions of Unionism in the Confederacy, see Inscoe and Kenzer, *Enemies of the Country*. For a valuable state study of Unionism that has applicability to the rest of the Confederacy, see Myers, *Rebels against the Confederacy*.

79. On nostalgia, see Anderson, "Dying of Nostalgia"; and Clarke, "So Lonesome I Could Die."

80. Christian Marion Epperly to Mary Epperly, April 24, 1863, Epperly Papers, NYHS. All subsequent Epperly correspondence is from this source.

81. Christian Marion Epperly to Mary Epperly, January 27, 1863.

82. Christian Marion Epperly to Mary Epperly, August 1, 1863.

83. Mary Epperly to Christian Marion Epperly, August 9, 1863.

84. Christian Marion Epperly to Mary Epperly, August 27, 1863.

85. Christian Marion Epperly to Mary Epperly, August 27, 1863.

86. Christian Marion Epperly to Mary Epperly, August 27, 1863.

87. Mary Epperly to Christian Marion Epperly, August 16 and 21, 1863.

88. Giesberg, *Army at Home*, 20. On the continued presence of men on the Confederate home front, see Wetherington, *Plain Folk's Fight*, 152. For an excellent examination of civilian life in Floyd County, see Dotson, "'The Grave and Scandalous Evil.'"

89. Guy S. Taylor to Sarah Taylor, March 19, 1865, in Alderson and Alderson, *Letters Home to Sarah*, 233.

90. Fifty-Fourth Virginia Infantry Regiment Order Book, War Department Collection of Confederate Records, Record Group 109, NA.

91. Christian Marion Epperly to Mary Epperly, February 1, 1864.

92. Christian Marion Epperly to Mary Epperly, October 16, 1864.

93. Christian Marion Epperly to Mary Epperly, November 8, 1864.

94. Christian Marion Epperly to Mary Epperly, September 25, 1864.

95. Christian Marion Epperly to Sarah C. Phleiger, March 12, 1865.

96. Court-martial of Sergeant William Walker, Third South Carolina Infantry (formed part of the Twenty-First United States Colored Infantry Regiment, January–February 1864), Records of the Office of the Judge Advocate General (Army), Record Group 153, NA. A complete transcription of the Walker case can be found in Carmichael, "The Court-martial Trial of Sergeant William Walker." For an outstanding discussion of military law, the inequity of black soldier pay, and the importance of the William Walker case, see Westwood, "The Cause and Consequence of a Union Black Soldier's Mutiny and Execution."

97. On the experience of African American soldiers, see Berlin, Reidy, and Rowland, *Freedom*; Glatthaar, *Forged in Battle*; Trudeau, *Like Men of War*; Luke and Smith, *Soldiering for Freedom*; John David Smith, *Black Soldiers in Blue*; and Ash, *Firebrand of Liberty*.

98. Westwood, "The Cause and Consequence of a Union Black Soldier's Mutiny and Execution," 224–27.

99. Court-martial of William Wolf, Battery G, First Pa. Artillery, Records of the Office of the Judge Advocate General (Army), Record Group 153, NA.

100. On issues of manhood and German American soldiers, see Honeck, "Men of Principle."

101. Court-martial of Sergeant William Walker, NA; Valuska and Keller, *Damn Dutch*; and Kurtz, *Excommunicated from the Union*.

102. "Document 158 A.: Officers of a South Carolina Black Regiment to the Adjutant

General of the Army" (Col. A. G. Bennett et al. to Brig. Genl. L. Thomas, November 21, 1863), in Berlin, Reidy, and Rowland, *Freedom*, 390.

103. Document 158 B, Commander of a South Carolina Black Regiment in the Headquarters of the Department of the South and the Commander of U.S. Forces at Hilton Head to Superintendent of Contrabands in the Department of the South, William B. Barton to Rufus Saxton, December 5, 1863, in Berlin, Reidy, and Rowland, *Freedom*, 390.

104. Court-martial of Sergeant William Walker, NA.

105. Charles Biddlecom to Esther Biddlecom, February 9, 1864, in Aldridge, *No Freedom Shrieker*, 106.

106. Hinman, *Corporal Si Klegg*, 588.

107. On the responsibilities of rank, see Fifty-Fourth Virginia Infantry Regiment Order Book, 10, NA.

108. This insight comes from W. Johnson, *River of Dark Dreams*, 217.

109. Broomall, *Private Confederacies*.

110. Joshua K. Callaway to Dulcinea Callaway, June 26, 1863, in Hallock, *Civil War Letters of Joshua K. Callaway*, 101–2.

111. Examples of stealing in the ranks include William Henry King Diary, July 17, 1862, in Joiner, Joiner, and Cardin, *No Pardons to Ask*, 40–41; Guy C. Taylor to Sarah Taylor, October 25, 1864, in Alderson and Alderson, *Letters Home to Sarah*, 138–39; and David Beem to Hala Beem, November 22, 1863, David Enoch Beem Papers, IHS. On the money stolen in the mail, see Charles Biddlecom to Esther Biddlecom, March 31, 1864, in Aldridge, *No Freedom Shrieker*, 127.

112. Hinman, *Corporal Si Klegg*, 188. On the financial exploitation of Civil War soldiers, see Steven J. Ramold's immensely important work *Baring the Iron Hand*.

113. Sears, *For Country, Cause, and Leader*, 170–71.

114. Jonathan Sproul to Brother James, September 9, 1862, in John Nau Collection, DL1069.1, Houston, Texas. The men in the Thirty-Sixth Wisconsin Infantry were less theatrical than those of the Eighty-Seventh New York in putting martinets in their place. "Their was one sargent in our reg. that was to big for his own good he began to insult a man that stood on gard," Private Guy Taylor wrote home. The sergeant stepped too close to the guard, who took the butt of his musket and walloped the offending officer over the head. "He fell like a ded man," Taylor added, and when the sergeant was revived, "he did not dair to arrest the gard he was afraid that he would get a hardeer nock another time so he let it drop, and bore the pain of a soar head." See Guy S. Taylor to Sarah Taylor, January 17, 1865, in Alderson and Alderson, *Letters Home to Sarah*, 195.

115. Giesberg, *Sex and the Civil War*, 36.

### CHAPTER 2

1. Alexander Keever to Ruth Keever, January 3, 1864; February 4, 1865; and March 5, 1865, in Keever, *Keever Civil War Letters*, 23, 46, 49.

2. I have built on George C. Rable's conclusions about the flexible nature of providential thinking and how soldiers were able to draw from it as an explanatory device in a range of situations. See Rable, *God's Almost Chosen Peoples*, 270, 347, 363, 372, 395.

3. Mark Noll argues that American intellectuals did not move away from providential

reasoning until the 1870s, following in the wake of European thinkers who questioned theological certainties during the Civil War. Noll's keen insights minimize the ways that Civil War soldiers struggled to put their complete trust in traditional Christianity. Noll, *The Civil War as a Theological Crisis*, 92.

4. The Christian belief that God controlled all events and that humans had the capacity to read and interpret the ways of Providence was foundational to how the vast majority of Americans thought on the eve of the Civil War. Even though no man could pass through the bloody gauntlet of war without experiencing a moment of metaphysical confusion, one should not deduce that there was a loss of religion. Rable also makes a similar point, but his discussion of soldiers focuses on the struggles of believing and acting as dutiful Christians while wearing the uniform. He largely overlooks the issues of epistemology. There were plenty of men who embraced Christianity even as they wondered whether anybody really knew what God was doing. On the role of Providence and the continuity of religious thought through the Civil War, see Noll, *The Civil War as a Theological Crisis*, esp. chapter 5; Moorhead, *American Apocalypse*, esp. chapter 4; Rable, *God's Almost Chosen Peoples*, 5, 88, 142, 144–46; and Woodworth, *While God Is Marching On*, 292–93.

Other scholars have focused on the depth of religious faith in the ranks, how it served soldiers, and the challenges of living a Christian life in the army. Such scholars include Faust, "Christian Soldiers"; Scott, *A Visitation of God*, esp. chapter 5; Rolfs, *No Peace for the Wicked*, esp. chapter 6; Sheehan-Dean, *Why Confederates Fought*, 109–10; Noe, *Reluctant Rebels*, 125–30; McPherson, *For Cause and Comrades*, esp. chapter 5; Phillips, *Diehard Rebels*, esp. chapter 1; Mitchell, *Civil War Soldiers*, 173–74; and Carmichael, *The Last Generation*, 207–10. Most of these historians have explored the role of religion in shaping political attachments, how meaning was made from the killing and carnage of war, and its impact on morale. *The War for the Common Soldier* shifts the line of inquiry away from the functionality of religion to how soldiers navigated moments of epistemological confusion within the physical reality of the military. In his brilliant discussion of Northern intellectuals, Louis Menand discovered that many of these men started to question the idea that the world was governed by fixed principles, and in its place advocated a more pragmatic approach to understanding life. My interpretive approach leans heavily on his *The Metaphysical Club*, esp. chapters 1 and 3. For another scholar who has noted that Civil War soldiers struggled to determine what was real, see Lisa Long, *Rehabilitating Bodies*, 10–11. For a general treatment of the religious history of the Civil War, see Miller, Stout, and Wilson, *Religion and the American Civil War*; and Shattuck, *A Shield and Hiding Place*.

5. A thoughtful explanation of providential thinking in the United States can be found in Rable, *God's Almost Chosen Peoples*, esp. chapters 3 and 4; and Rolfs, *No Peace for the Wicked*, 104–7.

6. Rable, *God's Almost Chosen Peoples*, 54.

7. Shi, *Facing Facts*, 4–5.

8. Cushman, *Bloody Promenade*, 102–3.

9. On the sights and sounds of Civil War armies in motion, see Sternhell, *Routes of War*, esp. chapter 2.

10. William H. Berrier to his wife, April 19, 1865, William H. Berrier Papers, FSNMP.

11. This insight comes from Trachtenberg, *Reading American Photographs*, 75.

12. Henry Biggs to his sister, August 28, 1864, Biggs Family Papers, DU. For other

examples of soldiers claiming that observation was the only way of determining reality, see Charles Biddlecom, July 2, 1864, in Aldridge, *No Freedom Shrieker*, 181–82.

13. Charles Bowen to his mother, June 25, 1864, in Cassedy, *Dear Friends at Home*, 508. On the news reporting of black troops at Petersburg, see Levin, "The Devil Himself," 264–82.

14. Woodworth, *While God Is Marching On*, 192–93.

15. Faust, *This Republic of Suffering*, 193.

16. Reuben A. Pierson to Mary Catherine Pierson, August 3, 1862, in Cutrer and Parrish, *Brothers in Gray*, 109–10.

17. Reuben A. Pierson to James F. Pierson, September 17, 1862, in Cutrer and Parrish, *Brothers in Gray*, 121.

18. Reuben A. Pierson to James F. Pierson, September 7, 1862, in Cutrer and Parrish, *Brothers in Gray*, 118.

19. Reuben A. Pierson to James F. Pierson, September 7, 1862.

20. Reuben A. Pierson to William H. Pierson, June 1, 1863, in Cutrer and Parrish, *Brothers in Gray*, 201. This insight comes from Faust, *This Republic of Suffering*, 175–76.

21. Schantz, *Awaiting the Heavenly Country*, 2.

22. Sweet, *Traces of War*.

23. Rable, *God's Almost Chosen Peoples*, esp. 75–80 and chapter 10.

24. Phillip Hamlin to his family, July 24, 1861, Phillip Hamlin Papers, GNMP.

25. For this scholarly perspective, see Rable, chapters 11 and 12.

26. Reuben A. Pierson to Nancy Collins Pierson, April 24, 1863, in Cutrer and Parrish, *Brothers in Gray*, 186.

27. Reuben A. Pierson to William Pierson, August 22, 1863, in Cutrer and Parrish, *Brothers in Gray*, 208–10.

28. Reuben A. Pierson to William Pierson, August 22, 1863, in Cutrer and Parrish, *Brothers in Gray*, 209.

29. Reuben A. Pierson to William Pierson, March 22, 1864, in Cutrer and Parrish, *Brothers in Gray*, 230.

30. Oliver Wendell Holmes Jr. to his mother, June 7, 1864, in Howe, *Touched with Fire*, 143. My insight into Holmes comes from Menand's *The Metaphysical Club*, esp. chapter 13.

31. Reuben A. Pierson to Mary Catherine Pierson, March 28, 1864, in Cutrer and Parrish, *Brothers in Gray*, 230–31.

32. This insight comes from Menand, *The Metaphysical Club*, 352.

33. John S. Willey to his wife, April 27, 1862, Harrisburg Civil War Round Table Collection, U.S. Army Military History Institute, Carlisle, Pa. For a similar perspective, see Andrew Jackson Dawson to his wife, December 26, 1864, Andrew Jackson Dawson Papers, UVA; and Charles Biddlecom to his wife, December 25, 1863, in Aldridge, *No Freedom Shrieker*, 71.

34. On the relationship between poor Confederate soldiers and their wives, see McCurry, *Confederate Reckoning*, esp. chapter 4; Bynum, *The Long Shadow*, esp. chapter 2; and Whites, "Civil War as a Crisis in Gender." On the situation between Northern soldiers, their wives, and the politics and economics of war, see Silber, *Daughters of the Union*, esp. chapters 1 and 2.

35. Alexander Keever to Ruth Keever, January 15, 1865, in Keever, *Keever Civil War Letters*, 45. All subsequent Keever correspondence is from this source.

36. The war did not disabuse members of the American medical community of the importance of cheerfulness in promoting an unconquerable willpower in the field. See Dunster, "Comparative Mortality," 182.

37. Alexander Keever to Ruth Keever, February 4, 1865, 46.

38. Proverbs 30:30; Proverbs 15:13; and Proverbs 15:15.

39. Quoted from Power, *Lee's Miserables*, 261.

40. Amos Judson, "Headquarters Eighty-Third Regiment, Camp Near Yorktown—April 12, 1862," *Erie (Pa.) Dispatch*, Judson Papers, MU.

41. "The Nation and Army," *Harper's Weekly*, July 4, 1863; "The Governor's First Word," *Harper's Weekly*, January 14, 1865; "Outlines from the Outpost," *Southern Illustrated News*, June 20, 1863; and Dunster, "Comparative Mortality," 184.

42. On the medical treatment of African American soldiers, see Gretchen Long, *Doctoring Freedom*; Humphreys, *Marrow of Tragedy*.

43. "The Voice of the Army, Camp 56th Virginia Regiment," *Richmond (Va.) Enquirer*, February 18, 1865.

44. Examples of the resolutions include "Spirit of the Army," *Richmond (Va.) Whig*, January 27, 1865; "Spirit of the Army: Palmetto Battery"; "Spirit of the Army: Hurt's Alabama Battery, Chew's Maryland Battery, and Price's Virginia Battery"; "Spirit of the Army: Second Regiment Virginia Cavalry," *Richmond (Va.) Examiner*, February 18, 1865; "Resolutions, 8th Virginia, 18th Virginia and Taylor's Battery in 'Spirit of the Army,'" *Richmond (Va.) Whig*, February 24, 1865; and "Spirit of the Army," *Richmond (Va.) Dispatch*, February 28, 1865.

45. For examples of morale studies that rely on a broad polling of soldier reactions, see Power, *Lee's Miserables*; Daniel, *Soldiering in the Army of Tennessee*; and Woodworth, *Nothing but Victory*.

46. I believe that emotion is a form of cognition, and I draw heavily from Reddy, *The Navigation of Feeling*, esp. chapter 1.

47. Alexander Keever to Ruth Keever, February 29, 1865, 47.

48. Alexander Keever to Ruth Keever, January 3, 1864, and January 15, 1865, 44.

49. Alexander Keever to Ruth Keever, February 29, 1865, 47. This letter is misdated and was written before February 25, 1865.

50. Alexander Keever to Ruth Keever, February 25, 1865, 48.

51. Alexander Keever to Ruth Keever, February 25, 1865.

52. Alexander Keever to Ruth Keever, March 5, 1865, 49–50.

53. William T. Shepherd to his mother, April 21, 1861, in Hackemer, *To Rescue My Native Land*, 5.

54. William T. Shepherd to his mother, April 21, 1861.

55. Shepherd quotes from his father's letter in his April 23, 1861, letter back to his father, in Hackemer, *To Rescue My Native Land*, 7.

56. William T. Shepherd to his father, April 23, 1861, in Hackemer, *To Rescue My Native Land*, 7–8.

57. Clarke, *War Stories*, 24.

58. William T. Shepherd to his father, November 24, 1861, in Hackemer, *To Rescue My Native Land*, 12.

59. William T. Shepherd to his mother, April 21, 1861, in Hackemer, *To Rescue My Native Land*, 5.

60. William T. Shepherd to [Cousin Maria], August 13, 1861, in Hackemer, *To Rescue My Native Land*, 59.

61. William T. Shepherd to [Cousin Maria], August 13, 1861.

62. William T. Shepherd to his parents, November 1, 1861, in Hackemer, *To Rescue My Native Land*, 93–94.

63. On the move from conciliation to hard war, see Grimsley, *The Hard Hand of War.*

64. Dilbeck, *A More Civil War*, 161.

65. William T. Shepherd to his father and mother, November 14, 1861, in Hackemer, *To Rescue My Native Land*, 105–6.

66. William T. Shepherd to his parents, February 23, 1862, in Hackemer, *To Rescue My Native Land*, 151–52.

67. William T. Shepherd to his parents, February 23, 1862.

68. William R. J. Pegram to Virginia Johnson (Pegram) McIntosh, August 14, 1862, Pegram-Johnson-McIntosh Papers, VHS.

69. For an excellent overview of soldier reactions to Shiloh, see Reaves and Frank, "Seeing the Elephant," esp. chapter 4.

70. William T. Shepherd to Sister Becca, April 14, 1862, in Hackemer, *To Rescue My Native Land*, 165–66.

71. This insight comes from Roeder, *Censored War*, 154–55.

72. William T. Shepherd to his father, April 30, 1862, in Hackemer, *To Rescue My Native Land*, 186.

73. William T. Shepherd to his sister Becca, June 7, 1862, in Hackemer, *To Rescue My Native Land*, 197–98.

74. William T. Shepherd to his sister Becca, June 7, 1862.

75. William T. Shepherd to his cousin Willie, August, 13, 1861, in Hackemer, *To Rescue My Native Land*, 58.

76. William T. Shepherd to his sister Becca, February 19, 1864, in Hackemer, *To Rescue My Native Land*, 296.

77. William T. Shepherd to his mother and father, March 28, 1864, in Hackemer, *To Rescue My Native Land*, 302.

78. William T. Shepherd to his father and mother, September 7, 1862, in Hackemer, *To Rescue My Native Land*, 224.

79. On Confederate nationalism, see Rubin, *A Shattered Nation.*


CHAPTER 3

1. Reuben A. Pierson to Mary Catherine Pierson, August 3, 1862, in Cutrer and Parrish, *Brothers in Gray*, 110–11.

2. Reuben A. Pierson to Mary Catherine Pierson, August 3, 1862, 112.

3. Victorian writing guides that stress the importance of representing life in hard facts and the need to awaken nobler sympathies of the correspondent through prose include the compilation assembled by D. Appleton, *Appleton's Complete Letter Writer*, xviii–xx; and *The Fashionable American Letter Writer*, xix–xx.

4. The introduction contains a fuller description of sentimentalism.

5. This insight draws from Fabian, *Unvarnished Truth*, 141.

6. An overview of David E. Beem's life can be found at http://www.indianahistory.org/our-collections/collection-guides/david-enoch-beem-papers-1821-1923-1954.pdf.

7. Fahs, "The Sentimental Soldier in Popular Civil War Literature, 1861–65."

8. Mahala Beem to David E. Beem, July 25, 1862, David Enoch Beem Papers, IHS, hereafter cited as Beem Papers.

9. Mahala Beem to David E. Beem, July 25, 1862.

10. David E. Beem to Mahala Beem, July 27, 1862, Beem Papers.

11. David E. Beem to Mahala Beem, July 27, 1862.

12. Clarke, *War Stories*, 100, 110.

13. David E. Beem to Mahala Beem, July 27, 1862, Beem Papers.

14. Quoted from Sears, *Landscape Turned Red*, 240.

15. Sears, *Landscape Turned Red*.

16. David Beem to Mahala Beem, September 18, 1862, Beem Papers.

17. David Beem to Mahala Beem, September 18, 1862.

18. David Beem to Emaline Lundy, September 20, 1862, Beem Papers.

19. David Beem to Emaline Lundy, September 20, 1862.

20. Clarke, *War Stories*, 69.

21. David Beem to Emaline Lundy, September 20, 1862, Beem Papers.

22. David Beem to Mahala Beem, September 24, 1862, Beem Papers.

23. David Beem to Mahala Beem, September 24, 1862.

24. David Beem to Mahala Beem, September 28, 1862, Beem Papers.

25. David Beem to Mahala Beem, October 7, 1862, Beem Papers.

26. David Beem to Mahala Beem, October 9, 1862, Beem Papers.

27. David Beem to Mahala Beem, October 17, 1862, Beem Papers.

28. Linderman, *Embattled Courage*, esp. chapters 8, 11, and 12.

29. Fred T. Brown to David Beem, October 17, 1862, Beem Papers.

30. David Beem to Mahala Beem, October 23, 1863, Beem Papers.

31. David Beem to Mahala Beem, July 5, 1863, Beem Papers.

32. David Beem to Belle Beem, January 19, 1864, Beem Papers.

33. On Southern manhood, see Glover, *Southern Sons*.

34. Thanks to the expertise of Keith Bohannon, I was able to piece together the prewar life and military record of Wright Vinson. See Seventh Census of the United States, 1850, Houston County, Georgia; and Wright Vinson, Fifty-Seventh Georgia Infantry Regiment, Compiled Service Records, NA.

35. Wright Vinson to Christiana Vinson, May 27, 1862, Wright Vinson Civil War Letters, GDAH, hereafter cited as Vinson Letters. For a summary of Vinson's military service in the Fifty-Seventh Georgia Infantry, see Walker, *Hell's Broke Loose in Georgia*.

36. Wright Vinson to Christiana Vinson, December 15, 1862, Vinson Letters.

37. Wright Vinson to Christiana Vinson, June 20, 1862, Vinson Letters.

38. Wright Vinson to Christiana Vinson, June 26, 1862, Vinson Letters.

39. Wright Vinson to Christiana Vinson, November 23, 1862, Vinson Letters.

40. Wright Vinson to Christiana Vinson, June 26, 1862, Vinson Letters.

41. Wright Vinson to Christiana Vinson, November 6, 1862, Vinson Letters.

42. Wright Vinson to Christiana Vinson, September 1, [1862], Vinson Letters.

43. Wright Vinson to Christiana Vinson, August 21, [1862], Vinson Letters.

44. Wright Vinson to Christiana Vinson, November 11, 1862, Vinson Letters.

45. Wright Vinson to Christiana Vinson, December 15, 1862, Vinson Letters.

46. Wright Vinson to Christiana Vinson, December 1, 1862, Vinson Letters.

47. On the abjection of the self in the writings of the poor and semiliterate, see Davis, "Abjection and White Trash Autobiography," 188–89.

48. Wright Vinson to Christiana Vinson, August 12, 1862, Vinson Letters.

49. M. W. Casswell to Christiana Vinson, January 18, 1863, Vinson Letters.

50. On John Crawford's education at private academies before entering the Citadel, see Moore, *Upcountry South Carolina*, xix–xx.

51. David Anderson to John Crawford Anderson, December 2, 1861; Mary Elizabeth Anderson to John Crawford Anderson, December 27, 1861; Hettie Brockman to John Crawford Anderson, October 3, 1861; and John Crawford Anderson to Mary Elizabeth Anderson, in Moore, *Upcountry South Carolina*, 47, 58, 60, 72–73.

52. On ambition, honor, and the desire to earn the approval of women in Confederate soldier culture, see Berry, *All That Makes a Man*.

53. John Crawford Anderson to Nettie Anderson, February 20, 1862, in Moore, *Upcountry South Carolina*, 72.

54. John Crawford Anderson to Nettie Anderson, February 20, 1862.

55. John Crawford Anderson to Nettie Anderson, June 12, 1862, in Moore, *Upcountry South Carolina*, 91.

56. John Crawford Anderson to Emma [?], December 7, 1863, in Moore, *Upcountry South Carolina*, 122.

57. John Crawford Anderson to Emma [?], December 7, 1863.

58. John Crawford Anderson to Mary Elizabeth Anderson, October 17, 1864, in Moore, *Upcountry South Carolina*, 147.

59. John Crawford Anderson to Mary Elizabeth Anderson, March 9, 1865, in Moore, *Upcountry South Carolina*, 158.

60. John Crawford Anderson to Mary Elizabeth Anderson, October 17, 1864, in Moore, *Upcountry South Carolina*, 151.

61. John Crawford Anderson to Mary Elizabeth Anderson, October 17, 1864.

62. John Crawford Anderson to David Anderson, April 11, 1865, in Moore, *Upcountry South Carolina*, 163.

63. John Crawford Anderson to David Anderson, April 11, 1865.

64. William W. Hewell to his companion, July 9, 1863, William W. Hewell Letters, GDAH.

65. Grant, "The Lost Boys," 236–39.

66. Ellis, Montgomery, and Berry, *Private Voices: The Corpus of American Civil War Letters*, http://altchive.org/private-voices/, accessed October 23, 2017.


CHAPTER 4

1. Charles Bowen to Kate Bowen, June 21, 1864, in Cassedy, *Dear Friends at Home*, 503. All subsequent Bowen correspondence is from this source.

2. Charles Bowen to Kate Bowen, June 20, 1864, 499.

3. Charles Bowen to Kate Bowen, June 20, 1864, 500.

4. Charles Bowen to Kate Bowen, June 20, 1864.

5. Charles Bowen to Kate Bowen, August 2, 1864, 553.

6. On the historiographical debate on the physical and emotional impact of battle, see Foote, "Soldiers," 2:118–20.

7. This insight comes from Darnton, *Great Cat Massacre*, 260–61.

8. Quoted from Dunkelman, *Brothers One and All*, 122.

9. Fahs, *Imagined Civil War*, 109–10.

10. Bartholow, "The Various Influences Affecting the Physical Endurance," 7.

11. Hess, *Union Soldier in Battle*, 108.

12. Broomall, *Private Confederacies*.

13. William T. Sherman to Thomas Ewing Sherman, April 11, 1862, in Simpson and Berlin, *Sherman's Civil War*, 202.

14. William T. Sherman to Ellen Ewing Sherman, April 24, 1862, in Simpson and Berlin, *Sherman's Civil War*, 208.

15. Mark M. Smith, *Smell of Battle*, 42–43.

16. Orr, "Surrendering at Gettysburg."

17. Court-martial of Thomas B. Rodgers, 140th Pennsylvania Infantry, Records of the Office of the Judge Advocate General (Army), Record Group 153, NA.

18. For revealing case studies of Civil War tactics from an archaeological perspective, see Geier, Scott, and Babits, *From These Honored Dead*.

19. Court-martial of George Gillis, Seventy-Seventh New York, Records of the Office of the Judge Advocate General (Army), Record Group 153, NA.

20. On the rumor grapevine in shaping perceptions of war, see Phillips, *Diehard Rebels*, esp. chapter 4.

21. Milton McJunkin to his mother, July 12, 1862, in Palm, Sauers, and Schroeder, *Bloody 85th*, 43; and John Futch to Martha Futch, May 28, 1863, Futch Brothers Papers, NCSA.

22. On capital punishments, see Johnson, Johnson, and Williams, *All Were Not Heroes*; Perry, *Civil War Courts-Martial of North Carolina Troops*; and Ramold, *Baring the Iron Hand*.

23. Robert Rodes Brigade Order Book, NA.

24. William A. Dunklin to Jennie T. Dunklin, April 6, 1863, Virginia T. Dunklin Papers, Georgia Historical Society, Savannah, Georgia.

25. *OR* 21: 859–60.

26. Reardon, *With a Sword in One Hand*, 90–91.

27. Bartholow, "The Various Influences Affecting the Physical Endurance," 30; Keen, Mitchell, and Morehouse, "On Malingering," 377, 383–84; and Woodward, *Outlines of the Chief Camp Diseases*, 376.

28. On the concept of courage, see Linderman, *Embattled Courage*, esp. chapter 1.

29. On the influence of racial perceptions in shaping the military expectations of African Americans and other ethnic groups, see Gretchen Long, *Doctoring Freedom*, esp. chapter 3; Samito, *Becoming American under Fire*, esp. chapters 3 and 5; Gleeson, *Green and the Gray*, esp. chapter 3; Bruce, *Harp and the Eagle*, 69–83; and Keller, *Chancellorsville and the Germans*, esp. chapter 5.

30. On killing as the crucial element in black soldiers' claims to citizenship, see Emberton's superb piece "'Only Murder Makes Men.'" On the interconnectedness of ethnicity, courage, and citizenship, see Samito, "Thomas F. Meagher, Patrick R. Guiney, and the Meaning of the Civil War for Irish America."

31. Bartholow, *Manual of Instructions for Enlisting and Discharging Soldiers*, 95, 96.

32. See Bartholow, "Various Influences Affecting the Physical Endurance," 5. On perceptions of the black body during the Civil War, see Humphreys, *Intensely Human*, 18–19. On the medical care of black soldiers, see Downs, *Sick from Freedom*, esp. chapter 1; and Gretchen Long, *Doctoring Freedom*.

33. Downs, "'Who Got Bloody?,'" 211–12.

34. On Civil War soldiers as psychiatric casualties and how battlefield trauma was understood, see Dean, "'We Will All Be Lost and Destroyed.'"

35. Oppenheim, *"Shattered Nerves,"* 8.

36. Bartholow, "Various Influences Affecting the Physical Endurance," 38.

37. This insight is gained from Barbian, Sledzik, and Reznick, "Remains of War."

38. Bartholow, "Various Influences Affecting the Physical Endurance," 8; and Grant, "Civil War Cybernetics."

39. Calhoun, "Nostalgia," 132.

40. On medical self-understandings in the nineteenth century, see Rosenberg, "Body and Mind in Nineteenth-Century Medicine," 185–97.

41. Devine, *Learning from the Wounded*, esp. the introduction and chapter 1; and Meier, "U.S. Sanitary Commission Physicians."

42. Keen, Mitchell, and Morehouse, "On Malingering," 369.

43. Chisolm, *Manual of Military Surgery*, 447.

44. Keen, Mitchell, and Morehouse, "On Malingering," 374–75.

45. Young, *Harmony of Illusions*, 13–19.

46. Chisolm, *Manual of Military Surgery*, 445.

47. Quoted in Glatthaar, *Forged in Battle*, 191.

48. For the argument that the rifled weapon was a revolutionary force on Civil War battlefields, see Linderman's *Embattled Courage*, esp. chapter 7.

49. For this perspective, see Grant, "Lost Boys."

50. Hess, *Rifle Musket in Civil War Combat*, 92.

51. DeGruccio, "Letting the War Slip through Our Hands," 17.

52. I take my methodological cue directly from Darnton, *Great Cat Massacre*, 109.

53. Francis Adams Donaldson to Auntie, December 27, 1862, in Acken, *Inside the Army of the Potomac*, 175. All subsequent Donaldson correspondence is from this source.

54. An outstanding overview of Donaldson's life can be found in Acken, *Inside the Army of the Potomac*, 1–18.

55. Francis Adams Donaldson to Auntie, December 27, 1862, 179.

56. Francis Adams Donaldson to Auntie, December 27, 1862, 181–82.

57. Francis Adams Donaldson to Auntie, December 27, 1862.

58. Francis Adams Donaldson to Auntie, December 27, 1862, 183.

59. Francis Adams Donaldson to Auntie, December 27, 1862, 183–84.

60. Francis Adams Donaldson to Auntie, December 27, 1862, 191, 193–94.

61. Neely and Holzer, *Union Image*, 199–206; "The Attack on Fredericksburg—The Forlorn Hope Scaling the Hill," "The Bombardment of Fredericksburg by the Army of the Potomac," and "The Battle as Seen by the Reserve," December 27, 1862, *Harper's Weekly*, http://ezpro.cc.gettysburg.edu:2841/IssueTocView.asp?titleId=HW&volumeId=1862&issueId=1227, accessed July 1, 2017. See also "The Attack on the Rebel Works at

Fredericksburg by the Centre Grand Division of the Army of the Potomac on December 13, 1862, Sketched by Mr. A. R. Waud," "Our Soldiers in the Streets of Fredericksburg—Drawn by Mr. A. R. Waud," and "Major General Franklin's Grand Division Crossing the Rappahannock on 12th December 1862," *Harper's Weekly*; "[From a Sketch by Mr. Davis]," January 3, 1863, *Harper's Weekly*, http://ezpro.cc.gettysburg.edu:2841/IssueTocView.asp?titleId=HW&volumeId=1863&issueId=0103, accessed July 1, 2017; and "Gallant Charge of Humphrey's Division at the Battle of Fredericksburg—Sketched by Mr. A. R. Waud," January 10, 1863, *Harper's Weekly*, http://ezpro.cc.gettysburg.edu:2841/IssueTocView.asp?titleId=HW&volumeId=1863&issueId=0110, accessed July 1, 2017.

62. Francis Adams Donaldson to Auntie, December 27, 1862, 187, 188.

63. Charles Biddlecom to Esther Biddlecom, July 1 and July 16, 1864, in Aldridge, *No Freedom Shrieker*, 179, 192. All subsequent Biddlecom correspondence is from this source.

64. Charles Biddlecom to Esther Biddlecom, October 6, 1863, 47.

65. Charles Biddlecom to Esther Biddlecom, October 6, 1863.

66. Charles Biddlecom to Esther Biddlecom, October 6, 1863.

67. Charles Biddlecom to Esther Biddlecom, November 12, 1863, 56.

68. Charles Biddlecom to Esther Biddlecom, November 20, 1863, 59.

69. Charles Biddlecom to Esther Biddlecom, November 20, 1863, 60.

70. Charles Biddlecom to Esther Biddlecom, December 27, 1863, 75.

71. Charles Biddlecom to Esther Biddlecom, December 27, 1863, 71, 72.

72. Charles Biddlecom to Esther Biddlecom, January 15, 1864, 85, 86.

73. Charles Biddlecom to Esther Biddlecom, March 19, 1864, 121.

74. Charles Biddlecom to Esther Biddlecom, March 19, 1864, 121–22.

75. Charles Biddlecom to Esther Biddlecom, March 31, 1864, 126.

76. Charles Biddlecom to Esther Biddlecom, March 19, 1864, 121–22.

77. Charles Biddlecom to Esther Biddlecom, June 12, 1864, 158.

78. Charles Biddlecom to Esther Biddlecom, July 1, 1864, 179.

79. Charles Biddlecom to Esther Biddlecom, June 12, 1864, 159, 157.

80. Charles Biddlecom to Esther Biddlecom, June 28, 1864, 176.

81. Charles Biddlecom to Esther Biddlecom, July 9, 1864, 186–87.

82. Ambrose H. Hayward to his father, December 2, 1862, in Orr, *Last to Leave the Field*, 194–95.

83. Ambrose H. Hayward to his father, December 2, 1862, 202, 201.

84. My observations draw from Mark M. Smith, *Smell of Battle*, 136.

85. Charles W. Trueheart to Minny Trueheart, November 8, 1864, in Williams, *Rebel Brothers*, 130.

86. My thinking on the importance of looking beyond the truthfulness or falseness of discourse comes from Farge, *Allure of the Archives*, 28.

87. Gordon, *A Broken Regiment*; and Sommerville, "'Will They Ever Be Able to Forget?'"

CHAPTER 5

1. "Military Execution at Dalton, Ga.—Fourteen Men Shot for Desertion," *San Francisco Daily Evening Bulletin*, July 7, 1864.

2. There are conflicting accounts of how many men survived the initial volley. Some

soldiers claim that only two were living. "Military Execution at Dalton, Ga.," *San Francisco Daily Evening Bulletin*, July 7, 1864; James Clark to Martha Clark, June 16, 1864, in Jordan, *North Carolina Troops*, 14:236–37; "Thomas W. Patton Recollections," in Jordan, *North Carolina Troops*, 14:463.

3. Jacoby, *Shadows at Dawn*, 225.

4. Foote, "Soldiers," 1:124.

5. McPherson, *For Cause and Comrades*, 168.

6. Lonn, *Desertion during the Civil War*, 29–30, 149–50.

7. Cashin, "Deserters, Civilians, and Draft Resistance in the North," 262–85.

8. On the Confederate draft riot, see McCurry, *Confederate Reckoning*, esp. chapter 5.

9. On the effects of Unionism, see Myers, *Rebels against the Confederacy*.

10. Outstanding discussions of deserter resistance in Pennsylvania can be found in Sandow, *Deserter Country*; and Palladino, *Another Civil War*.

11. Useful overviews of desertion include Weitz, *More Damning Than Slaughter*; and Cashin, "Deserters, Civilians, and Draft Resistance in the North."

12. Sheehan-Dean, *Why Confederates Fought*, 51.

13. This insight draws from Blair, *Virginia's Private War*, 88–89.

14. McGuire, "Desertion during the Civil War."

15. Radley, *Rebel Watchdog*, 107.

16. *OR* 34 (pt. 4): 188.

17. This insight comes from Sheehan-Dean, *Why Confederates Fought*, 102–6.

18. Kautz, *Customs of Service*, 213–14.

19. "May 12, 1863 Circular," Twentieth Indiana Regimental Letter and Order Book, Records of the Adjutant Generals Office, 1780s–1917: Records of Volunteer Union Organizations, Record Group 94, NA.

20. For an excellent summary of the military justice system in Civil War armies, see Foote, *Gentlemen and the Roughs*, 12–16.

21. For a diary recording of a Confederate court-martial at the regimental level, see Driver, "Diary of Captain John D. Lilley."

22. On the irregularities in the process of courts-martial on the Union side, see Ramold, *Baring the Iron Hand*, esp. chapter 8.

23. Farge, *Allure of the Archives*, 28.

24. For a summary of William Allen's military service, see Riggs, *13th Virginia Infantry*. A slightly different version of Allen's record can be found in Turner, *Allen Family of Amherst County*. My thanks to Robert E. L. Krick for sorting out the confusing layers of Allen's Compiled Service Record, particularly Allen's status as a conscript and deserter.

25. William T. Allen to his mother, May 21, 1863, Allen Family Papers, WL, hereafter cited as Allen Papers.

26. Turner, *Allen Family of Amherst County*, xi–xiii.

27. Hubbs, *Guarding Greensboro*, 170–71.

28. Giesberg, *Army at Home*, 32.

29. William T. Allen to his mother, May 21, 1863, Allen Papers.

30. William T. Allen to his mother, May 21, 1863.

31. William T. Allen to Ellen, June 1, 1863, Allen Papers.

32. William T. Allen to Ellen, June 1, 1863.

33. William T. Allen to Ellen, June 1, 1863.

34. William T. Allen to Ellen, April 20, 1864, Allen Papers.

35. For examples of Confederate loyalists coming under attack from Unionists and bands of deserters, see Wetherington, *Plain Folk's Fight*, 221–30. On the eruption of violence over the draft and deserter bands, see Weber, *Copperheads*, 67–68, 107–12.

36. William T. Allen to Henry, March 24, 1865, Allen Papers.

37. *OR* 46 (pt. 3): 1357.

38. Tinsley Allen to Sallie [Allen], March 30, 1865, Allen Papers.

39. Ayers, "Loyalty and America's Civil War," Forty-Ninth Annual Fortenbaugh Memorial Lecture, 8. Other scholars who see loyalties as more fluid in their construction include Browning, *Shifting Loyalties*.

40. A useful discussion of the Northern draft, its implementation, and how draftees, bounty men, and substitutes were perceived in the army can be found in Gallman, *Defining Duty*, esp. chapter 5.

41. Luskey, "Mercenaries or Patriots?," Civil War Institute Annual Conference.

42. Murdock, *One Million Men*, 289–90.

43. Murdock, *One Million Men*, 305.

44. The insights and details of this paragraph draw heavily from Murdock, *One Million Men*, 336.

45. Francis Adams Donaldson to Auntie, July 28 and July 31, 1863, in Acken, *Inside the Army of the Potomac*, 322–23.

46. Acken, *Inside the Army of the Potomac*, 471.

47. Francis Adams Donaldson to Auntie, August 6, 1863, in Acken, *Inside the Army of the Potomac*, 324.

48. Court-martial of John Rainese (alias Gion Rionese), 118th Pennsylvania Infantry, File No. MM 687, Records of the Office of the Judge Advocate General (Army), Record Group 153, NA.

49. Court-martial of John Folaney (alias Geacinto Lerchize), 118th Pennsylvania Infantry, File No. MM 687, Records of the Office of the Judge Advocate General (Army), Record Group 153, NA.

50. Court-martial of Charles Walter (alias C. Zene) Recruit, 118th Pennsylvania Infantry, File No. MM 687, Records of the Office of the Judge Advocate General (Army), Record Group 153, NA; Court-martial of Emile Lai (alias E. Duffie) Recruit, 118th Pennsylvania Infantry, File No. MM 687, Records of the Office of the Judge Advocate General (Army), Record Group 153, NA; Court-martial of George Kuhne (or Kuhn, alias G. Weik or Week) Recruit, 118th Pennsylvania Infantry, File No. MM 687, Records of the Office of the Judge Advocate General (Army), Record Group 153, NA.

51. Court-martial of Charles Walter (alias C. Zene) Recruit, 118th Pennsylvania Infantry, File No. MM 687, Records of the Office of the Judge Advocate General (Army), Record Group 153, NA; Court-martial of Emile Lai (alias E. Duffie) Recruit, 118th Pennsylvania Infantry, File No. MM 687, Records of the Office of the Judge Advocate General (Army), Record Group 153, NA; Court-martial of George Kuhne, NA.

52. For a copy of General Orders No. 84, see Survivors' Association, *History of the Corn Exchange Regiment*, 296.

53. Charles Walter, Gion Reanese, Emil Lai, Gion Folaney, and George Kuhn to George

Gordon Meade, August 23, 1863, in Survivors' Association, *History of the Corn Exchange Regiment*, 296–97. The correspondence between Lincoln and Meade can be found in *OR* 29 (pt. 2): 102–3.

54. Francis Adams Donaldson to Jacob, August 25, 1863, in Acken, *Inside the Army of the Potomac*, 334.

55. Francis Adams Donaldson to Jacob, August 25, 1863, 335–36.

56. "Army of the Potomac; Execution of Deserters—The Preparations—The Final Executions, &c.," *New York Times*, September 2, 1863; and "Execution of the Five Deserters," *Albany (N.Y.) Evening Journal*, September [?], 1863.

57. The sample includes "Further Particulars of the Execution of Deserters," *Illustrated New Age* (Philadelphia), September 1, 1863; "Execution of the Five Deserters," *Albany (N.Y.) Evening Journal*, September 5, 1863; "Meade's Army. Seven Men Shot for Desertion, Eight Condemned; But One Pardoned. Five of the Men 'Professional' Substitutes. Sketch of Some of the Prisoners. The Military—The Funeral Procession. The Place of Execution. One of the Prisoners Shot Three Times," *New York Herald*, August 31, 1863; "General Meade: Order Condemning the Deserters to Death—Professional Substitutes and Their Devices to Enable Them to Desert," *New York Herald*, September 6, 1863; "Army of the Potomac: Execution of Deserters—The Preparations—The Final Execution," *New York Times*, September 9, 1863; "Rappahannock Station, August 30, 1863," *Rochester (N.Y.) Democrat and American*, September 9, 1863; "From the 1st N.J. Artillery," *Newark (N.J.) Daily Advertiser*, September 4, 1863; "From the Army of the Potomac, an Impressive Military Execution—A Solemn Warning to Deserters," *Chicago Tribune*, August 31, 1863; "Warning to Substitutes and Deserters," *New York Times*, August 31, 1863; "Execution of Five Substitutes for Desertion," *Vermont Watchman and State Journal* (Montpelier), September 4, 1863; "Deserter's Fate," *Frank Leslie's Illustrated*, September 26, 1863; "From the Army of the Potomac," *Philadelphia Inquirer*, August 28, 1863; "From the Army of the Potomac—The Doomed Deserters," *New York Times*, August 31, 1863; and "Execution of the Five Deserters," *Albany (N.Y.) Evening Journal*, September 2, 1863; [Alfred Waud], "The Execution of Deserters," *Harper's Weekly*, September 26, 1863.

58. "Further Particulars of the Execution of Deserters," *Illustrated New Age* (Philadelphia), September 1, 1863.

59. Ramold, *Baring the Iron Hand*, 258.

60. Henry Kline to Cousin Mary, August 29, 1863, Shapell Manuscript Foundation, Herzilya, Israel.

61. Marshall, *Company "K."*

62. Survivors' Association, *History of the Corn Exchange Regiment*, 298.

63. [Waud], "The Execution of Deserters."

64. Marsena Rudolph Patrick Diary, July 9, 1864, in Sparks, *Inside Lincoln's Army*, 398–99.

65. John A. H. Foster to Mary Jane Foster, April 27, 1864, in Arden and Powell, *Letters from the Storm*, 197, 198. All subsequent Foster correspondence is from this source.

66. John A. H. Foster to Mary Jane Foster, May 4, 1864, 205.

67. Theodore Lyman Diary, May 17, 1864, in Agassiz, *Meade's Headquarters*, 117.

68. Krick, *9th Virginia Cavalry*, 34.

69. Theodore Lyman Diary, May 17, 1864, in Agassiz, *Meade's Headquarters*, 117.

70. John A. H. Foster to Mary Jane Foster, May 10, 1864, 207.

71. John A. H. Foster to Mary Jane Foster, May 13, 1864, 208.

72. *OR* 22 (pt. 2): 77.

73. John A. H. Foster to Mary Jane Foster, May 13, 1864, 208–9.

74. Reardon, *With a Sword in One Hand*, 110.

75. Charles Bowen Diary, May 12, 1864, in Cassedy, *Dear Friends at Home*, 465. Bowen sent his diary entries home for his family to read.

76. Theodore Lyman Diary, May 17, 1864, in Agassiz, *Meade's Headquarters*, 117.

77. Starbird's petition to Edwin Stanton as well as the documents of his movements among various commands can be found in John D. Starbird, Co. K, Nineteenth Massachusetts Infantry, Civil War Compiled Service Records, Records of the Adjutant General's Office, 1780s–1917, Record Group 94, NA. The report that Senator Wilson interfered can be found in the Franklin Dyer Diary, May 20, 1864, in Chesson, *Journal of a Civil War Surgeon*, 156.

78. Lieutenant John E. Hodgkins of the Nineteenth Massachusetts knew of Starbird's repeat offenses. He wrote in his diary on May 20: "He [Starbird] deserted from our Regiment about two years since, joined another, getting a bounty for so doing and in a short time joined still another, getting another bounty, all of which was taken into consideration." See Turino, *Civil War Diary of J. E. Hodgkins*, 88.

79. Court-martial of John D. Starbird, Nineteenth Massachusetts Infantry, File No. 1943, Records of the Office of the Judge Advocate General (Army), Record Group 153, NA.

80. Robert S. Robertson Diary, May 18, 1864, in Walker and Walker, "Diary of the War by Robt. S. Robertson," 189.

81. George Gordon Meade to Joseph Holt, July 5, 1864, Court-martial of John D. Starbird, NA.

82. Robert S. Robertson Diary, May 18, 1864, in Walker and Walker, "Diary of the War by Robt. S. Robertson," 189.

83. Court-martial of John D. Starbird, NA.

84. Court-martial of John D. Starbird, NA; Gibbon, *Personal Recollections of the Civil War*, 222; Banes, *History of the Philadelphia Brigade*, 258–59.

85. Jacob Bechtel to George Bechtel, May 20, 1864, Jacob Bechtel Papers, bound vol. 257, FSNMP.

86. Franklin Dyer Diary, May 20, 1864, in Chesson, *Journal of a Civil War Surgeon*, 156.

87. Gibbon, *Personal Recollections of the Civil War*, 224.

88. General Orders from [?], May 20, 1864, Court-martial of John D. Starbird, NA.

89. *OR* 36 (pt. 3): 135.

90. These insights come from Carol Reardon's superb analysis of the Army of the Potomac during the Overland Campaign. See Reardon, *With a Sword in One Hand*, esp. chapter 3.

91. Gibbon, *Personal Recollections of the Civil War*, 225, 226.

92. Marsena Rudolph Patrick Diary, June 13, 1864, in Sparks, *Inside Lincoln's Army*, 383.

93. R-R, Co. H, Eighth Ala., "In the Trenches, Near Gaines' Mill, Jun 8, 1864," *Mobile (Ala.) Advertiser & Register*, June 21, 1864.

94. On Davis's amnesty proclamation, see Glatthaar, *General Lee's Army*, 416.

95. The actions of the men who deserted from the Third North Carolina have been culled from a number of wartime papers, including "Military Murders," *Richmond (Va.) Examiner*, August 31, 1863, 2; "Death of Lieut. Richardson Mallett," *Fayetteville (N.C.)*

*Observer*, August 31, 1863, 2; and "Sentenced to Death," *Richmond (Va.) Whig*, September 5, 1863, 1. A fine secondary treatment of this incident and the subsequent execution of these North Carolina soldiers can be found in Blair, *Tragedy at Montpelier*.

96. Quoted from Blair, *Tragedy at Montpelier*, 79.

97. An outstanding biographical summary of the deserters shot in the Third North Carolina Infantry can be found in Perry, *Civil War Courts-Martial of North Carolina Troops*, 161–71.

98. John Futch to Martha Futch, August 16, 1863, Futch Brothers Papers, NCSA, hereafter cited as Futch Papers.

99. John Futch to Martha Futch, August 20, 1863, Futch Papers.

100. Eighth Census of the United States, 1860, New Hanover County, N.C.

101. John Futch to Martha Futch, February 5, 1863, Futch Papers.

102. John Futch to Martha Futch, April 9, 1863, Futch Papers.

103. John Futch to Martha Futch, February 13, 1863, Futch Papers.

104. Martha Futch to John Futch, March 29, 1863, Futch Papers.

105. Martha Futch to John Futch, March 5, 1862, Futch Papers.

106. Martha Futch to John Futch, April 14, 1863, Futch Papers.

107. John Futch to Martha Futch, April 20, 1863, Futch Papers.

108. Martha Futch to John Futch, April 3, 1863, Futch Papers.

109. Martha Futch to John Futch, April 14, 1863, Futch Papers.

110. John Futch to Martha Futch, May 9, 1863, Futch Papers.

111. John Futch to Martha Futch, May 9, 1863.

112. John Futch to Martha Futch, May 28, 1863, Futch Papers.

113. John Futch to Martha Futch, May 20, 1863, Futch Papers.

114. John Futch to Martha Futch, June 19, 1863, Futch Papers.

115. John Futch to Martha Futch, June 2, 1863, Futch Papers.

116. John Futch to Martha Futch, August 2, 1863, Futch Papers.

117. John Futch to Martha Futch, July 15, 1863, Futch Papers.

118. Faust, *This Republic of Suffering*, 11.

119. Glatthaar, *General Lee's Army*, 283–85.

120. John Futch to Martha Futch and to his mother, August 2, 1863, Futch Papers.

121. John Futch to Martha Futch, July 31, 1863, Futch Papers.

122. Stowe, *Intimacy and Power in the Old South*, 49.

123. John Futch to Martha Futch, July 19, 1863, Futch Papers.

124. Sheehan-Dean, *Why Confederates Fought*, 193.

125. John Futch to Martha Futch, February 21, 1863, Futch Papers.

126. John Futch to Martha Futch, July 31, 1863, Futch Papers.

127. Jefferson Davis, "Proclamation," in *OR* 4 (pt. 2): 687.

128. Gallagher, *Becoming Confederates*, esp. chapter 1.

129. Robert E. Lee to Jefferson Davis, August 8, 1863, in Dowdey, *Wartime Papers of R. E. Lee*, 589.

130. Robert E. Lee, "General Orders No. 80," *Raleigh Register*, August 1, 1863.

131. "A Deserter's Confession," *Carolina Watchman* (Salisbury, N.C.), September 14, 1863.

132. "A Deserter's Confession."

133. James Zimmerman to Adaline Zimmerman, August 23, 1863, James Zimmerman Papers, DU, hereafter cited as Zimmerman Papers.

134. Edward Johnson to George Steuart, September 4, 1863, George H. Steuart Papers, MOC.

135. Edward Johnson to George Steuart, September 4, 1863.

136. "From Gen. Lee's Army," *Richmond (Va.) Enquirer,* September 15, 1863.

137. "From Gen. Lee's Army." For descriptions of other executions that occurred in the Army of Northern Virginia in the fall of 1863, see "From the North Carolina Soldiers," *Fayetteville (N.C.) Observer,* October 5, 1863, 2; and "Military Execution," *Richmond (Va.) Whig,* October 15, 1863.

138. Thomas J. Armstrong to his father, September 8, 1863, Thomas J. Armstrong Papers, Special Collections, William Madison Randall Library, UNCW.

139. Perry, *Civil War Courts-Martial of North Carolina Troops,* 167–68.

140. J. R. Hawley to Zebulon Vance, November 25, 1863, Zebulon Baird Vance Papers #3952, UNC.

141. "The Execution of Ten Men," *Fayetteville (N.C.) Observer,* September 17, 1863.

142. "The Execution of Ten Men." For examples of newspaper editors vilifying deserters as part of a broader campaign in support of military executions, see "From the North Carolina Soldiers," *Fayetteville (N.C.) Observer,* October 5, 1863; "Military Execution," *Richmond (Va.) Whig,* October 15, 1863; and "Deserters," *Richmond (Va.) Whig,* September 12, 1863.

143. McGuire, "Desertion during the Civil War."

144. The insights of this paragraph come from Brubaker and Cooper, "Beyond 'Identity.'"

145. John A. H. Foster to Mary Jane Foster, April 12, 1863, in Arden and Powell, *Letters from the Storm,* 101.

146. James Zimmerman to Adaline Zimmerman, August 23, 1863, Zimmerman Papers.

147. James Calvin Zimmerman to Adaline Zimmerman, October 2, 1863, Zimmerman Papers.

148. Drew Gilpin Faust explores how Civil War soldiers conceived of the right way to die. See "The Civil War Soldier and the Art of Dying." Discussions of the psychological effects of ritual executions on the army include Linderman, *Embattled Courage,* 58–59, 174–77; and Dean, *Shook over Hell,* 68–69.

149. Quoted from Berkey, "Rockingham Rebellion."

CHAPTER 6

1. Amos Judson, "Army Correspondence: How a Man Feels Going into Battle," *Erie (Pa.) Dispatch,* undated, Judson Papers, MU.

2. Thomas Taylor to his wife, July 17, 1863, in Alderson and Alderson, *Letters Home to Sarah,* 124–25.

3. Some of the best examples of this approach to soldier reactions to military affairs include Gallagher, "Lee's Army Has Not Lost Any of Its Prestige" and "Our Hearts Are Full of Hope"; Noe, *Reluctant Rebels,* esp. chapter 8; and Daniel, *Soldiering in the Army of Tennessee,* esp. chapter 9.

4. I take my methodological cues on the difference between what historical actors thought and how they thought from Darnton, *Great Cat Massacre,* 3–7; and Farge, *Allure of the Archives,* 28–29.

5. While Southerners were critical of Confederate leadership in the aftermath of defeats at Gettysburg and Vicksburg, there is little evidence of soldiers using ridicule to implicate all of society as being responsible for military defeats. See Gallagher, "Lee's Army Has Not Lost Any of Its Prestige."

6. My understanding of pragmatism comes entirely from Menand's *The Metaphysical Club*.

7. O'Brien, *Conjectures of Order*, 2:676–79.

8. Robert E. Lee to Jefferson Davis, August 8, 1863, in Dowdey, *Wartime Papers of R. E. Lee*, 589; William Gordon McCabe to Mary Evans Pegram Anderson, April 7, 1865, Pegram-Johnson-McIntosh Papers, VHS; and Adaline Zimmerman to James Calvin, August 16, 1863, Zimmerman Papers.

9. Rubin, *Shattered Nation*, 142–43.

10. This insight draws from Roth, *Ironist's Cage*, 148–61.

11. Any discussion of the South within a global context should begin with C. Vann Woodward's *Burden of Southern History*. Laura F. Edwards explores the range of problems in arguing for Southern differences, insisting that any attempt to assert Southern distinctiveness has separated the South from broader trends of United States and global history. She is correct that the political and ideological problems confronting antebellum Southerners, especially regarding slavery and emancipation, were dilemmas that faced other ruling classes across the globe. While I agree with her assessment that the South should not represent or explain problems that have long persisted in American society, she unfortunately sees any claim of Southern exceptionalism as an attempt to separate the South from a national and international context. Different ways of knowing or sensibilities do not necessarily segregate the South from the rest of the world. See Edwards, "Southern History as U.S. History."

12. The literature comparing the North and South is especially vast. Excellent discussions of the field can be found in Smith, *Debating Slavery*, 11–14, 16–30; Kolchin, *Sphinx on the American Land*, esp. chapter 1; and Barnes, Schoen, and Towers, "Introduction: Reimagining the Old South."

13. The historiographical tropes of new and old or traditional and modern—long used to describe the antebellum South—have finally been overturned by historians studying the South's middle class. The leading advocates of this revisionist school include Wells, *Origins of the Southern Middle Class*; Byrne, *Becoming Bourgeois*; and Green, *Military Education*. Their work has shattered the image of the Old South as antimodern, traditional, and insulated from the rest of the world, for they have made a convincing case that countless Southerners were committed to ideas of respectability, privacy, and hard work and were part of a transatlantic bourgeois Victorian culture.

14. Wyatt-Brown, *Southern Honor*, 49; Stowe, *Intimacy and Power in the Old South*, 252; Fox-Genovese, "The Anxiety of History"; Simpson, *Man of Letters*; and Greenberg, *Honor and Slavery*, 85.

15. An excellent summary of the historiographical discussion of Northern and Southern masculinity can be found in Wongsrichanalai, *Northern Character*, 4–7.

16. This insight is drawn from White, "The Value of Narrativity in the Representation of Reality," 3–5.

17. Faust's examples of wartime irony come entirely from the pens of Northern soldiers and writers. See Faust, *This Republic of Suffering*, 194.

18. On the press's savage treatment of Confederate generals and politicians, see Hess, *Braxton Bragg*; and Andrews, *The South Reports the Civil War*.

19. During the Civil War the Confederacy boasted only one noted humorist, Charles Henry Smith, who wrote under the pen name Bill Arp. His stories advanced the Southern cause at the expense of self-criticism, although he was not opposed to pointing out problems with the Confederate war effort, especially when it came to men who managed to stay out the army. See Arp (Charles Henry Smith), *Bill Arp's Peace Papers*, xii; and Parker, *Alias Bill Arp*.

20. My insights about political satire come from Malcolm Gladwell, "The Satire Paradox," *Revisionist History* (podcast), accessed July 1, 2017.

21. George Breck, "The 'Masterly Retreat,'" *Lebanon (Pa.) Courier*, December 24, 1862, bound vol. 215, FSNMP.

22. Daniel, *Soldiering in the Army of Tennessee*, esp. chapter 9.

23. An excellent overview of humor in the Civil War can be found in Grinspan's "'Sorrowfully Amusing.'"

24. John Mayfield's findings about the function of humor in the Confederacy are in keeping with my conclusions, though Mayfield sees much greater potential for irony in the antebellum South than I do. See his *Counterfeit Gentlemen*, xxvii–xxviii. A superb analysis of humor in Civil War armies can be found in Fahs, *Imagined Civil War*, esp. chapter 6. On humor in general and its relationship to ironic detachment, see Wickberg, *Senses of Humor*, 98.

25. James Bailey, "Life in the Seventeenth," *Danbury (Conn.) Times*, September 3, 1863.

26. On Civil War journalism, see Coopersmith, *Fighting Words*, xv–xvi. For examples of a similar journalistic style commonly found in Southern papers, see Styple, *Writing and Fighting from the Army of Northern Virginia* and *Writing and Fighting the Confederate War*.

27. Melvin Dwinell to "Dear Courier," *Rome (Ga.) Courier*, October 6, 1862.

28. Melvin Dwinell to "Dear Courier," *Rome (Ga.) Courier*, September 27, 1862.

29. James Bailey, "Life in the Seventeenth," *Danbury (Conn.) Times*, January 15, 1863.

30. Gallman, *Defining Duty in the Civil War*, 59–60.

31. Rable, *Fredericksburg! Fredericksburg!*, 347–49.

32. Confederate self-criticisms often avoided the language of shame while also ignoring the implications of battlefield defeat. See Robert T. Scott to Fanny Scott, July 29, 1863, Scott Family Papers, VHS; Hodijah Lincoln Meade to Charlotte Randolph (Meade) Lane, July 19, 1863, Meade Family Papers, VHS; James Keith to Isham Keith Sr., July 18, 1863, Keith Family of Woodburne, Fauquier Co., Va., Papers, VHS; and Thomas Claybrook Elder to Anna Fitzhugh (May) Elder, July 15, 1863, Thomas Claybrook Elder Papers, VHS.

33. Quoted from Burlingame, *Abraham Lincoln*, 2:331. For other examples of Lincoln employing humor after a military setback, see Burlingame, *Abraham Lincoln*, 2:446–47.

34. On Lincoln's admiration of Northern humorists, see Thomas, "Lincoln's Humor," 14. A fine comparison of Lincoln and Davis can be found in Dirck, *Lincoln and Davis*, 218.

35. Neely, Holzer, and Boritt, *Confederate Image*, 31–41.

36. Halloran, *Thomas Nast*, 88.

37. William H. Morse Diary, June 8, 1864, FSNMP.

38. Quoted from Robertson, *Soldiers Blue and Gray*, 143.

39. For this scholarly perspective, see McPherson, *What They Fought For*, 18, 21–24, 38–40.

40. Robert Pratt to Sid Pratt, December 15, 1862, Pratt Family Papers, FSNMP.

41. James Coye to his wife and children, January 17, 1863, James Coye Papers, in the private possession of David Coye.

42. Jacob Bechtel to Candis Hannawalt, February 10, 1863, Jacob Bechtel Papers, FSNMP. Similar reactions from Northern soldiers after Fredericksburg can be found in Rable, *Fredericksburg! Fredericksburg!*, 359.

43. "From the 10th Connecticut: Picket Trenches before Petersburg, Va.," *Hartford (Conn.) Daily Courant*, September 14, 1861.

44. Ambrose Henry Hayward to his father, November 14, 1863, Ambrose Henry Hayward Papers, Special Collections, Musselman Library, GC.

45. Fahs, *Imagined Civil War*, 94.

46. On the admission of Northern inferiority to Lee's army, see Adams, *Our Masters the Rebels*.

47. Charles Bowen to Kate Bowen, June 10, 1863, in Cassedy, *Dear Friends at Home*, 281–82.

48. On discourse of the sentimental Union soldier and the elevation of the individual soldier as the master of the enemy, see Fahs, *Imagined Civil War*, esp. chapter 3.

49. On the moderation of the Union military policy against the Confederacy, see Grimsley, *The Hard Hand of War*.

50. For an invaluable examination of the attitudes of Sherman's men toward hard war, see Glatthaar, *March to the Sea and Beyond*, 76–80. An innovative book on how Confederate women responded to the violation of their domestic space can be found in Frank, *The Civil War*. On the collected memories of Sherman's March, see Rubin, *Through the Heart of Dixie*.

51. Neff, *Honoring the Civil War Dead*, 64.

52. John W. Haley diary entry, December 13, 1862, in Silliker, *Rebel Yell and the Yankee Hurrah*, 60.

53. Roland E. Bowen to his mother, December 20, 1862, in Coco, *From Ball's Bluff to Gettysburg and Beyond*, 142.

54. In the 111th Ohio Infantry, for instance, a debating society assigned soldiers to defend the Confederacy's right to secede, and those particular men, regardless of their political beliefs, had to assume the Southern perspective on this position. Not everyone saw this as an exercise in intellectual freedom, and one soldier who was too outspoken in his defense of the Confederacy was court-martialed. See the court-martial of Lt. Mordecai P. Bean, 111th Ohio, Records of the Office of the Judge Advocate General (Army), Record Group 153, NA. For additional examples of Northern soldiers having to take the Southern perspective, see Andersen, *Civil War Diary of Allen Morgan Geer*, 142, 147, 149, 136.

55. John W. Haley diary entry, December 13, 1862, in Silliker, *Rebel Yell and the Yankee Hurrah*, 60.

56. William B. Bailey to his family, January 16, 1863, Coco Collection, USAHEC.

57. "A Letter from the Battlefield," *Charleston (S.C.) Daily Courier*, December 30, 1862.

58. Charles W. McArthur to James Vaughan, May 23, 1863, Charles W. McArthur Collection, KMNMP. Historians who have written about fraternization and have not recorded Confederates expressing empathy for the enemy include Power, *Lee's Miserables*, 127–28; Daniel, *Soldiering in the Army of Tennessee*, 157; and Ballard, *Vicksburg*, 273–74.

59. This insight is drawn from Enstad's "On Grief and Complicity."

60. Phillips, "A Brothers' War?," 71.

61. For a masterful account of the demonization and racialization of Union soldiers, see Rable, *Damn Yankees!*

62. Alexander S. Pendleton to Kate Corbin, June 28, 1863, William Nelson Pendleton Papers, UNC. Confederates were not oblivious to the outrages committed by their own troops, but they did not interpret their own misdeeds as a consequence of racial makeup. See William Pitt Chambers Diary, April 16, 1864, in Baumgartner, *Blood and Sacrifice*, 131–32.

63. Brown, "North Carolinian Ambivalence," 13–17.

64. William Wagner to Nancy Wagner, July 16, 1863, in Hatley and Huffman, *Letters of William F. Wagner*, 55. All subsequent Wagner correspondence is from this source.

65. William Wagner to Nancy Wagner, July 18, 1863, 57.

66. William Wagner to Nancy Wagner, August 2, 1863, 62.

67. William Wagner to Nancy Wagner, August 15, 1863, 65.

68. William Wagner to Nancy Wagner, August 15, 1863.

69. Alexander McNeill to Almirah Haseltine "Tinie" Simmons, July 17 and August 21, 1863, in Wyckoff, *Civil War Letters of Alexander McNeill*, 318–19, 337.

70. Alexander McNeill to "Tinie" Simmons, December 7, 1864, in Wyckoff, *Civil War Letters of Alexander McNeill*, 530.

71. Rable, *Damn Yankees!*, 43.

72. Although some historians have criticized Chandra Manning for exaggerating the degree to which Union soldiers embraced the cause of black freedom, her research conclusively demonstrates that Northern soldiers were mentally agile in coming to grips with the revolutionary turn to emancipation. See *What This Cruel War Was Over*, 218–19. For an interpretation that stresses Northern soldiers' commitment to the Union rather than emancipation, see Gallagher, *Union War*.

73. On the African American military experience, see Berlin, Reidy, and Rowland, *Freedom*; and Luke and Smith, *Soldiering for Freedom*.

74. Emberton, *Beyond Redemption*, 131.

75. Charles Bowen to his mother, June 25, 1864, in Cassedy, *Dear Friends at Home*, 509.

76. Charles W. Wills to his family, June 26, 1863, in Kellogg, *Army Life of an Illinois Soldier*, 183–84; and Samito, *Becoming American under Fire*, 5.

77. Alice Fahs offers a compelling analysis of Northern popular culture and the representation of the black military experience. See Fahs, *Imagined Civil War*, esp. chapter 5.

78. Alexander, *Fighting for the Confederacy*, 462.

79. Thomas A. Smith to his sister, August 4, 1864, Thomas Smith Letters, 1862–1865, UVA.

80. This observation comes from the superb work of Kevin M. Levin. See Levin's *Remembering the Battle of the Crater*.

81. McCurry, *Confederate Reckoning*, 31. Secondary scholarship confirms that Confederates folded into themselves when confronting the incongruities of their society, lacking the mechanism or sensibility that would have afforded them distance to interrogate their experience from a critical angle. See also Faust, *Creation of Confederate Nationalism*, 83–84; and Rable, *Confederate Republic*, 277, 283.

82. For a discussion of Confederate views on black troops paralleling Alexander's, see Glatthaar, *General Lee's Army*, 305–6.

83. Hale, *Making Whiteness*, 67–70.

84. For a penetrating analysis of the racial understandings of nonslaveholders, see Genovese, "Yeomen Farmers in a Slaveholders' Democracy."

85. For a superb examination of the debates surrounding the enlistment of slaves as Confederate soldiers, see Levine, *Confederate Emancipation*, 115.

86. Quoted from Levine, *Confederate Emancipation*, 114, 115.

87. Phillips's study group in *Diehard Rebels* reinforces my claims of an absolutist perspective among slaveholding Confederates. Chapters 3 and 4 in his immensely important book are especially relevant to my argument.

88. The existence of Confederate nationalism is no longer in dispute among scholars, thanks to the work of Gary Gallagher, Anne Sarah Rubin, and Michael T. Bernath. What remains unstudied is how Southern soldiers, when facing a crumbling material reality and a desperate military and political situation, could imagine alternatives that defied a commonsense reading of reality. The concept of sensibilities helps us to understand distinct modes of perceiving and the very ways that people processed information. Bertram Wyatt-Brown utilized a sensibility approach in his "Death of a Nation," in *Shaping of Southern Culture*, 230–54. On the durability of Confederate nationalism, see Gallagher, *Confederate War*; Rubin, *Shattered Nation*; and Bernath, *Confederate Minds*.

89. Samuel Walkup Diary, March 6, 1865, Samuel Walkup Papers, UNC.

90. Gallagher's *Becoming Confederates* and his essays in *Lee: His Army in Confederate History* demonstrate the centrality of Lee to the hopes of all Confederate people.

91. William Biggs to his sister, December 14, 1864, Biggs Family Papers, DU.

92. William Biggs to his sister, December 14, 1864.

93. William Biggs to his sister, December 14, 1864, and January 25, 1865, Biggs Family Papers, DU.

94. Gallagher, *Confederate War*, esp. chapters 1 and 2.

95. For an elaboration of the political moderation of Union soldiers, see Hess, *Liberty, Virtue, and Progress*; and Gallagher, *Union War*.

96. For a useful argument about partisan divisions in the Union army, see White, *Emancipation in the Union Army*.

97. Guy Taylor to Sarah Taylor, April 23, 1865, in Alderson and Alderson, *Letters Home to Sarah*, 254.


CHAPTER 7

1. The best treatment of the Appomattox surrender proceedings can be found in Varon, *Appomattox*.

2. This insight comes from Trachtenberg, *Reading American Photographs*, 75.

3. The transition into veteranhood has been explored in rich and innovative ways by scholars, some of whom include Marten, *Sing Not War*; Gannon, *The Won Cause*; Brian Craig Miller, *Empty Sleeves*; Jordan, *Marching Home*; McClurken, *Take Care of the Living*; Silkenat, *Moments of Despair*, esp. chapters 2 and 5; McConnell, *Glorious Contentment*; and Harris, *Across the Bloody Chasm*.

4. On Confederates who were in Appomattox denial, see Phillips, *Diehard Rebels*, chapter 5.

5. Schivelbusch, *Culture of Defeat*, 38.

6. Waugh, "'I Only Knew What Was in My Mind.'"

7. John Smith to his mother, May 28, 1865, John Smith Papers, Pennsylvania Historical Society, hereafter cited as Smith Papers.

8. John Smith to his mother, April 28, 1865, Smith Papers.

9. William Berrier to his wife, April 10, 1865, William Berrier Papers, FSNMP.

10. Hezekiah M. McCorkle Diary, May 1, 1865, Civil War Miscellany—Personal Papers, GDAH; and Soloman Norman Brantley Questionnaire, Seventh Tennessee Cavalry, Tennessee Civil War Veterans' Questionnaires, Tennessee State Library and Archives, Nashville, Tenn.

11. John Crawford Anderson to David Anderson, April 11, 1865, in Moore, *Upcountry South Carolina Goes to War*, 163.

12. George K. Griggs Diary, April 10, 1865, George K. Griggs Papers, MOC; Hezekiah M. McCorkle Diary, April 30, 1865, GDAH; and Edward Valentine Jones Diary, April 9, 1865, ANHP.

13. John Smith to his mother, April 11, 1865, Smith Papers. For a similar Union account of the famous apple tree, see Jacob J. Zorn Diary, April 11, 1865, in Croner, *A Sergeant's Story*, 165.

14. Jacob J. Zorn Diary, April 10, 1865, in Croner, *A Sergeant's Story*, 165.

15. N. H. Panghorn to his parents, April 19, 1865, J. H. Panghorn Papers, ANHP.

16. John Smith to his mother, April 18, 1865, Smith Papers.

17. John Smith to his mother, April 18, 1865.

18. David Pierson to William H. Pierson, April 27, 1865, in Cutrer and Parrish, *Brothers in Gray*, 256, 257.

19. David Pierson to William H. Pierson, May 9, 1865, in Cutrer and Parrish, *Brothers in Gray*, 259.

20. Quoted from Wyatt-Brown, *Shaping of Southern Culture*, 234.

21. Andrews, *Footprints of a Regiment*, 180.

22. For a brilliant analysis on Southern masculinity, see Berry, *All That Makes a Man*, 11.

23. Samuel T. Foster Diary, April 22, 1865, in Brown, *One of Cleburne's Command*, 166.

24. William R. Aylett to Alice Roane Aylett, July 20, 1863, Aylett Family Papers, VHS.

25. Studies that explore the minds of defeated Confederates include Genovese, *A Consuming Fire*; Wyatt-Brown, *A Warring Nation*, chapters 4 and 5; Gallagher, *Confederate War*, esp. chapter. 4; Carmichael, *The Last Generation*, chapter 7; and Phillips, *Diehard Rebels*, esp. chapter 5.

26. John H. Chamberlayne to Edward P. Chamberlayne and Lucy Parke Chamberlayne, April 12, 1865, in Chamberlayne, *Ham Chamberlayne*, 322. All subsequent Chamberlayne correspondence is from this source.

27. See the introduction of Chamberlayne, *Ham Chamberlayne*.

28. On the role of ambition and the desire for the approval of women among Confederate soldiers, see Berry's *All That Makes a Man*.

29. Stott, "'What Exile from Himself Can Flee?'"

30. John H. Chamberlayne to George W. Bagby, June 20, 1865, 329, 330.

31. John H. Chamberlayne to Sally Grattan, August 1, 1865, 329, 333.

32. Schivelbusch, *Culture of Defeat*, 2.

33. John H. Chamberlayne to Sally Grattan, August 1, 1865, 333.

34. Rosen, *Terror in the Heart of Freedom*, 188–96.

35. John H. Chamberlayne to Sally Grattan, August 1, 1865, 329, 334.

36. John H. Chamberlayne to Sally Grattan, August 1, 1865.

37. Hezekiah M. McCorkle Diary, April 21, 1865, GDAH.

38. Varon, *Appomattox*, 70.

39. Henry A. Chambers Diary, April 9, 1865, in Pearce, *Diary of Captain Henry A. Chambers*, 262.

40. William Gordon McCabe to Mary Evans Pegram Anderson, April 7, 1865, in Early Family Papers, 1764–1956, VHS; and William Daniel Dixon Diary, April 17, 1865, in Durham, *Blues in Gray*, 276–77.

41. My insights on General Orders No. 9 parallel the conclusions of Varon, *Appomattox*, chapter 3.

42. Email correspondence with Appomattox Court House National Historical Park chief historian, Patrick Schroeder, April 25, 2016.

43. Andrews, *Footprints of a Regiment*, 179.

44. The anecdotes from Perry and Roller are taken directly from Varon, *Appomattox*, 104–5.

45. This insight draws from Schivelbusch, *Culture of Defeat*, 63.

46. William H. Ellis Diary, April 12, 1865, William H. Ellis Papers, Louisiana and Lower Mississippi Valley Collections, Special Collections, Hill Memorial Library, LSU.

47. General Orders No. 22, May 2, 1865, *OR* 47 (pt. 1): 1061. The best account of Johnson's surrender can be found in Bradley, *This Astounding Close*.

48. *OR* 49 (pt. 2): 1289–90.

49. General Orders No. 22, May 2, 1865, *OR* 47 (pt. 1): 1061.

50. *OR* 49 (pt. 2): 1289–90.

51. On the generosity of Grant's terms and the relatively peaceful demobilization of Confederate armies in comparison to other civil wars, see Janney, *Remembering the Civil War*, esp. chapter 2; and Varon, *Appomattox*, esp. chapter 2.

52. Quoted from Wyatt-Brown, *Shaping of Southern Culture*, 231.

53. On the attitudes of Sherman's men toward Southern whites, see Glatthaar, *March to the Sea and Beyond*, esp. chapter 4.

54. Joshua L. Chamberlain to Sarah B. Chamberlain, April 13, 1865, Joshua Lawrence Chamberlain Collection, George J. Mitchell Department of Special Collections and Archives, BC.

55. Marvel, *Lee's Last Retreat*.

56. N. H. Panghorn to his parents, April 19, 1865, J. H. Panghorn Papers, ANHP.

57. For an example of a battle flag made of silk bridal clothes, see the online American Civil War Museum, object record for catalog no. 0985.13.01747, http://moconfederacy .pastperfectonline.com/webobject/84DE6B99-90DB-4FA1-BDE7-971812234980, accessed January 19, 2018. On the symbolism of Confederate flags and how Confederate banners became sacred emblems, see Bonner, *Colors and Blood*, esp. chapters 4 and 5.

58. Joshua L. Chamberlain to Sarah B. Chamberlain, April 13, 1865, Chamberlain Collection, BC.

59. On the methodology of material culture, see Cashin, "Trophies of War"; and Harrison, "Mementos and the Souls of Missing Soldiers."

60. John Smith to his mother, April 15, 1865, Smith Papers.

61. John Smith to his mother, April 28, 1865, Smith Papers.

62. John Smith to his mother, April 15, 1865, Smith Papers.

63. John Smith to his mother, April 18, 1865, Smith Papers.

64. Joseph Whitehorne Diary, April 12, 1865, UNC, hereafter cited as Whitehorne Diary.

65. N. H. Panghorn to his parents, April 19, 1865, J. H. Panghorn Papers, ANHP.

66. Whitehorne Diary, April 12, 1865.

67. McCarthy, *Detailed Minutiae of Soldier Life*, 159–60, 174.

68. R. M. Crumpler Diary, April 12, 1865, Papers of Miss Georgia Hicks, NCSA.

69. Whitehorne Diary, April 10, 1865.

70. McCarthy, *Detailed Minutiae of Soldier Life*, 159–60, 174.

71. Whitehorne Diary, April 10, 1865.

72. John Kennedy Coleman Diary, April 20, 1865, John Kennedy Coleman (1847–1907) Collection, South Caroliniana Library, University of South Carolina, Columbia.

73. Hsieh, "Go to Your Gawd Like a Soldier," 559–66.

74. Fulton, *Family Record and War Reminiscences*, 144–45.

75. McCarthy, *Detailed Minutiae of Soldier Life*, 193.

76. Lepper and Lepper, Cyrus Marion Roberts Diary, May 16, 1864, http://www.78ohio .org/Diaries/Capt%20Cyrus%20Marion%20Roberts%20Diary.htm#_Volume_3:___8%20 May%20to%2020%20May%201865.

77. Merrill, *The Seventieth Indiana*, 274–75.

78. Cruikshank Letters, May 15, 1865, http://www.salem-ny.com/1865letters.html.

79. Cruikshank Letters, May 15, 1865.

80. Schroyer App Diary, May 15, 1865, https://storiesretoldvideo.wordpress.com/2013 /06/15/chapter-70-may-11-17-1865-stories-from-along-the-homeward-march-the-app -brothers-in-the-civil-war/, hereafter cited as App Diary.

81. On the practical and cultural process of burying the Civil War dead, see Faust, *This Republic of Suffering*; and Morhous, *Reminiscences of the 123d*, 186–87.

82. App Diary, May 15, 1865. For a similar view, see Bauer, *Soldiering*, 244–45; and Underwood, *Thirty-Third Mass. Infantry*, 296–97.

83. The stump of the twenty-two-inch oak tree is now on display at the Smithsonian National Museum of American History in Washington, D.C.

84. John Smith to his mother, May 8, 1865, Smith Papers.

85. John Smith to his mother, May 8, 1865.

86. John Smith to his mother, June 13, 1865, Smith Papers.

87. John Smith to his mother, June 2, 1865, Smith Papers.

88. On the connections between the demobilization of Union armies and the antimilitaristic nature of Union soldiers, see Gallagher, *Union War*, 124–28.

89. William Berrier to his wife, May 29, 1865, William Berrier Papers, FSNMP.

90. John Smith to his mother, July 2, 1865, Smith Papers.

91. For an incisive analysis of soldier material culture, see Nelson, *Ruin Nation*, 228–39.

92. John Smith to his mother, June 2, 1865, Smith Papers.

93. *Sixth Corps*, May 1, 1865.

1. Insights in this paragraph come from David Burton, introduction to Howe, *Touched with Fire*, xi; and Menand, *The Metaphysical Club*, esp. chapters 2 and 3.

2. Oliver Wendell Holmes Jr. to his mother, June 7, 1864, in Howe, *Touched with Fire*, 142–43. All subsequent Holmes letters and diary entries are from this source.

3. Oliver Wendell Holmes Jr., diary entries for May 8 and 13, 1864, and Holmes to his parents, May 16, 1864, 109, 117, 122, 123.

4. Oliver Wendell Holmes Jr. to his mother, December 12, 1862, 74.

5. Oliver Wendell Holmes Jr. to his father, December 20, 1862, 79, 80.

6. Burton, introduction to Howe, *Touched with Fire*, xi.

7. Reuben Allen Pierson to William H. Pierson, May 8, 1863, in Cutrer and Parrish, *Brothers in Gray*, 190.

8. Ambrose H. Hayward to his father, May 9, 1863, in Orr, *Last to Leave the Field*, 143.

9. Oliver Wendell Holmes Jr. to his parents, May 30, 1864, 135.

10. Oliver Wendell Holmes Jr. to his parents, May 16, 1864, 122.

11. Oliver Wendell Holmes Jr. to his parents, June 24, 1864, 149–50.

12. Burton, introduction to Howe, *Touched with Fire*, xi.

13. While Jackson Lears does not differentiate between Northern and Southern soldiers and how they interacted with a culture of chance, his observations suggest the ways that military service, especially the experience of combat, challenged a providential reading of the world. Lears wisely points out that those at home, who were insulated from the front, could insist that Providence governed all. His conclusion that "the Civil War became the centerpiece of secularized providential thought" is a compelling and important point, and one that I find among Union and Confederate soldiers while they were at the front. See Lears, *Something for Nothing*, 143–45; and Charles Bowen to his grandmother, April 23, 1864, in Cassedy, *Dear Friends at Home*, 449.

14. My argument is friendly with Anne Rose's findings in *Victorian America and the Civil War*, esp. chapter 6.

15. For the best summation of the historiographical debate on the intellectual consequences of the Civil War, see Bernath, "Literature," [2]:998–99; Butler, "Reconstructions in Intellectual and Cultural Life"; and Foote and Wongsrichanalai, *So Conceived and So Dedicated*.

16. My observations draw from Currarino, "Toward a History of Cultural Economy," 567–68.

17. Charles Bowen to his family, December 27, 1863, Charles Bowen Papers, GNMP.

18. This insight comes from Luskey and Phillips, "Muster."

# bibliography

PRIMARY SOURCES

*Manuscript Collections*

**Appomattox Court House National Historical Park, Appomattox Court House, Va.**
Valentine Jones Folder
J. H. Panghorn Papers

**Bowdoin College, Brunswick, Maine**
Joshua Lawrence Chamberlain Collection

**David Coye Private Collection**
James Coye Papers

**Duke University, Durham, N.C.**
Biggs Family Papers
James Calvin Zimmerman Papers

**Fredericksburg and Spotsylvania National Military Park, Fredericksburg, Va.**
Jacob Bechtel Papers
William H. Berrier Papers
James Coye Papers
William H. Morse Diary
Pratt Family Papers
John Wesley Stewart Letter
*Lebanon (Pa.) Courier*

**Georgia Department of Archives and History, Morrow**
William W. Hewell Letters
Hezekiah M. McCorkle Diary, Civil War Miscellany—Personal Papers
Wright Vinson Civil War Letters

**Georgia Historical Society, Savannah**
Virginia T. Dunklin Papers
**Gettysburg College, Gettysburg, Pa.**
Ambrose Henry Hayward Papers
**Indiana Historical Society, Indianapolis**
David Beem Papers
**John Nau Collection, Houston, Tex.**
Gregory Nash Letter
Jonathan Sproul Papers
**Kennesaw Mountain National Military Park, Kennesaw, Ga.**
Charles W. McArthur Collection
**Louisiana State University, Baton Rouge**
William H. Ellis Papers
**Mercyhurst University, Erie, Pa.**
Judson Papers
**Museum of the Confederacy, Richmond, Va.**
George K. Griggs Papers
George Steuart Papers
Richard Brooke Gwathmey Sword and Belt, no. 00985.13.01085.
**National Archives, Washington, D.C.**
Seventh Census of the United States, 1850, Schedule 1,
Free Inhabitants, Houston County, Ga.
Eighth Census of the United States, 1860, Schedule 1, Free
Inhabitants, New Hanover County, N.C.
Twentieth Indiana Regimental Letter and Order Book, Records
of the Adjutant Generals Office, 1780s–1917: Records of
Volunteer Union Organizations, Record Group 94
Fifty-Fourth Virginia Infantry Regiment Order Book, War Department
Collection of Confederate Records, Record Group 109
Court-martial of Lt. Mordecai P. Bean, 111th Ohio, Records of the Office
of the Judge Advocate General (Army), Record Group 153
Court-martial of John Folaney (alias Geacinto Lerchize), 118th
Pennsylvania Infantry, File No. MM 687, Records of the Office
of the Judge Advocate General (Army), Record Group 153
Court-martial of Daniel Geary, Co. E. Seventy-Second New York Infantry, Records
of the Office of the Judge Advocate General (Army), Record Group, 153
Court-martial of George Gillis, Seventy-Seventh New York, Records of the
Office of the Judge Advocate General (Army), Record Group 153
Court-martial of Ransom S. Gordon, Co. E, Seventy-Second
New York Infantry, File No. 1481, Records of the Office of the
Judge Advocate General (Army), Record Group 153
Court-martial of Emile Lai (alias E. Duffie) Recruit, 118th
Pennsylvania Infantry, File No. MM 687, Records of the Office
of the Judge Advocate General (Army), Record Group 153
Court-martial of John Layman, Letters Received by the

Confederate Secretary of War (M437), War Department
    Collection of Confederate Records, Record Group 109
Court-martial of William Nixon, Fourteenth Indiana Infantry, Records of
    the Office of the Judge Advocate General (Army), Record Group 153
Court-martial of John Rainese (alias Gion Rionese), 118th
    Pennsylvania Infantry, File No. MM 687, Records of the Office
    of the Judge Advocate General (Army), Record Group 153
Court-martial of Thomas B. Rodgers, 140th Pennsylvania Infantry, Records
    of the Office of the Judge Advocate General (Army), Record Group 153
Court-martial of John D. Starbird, Nineteenth Massachusetts Infantry, File No. 1943,
    Records of the Office of the Judge Advocate General (Army), Record Group 153
Court-martial of Sergeant William Walker, 3rd South Carolina
    Infantry (formed part of the Twenty-First United States Colored
    Infantry Regiment, January–February 1864), Records of the Office
    of the Judge Advocate General (Army), Record Group 153
Court-martial of Charles Walter (alias C. Zene) Recruit, 118th
    Pennsylvania Infantry, File No. MM 687, Records of the Office
    of the Judge Advocate General (Army), Record Group 153
Court-martial of William Wolf, Battery G, First Pa. Artillery, Records of the
    Office of the Judge Advocate General (Army), Record Group 153
Lafayette Guild Letterbook
Orders and Circulars Issued by the Army of Northern Virginia, War
    Department Collection of Confederate Records, Record Group 109
Robert Rodes Brigade Order Book, War Department Collection
    of Confederate Records, Record Group 109
John D. Starbird, Co. K, Nineteenth Massachusetts Infantry,
    Civil War Compiled Service Records, Records of the Adjutant
    General's Office, 1780s–1917, Record Group 94
Wright Vinson, Fifty-Seventh Georgia Infantry Regiment, Civil
    War Compiled Service Records, War Department Collection
    of Confederate Records, 1825–1927, Record Group 109
**New-York Historical Society, New York, N.Y.**
    Christian Marion Epperly Papers, Gilder Lehrman Collection
**North Carolina State Archives, Raleigh**
    Futch Brothers Papers
    Papers of Miss Georgia Hicks, Historian, Daughters of the Confederacy
**Pennsylvania Historical Society, Philadelphia**
    John Smith Papers
**Shapell Manuscript Foundation, Herzliya, Israel**
    Henry Kline Letter
**Southern Historical Collection, Wilson Library,**
    **University of North Carolina at Chapel Hill**
    L. C. Glenn Papers
    William Nelson Pendleton Papers
    Zebulon Baird Vance Papers

Richard Woolfolk Waldrop Papers
Samuel Walkup Papers
J. E. Whitehorne Diary
**Tennessee State Library and Archives, Nashville**
Tennessee Civil War Veterans' Questionnaires
**United States Army Heritage and Education Center, Carlisle, Pa.**
William Bailey Letter, Coco Collection
Harrisburg Civil War Round Table Collection
**University of Michigan, Ann Arbor**
William Ellis Jones Diary
**University of North Carolina at Wilmington**
Thomas J. Armstrong Papers
**University of South Carolina, Columbia**
John Kennedy Coleman Collection
**University of Virginia, Charlottesville**
Andrew Dawson Papers
Thomas Smith Letters
Micajah Woods Papers
**Virginia Historical Society, Richmond**
Aylett Family Papers
Early Family Papers, 1764–1956
Thomas Claybrook Elder Papers
Keith Family of Woodburn, Fauquier Co., Va. Papers
Meade Family Papers
Pegram-Johnson-McIntosh Papers
Scott Family Papers
**Washington and Lee University, Lexington, Va.**
Allen Family Papers, Rockbridge Historical Society Collection
**West Virginia University, Morgantown**
Henry J. Mugler Diary

## Books

Acken, J. Gregory, ed. *Inside the Army of the Potomac: The Civil War Experience of Captain Francis Adams Donaldson*. Mechanicsburg, Pa.: Stackpole Books, 1998.

Agassiz, George R., ed. *Meade's Headquarters, 1863–1865: Letters of Colonel Theodore Lyman, from the Wilderness to Appomattox*. Boston: Atlantic Monthly Press, 1922.

Alderson, Kevin, and Patsy Alderson, eds. *Letters Home to Sarah: The Civil War Letters of Guy C. Taylor, 36th Wisconsin Volunteers*. Madison: University of Wisconsin Press, 2012.

Aldridge, Katherine M., ed. *No Freedom Shrieker: The Civil War Letters of Union Soldier Charles Biddlecom*. Ithaca, N.Y.: Paramount Market, 2012.

Alexander, Edward Porter. *Fighting for the Confederacy: The Personal Recollections of General Edward Porter Alexander*. Edited by Gary W. Gallagher. Chapel Hill: University of North Carolina Press, 1989.

Andersen, Mary Ann, ed. *The Civil War Diary of Allen Morgan Geer*. Tappan, N.Y.: R. C. Appleman, 1977.

Andrews, W. H. *Footprints of a Regiment: A Recollection of the 1st Georgia Regulars, 1861–1865*. Edited by Richard M. McMurry. Atlanta: Longstreet, 1992.

Arden, Linda Foster, and Walter L. Powell, eds. *Letters from the Storm: The Intimate Civil War Letters of Lt. J. A. H. Foster, 155th Pennsylvania Volunteers*. Chicora, Pa.: Mechling Bookbindery, 2010.

Arp, Bill. *Bill Arp's Peace Papers: Columns on War and Reconstruction, 1861–1873*. Columbia: University of South Carolina Press, 2009.

Bartholow, Roberts. *A Manual of Instructions for Enlisting and Discharging Soldiers: With Special Reference to the Medical Examination of Recruits, and the Detection of Disqualifying and Feigned Diseases*. Philadelphia: J. B. Lippincott & Co., 1864.

———. "The Various Influences Affecting the Physical Endurance, the Power of Resisting Disease Etc., of the Men Composing the Volunteer Armies of the United States." In *Sanitary Memoirs of the War of the Rebellion: Collected and Published by the United States Sanitary Commission: Contributions Relating to the Causation and Prevention of Disease, and to Camp Diseases; Together with a Report of the Diseases, Etc., among the Prisoners at Andersonville, Ga.*, edited by Austin Flint, 3–41. New York: Hurd and Houghton, 1867.

Bauer, Jack, ed. *Soldiering: Civil War Diary of Rice C. Bull, 123rd New York Volunteer Infantry*. San Rafael, Calif.: Presidio, 1977.

Baumgartner, Richard A., ed. *Blood and Sacrifice: The Civil War Journal of a Confederate Soldier*. Huntington, W.Va.: Blue Acorn, 1994.

Berlin, Ira, Joseph P. Reidy, and Leslie S. Rowland, eds. *Freedom: A Documentary History of Emancipation, 1861–1865. Series II, The Black Military Experience*. New York: Cambridge University Press, 1982.

Blomquist, Ann K., and Robert A. Taylor, eds. *This Cruel War: The Civil War Letters of Grant and Malinda Taylor*. Macon, Ga.: Mercer University Press, 2000.

Brown, Norman D., ed. *One of Cleburne's Command: The Civil Reminiscences and Diary of Capt. Samuel T. Foster, Granbury's Texas Brigade, C.S.A.* Austin: University of Texas Press, 1980.

Carmichael, Peter S. "The Court-martial Trial of Sergeant William Walker." In *Slavery in North America: From the Colonial Period to Emancipation*, edited by Mark M. Smith, 237–64. London: Pickering & Chatto, 2009.

Cassedy, Edward K., ed. *Dear Friends at Home: The Civil War Letters and Diaries of Sergeant Charles T. Bowen, Twelfth United States Infantry, 1861–1864 (The Army of the Potomac)*. Baltimore: Butternut & Blue, 2001.

Chamberlayne, C. G., ed. *Ham Chamberlayne—Virginian: Letters and Papers of an Artillery Officer in the War for Southern Independence, 1861–1865*. Richmond: Dietz, 1932.

Chesson, Michael B., ed. *The Journal of a Civil War Surgeon, J. Franklin Dyer*. Lincoln: University of Nebraska Press, 2003.

Chisolm, J. Julian. *A Manual of Military Surgery, for the Use of Surgeons in the Confederate States Army; with Explanation Plates of All Useful Operations*. Columbia, S.C.: Evans and Cogswell, 1864.

Cockrell, Monroe F., ed. *Gunner with Stonewall: Reminiscences of William Thomas Poague*. 1957; reprint, Wilmington, N.C.: Broadfoot, 1987.

Coco, Gregory A., ed. *From Ball's Bluff to Gettysburg and Beyond: The Civil War Letters of Private Roland E. Bowen, 15th Massachusetts Infantry, 1861–1864*. Gettysburg, Pa.: Thomas, 1994.

Corbin, Richard Washington. *Letters of a Confederate Officer to His Family in Europe during the Last Year of the War of Secession*. 1902: reprint, Baltimore: Butternut & Blue, 1993.

Craighill, William P. *The 1862 Army Officer's Pocket Companion: A Manual for Staff Officers in the Field*. New York: D. Van Nostrand, 1862.

Croner, Barbara M., ed. *A Sergeant's Story: Civil War Diary of Jacob J. Zorn*. Apollo, Pa.: Closson, 1999.

Cutrer, Thomas W., and T. Michael Parrish, eds. *Brothers in Gray: The Civil War Letters of the Pierson Family*. Baton Rouge: Louisiana State University Press, 1997.

Dowdey, Clifford, ed. *The Wartime Papers of R. E. Lee*. New York: Bramhall House, 1961.

Durham, Roger S., ed. *Blues in Gray: The Civil War Journal of William Daniel Dixon Durham and the Republican Blues Daybook*. Knoxville: University of Tennessee Press, 2001.

Fulton, William Frierson, II. *Family Record and War Reminiscences*. N.p.: William Frierson Fulton III, 1919.

Gibbon, John. *Personal Recollections of the Civil War*. Dayton: Morningside Bookstore, 1978.

Hackemer, Kurt H., ed. *To Rescue My Native Land: The Civil War Letters of William T. Shepherd, First Illinois Light Artillery*. Knoxville: University of Tennessee Press, 2005.

Hallock, Judith Lee, ed. *The Civil War Letters of Joshua K. Callaway*. Athens: University of Georgia Press, 1997.

Hassler, William W., ed. *The General to His Lady: The Civil War Letters of William Dorsey Pender to Fanny Pender*. Chapel Hill: University of North Carolina Press, 2011.

Hatley, Joe M., and Linda B. Huffman, eds. *Letters of William F. Wagner, Confederate Soldier*. Wendell, N.C.: Broadfoot's Bookmark, 1983.

Hinman, Wilbur F. *Corporal Si Klegg and His "Pard."* 1877; reprint, Lincoln: University of Nebraska Press, 2009.

Holcomb, Julie, ed. *Southern Sons, Northern Soldiers: The Civil War Letters of the Remley Brothers, 22nd Iowa Infantry*. DeKalb: Northern Illinois University Press, 2003.

Howe, Mark De Wolfe, ed. *Touched with Fire: Civil War Letters and Diary of Oliver Wendell Holmes, Jr.* New York: Fordham University Press, 2000.

Hunter, Edna J., ed. *One Flag, One Country, and Thirteen Greenbacks a Month: Letters from a Civil War Private and His Colonel*. San Diego: Hunter, 1980.

Jackson, Mary Virginia, ed. *Kiss Sweet Little Lillah for Me: Civil War Letters of William Thomas Jackson, Company A, Eighth Alabama Infantry Regiment*. Birmingham: Ebsco Media, 2000.

Joiner, Gary D., Marilyn S. Joiner, and Clifton D. Cardin, eds. *No Pardons to Ask, nor Apologies to Make: The Journal of William Henry King Grays 28th Louisiana Infantry Regiment*. Knoxville: University of Tennessee Press, 2006.

Jordan, Weymouth T., Jr., ed. *North Carolina Troops, 1861–1865: A Roster*. 18 vols. Raleigh: North Carolina Division of Archives and History, 1988.

Judson, Amos. *History of the Eighty-Third Regiment Pennsylvania Volunteers*. Erie, Pa.: B. F. H. Lynn, Publisher, 1866.

Kautz, August V. *Customs of Service for Non-Commissioned Officers and Soldiers*. 1865; reprint, Mechanicsburg, Pa.: Stackpole Books, 2001.

Keever, Elsie, ed. *Keever Civil War Letters*. N.p.: E. H. Keever, 1989.

Kellogg, Mary, ed. *Army Life of an Illinois Soldier: Including a Day-by-Day Record of Sherman's March to the Sea: Letters and Diary of Charles W. Wills*. Carbondale: Southern Illinois University Press, 1996.

Lassen, Coralou Peel, ed. *Dear Sarah: Letters Home from a Soldier of the Iron Brigade*.
Bloomington: Indiana University Press, 1999.

McCarthy, Carlton. *Detailed Minutiae of Soldier Life in the Army of Northern Virginia, 1861–1865*. Richmond: Carlton McCarthy and Company, 1882.

McClenthen, Charles S. *Narrative of the Fall & Winter Campaign, by a Private Soldier of the 2nd Div. 1st Army Corps, Containing a Detailed Description of the "Battle of Fredericksburg, at the Portion of the Line Where the 2nd Div. Were Engaged, with Accurate Statements of the Loss in Killed, Wounded and Missing, in Each Regiment."* Syracuse: Masters & Lee, 1863.

Messent, Peter, and Steve Courtney, eds. *The Civil War Letters of Joseph Hopkins Twichell: A Chaplain's Story*. Athens: University of Georgia Press, 2006.

Moore, Tom Craig, ed. *Upcountry South Carolina Goes to War: Letters of the Anderson, Brockman, and Moore Families, 1853–1865*. Columbia: University of South Carolina Press, 2009.

Morhous, Henry C. *Reminiscences of the 123d Regiment, N.Y.S.V., Giving a Complete History of Its Three Years Service in the War*. Greenwich, N.Y.: People's Journal, 1879.

Orr, Timothy J., ed. *Last to Leave the Field: The Life and Letters of First Sergeant Ambrose Henry Hayward, 28th Pennsylvania Infantry*. Knoxville: University of Tennessee Press, 2010.

Palm, Ronn, Richard Sauers, and Patrick A. Schroeder, eds. *The Bloody 85th: The Letters of Milton McJunkin, a Western Pennsylvania Soldier in the Civil War*. Daleville, Va.: Schroeder, 2000.

Parker, David, ed. *Alias Bill Arp: Charles Henry Smith and the South's "Goodly Heritage."* Athens: University of Georgia Press, 1991.

Pearce, T. H., ed. *Diary of Captain Henry A. Chambers*. Wendell, N.C.: Broadfoot's Bookmark, 1983.

Rauscher, Frank J. *Music on the March, 1862–65, with the Army of the Potomac. 114th regt. P.V., Collis Zouaves*. Philadelphia: Press of Wm. F. Fell & Co., 1892.

Sears, Stephen W., ed. *For Country, Cause, and Leader: The Civil War Journal of Charles B. Haydon*. Boston: Houghton Mifflin Harcourt, 1993.

Silliker, Ruth L., ed. *The Rebel Yell and the Yankee Hurrah: The Civil War Journal of a Maine Volunteer*. Camden, Maine: Down East Books, 1985.

Simpson, Brooks D., and Jean V. Berlin, eds. *Sherman's Civil War: Selected Correspondence of William T. Sherman, 1860–1865*. Chapel Hill: University of North Carolina Press, 1999.

Smith, Barbara Bentley, and Nina Bentley Baker, eds. *Burning Rails as We Pleased: The Civil War Letters of William Garrigues Bentley, 104th Ohio Volunteer Infantry*. Jefferson, N.C.: McFarland & Company, 2004.

Sparks, David S., ed. *Inside Lincoln's Army: The Diary of Marsena Rudolph Patrick, Provost Marshal General, Army of the Potomac*. New York: Thomas Yoseloff, 1964.

Styple, William B., ed. *Writing and Fighting from the Army of Northern Virginia: A Collection of Confederate Soldier Correspondence*. Kearny, N.J.: Belle Grove, 2003.

———. *Writing and Fighting the Confederate War: The Letters of Peter Wellington Alexander, Confederate War Correspondent*. Kearny, N.J.: Belle Grove, 2002.

Survivors' Association. *History of the Corn Exchange Regiment, 118th Pennsylvania Volunteers, from Their First Engagement at Antietam to Appomattox*. Philadelphia: J. L. Smith, 1888.

Turino, Kenneth C., ed. *The Civil War Diary of J. E. Hodgkins: 19th Massachusetts Volunteers from August 11, 1862, to June 3, 1865.* Camden, Maine: Picton, 1994.

Turner, Charles W., ed. *The Allen Family of Amherst County, Virginia: Civil War Letters.* Berryville, Va.: Rockbridge, 1995.

Underwood, Adin B. *Thirty-Third Mass. Infantry Regiment, 1862–1865* ... Boston: A. Williams & Co., 1881.

Wilkeson, Frank. *Recollections of a Private Soldier in the Army of the Potomac.* New York: Putnam's, 1886; reprint, Lincoln: University of Nebraska Press, 1997.

Williams, Edward B., ed. *Rebel Brothers: The Civil War Letters of the Truehearts.* College Station: Texas A&M University Press, 1995.

Woodward, Joseph Janvier. *Outlines of the Chief Camp Diseases of the United States Armies as Observed during the Present War: A Practical Contribution to Military Medicine.* Philadelphia: J. B. Lippincott & Co., 1863.

Wyckoff, Mac, ed. *The Civil War Letters of Alexander McNeill, 2nd South Carolina Infantry Regiment.* Columbia: University of South Carolina Press, 2016.

### Journals

Calhoun, J. Theodore. "Nostalgia, as a Disease of Field Service: A Paper Read before the Medical Society of the 2nd Division, 3rd Corps, Army of Potomac, February 10th, 1864." *Medical and Surgical Reporter* 11 (February 27, 1864): 130–32.

———. "Rough Notes of an Army Surgeon's Experience, during the Great Rebellion." *Medical and Surgical Reporter* 11 (March 12, 1864): 159–60.

Driver, Robert, ed. "Diary of Captain John D. Lilley." *Augusta Historical Bulletin* 28, no. 1 (Spring 1992): 12–25.

Walker, Charles N., and Rosemary Walker, eds. "Diary of the War by Robt. S. Robertson." *Old Fort News* 28, no. 4 (December 1965).

### Government Publications

*Regulations for the Army of the Confederate States, 1863. Corrected and Enlarged with a Revised Index.* Richmond: J. W. Randolph, 1863; reprint, Harrisburg, Pa.: National Historical Society, 1980.

*Revised Regulations for the Army of the United States, 1861.* Philadelphia: G. L. Brown, Printer, 1861.

U.S. War Department. *The War of the Rebellion: A Compilation of the Official Records of the Union and Confederate Armies.* 128 vols. Washington, D.C.: Government Printing Office, 1880–1901.

### Newspapers

*Albany (N.Y.) Evening Journal*
*Carolina Watchman* (Salisbury, N.C.)
*Charleston (S.C.) Daily Courier*
*Chicago Tribune*
*Danbury (Conn.) Times*
*Fayetteville (N.C.) Observer*
*Frank Leslie's Illustrated*
*Harper's Weekly*

*Hartford (Conn.) Daily Courant*
*Illustrated New Age* (Philadelphia)
*Lebanon (Pa.) Courier*
*Mobile (Ala.) Advertiser & Register*
*New York Herald*
*New York Times*
*Newark (N.J.) Daily Advertiser*
*Philadelphia Inquirer*

Raleigh Daily Progress
Raleigh Register
Richmond (Va.) Dispatch
Richmond (Va.) Enquirer
Richmond (Va.) Examiner
Richmond (Va.) Whig
Rochester (N.Y.) Democrat and American

Rome (Ga.) Courier
San Francisco Daily Evening Bulletin
Sixth Corps
Southern Illustrated News
Vermont Watchman and State
Journal (Montpelier)

## SECONDARY SOURCES

### Books

Adams, Michael C. C. *Living Hell: The Dark Side of the Civil War*. Baltimore: Johns Hopkins University Press, 2014.

———. *Our Masters the Rebels: A Speculation on Union Military Failure in the East, 1861–1865*. Cambridge, Mass.: Harvard University Press, 1978.

Andrews, J. Cutler. *The North Reports the Civil War*. Pittsburgh: University of Pittsburgh Press, 1955.

———. *The South Reports the Civil War*. Princeton, N.J.: Princeton University Press, 1970.

Appleton, D. *Appleton's Complete Letter Writer: The Useful Letter Writer. Comprising a Succinct Treatise on the Epistolary Art; and Forms of Letters for All the Ordinary Occasions of Life*. New York: D. Appleton and Company, 1854.

Ash, Stephen V. *Firebrand of Liberty: The Story of Two Black Regiments That Changed the Course of the Civil War*. New York: W. W. Norton & Company, 2008.

Ballard, Michael B. *Vicksburg: The Campaign That Opened the Mississippi*. Chapel Hill: University of North Carolina Press, 2004.

Banes, Charles H. *History of the Philadelphia Brigade: Sixty-Ninth, Seventy-First, Seventy-Second, and One Hundred and Sixth Pennsylvania Volunteers*. Philadelphia: Lippincott & Co., 1876.

Barton, Michael. *Goodmen: The Character of Civil War Soldiers*. University Park: Pennsylvania State University Press, 1981.

Bernath, Michael T. *Confederate Minds: The Struggle for Intellectual Independence in the Civil War South*. Chapel Hill: University of North Carolina Press, 2010.

Berry, Stephen W. *All That Makes a Man: Love and Ambition in the Civil War South*. New York: Oxford University Press, 2002.

Blair, Jayne E. *Tragedy at Montpelier: The Untold Story of Ten Confederate Deserters from North Carolina*. Westminster, Md.: Heritage Books, 2004.

Blair, William. *Virginia's Private War: Feeding Body and Soul in the Confederacy, 1861–1865*. New York: Oxford University Press, 1998.

———. *With Malice toward Some: Treason and Loyalty in the Civil War Era*. Chapel Hill: University of North Carolina Press, 2014.

Bledsoe, Andrew S. *Citizen-Officers: The Union and Confederate Volunteer Junior Officer Corps in the American Civil War*. Baton Rouge: Louisiana State University Press, 2015.

Bonner, Robert E. *Colors and Blood: Flag Passions of the Confederate South*. Princeton, N.J.: Princeton University Press, 2002.

———. *The Soldier's Pen: Firsthand Impressions of the Civil War*. New York: Farrar, Straus and Giroux, 2006.

Bradley, Mark. *This Astounding Close: The Road to Bennett Place*. Chapel Hill: University of North Carolina Press, 2000.

Brady, Lisa. *War upon the Land: Military Strategy and the Transformation of Southern Landscapes during the American Civil War*. Athens: University of Georgia Press, 2012.

Broomall, James J. *Private Confederacies: The Emotional Worlds of Southern Men as Citizens and Soldiers*. Forthcoming in 2019 from the University of North Carolina Press.

Browning, Judkin. *Shifting Loyalties: The Union Occupation of Eastern North Carolina*. Chapel Hill: University of North Carolina Press, 2011.

Bruce, Susannah Ural. *The Harp and the Eagle: Irish-American Volunteers and the Union Army, 1861–1865*. New York: New York University Press, 2006.

Burke, Peter. *What Is Cultural History?* Cambridge: Polity, 2008.

Burlingame, Michael. *Abraham Lincoln: A Life*. 2 vols. Baltimore: Johns Hopkins University Press, 2008.

Bynum, Victoria E. *The Long Shadow of the Civil War: Southern Dissent and Its Legacies*. Chapel Hill: University of North Carolina Press, 2010.

Byrne, Frank J. *Becoming Bourgeois: Merchant Culture in the South*. Lexington: University Press of Kentucky, 2006.

Carmichael, Peter. *The Last Generation: Young Virginians in Peace, War, and Reunion*. Chapel Hill: University of North Carolina Press, 2005.

Clarke, Frances M. *War Stories: Suffering and Sacrifice in the Civil War North*. Chicago: University of Chicago Press, 2011.

Coddington, Richard S. *Faces of the Civil War: An Album of Union Soldiers and Their Stories*. Baltimore: Johns Hopkins University Press, 2004.

Coopersmith, Andrew S. *Fighting Words: An Illustrated History of Newspaper Accounts of the Civil War*. New York: New Press, 2004.

Cushman, Stephen. *Belligerent Muse: Five Northern Writers and How They Shaped Our Understanding of the Civil War*. Chapel Hill: University of North Carolina Press, 2014.

———. *Bloody Promenade: Reflections on a Civil War Battle*. Charlottesville: University of Virginia Press, 1999.

Daniel, Larry J. *Soldiering in the Army of Tennessee: Portrait of Life in a Confederate Army*. Chapel Hill: University of North Carolina Press, 1991.

Darnton, Robert. *The Great Cat Massacre: And Other Episodes in French Cultural History*. New York: Vintage Books, 1984.

Dean, Eric T., Jr. *Shook over Hell: Post-Traumatic Stress, Vietnam, and the Civil War*. Cambridge, Mass.: Harvard University Press, 1999.

Devine, Shauna. *Learning from the Wounded: The Civil War and the Rise of American Medical Science*. Chapel Hill: University of North Carolina Press, 2014.

Dilbeck, D. H. *A More Civil War: How the Union Waged a Just War*. Chapel Hill: University of North Carolina Press, 2016.

Dirck, Brian R. *Lincoln and Davis: Imagining America, 1809–1865*. Lawrence: University Press of Kansas, 2001.

Downs, Jim. *Sick from Freedom: African-American Illness and Suffering during the Civil War and Reconstruction*. New York: Oxford University Press, 2012.

Dunkelman, Mark H. *Brothers One and All: Esprit de Corps in a Civil War Regiment*. Baton Rouge: Louisiana State University Press, 2004.

Emberton, Carole. *Beyond Redemption: Race, Violence, and the American South after the Civil War*. Chicago: University of Chicago Press, 2015.

Fabian, Ann. *The Unvarnished Truth: Personal Narratives in Nineteenth-Century America*. Berkeley: University of California Press, 2002.

Fahs, Alice. *The Imagined Civil War: Popular Literature of the North and South, 1861–1865*. Chapel Hill: University of North Carolina Press, 2001.

Farge, Arlette. *The Allure of the Archives*. New Haven, Conn.: Yale University Press, 2013.

*The Fashionable American Letter Writer, or, the Art of Polite Correspondence*. Newark: Benjamin Olds, 1839.

Faust, Drew Gilpin. *The Creation of Confederate Nationalism: Ideology and Identity in the Civil War*. Baton Rouge: Louisiana State University Press, 1988.

———. *This Republic of Suffering: Death and the American Civil War*. New York: Alfred A. Knopf, 2008.

Foote, Lorien. *The Gentlemen and the Roughs: Violence, Honor, and Manhood in the Union Army*. New York: NYU Press, 2010.

Foote, Lorien, and Kanisorn Wongsrichanalai, eds. *So Conceived and So Dedicated: Intellectual Life in the Civil War–Era North*. New York: Fordham University Press, 2015.

Ford, Lacy K., Jr. *The Origins of Southern Radicalism: The South Carolina Upcountry*. New York: Oxford University Press, 1988.

Frank, Joseph Allan. *With Ballot and Bayonet: The Political Socialization of American Civil War Soldiers*. Athens: University of Georgia Press, 1998.

Frank, Lisa Tendrich. *The Civil War: Confederate Women and Union Soldiers during Sherman's March*. Baton Rouge: Louisiana State University Press, 2015.

Frassanito, William A. *Grant and Lee: The Virginia Campaigns, 1864–1865*. New York: Charles Scribner's Sons, 1983.

Fussell, Paul. *The Great War and Modern Memory*. New York: Oxford University Press, 1975.

Gallagher, Gary W. *Becoming Confederates: Paths to a New National Loyalty*. Athens: University of Georgia Press, 2013.

———. *The Confederate War: How Popular Will, Nationalism and Military Strategy Could Not Stave Off Defeat*. Cambridge, Mass.: Harvard University Press, 1999.

———. *Lee: His Army in Confederate History*. Chapel Hill: University of North Carolina Press, 2001.

———. *The Union War*. Cambridge, Mass.: Harvard University Press, 2011.

Gallman, J. Matthew. *Defining Duty in the Civil War: Personal Choice, Popular Culture, and the Union Home Front*. Chapel Hill: University of North Carolina Press, 2015.

Gannon, Barbara. *The Won Cause: Black and White Comradeship in the Grand Army of the Republic*. Chapel Hill: University of North Carolina Press, 2011.

Geier, Clarence R., David G. Orr, and Matthew B. Reeves, eds. *Huts and History: The Historical Archaeology of Military Encampment during the American Civil War*. Gainesville: University Press of Florida, 2006.

Geier, Clarence R., Douglas D. Scott, and Lawrence E. Babits, eds. *From These Honored Dead: Historical Archaeology of the American Civil War*. Gainesville: University Press of Florida, 2014.

Genovese, Eugene D. *A Consuming Fire: The Fall of the Confederacy in the Mind of the White Christian South*. Athens: University of Georgia Press, 1998.

Giesberg, Judith. *Army at Home: Women and the Civil War on the Northern Home Front.* Chapel Hill: University of North Carolina Press, 2009.

———. *Sex and the Civil War: Soldiers, Pornography, and the Making of American Morality.* Chapel Hill: University of North Carolina Press, 2017.

Ginzburg, Carlo. *The Cheese and the Worms: The Cosmos of a Sixteenth-Century Miller.* Baltimore: Johns Hopkins University Press, 1980.

Glatthaar, Joseph T. *Forged in Battle: The Civil War Alliance of Black Soldiers and White Officers.* New York: Free Press, 1990.

———. *General Lee's Army: From Victory to Collapse.* New York: Free Press, 2008.

———. *The March to the Sea and Beyond: Sherman's Troops in the Savannah and Carolinas Campaign.* New York: New York University Press, 1986.

Gleeson, David T. *The Green and the Gray: The Irish in the Confederate States of America.* Chapel Hill: University of North Carolina Press, 2013.

Glover, Lori. *Southern Sons: Becoming Men in the New Nation.* Baltimore: Johns Hopkins University Press, 2009.

Gordon, Lesley J. *A Broken Regiment: The 16th Connecticut's Civil War.* Baton Rouge: Louisiana State University Press, 2014.

Gottfried, Bradley M. *The Maps of Gettysburg: An Atlas of the Gettysburg Campaign, June 3–July 13, 1863.* New York: Savas Beatie LLC, 2007.

Green, Jennifer R. *Military Education and the Emerging Middle Class in the Old South.* New York: Cambridge University Press, 2008.

Greenberg, Kenneth S. *Honor and Slavery.* Princeton, N.J.: Princeton University Press, 1996.

Griffith, Paddy. *Battle Tactics of the Civil War.* New Haven, Conn.: Yale University Press, 1987.

Grimsley, Mark. *The Hard Hand of War: Union Military Policy toward Southern Civilians, 1861–1865.* New York: Cambridge University Press, 1995.

Hale, Grace Elizabeth. *Making Whiteness: The Culture of Segregation in the South, 1890–1940.* New York: Vintage, 1998.

Haller, John S., Jr. *American Medicine in Transition, 1840–1910.* Urbana: University of Illinois Press, 1981.

Halloran, Fiona Deans. *Thomas Nast: The Father of Modern Political Cartoons.* Chapel Hill: University of North Carolina Press, 2012.

Hardy, Michael C. *The Fifty-Eighth North Carolina Troops: Tar Heels in the Army of Tennessee.* Jefferson, N.C.: McFarland, 2010.

Harris, M. Keith. *Across the Bloody Chasm: The Culture of Commemoration among Civil War Veterans.* Baton Rouge: Louisiana State University Press, 2014.

Hartwig, D. Scott. *To Antietam Creek: The Maryland Campaign of September 1862.* Baltimore: Johns Hopkins University Press, 2012.

Harvey, Eleanor Jones. *The Civil War in American Art.* Washington, D.C.: Smithsonian American Art Museum and Yale University Press, 2012.

Hess, Earl J. *Braxton Bragg: This Most Hated Man of the Confederacy.* Chapel Hill: University of North Carolina Press, 2016.

———. *Field Armies and Fortifications in the Civil War.* Chapel Hill: University of North Carolina Press, 2005.

———. *Liberty, Virtue, and Progress: Northerners and Their War for the Union*. New York: New York University Press, 1988.

———. *The Rifle Musket in Civil War Combat: Reality and Myth*. Lawrence: University of Kansas Press, 2008.

———. *Trench Warfare under Grant and Lee: Field Fortifications in the Overland Campaign*. Chapel Hill: University of North Carolina Press, 2007.

———. *Union Soldier in Battle: Enduring the Ordeal of Combat*. Lawrence: University Press of Kansas, 1997.

Houghton, Walter E. *The Victorian Frame of Mind, 1830–1870*. New Haven, Conn.: Yale University Press, 1985.

Hsieh, Wayne Wei-Siang. *West Pointers and the Civil War: The Old Army in War and Peace*. Chapel Hill: University of North Carolina Press, 2009.

Hubbs, G. Ward. *Guarding Greensboro: A Confederate Company in the Making of a Southern Community*. Athens: University of Georgia Press, 2003.

Humphreys, Margaret. *Intensely Human: The Health of Black Soldiers in the American Civil War*. Baltimore: Johns Hopkins University Press, 2008.

———. *Marrow of Tragedy: The Health Crisis of the American Civil War*. Baltimore: Johns Hopkins University Press, 2013.

Inscoe, John C., and Robert C. Kenzer, eds. *Enemies of the Country: New Perspectives on Unionists in the Civil War South*. Athens: University of Georgia Press, 2001.

Jacoby, Karl. *Shadows at Dawn: An Apache Massacre and the Violence of History*. New York: Penguin, 2009. Kindle edition.

Janney, Caroline E. *Remembering the Civil War: Reunion and the Limits of Reconciliation*. Chapel Hill: University of North Carolina Press, 2013.

Johnson, Edward C., Gail R. Johnson, and Melissa Johnson Williams. *All Were Not Heroes: A Study of "the List of U.S. Soldiers Executed by U.S. Military Authorities during the Late War."* Chicago: W. Gunnison, 1997.

Johnson, Walter. *River of Dark Dreams: Slavery and Empire in the Cotton Kingdom*. Cambridge, Mass.: Belknap Press of Harvard University Press, 2013.

Jordan, Brian Matthew. *Marching Home: Union Veterans and Their Unending Civil War*. New York: W. W. Norton & Company, 2015.

Keller, Christian B. *Chancellorsville and the Germans: Nativism, Ethnicity, and Civil War Memory*. New York: Fordham University Press, 2007.

Kolchin, Peter. *A Sphinx on the American Land: The Nineteenth-Century South in Comparative Perspective*. Baton Rouge: Louisiana State University Press, 2003.

Krick, Robert K. *9th Virginia Cavalry*. Lynchburg, Va.: H. E. Howard, 1982.

Kurtz, William B. *Ex-communicated from the Union: How the Civil War Created a Separate Catholic America*. New York: Fordham University Press, 2016.

Lears, T. J. Jackson. *Something for Nothing: Luck in America*. New York: Penguin, 2003.

Levin, Kevin M. *Remembering the Battle of the Crater*. Lexington: University Press of Kentucky, 2012.

Levine, Bruce. *Confederate Emancipation: Southern Plans to Free and Arm Slaves during the Civil War*. New York: Oxford University Press, 2006.

Linderman, Gerald. *Embattled Courage: The Experience of Combat in the American Civil War*. New York: Free Press, 1987.

Long, Gretchen. *Doctoring Freedom: The Politics of African American Medical Care in Slavery and Emancipation.* Chapel Hill: University of North Carolina, 2012.

Long, Lisa. *Rehabilitating Bodies: Health, History, and the American Civil War.* Philadelphia: University of Pennsylvania Press, 2004.

Lonn, Ella. *Desertion during the Civil War.* Lincoln: University of Nebraska Press, 1998.

Luke, Bob, and John David Smith. *Soldiering for Freedom: How the Union Army Recruited, Trained, and Deployed the U.S. Colored Troops.* Baltimore: Johns Hopkins University Press, 2014.

Manning, Chandra. *What This Cruel War Was Over: Soldiers, Slavery, and the Civil War.* New York: Knopf, 2007.

Marshall, D. Porter. *Company "K" 155th Pennsylvania Volunteer Zouaves (1888).* N.p.: Kessinger, 2010.

Marten, James Alan. *Sing Not War: The Lives of Union and Confederate Veterans in Gilded Age America.* Chapel Hill: University of North Carolina Press, 2011.

Marvel, William. *Lee's Last Retreat: The Flight to Appomattox.* Chapel Hill: University of North Carolina Press, 2002.

Mayfield, John. *Counterfeit Gentlemen: Manhood and Humor in the Old South.* Gainesville: University Press of Florida, 2009.

McClurken, Jeffrey W. *Take Care of the Living: Reconstructing Confederate Veteran Families in Virginia.* Charlottesville: University of Virginia Press, 2009.

McConnell, Stuart. *Glorious Contentment: The Grand Army of the Republic, 1865–1900.* Chapel Hill: University of North Carolina Press, 1992.

McCurry, Stephanie. *Confederate Reckoning: Power and Politics in the Civil War South.* Cambridge, Mass.: Harvard University Press, 2012.

McKnight, Brian D., and Barton A. Myers, eds. *The Guerrilla Hunters: Irregular Conflicts during the Civil War.* Baton Rouge: Louisiana State University Press, 2017.

McPherson, James. *For Cause and Comrades: Why Men Fought in the Civil War.* New York: Oxford University Press, 1997.

———. *What They Fought For, 1861–1865.* New York: Knopf Doubleday, 1994.

Meier, Kathryn Shively. *Nature's Civil War: Common Soldiers and the Environment in 1862 Virginia.* Chapel Hill: University of North Carolina Press, 2013.

Menand, Louis. *The Metaphysical Club: The Story of Ideas in America.* New York: Farrar, Straus and Giroux, 2001.

Merrill, Samuel. *The Seventieth Indiana: The Volunteer Infantry: In the War of the Rebellion.* Indianapolis: Bowen-Merrill, 1900.

Miller, Brian Craig. *Empty Sleeves: Amputation in the Civil War South.* Athens: University of Georgia Press, 2015.

Miller, Randall, Harry S. Stout, and Charles Reagan Wilson, eds. *Religion and the American Civil War.* New York: Oxford University Press, 1998.

Miller, Richard F. *Harvard's Civil War: A History of the Twentieth Massachusetts Volunteer Infantry.* Hanover, N.H.: University Press of New England, 2005.

Mitchell, Reid. *Civil War Soldiers: Their Expectations and Their Experiences.* New York: Viking, 1988.

———. *The Vacant Chair: The Northern Soldier Leaves Home.* New York: Oxford University Press, 1993.

Moorhead, James H. *American Apocalypse: Yankee Protestants and the Civil War, 1860–1869*. New Haven, Conn.: Yale University Press, 1978.

Murdock, Eugene C. *One Million Men: The Civil War Draft in the North*. Madison: State Historical Society of Wisconsin, 1971.

Murphy, Terrence V. *10th Virginia Infantry*. Lynchburg, Va.: H. E. Howard, 1989.

Myers, Barton A. *Rebels against the Confederacy: North Carolina's Unionists*. New York: Cambridge University Press, 2014.

Neely, Mark E., and Harold Holzer. *The Union Image: Popular Prints of the Civil War North*. Chapel Hill: University of North Carolina Press, 2000.

Neely, Mark E., Harold Holzer, and Gabor S. Boritt. *The Confederate Image: Prints of the Lost Cause*. Chapel Hill: University of North Carolina Press, 1987.

Neff, John R. *Honoring the Civil War Dead: Commemoration and the Problem of Reconciliation*. Lawrence: University Press of Kansas, 2005.

Nelson, Megan Kate. *Ruin Nation: Destruction and the American Civil War*. Athens: University of Georgia Press, 2012.

Niebuhr, Reinhold. *The Irony of American History*. Chicago: University of Chicago Press, 1952.

Noe, Kenneth W. *Reluctant Rebels: The Confederates Who Joined the Army after 1861*. Chapel Hill: University of North Carolina Press, 2015.

Noll, Mark A. *The Civil War as a Theological Crisis*. Chapel Hill: University of North Carolina Press, 2006.

Nudelman, Franny. *John Brown's Body*. Chapel Hill: University of North Carolina Press, 2004.

O'Brien, Michael. *Conjectures of Order: Intellectual Life and the American South, 1810–1860*. 2 vols. Chapel Hill: University of North Carolina Press, 2004.

Oppenheim, Janet. *"Shattered Nerves": Doctors, Patients, and Depression in Victorian England*. New York: Oxford University Press, 1991.

Palladino, Grace. *Another Civil War: Labor, Capital, and the State in the Anthracite Regions of Pennsylvania, 1840–68*. Urbana: University of Illinois Press, 1990.

Perry, Aldo S. *Civil War Courts-Martial of North Carolina Troops*. Jefferson, N.C.: McFarland & Company, 2012.

Phillips, Jason. *Diehard Rebels: The Confederate Culture of Invincibility*. Athens: University of Georgia Press, 2007.

Power, J. Tracy. *Lee's Miserables: Life in the Army of Northern Virginia from the Wilderness to Appomattox*. Chapel Hill: University of North Carolina Press, 1998.

Prokopowicz, Gerald J. *All for the Regiment: The Army of the Ohio, 1861–1862*. Chapel Hill: University of North Carolina Press, 2001.

Rable, George C. *The Confederate Republic: A Revolution against Politics*. Chapel Hill: University of North Carolina Press, 1994.

———. *Damn Yankees! Demonization and Defiance in the Confederate South*. Baton Rouge: Louisiana State University Press, 2015.

———. *Fredericksburg! Fredericksburg!* Chapel Hill: University of North Carolina Press, 2002.

———. *God's Almost Chosen Peoples: A Religious History of the American Civil War*. Chapel Hill: University of North Carolina Press, 2010.

Radley, Kenneth. *Rebel Watchdog: The Confederate States Army Provost Guard.* Baton Rouge: Louisiana State University Press, 1989.

Ramold, Steven J. *Baring the Iron Hand: Discipline in the Union Army.* DeKalb: Northern Illinois University Press, 2010.

Reardon, Carol. *With a Sword in One Hand and Jomini in the Other: The Problem of Military Thought in the Civil War North.* Chapel Hill: University of North Carolina Press, 2012.

Reaves, George A., and Joseph Allen Frank. *"Seeing the Elephant": Raw Recruits at the Battle of Shiloh.* Urbana: University of Illinois Press, 2003.

Reddy, William M. *The Navigation of Feeling: A Framework for the History of Emotions.* New York: Cambridge University Press, 2001.

Reid, Brian Holden. *America's Civil War: The Operational Battlefield, 1861–1863.* Amherst, N.Y.: Prometheus, 2008.

Reinitz, Richard. *Irony and Consciousness: American Historiography and Reinhold Niebuhr's Vision.* Lewisburg, Pa.: Bucknell University Press, 1980.

Riggs, David F. *13th Virginia Infantry.* Lynchburg, Va.: H. E. Howard, 1988.

Robertson, James I., Jr. *Soldiers Blue and Gray.* Columbia: University of South Carolina Press, 1988.

Rockman, Seth. *Scraping By: Wage Labor, Slavery, and Survival.* Baltimore: Johns Hopkins University Press, 2009.

Roeder, George H., Jr. *Censored War: American Visual Experience during World War Two.* New Haven, Conn.: Yale University Press, 1993.

Rolfs, David. *No Peace for the Wicked: Northern Protestant Soldiers and the American Civil War.* Knoxville: University of Tennessee Press, 2009.

Rose, Anne C. *Victorian America and the Civil War.* New York: Cambridge University Press, 1992.

Rosen, Hannah. *Terror in the Heart of Freedom: Citizenship, Sexual Violence, and the Meaning of Race in the Postemancipation South.* Chapel Hill: University of North Carolina Press, 2009.

Roth, Michael S. *The Ironist's Cage: Memory, Trauma, and the Construction of History.* New York: Columbia University Press, 1995.

Rubin, Anne Sarah. *A Shattered Nation: The Rise and Fall of the Confederacy, 1861–1865.* Chapel Hill: University of North Carolina Press, 2005.

———. *Through the Heart of Dixie: Sherman's March and American Memory.* Chapel Hill: University of North Carolina Press, 2014.

Samito, Christian G. *Becoming American under Fire: Irish Americans, African Americans, and the Politics of Citizenship during the Civil War.* Ithaca, N.Y.: Cornell University Press, 2009.

Sandow, Robert M. *Deserter Country: Civil War Opposition in the Pennsylvania Appalachians.* New York: Fordham University Press, 2009.

Schantz, Mark S. *Awaiting the Heavenly Country: The Civil War and America's Culture of Death.* Ithaca, N.Y.: Cornell University Press, 2008.

Schivelbusch, Wolfgang. *The Culture of Defeat: On National Trauma, Mourning, and Recovery.* New York: Picador, 2001.

Scott, Sean A. *A Visitation of God: Northern Civilians Interpret the Civil War.* New York: Oxford University Press, 2011.

Sears, Stephen W. *Landscape Turned Red: The Battle of Antietam*. New York: Ticknor & Fields, 1983.

Shattuck, Gardiner H., Jr. *A Shield and Hiding Place: The Religious Life of the Civil War Armies*. Macon, Ga.: Mercer University Press, 1987.

Sheehan-Dean, Aaron. *Why Confederates Fought: Family and Nation in Civil War Virginia*. Chapel Hill: University of North Carolina Press, 2009.

————, ed. *View from the Ground: Experiences of Civil War Soldiers*. Lexington: University Press of Kentucky, 2007.

Shi, David E. *Facing Facts: Realism in American Thought and Culture, 1850–1920*. New York: Oxford University Press, 1995.

Silber, Nina. *Daughters of the Union: Northern Women Fight the Civil War*. Cambridge, Mass.: Harvard University Press, 2005.

Silkenat, David. *Moments of Despair: Suicide, Divorce, and Debt in Civil War Era North Carolina*. Chapel Hill: University of North Carolina Press, 2011.

Simpson, Lewis P. *The Man of Letters in New England and the South: Essays on the Literary Vocation in America*. Baton Rouge: Louisiana State University Press, 1973.

Smith, John David, ed. *Black Soldiers in Blue: African American Troops in the Civil War Era*. Chapel Hill: University of North Carolina Press, 2002.

Smith, Mark M. *Debating Slavery: Economy and Society in the Antebellum South*. New York: Cambridge University Press, 1998.

————. *How Race Is Made: Slavery, Segregation, and the Senses*. Chapel Hill: University of North Carolina Press, 2006.

————. *The Smell of Battle, the Taste of Siege: A Sensory History of the Civil War*. New York: Oxford University Press, 2015.

Sternhell, Yael A. *Routes of War: The World of Movement in the Confederate South*. Cambridge, Mass.: Harvard University Press, 2012.

Stowe, Stephen. *Intimacy and Power in the Old South: Ritual in the Lives of the Planters*. Baltimore: Johns Hopkins University Press, 1987.

Sutherland, Daniel E. *A Savage Conflict: The Decisive Role of Guerrillas in the American Civil War*. Chapel Hill: University of North Carolina Press, 2009.

Sweet, Timothy. *Traces of War: Poetry, Photography, and the Crisis of the Union*. Baltimore: Johns Hopkins University Press, 1990.

Taylor, Amy Murrell. *The Divided Family in Civil War America*. Chapel Hill: University of North Carolina Press, 2005.

Thornton, J. Mills, III. *Politics and Power in a Slave Society: Alabama, 1800–1860*. Baton Rouge: Louisiana State University Press, 1978.

Trachtenberg, Allen. *Reading American Photographs: Images as History, Mathew Brady to Walker Evans*. New York: Hill and Wang, 1989.

Trudeau, Noah Andre. *Like Men of War: Black Troops in the Civil War, 1862–1865*. Boston: Little, Brown, 1998.

Valencium, Conevery Bolton. *The Health of the Country: How American Settlers Understood Themselves and Their Land*. New York: Basic Books, 2002.

Valuska, David L., and Christian B. Keller. *Damn Dutch: Pennsylvania Germans at Gettysburg*. Mechanicsburg, Pa.: Stackpole Books, 2010.

Varon, Elizabeth R. *Appomattox: Victory, Defeat, and Freedom at the End of the Civil War*. New York: Oxford University Press, 2014.

Walker, Scott. *Hell's Broke Loose in Georgia: Survival in a Civil War Regiment.* Athens: University of Georgia Press, 2005.

Weber, Jennifer L. *Copperheads: The Rise and Fall of Lincoln's Opponents in the North.* New York: Oxford University Press, 2006.

Weitz, Mark A. *More Damning Than Slaughter: Desertion in the Confederate Army.* Lincoln: University of Nebraska Press, 2005.

Wells, Jonathan Daniel. *The Origins of the Southern Middle Class, 1800–1861.* Chapel Hill: University of North Carolina Press, 2004.

Wetherington, Mark V. *Plain Folk's Fight: The Civil War and Reconstruction in Piney Woods Georgia.* Chapel Hill: University of North Carolina Press, 2002.

White, Jonathan W. *Emancipation in the Union Army and the Reelection of Abraham Lincoln.* Baton Rouge: Louisiana State University Press, 2014.

Wickberg, Daniel. *The Senses of Humor: Self and Laughter in Modern America.* Ithaca, N.Y.: Cornell University Press, 1998.

Wiley, Bell I. *The Life of Billy Yank: The Common Soldier of the Union.* Indianapolis: Bobbs-Merrill, 1952.

————. *The Life of Johnny Reb: The Common Soldier of the Confederacy.* Indianapolis: Bobbs-Merrill, 1943.

Wongsrichanalai, Kanisorn. *Northern Character: College-Educated New Englanders, Honor, Nationalism, and Leadership in the Civil War Era.* New York: Fordham University Press, 2016.

Wood, Peter H. *Near Andersonville: Winslow Homer's Civil War.* Cambridge, Mass.: Harvard University Press, 2010.

Woodward, C. Vann. *Burden of Southern History.* Baton Rouge: Louisiana State University Press, 1968.

Woodward, Colin E. *Marching Masters: Slavery, Race, and the Confederate Army during the Civil War.* Charlottesville: University Press of Virginia, 2014.

Woodworth, Steven E. *Nothing but Victory: The Army of the Tennessee, 1861–1865.* New York: Alfred A. Knopf, 2005.

————. *While God Is Marching On: The Religious World of Civil War Soldiers.* Lawrence: University Press of Kansas, 2001.

Wyatt-Brown, Bertram. *The Shaping of Southern Culture: Honor, Grace, and War, 1760s–1880s.* Chapel Hill: University of North Carolina Press, 2001.

————. *Southern Honor: Ethics and Behavior in the Old South.* New York: Oxford University Press, 1982.

————. *A Warring Nation: Honor, Race, and Humiliation in America and Abroad.* Charlottesville: University of Virginia Press, 2014.

Young, Allan. *The Harmony of Illusions: Inventing Post-Traumatic Stress Disorder.* Princeton, N.J.: Princeton University Press, 1995.

### Articles and Essays

Anderson, David. "Dying of Nostalgia: Homesickness in the Union Army during the Civil War." *Civil War History* 46, no. 3 (September 2010): 247–82.

Barbian, Lenore, Paul S. Sledzik, and Jeffrey S. Reznick. "Remains of War: Walt Whitman, Civil War Soldiers, and the Legacy of Medical Collections." *Museum History Journal* 5 (January 2012): 7–28.

Barnes, L. Diane, Brian Schoen, and Frank Towers. "Introduction: Reimagining the Old South." In *The Old South's Modern Worlds: Slavery, Region, and Nation in the Age of Progress*, edited by L. Diane Barnes, Brian Schoen, and Frank Towers, 3–19. New York: Oxford University Press, 2011.

Bernath, Michael T. "Literature." In *A Companion to the U. S. Civil War*, 2 vols., edited by Aaron Sheehan-Dean, 2:998–99. Malden, Mass.: Wiley-Blackwell, 2014.

Brown, David. "North Carolinian Ambivalence: Rethinking Loyalty and Disaffection in the Civil War Piedmont." In *North Carolinians in the Era of the Civil War and Reconstruction*, edited by Paul D. Escott, 7–36. Chapel Hill: University of North Carolina Press, 2008.

Brubaker, Robert, and Frederick Cooper. "Beyond 'Identity.'" *Theory and Society* 29, no. 1 (February 2000): 1–47.

Butler, Leslie. "Reconstructions in Intellectual and Cultural Life." In *Reconstructions: New Perspectives on the Postbellum United States*, edited by Thomas J. Brown, 172–205. New York: Oxford University Press, 2006.

Carmichael, Peter S. "So Far from God and So Close to Stonewall Jackson: The Executions of Three Shenandoah Valley Soldiers." *Virginia Magazine of History and Biography* 111, no. 1 (2003): 33–66.

Cashin, Joan. "Deserters, Civilians, and Draft Resistance in the North." In *The War Was You and Me*, edited by Joan Cashin, 262–85. Princeton, N.J.: Princeton University Press, 2002.

————. "Trophies of War: Material Culture in the Civil War Era." *Journal of the Civil War Era* 3, no. 1 (September 2011): 339–67.

Clarke, Frances. "So Lonesome I Could Die: Nostalgia and Debates over Emotional Control in the Civil War North." *Journal of Social History* 41, no. 2 (Winter 2007): 253–82.

Currarino, Rosanne. "Toward a History of Cultural Economy." *Journal of the Civil War Era* 2, no. 4 (December 2012): 564–84.

Davis, David A. "Abjection and White Trash Autobiography." In *Storytelling, History, and the Postmodern South*, edited by Jason Phillips, 187–204. Baton Rouge: Louisiana State University Press, 2013.

Dean, Eric T., Jr. "'The Awful Shock and Rage of Battle': Rethinking the Meaning and Consequences of Combat in the Civil War." In *Battle: The Nature and Consequences of Civil War Combat*, edited by Kent Gramm, 92–109. Tuscaloosa: University of Alabama Press, 2008.

————. "'We Will All Be Lost and Destroyed': Post-traumatic Stress Disorder and the Civil War." *Civil War History* 37, no. 2 (1991): 138–53.

DeGruccio, Michael. "Letting the War Slip through Our Hands: Material Culture and the Weakness of Words in the Civil War Era." In *Weirding the War: Stories from the Civil War's Ragged Edges*, edited by Stephen Berry, 15–35. Athens: University of Georgia Press, 2011.

Dotson, Rand. "'The Grave and Scandalous Evil Infected to Your People': The Erosion of Confederate Loyalty in Floyd County, Virginia." *Virginia Magazine of History and Biography* 108 (Fall 2000): 393–434.

Downs, James. "'Who Got Bloody?': The Cultural Meanings of Blood during the Civil War and Reconstruction." In *The Cultural Politics of Blood*, edited by Kimberly Anne

Coles, Ralph Bauer, Zita Nunes, and Carla Peterson, 210–28. New York: Palgrave Macmillan, 2014.

Dunster, Edward S. "The Comparative Mortality in Armies from Wounds and Disease." In *Contributions Relating to the Causation and Prevention of Disease, and to Camp Diseases,* edited by Austin Flint, 169–92. New York: Hurd and Houghton, 1867.

Edwards, Laura F. "Southern History as U.S. History." *Journal of Southern History* 75 (August 2009): 563–64.

Emberton, Carole. "'Only Murder Makes Men': Reconsidering the Black Military Experience." *Journal of the Civil War Era* 2, no. 3 (September 2012): 368–93.

Enstad, Nan. "On Grief and Complicity: Notes toward a Visionary Cultural History." In *The Cultural Turn in U.S. History: Past, Present, and Future,* edited by James W. Cook, Lawrence B. Glickman, and Michael O'Malley, 319–41. Chicago: University of Chicago Press, 2008.

Fahs, Alice. "The Sentimental Soldier in Popular Civil War Literature, 1861–65." *Civil War History* 46, no. 2 (June 2000): 107–31.

Faust, Drew Gilpin. "Christian Soldiers: The Meaning of Revivalism in the Confederate Army." In *Southern Stories: Slaveholders in Peace and War,* edited by Drew Gilpin Faust, 88–109. Columbia: University of Missouri Press, 1992.

———. "The Civil War Soldier and the Art of Dying." *Journal of Southern History* 67 (2002): 3–38.

Foote, Lorien. "Soldiers." In *A Companion to the U. S. Civil War,* 2 vols., edited by Aaron Sheehan-Dean, 1:114–31. Malden, Mass.: Wiley-Blackwell, 2014.

Fox-Genovese, Elizabeth. "The Anxiety of History: The Southern Confrontation with Modernity." *Southern Cultures* Inaugural Issue (1993): 65–82.

Gallagher, Gary W. "Lee's Army Has Not Lost Any of Its Prestige: The Impact of Gettysburg on the Army of Northern Virginia and the Confederate Home Front." In *The Third Day at Gettysburg and Beyond,* edited by Gary W. Gallagher, 1–30. Chapel Hill: University of North Carolina Press, 1994.

———. "Our Hearts Are Full of Hope: The Army of Northern Virginia in the Spring of 1864." In *The Wilderness Campaign,* edited by Gary W. Gallagher, 36–65. Chapel Hill: University of North Carolina Press, 1997.

Genovese, Eugene D. "Yeomen Farmers in a Slaveholders' Democracy." *Agricultural History* 49, no. 2 (1975): 331–42. https://www.jstor.org/stable/3741274?seq=1#page _scan_tab_contents. Accessed March 16, 2016.

Glatthaar, Joseph T. "A Tale of Two Armies: The Confederate Army of Northern Virginia and the Union Army of the Potomac and Their Cultures." *Journal of the Civil War Era* 6, no. 3 (September 2016): 315–46.

Grant, Susan-Mary. "Civil War Cybernetics: Medicine, Modernity, and the Intellectual Mechanics of Union." In *So Conceived and So Dedicated: Intellectual Life in the Civil War–Era North,* edited by Lorien Foote and Kanisorn Wongsrichanalai, 41–63. New York: Fordham University Press, 2015.

———. "The Lost Boys: Citizen-Soldiers, Disabled Veterans, and Confederate Nationalism in the Age of People's War." *Journal of the Civil War Era* 2, no. 2 (June 2012): 233–59.

Grinspan, Jon. "'Sorrowfully Amusing': The Popular Comedy of the Civil War." *Journal of the Civil War Era* 1, no. 3 (September 2011): 313–38.

Harrison, Simon. "Mementos and the Souls of Missing Soldiers: Returning Effects of the Battlefield Dead." *Royal Anthropological Institute of Great Britain and Ireland* 14 (December 2008): 774–90.

Hartwig, D. Scott. "'Its All Smoke and Dust and Noise': The Face of Battle at Gettysburg." In *Battle: Nature and Consequences of Civil War Combat*, edited by Kent Gramm, 12–66. Tuscaloosa: University of Alabama Press, 2009.

Honeck, Mischa. "Men of Principle: Gender and the German American War for the Union." *Journal of the Civil War Era* 5, no. 1 (March 2015): 38–67.

Hsieh, Wayne Wei-Siang. "'Go to Your Gawd Like a Soldier': Transnational Reflections on Veteranhood." *Journal of the Civil War Era* 5, no. 7 (December 2015): 551–77.

Keen, William W., S. Weir Mitchell, and George R. Morehouse. "On Malingering, especially in Regard to Simulation of Diseases of the Nervous System." *American Journal of the Medical Sciences* 48 (October 1864): 367–93.

Lears, T. J. Jackson. "The Concept of Cultural Hegemony: Problems and Possibilities." *American Historical Review* 90, no. 3 (1985): 576–93.

Levin, Kevin M. "The Devil Himself Could Not Have Checked Them." In *Cold Harbor to the Crater: The End of the Overland Campaign*, edited by Gary W. Gallagher and Caroline E. Janney, 264–82. Chapel Hill: University of North Carolina Press, 2015.

Luskey, Brian, and Jason Phillips. "Muster: Inspecting Material Cultures of the Civil War." *Civil War History* 63, no. 2 (June 2017): 103–12.

Lyon, A. A. "Malingerers." *Southern Practitioner* 9 (September 1904): 558–64.

McCurry, Stephanie. "Women Numerous Armed: Gender and the Politics of Subsistence in the Civil War South." In *Wars within a War: Controversy and Conflict over the American Civil War*, edited by Joan Waugh and Gary W. Gallagher, 1–25. Chapel Hill: University of North Carolina Press, 2014.

Meier, Kathryn Shively. "U.S. Sanitary Commission Physicians and the Transformation of American Health Care." In *So Conceived and So Dedicated: Intellectual Life in the Civil War–Era North*, edited by Lorien Foote and Kanisorn Wongsrichanalai, 19–39. New York: Fordham University Press, 2015.

Minton, Amy R. "Defining Confederate Respectability: Morality, Patriotism, and Confederate Identity in Richmond's Civil War Public Press." In *Crucible of the Civil War: Virginia from Secession to Commemoration*, edited by Andrew J. Torget, Gary W. Gallagher, and Edward L. Ayers, 80–105. Charlottesville: University of Virginia Press, 2006. eBook Academic Collection (EBSCOhost), Ipswich, Mass. March 22, 2016.

Mitchell, Reid. "'Not the General but the Soldier': The Study of Civil War Soldiers." In *Writing the Civil War: The Quest to Understand*, edited by James M. McPherson and William J. Cooper, 81–95. Columbia: University of South Carolina Press, 1998.

Orr, Timothy J. "'All Manner of Schemes and Rascalities': The Politics of Promotion in the Union Army." In *This Distracted and Anarchical People: New Answers for Old Questions about the Civil War–Era North*, edited by Andrew L. Slap and Michael Thomas Smith, 83–103. New York: Fordham University Press, 2013.

Phillips, Jason. "Battling Stereotypes: Taxonomy of Common Soldiers in Civil War History." *History Compass* 6 (2008): 1–19.

———. "A Brothers' War? Exploring Confederates Perceptions of the Enemy." In *The View from the Ground: Experiences of Civil War Soldiers*, edited by Aaron Sheehan-Dean, 67–90. Lexington: University Press of Kentucky, 2007.

Robinson, Armstead L. "In the Shadow of Old John Brown: Insurrection Anxiety and Confederate Mobilization, 1861–1863." *Journal of Negro History* 65, no. 4 (1980): 279–97. https://www.jstor.org/stable/2716860?seq=1#page_scan_tab_contents. Accessed March 16, 2016.

Rosenberg, Charles E. "Body and Mind in Nineteenth-Century Medicine: Some Clinical Origins of the Neurosis Construct." *Bulletin of the History of Medicine* 63, no. 2 (1989): 185–97.

Rosenwein, Barbara H. "Worrying about Emotions in History." *American Historical Review* 107, no. 3 (June 2002): 821–45.

Samito, Christian G. "Thomas F. Meagher, Patrick R. Guiney, and the Meaning of the Civil War for Irish America." In *So Conceived and So Dedicated: Intellectual Life in the Civil War–Era North*, edited by Lorien Foote and Kanisorn Wongsrichanalai, 193–216. New York: Fordham University Press, 2015.

Sheehan-Dean, Aaron. "Justice Has Something to Do with It: Class Relations and the Confederate Army." *Virginia Magazine of History and Biography* 113, no. 4 (2005): 340–77.

Sommerville, Diane Miller. "'Will They Ever Be Able to Forget?': Confederate Soldiers and Mental Illness in the Defeated South." In *Weirding the War: Stories from the Civil War's Ragged Edges*, edited by Stephen Berry, 321–39. Athens: University of Georgia Press, 2011.

Sternhell, Yael A. "Revisionism Reinvented? The Antiwar Turn in Civil War Scholarship." *Journal of the Civil War Era* 3, no. 2 (June 2013): 239–56.

Thomas, Benjamin P. "Lincoln's Humor." In *"Lincoln's Humor" and Other Essays*, edited by Michael Burlingame, 3–22. Urbana: University of Illinois Press, 2002.

Waugh, Joan. "'I Only Knew What Was in My Mind': Ulysses S. Grant and the Meaning of Appomattox." *Journal of the Civil War Era* 2, no. 3 (September 2012): 307–36.

Weicksel, Sarah Jones. "The Dress of the Enemy: Clothing and Disease in the Civil War Era." *Civil War History* 63, no. 2 (June 2017): 133–50.

Westwood, H. C. "The Cause and Consequence of a Union Black Soldier's Mutiny and Execution." *Civil War History* 31, no. 3 (1985): 222–36.

White, Hayden. "The Value of Narrativity in the Representation of Reality." In *On Narrative*, edited by W. J. T. Mitchell, 1–23. Chicago: University of Chicago Press, 1980.

Whites, LeeAnn. "Civil War as a Crisis in Gender." In *Divided Houses: Gender and the Civil War*, edited by Catherine Clinton and Nina Silber, 3–21. New York: Oxford University Press, 1992.

Wickberg, Daniel. "Heterosexual White Male: Some Recent Inversions in American Cultural History." *Journal of American History* 92, no. 1 (June 2005): 136–57.

———. "Intellectual History vs. the Social History of Intellectuals." *Rethinking History* 5, no. 3 (2002): 383–95.

———. "What Is the History of Sensibilities? On Cultural Histories, Old and New." *American Historical Review* 112 (June 2007): 661–84.


## Lectures and Presentations

Ayers, Edward L. "Loyalty and America's Civil War." Lecture presented at the 49th Annual Fortenbaugh Memorial Lecture, Gettysburg College, Gettysburg, Pa., 2010 (pamphlet, Gettysburg College), 8.

Luskey, Brian. "Mercenaries or Patriots? Bounty Men in the Union Army." Paper presented at the Civil War Institute Annual Conference, Gettysburg College, Gettysburg, Pa., June 2017.

*Online Sources*

App, Larry A., ed. Michael Schroyer Diary, May 15, 1865. *Stories Retold Blog Site*, https:// storiesretoldvideo.wordpress.com/2013/06/15/chapter-70-may-11-17-1865-stories -from-along-the-homeward-march-the-app-brothers-in-the-civil-war/. Accessed May 8, 2016.

Berkey, Jonathan M. "Rockingham Rebellion," *Encyclopedia Virginia*, April 12, 2011. http://www.encyclopediavirginia.org/Rockingham_Rebellion#start_entry. Accessed March 6, 2016.

Billings, Todd. "Avoiding the Dead Ends of Providence: Monocausal Fatalism and Open Theism." February 2015. http://www.reformation21.org/articles/j-todd-billingsseries -of-4.php. Accessed March 3, 2016.

Cruikshank, R. Letters, May 15, 1865. *Civil War Letters, Town of Salem (N.Y.)*. http://www .salem-ny.com/1865letters.html. Accessed May 8, 2016.

Ellis, Michael, Michael Montgomery, and Stephen Berry. *Private Voices: The Corpus of American Civil War Letters*. http://altchive.org/private-voices/. Accessed October 23, 2017.

Lepper, Bradley T., and Mary E. Lepper, eds. Cyrus Marion Roberts Diary. http://www .78ohio.org/Diaries/Capt%20Cyrus%20Marion%20Roberts%20Diary.htm#_Volume _3:__8%20May%20to%2020%20May%201865. Accessed May 8, 2016.

McGuire, Samuel B. "Desertion during the Civil War." *New Georgia Encyclopedia*, December 24, 2014. http://www.georgiaencyclopedia.org/articles/history-archaeology /desertion-during-civil-war. Accessed March 1, 2016.

Orr, Timothy J. "Surrendering at Gettysburg: The Vindication of Major Thomas B. Rodgers, Pt. 1." *Tales from the Army of the Potomac*. https://talesfromaop.blogspot.com /2017/03/surrendering-at-gettysburg-vindication.html. Accessed February 7, 2018.

Stott, Andrew McConnell. "'What Exile from Himself Can Flee?': Byron and the Price of Exile." *Welcome to the Wordsworth Trust* (blog), March 27, 2014. https://wordsworth.org .uk/blog/2014/03/27/byron-exile/. Accessed April 2016.

# index

Page numbers appearing in *italics* refer to illustrations.

abolition, 257

absent without leave: and the blurring with desertion, 177, 178–79; and stabilized households, 179. *See also* desertion; discipline

absolutism, 25, 232, 233–34, 245, 252, 253, 254, 259, 262, 276, 277, 290–91

Adams, Marshall L. H., 204

African American soldiers: and mistreatment of, 55–56, 57; and breakdown of household economies, 58–59; as perceived by white soldiers, 64, 71–72, 83–84, 143, 153–54, 256–57; and perception of surgeons, 148–49; coerced by bounty brokers, 190; massacres of, 258–59

Age of Progress, 236

Alabama Infantry, Twenty-Eighth, 36, 38

*Albany Evening Journal*, 195

alcohol: and discipline, 27, 33–35, 127, 191; and combat, 144, 152, 159

Alexander, Edward Porter, 258, 259, 261

Allen, Tinsley, 188

Allen, William P., 182–89

"All Quiet along the Potomac Tonight," 28

Anderson, John Crawford, 122–30, 272

Antietam, 1–2, 106–7, *108*, 109, 241

anti-Semitism, 245

Appomattox, 266, 270, 271, 278; apple tree at, 266, 267, 273, 274, 275–76; Lee's Farewell Address (General Orders No. 9), 267, 282–86; and final campaign, 269–70, 271, 283; surrender proceedings, 270; and Confederate shame, 271–72, 280, 293–94; and looking to the future, 272–73, 274–75, 279, 280, 293–94; and die-hard Confederates, 275, 277–79, 283, 290; and denying Confederate defeat, 276–77; surrender parade, 287–89

armies. *See individual armies*

Armstrong, Thomas, 224

army debating societies, 251, 350n54

Army of the Cumberland, 60

Army of Northern Virginia, 125, 141; 1865 petitions, 84–85; determining loyalty, 184, 186, 187; Gettysburg Campaign, 208, 209, 213, 231–32, 233–34, 253–56; at Appomattox, 267, 271, 273, 283. *See*

*also* absolutism; combat; Confederate
soldiers; desertion; religion; slavery

Army of the Potomac, 17, 60, 102, 112, 133,
163, 164, 220–21; partisanship in, 22–23,
207; understanding defeat, 231, 239,
257, 267, 271; end of the war, 294, 304,
305. *See also* combat; desertion; ironic
detachment; religion; Union; Union
soldiers

Army of Tennessee, 48, 51, 53, 114, 246:
executions, 174–75, 267; surrender of,
272, 273, 276–77, 281, 283, 284, 287

Arnold, Ambrose, 135

Articles of War, 59, 180, 287

Atlanta Campaign, 179, 239

Aycock, W. F., 47

Ayers, Edward L., 189

Aylett, William Roane, 277–78

Bagby, George W., 279

Bailey, James (Manton), 240, 242–44

Bates, William, 281

battlefield defeats. *See* absolutism; ironic
detachment; morale

battlefield sounds, 70, 107, 271

Bechtel, Jacob L., 206

Beem, David E., 102–4, *105*, 106–13, 128, 129,
130

Beem, Mahala, 102–7, 109, 111–13

Berrier, William, 71, 271, 301

Beverly's Ford, 191, 192

Biddlecom, Charles, 23, 135, 160–66, 169–72

Bienville Parrish, La., 74

Biggs, Henry, 71

Biggs, William, 162

Blair, William A., 179

"bold soldier boy," 21, 30, 34. *See also*
sentimentalism

Boston Draft Riots, 177

bounty brokers, 190–91

bounty jumpers, 162, 190; and act of
desertion, 191–93, 204–5; little sympathy
for, 196–97

Bowen, Charles, 25–26, 30–33, 34, 35–36, 43,
49, 61, 65, 132–33, 203, 249–50, 257–58,
313, 315–16, 321

Bowen, Kate, 36

Bowen, Roland, 250–51

Bragg, Braxton, 25, 41, 118, 238

Breck, George, 239, 244

"broken down": as a soldiery description,
27, 45–46, 120, 160; and mental collapse,
215, 267. *See also* combat

Broomall, James, 61, 136

Brown, John, 258

Burnside, Ambrose, 158

Burton, David H., 309

Callaway, Joshua, 25, 26, 36–42, 44–47, 49,
53, 61–62, 65

camp: as place of sin, 21, 30–31, 32, 40,
64–65, 91, 116, 191; officer privilege, 21;
as hotbed of rumors, 22, 70–71, 97;
discipline, 25, 33–34, 37–38, 40–41, 53, 61,
142, 184–85; economies of, 26, 31, 32, 38;
scarcities in, 32; environmental impact
of, 37; poor conditions in, 37–39, 118; as a
soundscape, 39, 40, 60; routine of, 40–41,
96–97; and the work of soldiering, 55–57,
63–64; mutinies in, 59–60, 64; humor,
63–64; and pornography, 64; during a
siege, 187

Castle Thunder (Richmond), 209

Cedar Mountain, Battle of, 95

Chamberlayne, John H., 268–69, 278–82,
288, 289

Chambers, Henry, 283

Chancellorsville, Battle of, 140, 167, 180, 184,
249, 294, 296, 297, 309

Charleston, S.C., 122

cheerfulness. *See* emotions; letter writing

*Chicago Tribune*, 195

Chickamauga, Battle of, 46, 51

Christian Enlightenment, 68

Christianity. *See* metaphysical confusion;
Providence; religion

Citadel, 122, 127

citizen-soldier, 8, 9, 90, 172, 178

civilians: bonds with soldiers, 5, 65, 111–12,
136–37, 179, 211; and soldier uniforms,
20; and expectations of soldiers, 20, 21,
36–37, 100, 135, 141, 161; shamed soldiers,

22; estranged from soldiers, 78–79, 104–5, 106, 112–13, 126, 163, 227, 244, 305, 307, 310; and parental advice, 89–90, 122. *See also* household economy

class conflict, 227–28, 229

Cold Harbor, Battle of, 305

combat, 23–24; mental and physical strain, 3–4, 46, 75, 81–82, 94–97, 100–101, 106–7, 109–11, 132–33, 137, 141, 144, 146, 165, 183, 184, 202, 240, 254, 310–11; affirmed manliness, 7, 16, 69, 74–75, 93, 100, 123, 136, 149, 161, 165, 213; shaped by pragmatism, 24, 127–28; friendly fire, 27; inspired by comrades, 43; mourning the fallen, 43, 109; role of Providence, 69, 72–73, 74, 94–95, 213; importance of training, 76, 171; affirmed political beliefs, 93, 170; coping strategies, 93–94, 96; promoted savage feelings, 100, 136; emotional responses to, 100–101, 107–10, 119, 137, 165, 166–67, 170; ambivalent feelings toward, 110, 119–20, 130, 137, 169–70, 172, 306, 309; as a passage to adulthood, 124; historiographical debate of, 133–34; confusion of, 137–38, 155, 158–59; captured in battle, 138–39; and blurring of courage and cowardice, 140–41; and misunderstanding of trauma, 142–43; and range of rifled musket, 149, 150; and the absurd, 158; depicted in print culture, 158; strengthened devotion to cause, 169–170; and the cause of desertion, 184, 200–202; sounds of, 207, 137. *See also* courage; cowardice; letter writing; professionalism; willed behavior

Compiled Service Records (CSR), 182–83, 189

complicity, 249–50, 252–53, 264

comrades: conflicts among, 18–19, 33–35, 48–49, 63–64, 91, 203; emotional intimacy of, 20–21, 167, 169, 174, 213; and community bonds, 21, 23, 89; and visual and material culture, 21, 166; resentment of officers, 21–22, 55, 56, 59–60; united by hardship, 31–32, 45, 62–65, 263; divided over slavery, 42; and messes, 42, 43, 45,

62; mourning the dead, 43, 107, 109, 294–97; and racial divisions, 55, 56; and daily tasks of soldiering, 56–57; humiliation of fellow soldiers, 63–64; bonded through combat, 74–75, 96, 113, 165; refusal to shoot deserters, 186; and ethnic divisions, 191–92. *See also* camp; combat; Confederate soldiers; Union soldiers

Confederate Conscription Act (1862), 63, 114

*Confederate Image Prints of the Lost Cause, The,* 245

Confederate soldiers: enlistment of, 19, 22–23, 36–37, 191; and the importance of uniforms and material culture, 20–21, 24; and slavery, 37, 42–43, 115, 122, 127; resentment of authority, 41; committed to the cause, 45–46, 78–79, 123, 127, 171; demoralization of, 45–46, 212, 213, 215, 228; absence of nationalism, 48; antiwar sentiments, 48, 185; poor soldiers, 48–49, 52–53, 204; and honor, 49, 124; confided to wives, 49, 204; and relationship to household, 52, 183–84, 204, 212; engaged in mutiny, 53, 82, 123; desertion, 54, 79, 85–88, 184–85, 186; and silent on race, 54, 259–60; critical of civilians, 78–79, 101, 126; zealotry, 95, 261, 268, 277–78; and ambition, 100, 123, 124; as fathers, 121, 135; belief in bloodlines, 123; demonization of the enemy, 123, 253, 255–56; and defending household, 217; understanding defeat, 231–35, 237–38, 239–42, 254–56, 261–63; returning home, 272, 292–93. *See also* absolutism; camp; combat; deserters; discipline; emotion; household; religion

*Confederate War* (Gallagher), 263

contradictory conscience, 101, 135, 172, 183, 185, 220

Copperhead movement, 112, 227

Corinth, Miss., 37, 38–39

courage: relationship to sentimentalism, 3, 74–75, 100–101, 149; on display, 5–6, 7, 28, 75, 77, 93, 100–101; inspired by emotion, 83, 100–101; connected to godliness, 91,

93, 95, 109; harnessed by professionalism, 113; determined by bloodlines, 123; shaped by pragmatism, 135; blurred with cowardice, 138, 140–41; definition of, 142–43; flexible understanding of, 154–55, 159–61, 310; mocked, 242–43; and material culture, 315. *See also* combat

courts-martial, 57, 59, 138–39, 180–81, 191–93, 205–6, 209–10. *See also* military courts

cowardice: on the picket line, 26–27; the result of circumstances, 135; blurred with courage, 135, 154, 159–60; and rumor, 137, 138, 141; difficulties in prosecuting, 138; vagaries of, 138, 140–41; medical understanding of, 142–43; biological explanations of, 143–44, 160; surgeon's treatment of, 143–49; ruses of, 145–47; soldier admits to, 151–52; euphemisms for, 160; confused with desertion, 169, 202; and execution, 205

Crane, Stephen, 137

Crater, Battle of, 258

Cruikshank, R., 295–96

Culp's Hill, 214

cult of personality, 262

Curtin, Andrew, 23

Dalton, Ga., 174

*Danbury (Conn.) Times*, 240

Davis, Jefferson, 50–51, 186, 218–19, 238, 244

Davis, Pinky, 184

death: in camp, 38–39; sounds of, 39; sense of randomness, 39, 73, 106–7; desire for the "good death," 39, 109, 214; among comrades, 43, 47, 75, 106–9, 167, 169; and material culture, 47, 109–10, 214; expressed desire for, 49, 75–76; made sacred on the battlefield, 107–8, 119, 113; and burials, 109, 113, 214, 195–97, 294–97; and antisentimentalism, 121, 183, 188, 214, 250, 264, 295–96; and executions, 195–97, *198*, 199. *See also* combat

De Gruccio, Michael, 151

Democratic Party, 257, 258

deserters: as sympathetic figures, 31, 66, 186, 187, 224; and the breakdown of

households, 33, 178, 204, 212; reasons for staying in the army, 50, 81, 86, 184; reasons for leaving the army, 50–51, 85–88, 162, 184, 208, 218, 226–28; efforts to eradicate, 51–52, 126; and metaphysical confusion, 66–67, 79, 85; euphemism for, 164; seen as nonideological, 176; and strategies for escape, 176, 185, 186, 187–88, 191–93, 199–200, 208; numbers of, 177; inconsistent categorization of, 177, 178, 180; favorite hideouts of, 177, 178–89; confused with cowardice, 178–79, 202; before a court-martial, 180–81; treated unfairly by military courts, 181; and execution, 185, 187, 221–24, 263; as bounty men, 191–93, 204–5; finances of, 201; background of, 209–10; plotting escape, 210–11; as having a defective character, 219, 229; demonstrate political awareness, 225–28; and the evasive tactics of officers, 227; and the language of class, 227–28; as a nonrevolutionary act, 228

"Deserter's Confession, A," 220

diarrhea, 160, 161, 162

Dilbeck, D. H., 94

discipline, 18, 41; punishments, 4, 53, 61, 141–42, 184, 218; instilled by training, 24–25; in camp, 25, 37–38, 40–41, 53, 61, 185; along picket line, 26–27; and alcohol, 27, 33–35, 191; use of fines, 52–53; soldier resistance to, 55; through work details, 55–56; and emotional control, 83–84; promoted by surgeons, 144–46, 148–49, 164; and powerlessness in the ranks, 172, 187; and straggling, 199; breakdown over plundering, 207

disease and illness, 37–39, 115. *See also* military surgeons

dissent: imagining political alternatives, 54; black soldiers, 55–56; spurred by drudgery, 55–56; mutinies, 57–60, 63; expressed through noise and song, 59–60; and acts of humiliation, 63–64; expressed through the language of poor soldier, 64; and the absence of radicalism, 64–65; dismissed as a problem of character, 222, 229. *See also* desertion

Donaldson, Francis A., 152–56, 157, 158–60, 191–92, 194, 309–10

Downs, James, 143

draft, 63, 190. *See also* Confederate Conscription Act (1862)

duty: soldier's flexible conception of, 79, 112, 200, 310; imposed by the military, 126, 202–3, 305

Dwinell, Melvin, 240–41

economies, 26; lack of pay, 2, 16, 18, 32–33, 44, 52, 55, 57, 58, 141; sutlers, 3, 32, 51; and credit and debt, 32; and gambling, 32; and poverty, 32, 115, 120–21; constrained political choices, 33, 58, 62, 201, 215; and predatory practices, 38; and role of slavery, 42; connected to households, 43–44, 58–59, 118, 190–91, 204; cost of death, 47; soldier fines, 51–53, 180, 185; cost of furlough, 53; prevalence of stealing, 63, 213; demand for soldier labor, 63–64; entrepreneurship, 184, 297; trading with the enemy, 246. *See also* camp; household economy

Ellis, William, 285

Elmira, 161

emancipation, 170

emotion: expressed to wives, 36, 44–45, 49, 81–82, 106, 114–15, 117–19, 136–37, 162–63, 211, 212, 214; as a bond among comrades, 43, 61, 215; and the importance of being cheerful, 45, 69, 81–82, 109, 163, 272; management of, 81–85, 88–89, 90, 211; connected to medical knowledge, 82–83; and being a Christian, 83; and rage militaire, 90; and nostalgia, 91; in response to combat, 100–101, 107–10, 119, 137, 166–67, 270; expression of sympathy, 110–11, 135, 194, 264–65, 271, 307; and fear of savagery, 136; feelings of emptiness, 206; expression of fear, 213; and fatalism, 214; and mourning, 215

empathy, 247–48, 249–52, 264–65

enlistment, 20, 21, 26, 36–37, 55–56, 89–91, 103, 161, 179, 190–91, 192, 253–54

Enrollment Act of 1863, 190

epilepsy, 146

Epperly, Christian, 25, 26, 47–49, 50–54, 61, 64–65

*Erie (Pa.) Dispatch*, 230

executions, 22, 54–55, 63, 86, 127, 174, 206, 233, 263; in Confederate armies, 67, 174–75, 180, 185, 187, 221–25, 228, 229; and ritual proceedings, 154–55, 222–24; represented in print culture, 175, 197–98; recorded in official testimony, 175–76, 181–82; in Union armies, 193–95, 206–7; and reporting, 195, 220–21; reaction of soldiers to, 196–97, 206–7, 220–21, 224; as a deterrent, 224; acceptance of, 228–29; condemned portrayed as lacking character, 220, 222, 22

Fahs, Alice, 103

Farge, Arlette, 11

Faust, Drew Gilpin, 73, 238

*Fayetteville, (N.C.) Observer*, 225

Fields, Thomas D., 57–58

Fifth Corps (Army of the Potomac), 194

First Manassas, 122–23

Floyd County, Va., 48, 50, 51, 52, 54

Folaney, John, 192, 196

food, 49, 56, 115, 120, 131, 161, 210, 212

Foote, Lorien, 176

Forbes, Edwin, 197, 248

*For Cause and Comrades* (McPherson), 176

Forrest, Nathan Bedford, 285, 286

Fort Donelson, Tenn., 94–95

Fort Stedman, Va., 188

Fort Wagner, S.C., 72, 258

Fort Warren (Mass.), 204

Foster, John A. H., 199–203, 226–27

Foster, Samuel, 277

Fox-Genovese, Elizabeth, 236

*Frank Leslie's Budget of Fun*, 244

*Frank Leslie's Illustrated*, 197, 258

Fraternization, 246–47, 248, 248–49, 251. *See also* Confederate soldiers; Union soldiers

Fredericksburg, Battle of, 3–5, 30–31, 112, 146, 151–55, *156*, 157–60, 230–31, 239, 242–44, 247, 250, 306–9
Fredericktown, Mo., 91–94
Futch, Charley, 211, 213, 214, 215, 216, 217
Futch, John, 208–19, 221–24, 226, 259, 320
Futch, Martha, 211, 212, 213

Gallagher, Gary W., 263
Gallman, Matthew, 244
Gardner, Alexander, 75
Geary, Daniel, 199
General Orders No. 9, 282–86
General Orders No. 22, 285
Georgia Infantry: Second state troops, 114; Eighth, 240, 241; Fifty-Seventh, 114
Gettysburg, Battle of, 16, 77, 78, 112–13, 129, 138–39, 167, 210, 214, 218, 228, 233, 234, 240, 253, 254, 255, 256, 315, 316
Gibbon, John, 206
Giesberg, Judith, 52, 65, 184
Gillis, George, 140–41
Glatthaar, Joseph T., 8, 215
Goldsboro, N.C., 211
Gordon, John B., 288, 289
Gordon, Ransom, 199
Grand Review, 294, 299
Grant, Ulysses S., 264, 266, 270
Grattan, Sally, 280, 281
Greenberg, Kenneth, 236
Greensboro, N.C., 285, 287
Griffin, Charles, 194
Griggs, George, 273
Griggs, William, 139
guerrilla warfare, 48
Gwyn, James, 152, 155

Hagerstown, Md., 23
Haitian Revolution, 259
Halloran, Fiona Deans, 245
Hamlin, Philip, 40, 76
hard-war policy, 249, 253
*Harpers Weekly*, 158, 167, 197, 243, 258, 267
Harrison's Landing, Va., 104
Haydon, Charles, 25–28, 29, 30, 62, 65
Hayward, Ambrose, Henry, 166–67, *168*

Hess, Earl, 136
Hewell, William W., 129
Hinman, Wilbur F., 24
*History of the Peloponnesian War* (Thucydides), 129
Holmes, Oliver Wendell, Jr., 7, 78–79, 304–7, *308*, 309–13
Holt, Joseph, 205
Homer, Winslow, 17–18, *19*, 51, 62, 147
homesickness, 48, 49, 97, 215, 218
honor: as combat motivation, 6, 46, 69, 123, 133; in enlisting, 19–20, 122–23; resentment of officers, 23, 42–43; did not dictate soldier behavior, 49, 215, 226, 254; and distorted battlefield reporting, 78; and shame, 128, 142, 262; and civilians, 225; relationship to slavery, 232, 258–59, 277; connected to absolutism, 233; and material culture, 291
Hood, John Bell, 179
hospitals, 211; described on the battlefield, 1–2, 107; Confederate system of, 186–87
household economy, 13; soldier's dependency upon, 12, 14, 32, 43–44, 58, 59, 163–64, 183–84, 212; financial breakdown of, 36–37, 44, 52, 114, 118, 190–91, 204, 211, 254; receiving state support, 37, 52, 204, 212; and soldier political options, 58–59, 62, 63, 227. *See also* civilians; economies
Hubbs, G. Ward, 184
humor, 238–39, violent nature of, 63–64, 133, 153–54; and military defeat, 239–40, 241, 245

identity, 26
ideology, 73; relationship to combat, 1, 16; and motivation, 5–6, 326–27n21, 327n22, 330n76; expressed through material culture, 20, 132, 166; relationship to professionalization, 30, 33–35, 263; relationship to slavery, 37, 43, 122; and physical sacrifice, 46; destabilized by war, 70; and importance of circumstances, 79, 232–33; as a deterministic force, 90; subordinated to experience, 131, 172;

absence of, 185, and pragmatism, 309. *See also* Union

Illinois Artillery, First, 88, 90

illness. *See* disease and illness

*Illustrated New Age* (Philadelphia), 195

immigrant soldiers: charged with being unmanly, 57, 63, 143; as substitutes, 191; in military courts, 193

Indiana Infantry: Fourteenth, 102, 106–7, 113; Twentieth, 180

Indiana University, 103

*In Front of Yorktown* (Homer painting), 17–18, *19*, 62

ironic detachment, 230–31, 232, 235, 238, 240, 242–43, 244–46, 251, 256–57, 264

*Ivanhoe*, 153

Jackson, Miss., 121

Jackson, Stonewall, 245

James Island, S.C., 123

James River, 209, *219*

Johnson, Andrew, 299

Johnson, Edward, 222, 223

Johnson, Edward, division of (Army of Northern Virginia), 222, 224

Johnston, Joseph E., 54, 238, 245, 285, 286

Jones, Edward Valentine, 273

Judson, Amos, 83, 230, 233

Kautz, August, 180

Keever, Alexander, 66–67, 69, 73, 79–82, 85–88, 98–99

Kentucky Campaign (1862), 118–19

Kline, Henry, 196

Kuhne, George, 192, 193, 196

Lae, Emil, 193, 194, 196

*Lebanon (Pa.) Courier*, 239

Lee, Robert E., 231, 234; soldiers' belief in, 78, 84–85, 126, 183, 231, 260, 262, 276; proponent of executions, 187, 218–19, 221; and cult of personality, 262, 263; at Appomattox, 266–67, 270, 273, 274, 275, 283, 284–85, 286, 287

letter writing: and sentimentalism, 43, 101–2, 128, 129; mail service, 44; breaking into

soldier letters, 44, 210; the importance of writing cheerfully, 45, 81–83, 163; importance of audience, 74, 77, 100–101, 130–31, 171; spurred disagreement with civilians, 130; and battle narratives, 107, 109, 119, 124, 129, 132–33, 151, 156, 158–60, 237–38, 240; and emotional openness, 114, 212, 215; semiliterate and illiterate soldiers, 114–15, 117, 119, 121, 129–30, 210, 212, 213, 215; self-censorship, 117, 141, 213; and separation from families, 118, 184, 212; authorial authority, 125–26, 131, 313; grounded in daily experiences, 131; and judging morale, 176; and the cultural lens of absolutism, 232, 252

Levine, Bruce, 260

Lincoln, Abraham, 204, 230, 238, 244, 265, 270

Linderman, Gerald, 111

logistics, 208

Longstreet, James, 289

Lost Cause, 235, 269, 282, 285

Louisiana Infantry, Ninth, 74

loyalty, 84, 176, 183, 189, 227

Lundy, Potter, 109

Luskey, Brian, 190

Lyle, Peter, 23

Lyman, Theodore, 104

malingerers, 143, 145–46, 148

Mallet, Richardson, 209, 219, 224

manliness: and vulnerability, 6, 111, 114, 116–17, 120; inspired by women, 44, 73–74; and desire for reputation, 49, 133, 151, 161, 162, 170, 219; and the tasks of soldiering, 56, 172; absence of in immigrant soldiers, 57, 63; and the loss of restraint, 65; redefined through emotional expressiveness, 83–84, 217; defined by Christianity, 90–91; and militarized manliness, 121, 139, 172. *See also* emotion

March to the Sea, 255–56

Marshall, Charles, 282, 283

Marye's Heights (Va.), 151, 155, 230

Maryland Campaign (1862), 241

Massachusetts Infantry: Nineteenth, 204,

206; Twentieth, 305, 311; Fifty-Fourth, 72, 254

masturbation, 144, 146

material culture, 3; importance of uniforms, 20, 24, 27, 39, 166; and camp slaves, 42; important in civilian relationship with soldiers, 44; and demoralization, 45–46, 47; and death, 47, 107, 110, 214; battlefield relics, 93–94, 98, 137; and pragmatism, 127–28; and Confederate surrender, 266, 267, 273–76, 281–85, 288–90, 291; symbolized courage, 291, 299–300, 315; and return to the battlefields, 294–97, 298; and Grand Review, 299–300; and veteran courage, 300–301; and empathy for the enemy, 302

Mayfield, John, 240

McAbe, Samuel, 260–61

McCarthy, Carlton, 269, 282, 291, 292, 294

McClellan, George B., 33, 245

McNeill, Alexander, 255–56

McPherson, James, 176

Meade, George Gordon, 191–95, 203–4, 205

medical care. See military surgeons

Meier, Kathryn Shively, 9

Memphis, Tenn., 96

Menand, Louis, 7–8

Meridian, Miss., 287

messes. See comrades: and messes

Metaphysical Club, The (Menand), 9

Metaphysical confusion, 1, 3, 6, 25, 47–48, 255; and desertion, 66–69; and destabilization of knowledge, 70–72, 76, 98–99, 306; because of combat, 106–7

Metzner, Adolph, 117

Michigan Infantry: Second, 26; Twenty-Fourth, 1

militarized manliness, 121, 139, 309–10

military courts: the vagaries of cowardice, 138–39, 140–41; the role of partisanship, 139; at the regimental and company level, 141–42; inconsistent prosecution of desertion, 178–80, 202; procedures of courts-martial, 180–81, 185, 193–95; unfair treatment of defendants, 181, 204, 205–6, 221

military surgeons: and battlefield trauma, 142–44; perception of cowards, 143–44; treatment of battle fatigue, 144–45; resented by soldiers, 145, 148–49; examination of soldiers, 145–46; and medical discharges, 161, 164, 211–12

military training. See professionalization

Mine Run Campaign, 125, 127

Missionary Ridge, 46, 239

Mitchell, Reid, 20

Mobile, Ala., 261

Moorehead, James H., 68

morale, 71–72, 85, 176, 189, 231–32, 263

mutiny, 53, 55, 64, 123

Nashville, Tenn., 123

nature, 37–38, 91

Neeger, George, 43

Neff, John, 250

New Hanover County, N.C., 218

newspaper reporting: on executions, 195–96; demonizing deserters, 220, 222, 229; soldier skepticism of, 220, 230; on battles, 245–46

New York City Draft Riots, 177

New York Herald, 195

New York Infantry: Twenty-Eighth, 161; Thirty-Fifth, 204; Fortieth, 64; Sixty-First, 146; Seventy-Second, 199; Seventy-Seventh, 140; Eighty-Seventh, 64; 147th, 161, 162

New York Times, 195

nightmares, 81–82, 94

Noll, Mark, 67

North Carolina Infantry: Third, 208, 222, 224; Forty-First, 211; Forty-Sixth, 209; Fifty-Seventh, 254

Northern women: sentimentalized marriage, 2–3, 36; offering religious advice, 2–3, 103–4; impoverished, 33, 52; critical of the war, 102, 103, 112–13; chastised by soldiers, 104–5, 113; tensions with soldiers, 163–64. See also civilians; household economy

North vs. South, 235–36, 348n11, 348n13

nostalgia. See emotion

O'Brien, Michael, 234
officers: receive preferential treatment,
    20–2l; resented by enlisted men, 21,
    31; enforcers of discipline, 25, 37–38,
    53; show preferential treatment, 56;
    resistance against, 59–62, 63, 162;
    misread soldiers, 84–85; and limited
    understanding of soldier bodies,
    142, 207–8; mocked by men, 155; and
    desertion and AWOL, 178–79, 200–202;
    and drinking, 191; disguised as deserters,
    227
O'Sullivan, Timothy, 75
Overland Campaign, 126, 165, 169–70, 199
Owen County, Ind., 103, 104

Panghorn, N.H., 291
Pardington, John, 1–3, 4, 5–7, 16, 22
Pardington, N.H., 275
partisanship, 264, 311
Patrick, Marsena Rudolph, 199, 207, 208
Patterson, George, 222, 223
Pegram, William R. J., 95
Pender, William Dorsey, 42
Pennsylvania Artillery, Battery G, 56
Pennsylvania Infantry: Ninetieth, 23; 118th,
    152, 190, 191, 193, 290, 299, 301, 302; 140th,
    138–39; 155th, 199, 200
Perry, H., 284
Perryville, Battle of, 119
Petersburg, siege of: 66, 71, 72, 126, 127, 133,
    165, 171, 187, 208, 248, 257
Phillips, Jason, 253, 261
physical appearance: changes, of, 45, 121,
    133, 162, 166, 169–70; signified character,
    208
picket duty, 26–27, 41: relationship
    to sentimentalism, 26, 28; and the
    prevalence of rumor, 70, 71; and
    Confederate desertion, 186; dangers of,
    311. See also discipline; fraternization
"Picket Guard, The" (poem), 28
Pierson, Reuben A., 69, 73–74, 77–79,
    98–101, 131, 309
plundering: and pragmatism, 30; of
    Fredericksburg, 155; during the Overland

Campaign, 207; encouraged desertion,
    207
"Poor Soldier," language of, 45
poor soldiers, 42–43, 53; and physical
    suffering, 32–33, 53–54, 55–56, 118–21, 211–
    12, 215; breaking into letters of, 44, 48,
    110; relationship to household economy,
    52, 190, 204; denounce the humanity of
    war, 53–54, 226; and language of dissent,
    64, 65; and act of writing, 114–15, 202,
    213, 215–16; and sentimentalism, 114,
    115–16; and malleable sense of honor
    and manliness, 114, 119–20, 202, 215,
    226; and corrupt bounty brokers, 190;
    disadvantaged in military court system,
    204, 205–6; emotional intimacy among
    comrades, 213, 215
Pope, Ranty, 59
pornography, 64
Port Republic, Battle of, 100–101, 131
pragmatism: relationship to
    sentimentalism, 18, 127–28; and combat,
    24, 135, 159–60, 247; living off the land,
    30, 62; elevated individual conscience,
    35, 78–79, 112–13, 226–27, 305, 307; and
    self-care, 38; reflected in soldier dissent,
    59–60, 87; and flexible understanding
    of Providence, 67, 87–88, 98–99; and
    racial attitudes, 72, 256–58, 260–61; and
    a malleable sense of duty, 79, 87–88, 112,
    126, 200; and the reworking of manliness,
    111; relaxed ideological commitments,
    170–71, 233–34, 309; and codes of
    conduct, 172; and survival, 189, 200; and
    political questions, 189, 263; definition of,
    203–5, 311–12; and desertion, 226–27, 228;
    and Union hard war, 249; and wartime
    cultural change, 314–16
print culture, 158, 245–46, 258; and
    executions, 175, 197, 198, 199
Private Voices (Ellis, Montgomery, and
    Berry), 130
professionalization: relationship to
    discipline, 18, 23–24, 33–35, 37–38, 178–
    79; civilian impediments to, 23; valued by
    the troops, 27–28, 30, 33–35, 72, 76–77, 79,

126, 172, 305–6, 309, 313; training, 40–41; compatible with Christianity, 90–91; and loss of individualism, 124, 126–27; after a battle, 142; and the role of military surgeons, 144–46

Providence: and metaphysical confusion, 25, 66–70, 73, 79, 213, 333n4; spurred cynicism, 31; and pragmatism, 67, 79, 98; as foundational to American thought, 68, 70; and combat, 69, 72–73, 74, 94–95, 109; soldiers skeptical of, 69, 77–78; as a source of security, 72, 76, 231; and national loyalty, 85–88, 94; explaining battlefield outcomes, 231, 234, 272, 273. *See also* religion

punishments. *See* discipline; executions

Rable, George, 68, 70, 244
Rainese, John, 192, 193, 196
Ramold, Steven J., 196
Rapidan River (Va.), 186, 249
Rappahannock River (Va.), 191, 247
rations. *See* food
Reardon, Carol, 203
Reconstruction, 282, 293–94
*Red Badge of Courage* (Crane), 137
religion: and metaphysical confusion, 1–3, 6, 47–48, 66–70, 73, 85–86; and soldier wives, 2, 49, 54, 103, 104, 116; and inhumanity of war, 3, 53, 226, 230–31, 249, 254; as a source of comfort in battle, 3–4, 43, 89, 95, 107; as an ideology, 5–6; connected to manliness, 18, 99, 106, 225; and death, 39, 47; created a spirit of camaraderie, 40; and soldier isolation, 48, 54, 91; made flexible through pragmatism, 67–68, 86, 94, 226, 303; Christian Enlightenment, 68; importance of Providence, 68, 75–76, 95; verified in battle, 69, 91–92; and emotional management, 83, 136; as a source of patriotism, 76, 85, 88, 89, 278; as a source of emotional fortitude, 104, 115, 118; sanctioned executions, 229. *See also* Providence

Republican Party, 257
Reynolds, Alexander Welch, 174, 175
rheumatism, 146, 160, 161, 162, 164
Rhode Island Cavalry, Second, 204
Richmond Bread Riots, 177–78
rifled musket, 149, 150, 151
Ringgold, Battle of, 166, 167, 169
Roberts, Marion, 294–95
Robertson, Robert, 206
Rockingham Rebellion, 229
Rodgers, Thomas B., 138–39
Roller, John E., 284
Romantic literature, 123
*Rome (Ga.) Courier*, 240
Rose, George, 139
rumors: destabilization of knowledge, 27, 70–71, 96–97; trumped by the act of soldiering, 32; challenged providential thinking, 69; shaming of comrades, 69, 136, 137; and home front, 212

Samito, Christian, 257
Savannah, Ga., 114
Schantz, Mark, 75
Schivelbusch, Wolfgang, 280
Schroyer, Michael, 296–97
scientific racism, 143, 256
Scottsville, Va., 209
Second Inaugural, 265
Selma, Ala., 293
sentimentalism, 20, 127; and wartime marriage, 2–3, 36, 102–3, 106, 162–63, 118; and idealization of soldiering, 3, 123, 124, 136, 149; relationship to discipline, 18, 33–35, 65; idea of "bold soldier boy," 21, 34; displayed on the picket line, 26, 28; and death, 39, 75; extolled suffering, 39–40, 49, 111; and letter writing, 44–45, 103, 118; in contradiction to "poor soldier," 45, 48; challenged by combat, 73, 74–75, 106–7, 213, 242–43; influence on emotions, 106; and importance of sympathy, 111, 270, 271, and semiliterate soldiers, 114, 115–16, 118, 119–20; shift toward pragmatism, 127–28, 264, 311–12,

213; lived out on the battlefield, 149–51; and failure to realize it in the field, 163, 230–31; and broader cultural change, 314–15

Seven Days Campaign, 244

sexual violence, 116–17, 199

Shaw, Hugh, 139

Sheehan-Dean, Aaron, 179–80, 217

Shepherd, William T., 88–99, *89, 92*

Sherman, William T., 264

Shiloh, Battle of, 95–96, 136–37

shirking. *See* cowardice; military surgeons

sick call. *See* military surgeons

Simpson, Lewis, 236

Sixth Corps (Army of the Potomac), 207, 302

skulkers parade, 142

slavery, 118; body servants and camp laborers, 42–43; soldiers silent on race, 54, 259–60; and compared to soldiering, 115; as Confederate motivation, 122, 218–19, 277–78; arming of slaves, 127, 260–61; as related to Southern absolutism, 233, 237–38, 251

sleep deprivation, 207

Slow, George, 153

smallpox, 121

Smith, Charles Henry (Bill Arp), 238–39

Smith, John, 268–69, 272, 273, 275, 289, 290, 297, 299–302

Smith, Thomas, 258–59, 261

soldier self-care, 9, 38

South Carolina, 249

South Carolina Infantry (USCT), Third, 54, 57–60

*Southern Illustrated News,* 25

*Southern Punch,* 245

Southern women: expressed patriotic support, 44–25; soldiers confide to, 46, 49, 114–15, 116–18, 120, 141; against the war, 49–50; solicitous of soldier needs, 50, 54; instructed by soldiers, 82–83, 87, 118; subjected to sexual violence, 116–17, 199; blamed for desertion, 225. *See also* household economy; religion

South vs. North, 235–36, 348n11, 348n13

Spotsylvania, 43, 203, 205, 207, 294–95, 297

Sproul, Jonathan, 64

Stanton, William, 204

Starbird, John, 204–7

Stiles, Mary, 199

Stowe, Stephen, 236

straggling, 199, 202, 203

substitutes, 191

Sunken Lane (Antietam), 106, *108*

surgeons. *See* military surgeons

survival: soldier strategies of, 28–29, 38, 49–50, 54, 62, 81, 307–8; challenges to sentimentalism, 30–31, 250; and emotional management, 61, 81; trusting in God, 67; calculations of, 69, 86–88, 202, 311; impact on loyalty, 183; thrill of, 208, 271; removed from high politics, 226; and truces between pickets, 246, 247–48

sutlers, 31, 32–33, 82. *See also* camp; economies

sympathy. *See* emotions; sentimentalism

tactics, 135, 149, *150*

Taylor, Guy, 264–65

Taylor, Thomas, 231–32, 233

Thomas, George, 264

Thucydides, 129

Trans-Mississippi, 294

Trueheart, Charles, 171

Union: soldier convictions, 3, 104–5, 227, 264, 271; connected to home, 36; and emotion, 88–89; grounded in Christianity, 89–90, 97, 104; affirmed on the battlefield, 93, 97, 109, 170; cynical toward, 161; and pragmatism, 170; revealed in material culture, 301

Union soldiers: religious beliefs of, 1, 3; relationships with wives, 2–3, 36, 103, 104–5, 111, 112–13; importance of material culture, 3, 20, 166; enlistment, 20, 26, 89–90, 191; partisanship among, 23, 33, 139–40; becoming veterans, 30, 33–34, 35, 72; and hard war, 30, 94; critical of the war effort, 31, 161–64; united by hardship, 31–32; poor soldiers, 32, 58–59; denounced inhumanity of war, 32, 163; mutinies, 55, 57–60; racial attitudes, 72, 256–57; estranged from civilians, 78–79; love for Union, 88–90, 97–98, 104–5, 170; combat and political beliefs, 94–95, 106–7, 170–72; and the importance of Christianity, 104; influenced by honor, 104–5, 170; turned into martyrs, 109; bond with civilians, 111–12; acts of sexual violence, 116–17; discharge guidelines and returning home, 143, 269; bounty soldiers, 190, 191–93; opinion of immigrant soldiers, 190–92; and defeat, 230–31, 232, 237–38, 239; self-mockery, 238, 239, 242–44; empathy for the enemy, 247–50; returning to the battlefield, 294–98. *See also* absolutism; camp; combat; deserters; discipline; emotion; household; religion; Union

United States Infantry, Twelfth, 30, 72–73

Vance, Zebulon, 124
Varon, Elizabeth, 282
vengeance, 246–47
Vicksburg, Miss., 253
Vinson, Christiana, 114, 115, 116–17, 119, 120–21, 122
Vinson, Wright, 102, 114–22, 128, 129, 130
Virginia Infantry: Twelfth, 290; Thirteenth, 182, 186; Fifty-Fourth, 53; Fifty-Eighth, 183

Wagner, William, 253–55
Walker, William, 25–26, 54–59, 61
Walkup, Samuel, 261–62, 263
Walter, Charles, 192, 293, 296
Washington, D.C., 26, 201. *See also* Grand Review
Washington, George, 263
Watson, George W., 23
Waud, Alfred, 197, *198*, 264, 267, 274
Weicksel, Sarah Jones, 39
Western Theater, 43
Whitehorne, J. E., 290, 292
Wilderness, Battle of, 126, 164, 186, 200–201, 205, 227, 294, 295–96
willed behavior: valued by soldiers, 18, 74, 76–77, 99, 123, 278, 310, 313; and sentimentalism, 26, 81, 91; challenged by circumstances of war, 28; and controlling emotions, 90–91; and rise of professionalism, 126–27; and the battlefield, 135, 142–43, 149, 158, 160
Wills, Charles, 258
Wilmington, N.C., 262
Wilson, Henry, 204
Winchester, Va., 186
Wolk, Thomas D., 56–57
Woods, George W., 57
World War I, 148
Wyatt-Brown, Bertram, 236

Zook, Samuel, 138
Zorn, Jacob, 275